ULTRAMAFIC *and* RELATED ROCKS

ULTRAMAFIC *and* RELATED ROCKS

Edited by P. J. WYLLIE

JOHN WILEY & SONS, INC., *New York · London · Sydney*

Library of Congress Catalog Card Number: 67-19786
Printed in the United States of America

Contributors

S. BHATTACHARJI, *Brooklyn College, New York, U.S.A.*

C. F. DAVIDSON, *The University of St. Andrews, Fife, Scotland*

J. B. DAWSON, *The University of St. Andrews, Fife, Scotland*

H. I. DREVER, *The University of St. Andrews, Fife, Scotland*

H. von ECKERMANN, *Edeby Ripsa, Sweden*

R. B. FORBES, *University of Alaska, College, Alaska, U.S.A.*

G. W. FRANZ, *Southeast Missouri State College, Cape Birardeau, Missouri, U.S.A.*

I. G. GASS, *University of Leeds, Leeds, England*

D. P. GOLD, *The Pennsylvania State University, University Park, Pennsylvania, U.S.A.*

G. G. GOLES, *University of Oregon, Eugene, Oregon, U.S.A.*

D. H. GREEN, *The Australian National University, Canberra, Australia*

P. M. HURLEY, *Massachusetts Institute of Technology, Cambridge, Massachusetts, U.S.A.*

T. N. IRVINE, *Geological Survey of Canada, Ottawa, Canada*

E. D. JACKSON, *U.S. Geological Survey, Menlo Park, California, U.S.A.*

R. H. JAHNS, *Stanford University, Stanford, California, U.S.A.*

R. JOHNSTON, *The University of St. Andrews, Fife, Scotland*

H. KUNO, *Tokyo University, Tokyo, Japan*

D. M. LAPHAM, *State Geological Survey, Harrisburg, Pennsylvania, U.S.A.*

M. A. LAPPIN, *University of Aberdeen, Aberdeen, Scotland*

I. D. MacGREGOR, *Southwest Center for Advanced Studies, Dallas, Texas, U.S.A.*

V. R. MURTHY, *University of Minnesota, Minneapolis, Minnesota, U.S.A.*

M. J. O'HARA, *University of Edinburgh, Edinburgh, Scotland*

D. M. RAGAN, *Arizona State University, Tempe, Arizona, U.S.A.*

C. B. RALEIGH, *U.S. Geological Survey, Menlo Park, California, U.S.A.*

T. SIMKIN, *The University of Chicago, Chicago, Illinois, U.S.A.*

C. H. SMITH, *Geological Survey of Canada, Ottawa, Canada*

H. SØRENSEN, *Universitetets Mineralogisk-Geologiske Institute, Copenhagen, Denmark*

A. M. STUEBER, *Washington University, St. Louis, Missouri, U.S.A.*

H. P. TAYLOR, *California Institute of Technology, Pasadena, California, U.S.A.*

T. P. THAYER, *U.S. Geological Survey, Washington, D.C., U.S.A.*

B. G. J. UPTON, *University of Edinburgh, Edinburgh, Scotland*

K. D. WATSON, *University of California at Los Angeles, Los Angeles, California, U.S.A.*

P. J. WYLLIE, *The University of Chicago, Chicago, Illinois, U.S.A.*

Preface

This book was planned for advanced students, research workers, teachers in petrology, and enthusiastic undergraduates. It should also be of interest to solid-earth geophysicists because the International Upper Mantle project has focused attention on the implications of ultramafic rock studies for interpretations of upper mantle composition and mineralogy. The book is offered as a supplement to the standard textbooks on petrology, even the most detailed of which can devote only a few pages to the origin of any specific group of rocks. Several specialized volumes which perform a similar function for granites, carbonatites, basalts, and layered intrusions have been published recently, and these books fill a need that becomes more acute as the volume of research literature increases.

One aim of *Ultramafic and Related Rocks,* is to emphasize variety: the variety of rock types included in this book, the variety of field and petrographic associations, the variety of approaches being used to study these rocks and associations, and the variety of processes involved in their origin and formation. It does not claim to answer all the problems of the petrogenesis of ultramafic rocks. It attempts to provide a framework for classification and discussion; to survey the present state of our knowledge; to recognize the problems and examine the extent to which they have been solved; and, hopefully, to provide guidelines for future research. The comprehensive bibliography provides an entrance into the literature for those wishing to study in more detail any association of ultramafic rocks.

Adoption of a multiauthor approach which combines the experience of many experts has certainly produced variety, but it also introduces the usual problems of symposium volumes. I have avoided the format of one author-one chapter, with each chapter standing independently, but despite my attempts to organize the material into a continuous textbook I realize that there is overlap between contributions and that many gaps in coverage remain. There are irregularities in style from one article to another that will undoubtedly disturb some readers. I hope, however, that the variety of viewpoints presented will compensate for these deficiencies. Contributions were received between August 1965 and July 1966. Thirty-three authors prepared forty-one articles that I have grouped into twelve chapters. Chapter 1 describes briefly the petrographic types of ultramafic and ultrabasic rocks and presents classifications in terms of their field associations, tectonic environments, and conditions of formation. Chapters 2 to 9 contain groups of articles that deal with the various rock associations. Chapter 10 is concerned with ultramafic nodules and their bearing on the upper mantle. Chapter 11 brings together geochemical studies on rocks from several associations, and Chapter 12 is concerned specifically with the nature of the upper mantle and the origin of ultramafic and ultrabasic rocks in all petrographic associations.

I have tried to smooth the inevitable discontinuities in several ways. The opening chapter provides a framework within which the many articles can be located. I have written an introduction for each chapter which serves as an abstract for a group of articles and attempts to coordinate and relate the articles to other chapters by means of cross references. Cross references have also been inserted at many points in the text. The introductions summarize the main conclusions reached in each article, and in a sense, therefore, they constitute part of the final review article. This review includes many specific references to the preceding articles. It draws attention to the points of agreement and emphasizes points of disagreement among the contributors.

The increased application of new instrumental techniques to problems related to the origin of ultramafic rocks promises solutions to many problems, and much progress can be expected during the next few years. I hope that this book will continue to provide a useful framework outlining fields of study even as the results described in various parts of the framework become superseded by future results.

Peter J. Wyllie

Chicago, Illinois
June 1967

Acknowledgments

The acknowledgments of all contributors have been consolidated here in order to improve continuity within the text. The editor has taken the liberty of condensing the acknowledgments into a consistent pattern. The name of the author in italics is followed by the names of the people and organizations providing assistance or advice.

E. D. Jackson: E. N. Cameron, F. C. Calkins, and T. P. Thayer.

T. Simkin: R. B. Hargraves, H. H. Hess, S. Bhattacharji, H. I. Drever, C. Methuen, and colleagues at The University of St. Andrews, Princeton University, and the State University of New York at Binghamton.

S. Bhattacharji: R. Baragar, T. Simkin, W. Valentine, J. Emslie, L. C. Bhattacharji, Geological Survey of Canada, and the National Research Council of Canada.

T. N. Irvine: J. A. Noble, H. H. Schmitt, B. Raychaudhuri, E. J. Oliver, D. C. Findlay, H. P. Taylor, Jr., M. A. Lanphere, and G. D. Eberlain.

D. M. Ragan: National Science Foundation Grant GP-3189.

D. M. Lapham: J. Freedman, D. U. Wise, V. Gwinn, the National Science Foundation, and the Pennsylvania Geological Survey.

M. A. Lappin: M. Munro and F. E. Tocher.

C. B. Raleigh: D. T. Griggs, M. S. Paterson, J. C. Jaeger, the Australian National University, National Science Foundation Grant G-16105, and the Petroleum Research Fund of the American Chemical Society.

T. P. Thayer: D. L. Rossman, R. van Vloten, D. L. Southwick, C. A. Hopson, C. Ervin Brown, and E. D. Jackson.

J. B. Dawson: C. F. Davidson, R. Johnston, A. J. A. Janse, J. M.Rooke, J. L. Powell, and The Mineral Resources Division of the Overseas Geological Surveys, London.

B. G. J. Upton: M. J. O'Hara and K. G. Cox.

K. D. Watson: J. de Grosse, Mrs. O. L. Kurtz, D. L. Watson, L. S. Weymouth, D. M. Morton, E. D. Pittman, and the University of California.

G. W. Franz and P. J. Wyllie: National Science Foundation Grant GP-1870.

R. B. Forbes and H. Kuno: International cooperation of many colleagucs, thc National Science Foundation for a Faculty Fellowship (R. B. Forbes) at the University of Tokyo, and National Science Foundation Grant G-23660.

H. Kuno: H. Hayashi, G. A. MacDonald, P. Weiblen, H. Haramura, T. Saito, and the Japanese Government Fund for Scientific Research.

I. D. MacGregor: B. T. C. Davis.

P. J. Wyllie: T. Simkin, Mrs. I. L. Baltuska, and National Science Foundation Grant GP-4910.

Publication of Chapter 2-II and 7-IV by E. D. Jackson and T. P. Thayer respectively, was authorized by the Director, U.S. Geological Survey.

Contents

ULTRAMAFIC *and* RELATED ROCKS

1. *Ultramafic and Ultrabasic Rocks*

I. PETROGRAPHY AND PETROLOGY

P. J. Wyllie

A. Introduction: Nomenclature and Petrography

This chapter outlines the petrography of ultramafic and ultrabasic rocks, and presents a preliminary classification of the petrological associations in which they occur. Many of the associations, but not all of them, are described in detail in the following chapters. Within the classification there is a guide to the chapters dealing with the various associations, and for those associations inadequately covered in this volume reference is made to one or more review papers. This is followed by O'Hara's account of the mineral facies of ultrabasic rocks.

"Ultramafic and ultrabasic rocks" was to have been the title of this book, but two contributors objected to the word "ultrabasic" with such vehemence that I decided to call the book "Ultramafic and related rocks," an alternative suggested by one of the dissidents, and to slip my original title into Chapter 1. The terms "ultramafic" and "ultrabasic" relate, respectively, to mineralogical and chemical classifications of rocks, but both have been used rather loosely in the petrological literature. The definitions given by Williams, Turner, and Gilbert (1955) are widely used and will be accepted here, although this implies no guarantee that all of the contributors to this volume agree with these definitions. Rocks of the ultramafic clan are those with color indices of more than 70; that is, rocks containing more than 70 per cent of mafic minerals. Ultrabasic rocks are those containing less than 45 per cent SiO_2. Most ultramafic rocks are also ultrabasic and most ultrabasic rocks are also ultramafic, but there are exceptions.

Ultramafic rocks are composed largely of the dark-colored ferromagnesian or mafic minerals: olivine, pyroxenes, hornblendes, biotite, phlogopite, serpentine, and opaque minerals. Ultramafic monomineralic rocks composed of the following mafic minerals would certainly be ultrabasic, as shown by the SiO_2 content, by per cent, given in parentheses after each mineral: forsterite (42.9), fayalite (29.4), hornblende (an average value 37), biotite (an average value 43.1) serpentine (average value approximately 42). However, monomineralic rocks composed of pyroxenes, although definitely ultramafic, would not be ultrabasic because of their high SiO_2 content: enstatite (60), diopside (55.6), aegirine (52). Conversely, some rocks are ultrabasic but not ultramafic; the following light colored minerals could form hypothetical, monomineralic ultrabasic rocks: anorthite (43.2), nepheline (42.3), kalsilite (38.2), akermanite (44), gehlenite (22), and calcite (0).

The fifth edition of "Suggestions to authors of the reports of the United States Geological Survey" (1958) has this to say on terminology (pp. 63–64): " 'Basic' is objectionable for rocks; 'mafic' and 'ferromagnesian' are preferred. . . The use of 'ultrabasic' cannot always be avoided, but where 'ultramafic' is appropriate it may be used instead." Doubtless this recommendation has led to the adoption of "ultramafic" by many American petrologists, but a glance through the chapters of this volume confirms that "ultrabasic" is still widely used, particularly by European petrologists. The 1960 edition of the influential American book by Turner and Verhoogen uses "ultrabasic" more often than "ultramafic," the latter not even being listed in the index. There is a tendency for the terms ultramafic and mafic to be used in a chemical sense as well as in their defined mineralogical sense. This is unfortunate. Basic and ultrabasic magmas may crystallize to yield mafic and ultramafic rocks, but it is incorrect to refer to mafic and ultramafic magmas, unless these terms are redefined to embrace chemistry as well as mineralogy.

Mineralogical and chemical descriptions of many ultramafic and ultrabasic rocks are included within this volume, and these can be found in the appropriate sections via the index. Additional descriptions are available in textbooks of petrography, the fourth volume of Johannsen (1938) containing descriptions as well as historical accounts of rock discoveries and changing rock names. Because this book is regarded as a supplement to existing textbooks, only a brief petrographic outline is presented here. This summarizes the main combinations of essential minerals in the ultramafic clan.

Ultramafic and ultrabasic rocks are composed essentially of the minerals olivine (including monticellite), clinopyroxene, orthopyroxene, amphibole, biotite, and serpentine. Phlogopite and nepheline are significant constituents in some rocks. The presence of plagioclase feldspar in assemblages of the mafic minerals produces ultramafic and ultrabasic rocks related to the calc-alkalic series. Rocks of alkalic type are produced when assemblages of the above minerals coexist with the feldspathoids nepheline, melilite, leucite, analcite, and rarely kalsilite.

Each of the essential mafic minerals is represented by a monomineralic ultramafic rock: olivine by *dunite*, pyroxene by *pyroxenite*, amphibole by *hornblendite*, and biotite by *biotitite*. Various combinations of these minerals have been given names whose origins are described by Johannsen (1938, Vol. 4).

Peridotites are olivine-rich rocks containing pyroxenes, but with little or no feldspar. The *pyroxene-peridotites* include *wehrlite* (olivine plus diallage), *harzburgite* (olivine plus orthopyroxene) and *lherzolite* (olivine plus diallage plus orthopyroxene); these may be characterized by the accessory minerals plagioclase feldspar, spinel, or pyrope-rich garnet. *Hornblende-peridotites* vary in composition through to hornblendites and pyroxenites. *Mica-peridotites* contain biotite or phlogopite. The name *garnet-peridotite* is given to any peridotite containing accessory garnet. Alteration of olivine and pyroxene converts peridotites into *serpentinites.*

Pyroxenites are ultramafic, although many contain too much silica to be classified as ultrabasic rocks. Orthopyroxenites have been called *enstatolite, hypersthenite,* or *bronzitite,* and clinopyroxenites include *diopsidite* and *diallagite. Websterite* is composed of interlocking orthopyroxenes and clinopyroxenes. *Hornblende-pyroxenites, biotite-pyroxenites, melilite-pyroxenites,* and *melanite-pyroxenites* are known; *eclogite* is a garnet-pyroxenite composed essentially of pyrope and omphacite.

Hornblendites vary widely in mineralogy, and various combinations of hornblende, pyroxene, olivine, and biotite are known. *Scyelite,* for example, contains approximately equal proportions of hornblende, pyroxene, and biotite.

The important members of the mica-peridotite family are *kimberlite* and *alnoite.* There is continuous mineralogical gradation between these rocks and *carbonatites* (composed essentially of carbonates), which are certainly ultrabasic, although not ultramafic.

Many ultramafic rocks grade into mafic rocks by an increase in plagioclase feldspar; dunites grade into troctolites, pyroxenites grade into gabbros and norites, and hornblendites grade into diorites (the *appinite* suite). Increase of plagioclase feldspar in olivine-rich peridotites produce *picrites, augite-picrites,* and *hornblende-picrites,* which may be of tholeiitic type, or of alkalic type if the feldspar is accompanied by accessory feldspathoids such as analcite. There is complete mineralogical gradation between gabbro, diabase, or teschenite, and peridotites containing no feldspar.

Addition of feldspathoids to combinations of ultramafic minerals produces ultrabasic and ultramafic rocks with an impressive variety of names. The ultrabasic *ijolite* series is composed essentially of nepheline and aegirine-augite; the ultramafic members of the series, *jacupirangite* and *melteigite,* are *nepheline-pyroxenites.* The melilite-bearing ultramafic rocks include *uncompahgrite* (a melilite-pyroxenite); *turjaite* (biotite, melilite, and nepheline); *okaite* (melilite, biotite, and hauyne); and alnoite (melilite-mica-peridotite).

Effusive, fine-grained equivalents of most peridotites are unknown, although some serpentinites have been interpreted as submarine lava flows. *Meimechite,* recently described from the U.S.S.R., is the effusive equivalent of kimberlite. Porphyritic lavas enriched in olivine include *picrite-basalts* and *oceanites. Ankaramites* are similar lavas enriched in augite. Ultrabasic alkalic lavas consist of various combinations of olivine, nepheline, melilite, leucite, and kalsilite, which may be set in a glassy matrix; they include *nephelinite, melilitite, leucitite, katungite, ugandite,* and *madupite.* The most subsiliceous lava yet recorded is a carbonatite flow composed essentially of carbonates of sodium, calcium, and potassium.

The distribution of these ultramafic and ultrabasic rock types in petrographic associations is described in the next section. Following this classification, O'Hara in Section II describes the mineral facies of ultrabasic rocks. From the stability ranges of individual minerals, and then of mineral assemblages, it becomes possible to delineate the range of conditions for the formation of many ultramafic and ultrabasic rocks. With this facies classification before us, we then pass on, in Chapters 2 through 11, to detailed accounts of the rock types and associations, and of various approaches used to investigate the problems involved in their petrogenesis. Finally, in Chapter 12, after the mineralogy of the upper mantle is considered, O'Hara uses mineral parageneses to plot the positions of many rocks on his facies diagram to provide estimates of the depth and temperature at which the minerals in the rocks reached equilibrium. This is followed by a review of the conclusions reached by the 33 contributors to this volume. They confirm that we still have much to learn before agreement can be reached on the origins of ultramafic and ultrabasic rocks.

B. Ultramafic and Ultrabasic Rock Associations

There are many different rock types in the ultramafic clan, and these occur in a variety of field and petrographic associations. We may expect, therefore, that there is a variety of processes involved in the origin and emplacement of these rocks. The outline of ultramafic and ultrabasic rock associations that follows provides a framework for the more detailed accounts and petrogenetic discussions given in the succeeding chapters. Ten associations are listed, some of them with subdivisions. There is overlap between some of the associations, and gradation between some of the subdivisions. The outline is to be regarded only as a working classification to be modified as we learn more about the geology of these rocks.

1. The layered gabbro-norite-peridotite association in major intrusions. This association has been widely recognized, and most petrologists agree that the ultramafic rocks have been derived by crystal settling from a parent gabbroic magma of tholeiitic type. The ultramafic rocks form cumulates on the floors of magma chambers. There appear to be two extreme types, but future work may confirm gradational types between them:

1. The large differentiated gabbroic lopoliths or stratiform intrusions which may be thousands of square miles in area and just a few miles thick. These occur in regions not affected by contemporaneous orogeny.
2. The small funnel-shaped intrusions occurring in a volcanic association, of which the type example is the Skaergaard intrusion described in detail by Wager and Deer (1939; see Wager, 1963, and Taylor and Epstein, 1963, for bibliographies of additional studies on this intrusion).

The Stillwater, Great Dyke, and Bushveld intrusions are described by Jackson in Chapter 2-II, and the Muskox intrusion is described by Irvine and Smith in Chapter 2-III.

2. Ultramafic rocks in differentiated basic sills and in minor intrusions. Concentration of mafic minerals in basic sills, dykes, sheets, and laccoliths may produce ultramafic rocks. Two associations are recognized:

1. The alkalic diabase (or teschenite, or theralite)-picrite association.
2. The tholeiitic diabase-picrite association.

Drever and Johnston review many minor intrusions in Chapter 3-II, and Simkin in Chapter 3-III discusses the differentiation of specific sills in Skye. A third group of rocks may merit separate classification as:

3. Picritic minor intrusions. These are olivine-rich rocks of tholeiitic type which, according to Drever and Johnston in Chapter 3-V, have characteristics distinguishing them from picrites of differentiated sills.

3. Concentrically zoned dunite-peridotite association. Large and small cylindrical ultramafic bodies with concentric zoning from a dunite core to outer zones of peridotites occur in orogenic belts. They are usually emplaced in gabbro which does not appear to have a close genetic relationship to them. They have features distinguishing them from alpine-type intrusions of Group 4, and from cumulative ultramafic rocks in basic layered intrusions of Group 1, although gravity settling of minerals was an important process in the formation of some of them. Examples from Alaska and the Urals are described in Chapter 4 by Irvine and by Taylor.

4. Alpine-type peridotite-serpentinite association. This association includes large and small bodies distributed along deformed mountain chains and island arcs, usually along with gabbros or basic volcanic rocks. They have characteristics distinguishing them from other ultramafic associations occurring in orogenic zones (Benson, 1926; Thayer, Chapter 7). The different times of emplacement of alpine-type intrusions—preorogenic, synorogenic and postorogenic—produce alpine types of distinct mineral facies which provide a basis for their classification (O'Hara, Section II of this chapter). The following groups of alpine-type ultramafic intrusions are distinguished mainly on the basis of their present environment:

1. Serpentinites and peridotites occurring in strongly deformed but peripheral low-grade metamorphic zones, with greenschists, glaucophane schists, and even unmetamorphosed greywackes and lavas. This includes the ophiolite association discussed by Thayer, Chapter 7-IV-B-5; Sørensen, Chapter 7-II-C-1.
2. Serpentinites and peridotites occurring in regionally metamorphosed rocks of greenschist, epidote amphibolite, and amphibolite facies. An example is the Appa-

lachian ultramafic belt described by Jahns in Chapter 5-II (see also Lapham, Chapter 6-II; Thayer, Chapter 7-IV-D-1).

3. Peridotites and garnet peridotites associated with regionally metamorphosed rocks of upper amphibolite, granulite or eclogite facies. These are described by O'Hara, Chapter 5-IV, and Lappin, Chapter 6-III.

4. A distinctive group of high-temperature peridotite intrusions, of intermediate size (5 to 15 miles in diameter), with well defined dynamothermal metamorphic aureoles. These are discussed by Green in Chapter 7-III, and by Thayer in Chapter 7-IV-D-2.

5. Serpentinites of the oceans. It has been proposed that the main crustal layer beneath the oceans may be serpentinized peridotite, similar to those samples dredged from fault scarps on the mid-Atlantic ridge, from the Puerto Rico trench, and collected from St. Peter's and St. Paul's Rocks on the mid-Atlantic ridge. Hess has reviewed this association in the volume edited by Burk (1964) which includes studies on the serpentinite cores obtained from the AMSOC drill hole near Mayaguez, Puerto Rico.

6. Some metamorphic and metasomatic rocks in Group 10 are appropriately considered in the alpine association.

5. Minor associates of batholithic complexes. The "granitic" batholiths include rock types ranging in composition from ultrabasic to acid. There are at least three associations including ultrabasic rocks. In the first two, basic and ultrabasic members are usually concentrated as masses within the stocks forming satellites to the major complex:

1. Peridotite-pyroxenite-hornblendite-tonalite-granodiorite-granite.

2. Hornblendite-diorite-monzonite-syenite, the hornblende-rich varieties making up the appinite suite.

3. Ultrabasic lamprophyre dikes occurring as members of dike swarms associated with granitic or granodioritic complexes, and often converging on individual intrusive centres.

Joplin (1959) presented a review of the occurrence and origin of some of these basic and ultrabasic bodies. Ultrabasic lamprophyres also occur in association with alkalic ring complexes, Group 6(3), and dikes or sheets of alnoite (and other lamprophyres) may be distributed on a regional scale; compare Group 7(2).

6. Alkalic ultrabasic rocks in ring complexes. Alkalic ring complexes containing ultrabasic rocks are usually circular or elliptical in plan, with evidence for cylindrical or funnel shape in vertical section. They are usually a few miles in diameter, although they range from small diatremes to masses many miles across. The rock types may be arranged in concentric fashion, and many of them exhibit gravity layering. The complexes occur in stable or fractured continental regions following linear trends. Three series of rocks encountered in these complexes include ultrabasic rocks:

1. The subsiliceous alkalic series containing normative but not necessarily modal nepheline: peridotite-pyroxenite-biotitite-gabbro-diorite-syenite.

2. The peralkalic series including pyroxenites, biotitites, rocks of the ijolite family, melilite-rich rocks of the uncompahgrite family, and carbonatites.

3. Alnoite and kimberlite dykes and sheets associated with some of the carbonatite complexes in Group 6(2).

A review of the rocks of this association is given by Upton, in Chapter 9-II, and Gold describes the plutonic complexes of the Monteregian Petrographic Province in Chapter 9-III. In Chapter 8-IV, von Eckermann discusses the rocks in Group 6(3). Carbonatites and their place in this association have been described in a book edited by Tuttle and Gittins (1967).

7. Kimberlites. Kimberlites are rare rocks, occurring as small pipes, dikes or sheets confined to the interior and margins of stable continental areas. Three associations may be considered:

1. Clusters of pipes or diatremes, which tend to form elongate chains. These include the diamond-bearing kimberlites. Chapter 8 contains a review of these rocks by Dawson (Sections II and V), a review of Russian kimberlites by Davidson (Section III), and an account of some specific pipes in Arizona by Watson (Section IV).

2. Dikes and sheets of kimberlite (mica-peridotite) or alnoite distributed on a regional scale. In Chapter 9-V Watson reviews the suite in eastern North America extending along the stable area to the west of the Appalachian orogenic belt.

3. Dikes and sheets of alnoite and kimberlite associated with carbonatite complexes. Dawson (Chapter 8-II-C) refers to these as "central-complex kimberlites," and they have been listed previously under 6 (3).

8. Ultrabasic lavas. Ultrabasic lavas are listed apart from their plutonic equivalents and associates because the existence and nature of ultrabasic lavas is of critical importance in petrogenesis (cf. Bowen, 1928):

1. Ultrabasic or ultramafic lavas can be formed by enrichment of basic magma in mafic crystals, either by crystal settling before or after extrusion, or by flow differentiation during extrusion. Richter and Murata (1966) discuss olivine concentration in the lavas of Hawaii, Simkin (Chapter 3-III-D) mentions flows with features suggesting flow differentiation, and Mathews et al. (1964) show that gravity concentration of olivine can occur in basaltic pillows. The ultrabasic lavas of Cyprus described by Gass (1958) are believed to represent olivine-enriched basic magma. Rocks of the ophiolite suite may represent submarine lava flows enriched in mafic minerals (see Thayer Chapter 7-IV-B-5).

2. Alkalic ultrabasic lavas occur in the same cratogenic environment as the alkaline ultrabasic complexes of Group 6. In his review of the sodic, alkalic igneous suites of eastern Uganda, King (1965) noted that the ultrabasic lavas in the melanephelinite-nephelinite series correspond to the plutonic series pyroxenite-ijolite family-carbonatite of Group 6(2). He proposed that the alkali carbonatite lava flows observed by Dawson (1962) on Oldoinyo Lengai represented the final residuum, corresponding to the carbonatites of the plutonic series.

Potassic ultrabasic lavas containing leucite, melilite, and rarely kalsilite are represented by the ugandite-mafurite-katungite series of the Toro-Ankole volcanic province of Uganda, whose petrology and petrogenesis were discussed by Holmes (1950).

The Congo volcano of Mount Nyiragongo in the Virunga volcanic field is composed of both sodic and potassic ultrabasic lavas containing various proportions of nepheline, leucite, and melilite, along with their mafic minerals. Sahama (1962) has reviewed the petrology of this complex volcano.

3. An effusive equivalent of kimberlite, meimechite, is known in the U.S.S.R. both in lava-form and as a tuff, or lava-breccia. Meimechites are described briefly by Dawson in Chapter 8-II-H-7, and by Davidson in Chapter 8-III-B-9.

9. Ultrabasic nodules. Lavas and diatremes contain a variety of inclusions or nodules, including ultrabasic types, which may be cognate (cumulative) or accidental (exotic) xenoliths. These ultrabasic xenoliths occur in three environments:

1. Many alkali olivine-basalts contain nodules of peridotite (spinel-lherzolite), garnet peridotite, and eclogite, but only three examples are known of inclusions in tholeiitic basalts. Forbes and Kuno review the distribution and composition of the inclusions and their host basalts in Chapter 10-II, and Kuno describes a series of inclusions from a single volcano in Chapter 10-III.

2. Alkalic basic and ultrabasic lavas of Group 8 (2) contain inclusions of peridotite, pyroxenite, biotite pyroxenite, and biotite hornblendite. These are referred to by Upton in Chapter 9-II.

3. Kimberlite diatremes are crowded with xenoliths, including peridotites, garnet pyroxenites, and eclogites. Scapolite may occur in the xenoliths. These inclusions are discussed in Chapter 10-IV by Davidson, and in Chapter 10-V by O'Hara. They are also discussed in Chapter 8.

10. Metamorphic and metasomatic ultrabasic and ultramafic rocks. Any of the preceding types of ultrabasic or ultramafic rocks could become involved in regional metamorphism. Some of the alpine-type intrusions have had a complex history, and their origin may be obscured by deformation and recrystallization. Other ultramafic rocks in schists, amphibolites, and hornblende gneisses of the orogenic zones may be formed by metamorphic differentiation or by metasomatic processes, as described by Sørensen in Chapter 7-II.

II. MINERAL FACIES IN ULTRABASIC ROCKS

M. J. O'Hara

A. *Mineral Stabilities*

Most peridotites are formed from combinations of olivine, clinopyroxene, and orthopyroxene. Figure 1.1 shows the melting relationships for these minerals occurring in the system CaO-MgO SiO_2, and for assemblages of these minerals, and Fig. 1.2 shows the melting curves for the corresponding ultramafic rocks containing only small amounts of Al_2O_3 and FeO.

The stability limits of magnesian olivine set ultimate limits on the conditions of formation of peridotites. The stability of forsterite is limited by the melting curve shown in Fig. 1.1 (Davis and England, 1964) and by inversion to the spinel structure at very high pressures (Dachille and Roy, 1960a). Natural fayalite-bearing magnesian olivines of peridotites will melt over a temperature interval at slightly lower temperatures (Bowen and Schairer, 1935) and invert to the spinel form over a pressure interval at slightly lower pressures than pure forsterite (Boyd and England, 1960a). At still higher pressures a breakdown to periclase + ilmenite structure $MgSiO_3$ is predicted (Clark and Ringwood, 1964).

Magnesium-rich pyroxenes are also important constituents of natural anhydrous peridotites. The stability of enstatite is limited by inversion to protoenstatite at low pressures and by the melting curve (Fig. 1.1) at higher pressures (Boyd et al., 1964). There may be an inversion to corundum or ilmenite structure or a breakdown to a dense silica phase and an MgO-rich compound at very high pressures (Ringwood and Scabrook, 1963). 5 to 15 per cent iron-bearing molecule in solid solution lowers the temperature of the onset of melting, the temperature of inversion to what is probably the protoenstatite structure (Bowen and Schairer, 1935), and probably also lowers the pressure of inversion to high-pressure polymorphs. Entry of Al_2O_3 lowers the temperature of the onset of melting (Boyd and England, 1964a) and raises the temperature at which inversion to protoenstatite occurs (O'Hara and Schairer, 1963). Up to 10 per cent diopside can dissolve in enstatite at high temperature and pressure (Davis, 1963), greatly reducing the temperature of the onset of melting, and larger amounts can enter into protoenstatite and another high-temperature polymorph at low pressures (Boyd and Schairer, 1964).

Evidence of high-pressure polymorphs of olivine and pyroxene compositions is

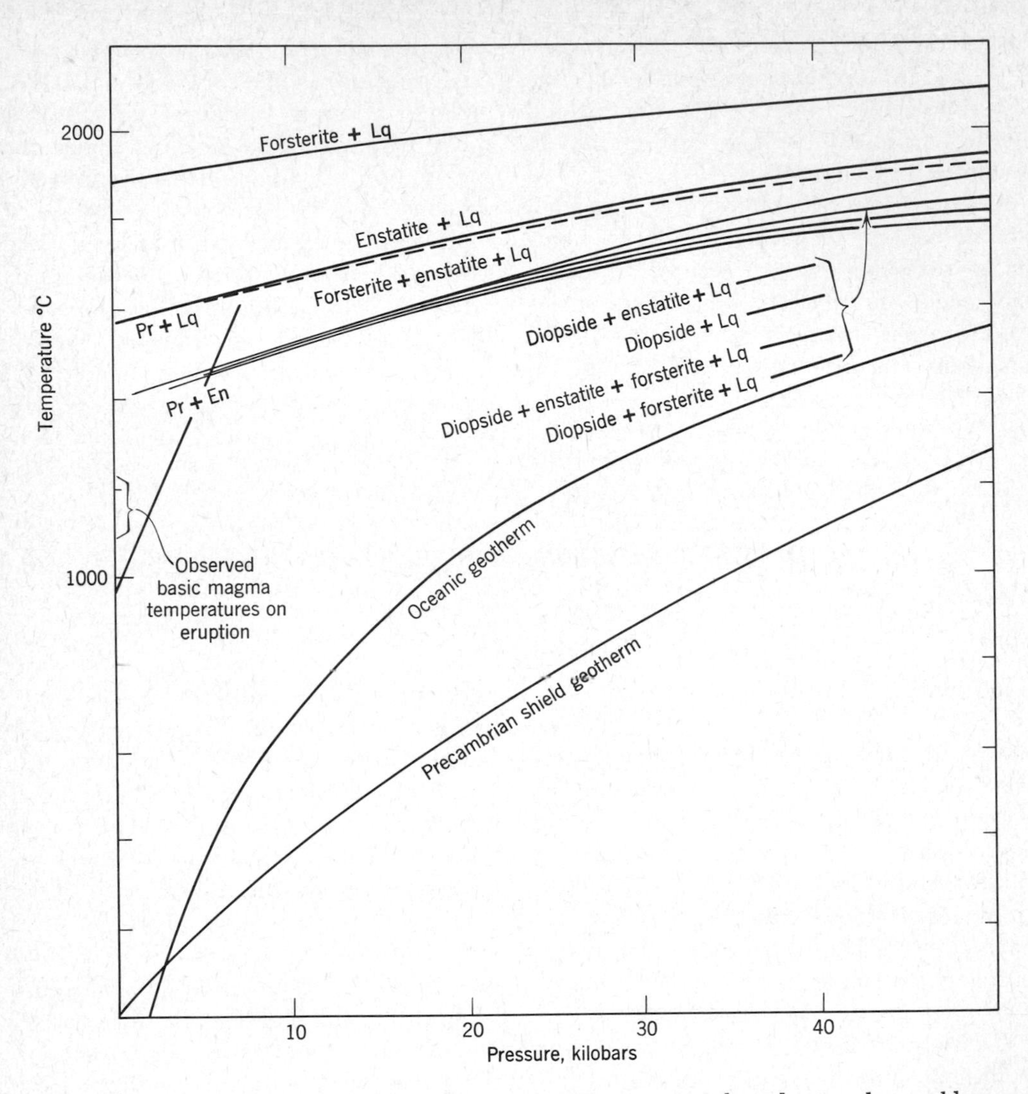

Fig. 1.1 Curves representing melting relationships of some minerals and mineral assemblages in the system $CaO\text{-}MgO\text{-}SiO_2$ (data sources given in the text). Suggested geotherms in this and in Fig. 1.4 are from Ringwood et al. (1964).

unknown from described natural ultrabasic rocks or meteorites unless the ilmenite-pyroxene intergrowths reported from fragments in some kimberlite pipes arise by breakdown of such a high-pressure phase. Magnesian olivine and magnesian orthopyroxene may coexist in anhydrous peridotites under all conditions where both phases are themselves stable up to the onset of melting of the mixture, which is the same as, or only slightly lower than, that of the onset of melting of the orthopyroxene (Fig. 1.1). Incongruent melting of orthopyroxene to olivine + liquid is restricted to low pressures (Boyd et al., 1964) and magnesian compositions (Bowen and Schairer, 1935). A small excess of MgO is observed in orthopyroxenes coexisting with olivine (Boyd and England, 1960b, Mercy and O'Hara, 1965a).

Diopsidic clinopyroxene can coexist with olivine and orthopyroxene in anhydrous peridotites over a range of conditions limited only by the onset of melting and the pressure stability of the individual phases. The melting curve of pure diopside

(Fig. 1.1) has been determined to high pressures (Boyd and England, 1963a). Diopsides coexisting with enstatite or protoenstatite at pressures from atmospheric to above 30 kilobars contain very large amounts of $MgSiO_3$ in solid solution at high temperatures (Boyd and Schairer, 1964; Davis, 1963; O'Hara, 1963a) but there is only a small effect on the temperature of melting. Diopside coexisting with olivine at low and high pressures contains an appreciable excess of MgO (Kushiro and Schairer, 1963; Kushiro, 1964a) and natural assemblages exhibit a small excess (Mercy and O'Hara, 1965a), slightly lowering the temperature of beginning of melting. Olivines coexisting with diopside at a high temperature may contain appreciable monticellite molecule in solid solution (Kushiro and Schairer, 1963) but in the presence of orthopyroxene as well this effect is negligible (Ross et al., 1954; O'Hara and Mercy, 1963). A high-pressure phase transition or breakdown is likely (Ringwood and Seabrook, 1963).

The temperature of the onset of melting of the forsterite + diopside + orthopyroxene assemblage is close to that of diopside itself (Kushiro and Schairer, 1963; Kushiro, 1964a) and marks the upper temperature limit of the stability of three-phase lherzolite assemblages (Fig. 1.1). FeO, Al_2O_3 and other components in the minerals of natural peridotites lower the practical upper limit set by the experimental data, as shown in Fig. 1.2.

The data illustrated in Fig. 1.1 represent the conditions under which Al_2O_3-free dunite (olivine), harzburgite (olivine + orthopyroxene), websterite (clinopyroxene + orthopyroxene), wehrlite (olivine + clinopyroxene), and lherzolite (olivine + clinopyroxene + orthopyroxene) crystallize from, equilibrate with, or yield by partial melting an ultrabasic Al_2O_3-free magma of their own bulk composition. Note the narrow temperature range for coexistence of clinopyroxene-bearing peridotites with liquid. The high temperatures of the melting curves, the large temperature interval between the geothermal gradients and the melting curves, and the discrepancy between observed magma temperatures and the minimum temperatures for existence of true ultrabasic magmas are important points in the argument against the existence of ultrabasic liquids in the earth's upper mantle and crust (Bowen, 1928). Another cogent reason against the existence of liquid peridotite magmas is found when the proportion is considered in which the minerals would precipitate together. At 20 kb, for example, a liquid-precipitating olivine and orthopyroxene in the system CaO-MgO-SiO_2 would yield rocks extremely rich in orthopyroxene, whereas the liquid precipitating olivine + two pyroxenes would precipitate clinopyroxene, with minor olivine and only a trace of orthopyroxene (Kushiro, 1964a). Natural harzburgites and lherzolites do not satisfy these requirements.

The temperatures and pressures at which certain ultramafic rocks very poor in Al_2O_3 and FeO will precipitate from ultrabasic liquids of their own composition are shown in Fig. 1.2. FeO enters into solid solution in the crystalline phases already discussed, but the presence of Al_2O_3 makes possible the formation of plagioclase feldspar as well. Four-phase lherzolites may precipitate from, or otherwise coexist, with suitable dry basic liquids under conditions bounded by the two lowest curves. The curves bounding the ranges of conditions under which various ultramafic rock types can form by accumulation from suitable magmas are indicated at the right hand side of Fig. 1.2. The majority of natural igneous ultrabasic rocks, such as the lower parts of large layered intrusions and nodules in basalts, are probably formed under conditions very close to the lowest curve in Fig. 1.2. The compositions of the liquids from which these ultramafic rocks will precipitate become decreasingly ultrabasic and increasingly rich in Al_2O_3, FeO, and Na_2O; that is, increasingly basaltic as the temperature falls.

The mutual solubility of coexisting py-

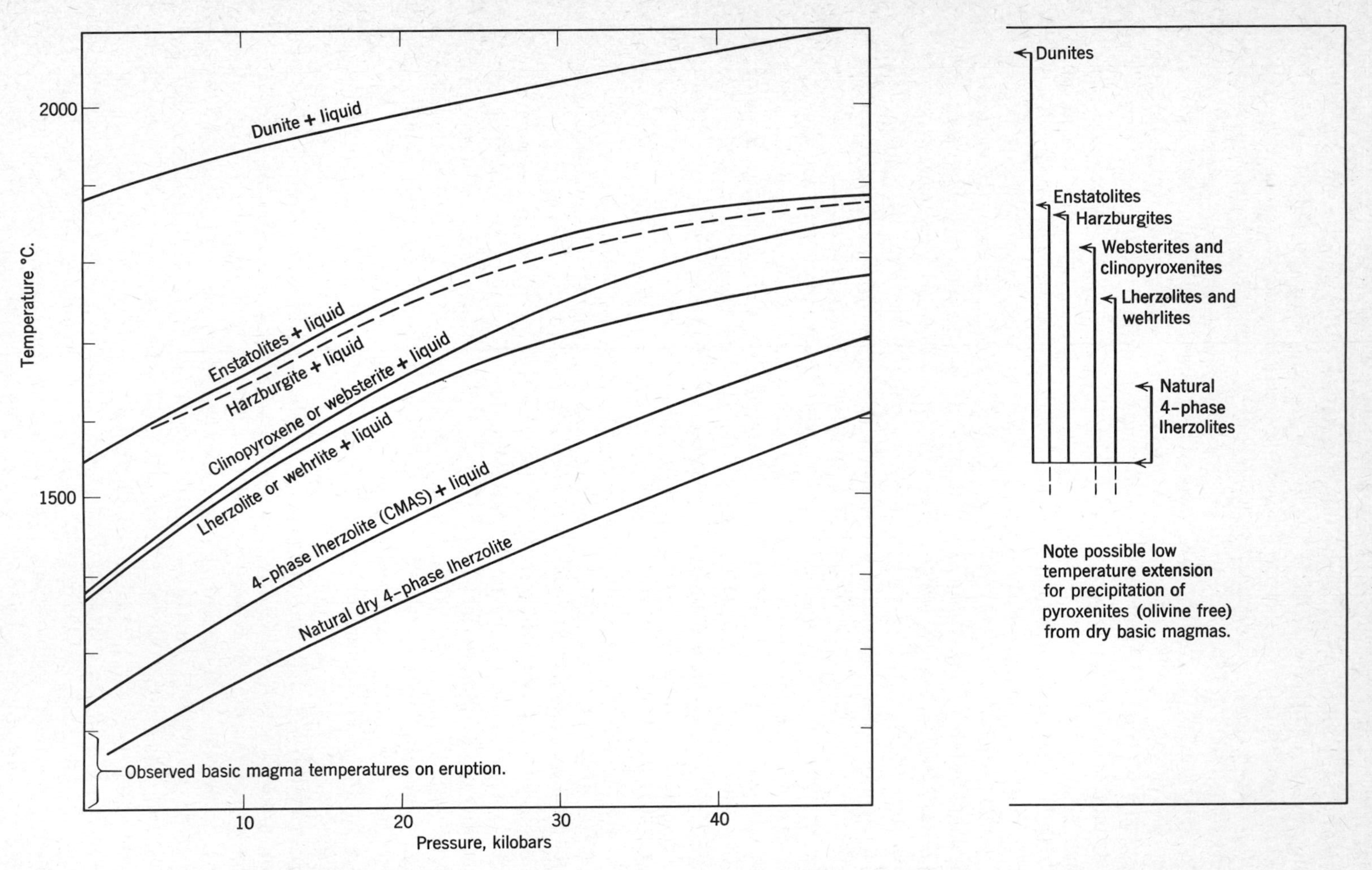

Fig. 1.2 Temperatures and pressures at which certain ultramafic rock types very poor in Al_2O_3 and FeO can be expected to precipitate from dry liquids *of their own* (*ultrabasic*) *composition* are shown by the upper five curves. Data sources are reviewed in the text. The two lower curves give the temperatures and pressures at which 4-phase lherzolites might precipitate from dry Al_2O_3—rich liquids which are *not* of the same composition as the accumulate. The right-hand half of the figure displays the wide temperature ranges over which these same ultramafic rock types might accumulate from suitable dry basic liquids at 40 kb.

roxenes potentially affords a useful geologic thermometer, almost independent of pressure (Davis, 1963). The influence of Al_2O_3, Cr_2O_3 and FeO upon the mutual solubility is known to be substantial, however, and is greatly dependent upon pressure (O'Hara and Mercy, 1963; O'Hara, 1963a,b; O'Hara and Schairer, 1963; Davis, 1964) and the solubility of excess MgO in the pyroxenes coexisting with olivine may further affect their mutual solubility. Entry of aegirine and jadeite molecules into the clinopyroxene will further influence the solvus limits; hence precise temperature estimates cannot yet be made on this basis.

The distribution of Mg and Fe between coexisting olivine and calcium-poor pyroxene has yielded no unambiguous criteria of conditions of crystallization of ultrabasic assemblages. Magnesian olivines have higher Fe/Mg ratios than coexisting equilibrium calcium-poor pyroxenes at low pressure (Bowen and Schairer, 1935). Garnet peridotites, pyrenean spinel-lherzolites and chondrite meteorites are known to have olivines with higher Fe/Mg ratio than coexisting orthopyroxene (O'Hara, 1963c; O'Hara and Mercy, 1963; Mason, 1962; Keil and Fredriksson, 1964; Mercy and O'Hara, 1965a) while peridotite nodules in basalts, some alpine-type peridotites, many accumulative ultrabasic rocks, basic lavas and achondrite meteorites are known to contain olivines whose Fe/Mg ratios are equal to or lower than those of coexisting orthopyroxene (O'Hara, 1963c; Challis, 1965a). Alternative interpretations of this situation either assume thermodynamic equilibrium and attribute the differences to differing conditions of crystallization (Ramberg and de Vore, 1951; Bartholomé, 1962), or attribute differences to variable departure from the equilibrium state (O'Hara, 1963c). Keil and Fredriksson (1964) differ from the other authors in ascribing chondrite assemblages, which conform with the expected equilibrium distribution, to extreme disequilibrium crystallization. However, assemblages from olivine-pigeonite chondrites in which the composition of the minerals vary greatly from grain to grain are ascribed to less extreme disequilibrium. It is difficult to reconcile this hypothesis with opinions on the petrology of terrestrial peridotites.

Jadeite is a minor component in the clinopyroxenes of peridotites, and jadeite-rich pyroxenes occur within a few ultrabasic masses. Pure jadeite is stable at high pressures only and melts at much lower temperatures than diopside (Bell and Davis, 1965); hence partial melting or fractional crystallization at high pressure is likely to enrich Na relative to Ca in the liquid phase (contrast Harris and Rowell, 1960). Jadeite-bearing clinopyroxenes are likely to become stable in ultrabasic rocks at pressures somewhat lower than those required to stabilize pure jadeite in a silica-poor environment, and at a pressure appreciably lower than required to stabilize jadeite-rich omphacites in quartz-bearing eclogites. Consequently, the appearance of jadeite-bearing clinopyroxene in ultrabasic rocks is not necessarily an indicator of eclogite facies, or garnet-lherzolite facies conditions (see below).

B. Mineral Facies in the System CaO-MgO-Al_2O_3-SiO_2-H_2O

Anhydrous ultrabasic rocks commonly contain small amounts of phases other than olivine and the two pyroxenes. These phases are rich in Al_2O_3 particularly, but may contain substantial amounts of Fe_2O_3 and Cr_2O_3 also. The nature of the Al_2O_3-rich phase which may coexist with olivine and two pyroxenes in magnesian assemblages varies with the conditions of crystallization, and is used to define three important mineral facies. It is convenient to discuss the situation arising in the system CaO-MgO-Al_2O_3-SiO_2-H_2O (CMASH) first, and then to take into account the greater number of components present in natural rocks by generalizing the rigid definitions of mineral facies based upon this system.

Arabic numerals are used to denote subsolidus reactions, or facies boundaries, and melting reactions for mineral assemblages. Roman numerals are used to denote mineral assemblages or facies stable between pairs of reaction boundaries. Reversible equations are written where the reactions are known, but the equations are not balanced because solid solution difficulties are overwhelming. The liquid and vapor compositions are unknown in reactions involving these phases. Some of the less well known reactions are listed simply as phase assemblages, but these are distinguishable from the facies by the arabic numerals. Some reactions are just described in qualitative terms. Some of the reactions are considered in more detail in Chapter 7-III, by Green, and in Chapter 12-II, by MacGregor.

1. Anhydrous facies. In the absence of H_2O, compositions in CMAS which simulate natural ultrabasic rocks may crystallize to forsterite plus two Al_2O_3-saturated pyroxenes plus an Al_2O_3-rich phase that is anorthite at low pressures, spinel at intermediate pressures, and pyrope-rich garnet at high pressures. Forsterite, clinopyroxene plus enstatite or protoenstatite, may coexist with two Al_2O_3-rich phases (any two of anorthite, spinel, garnet, and "basaltic" liquid) in univariant equilibria. Three subsolidus univariant equilibria forming facies boundaries are:

Protoenstatite = enstatite 1
(coexisting with forsterite + diopside + anorthite)
Forsterite + anorthite = diopside + enstatite + spinel 2
Diopside + enstatite + spinel = forsterite + garnet 3

Four univariant melting reactions give the beginning of melting of Al_2O_3-saturated lherzolite assemblages:

Forsterite + diopside + protohypersthene + anorthite + liquid ... 4
Forsterite + diopside + enstatite + anorthite + liquid 5
Forsterite + diopside + enstatite + spinel + liquid 6
Forsterite + diopside + enstatite + garnet + liquid 7

The liquid composition varies in the equilibria 4–7 from "basaltic" to "picritic" (O'Hara, 1965a).

Sufficient experimental data are available to outline the positions of these reactions in the P-T diagram, Fig. 1.3. The position of reaction 3 is an estimate based on the assumption that the stability of calcium-bearing garnet with forsterite begins at lower pressures than that of pyrope with forsterite investigated by MacGregor (1964). The curves outline the range of pressure-temperature conditions appropriate to four mineral facies:

Protohypersthene-plagioclase-lherzolite facies I
(forsterite + diopside + protoenstatite + anorthite)
Orthopyroxene-plagioclase-lherzolite facies II
(forsterite + diopside + enstatite + anorthite)
Spinel-lherzolite facies III
(forsterite + diopside + enstatite + spinel)
Garnet-lherzolite facies IV
(forsterite + diopside + enstatite + garnet)

Figure 1.3 may be compared with Fig. 1.2 to reveal how dunite, harzburgite, lherzolite etc. containing Al_2O_3-saturated pyroxenes may accumulate from basic liquids, or be left as crystalline residua during partial melting to produce basic liquids, at much lower temperatures in the Al_2O_3-bearing system.

Two subfacies of the spinel-lherzolite facies (III) may be recognized on the basis of the stabilization of garnet in anhydrous compositions by the univariant reaction involving:

Enstatite + spinel + anorthite + diopside + garnet 17

which must occur at a pressure between reactions 2 and 3, and will be observed in

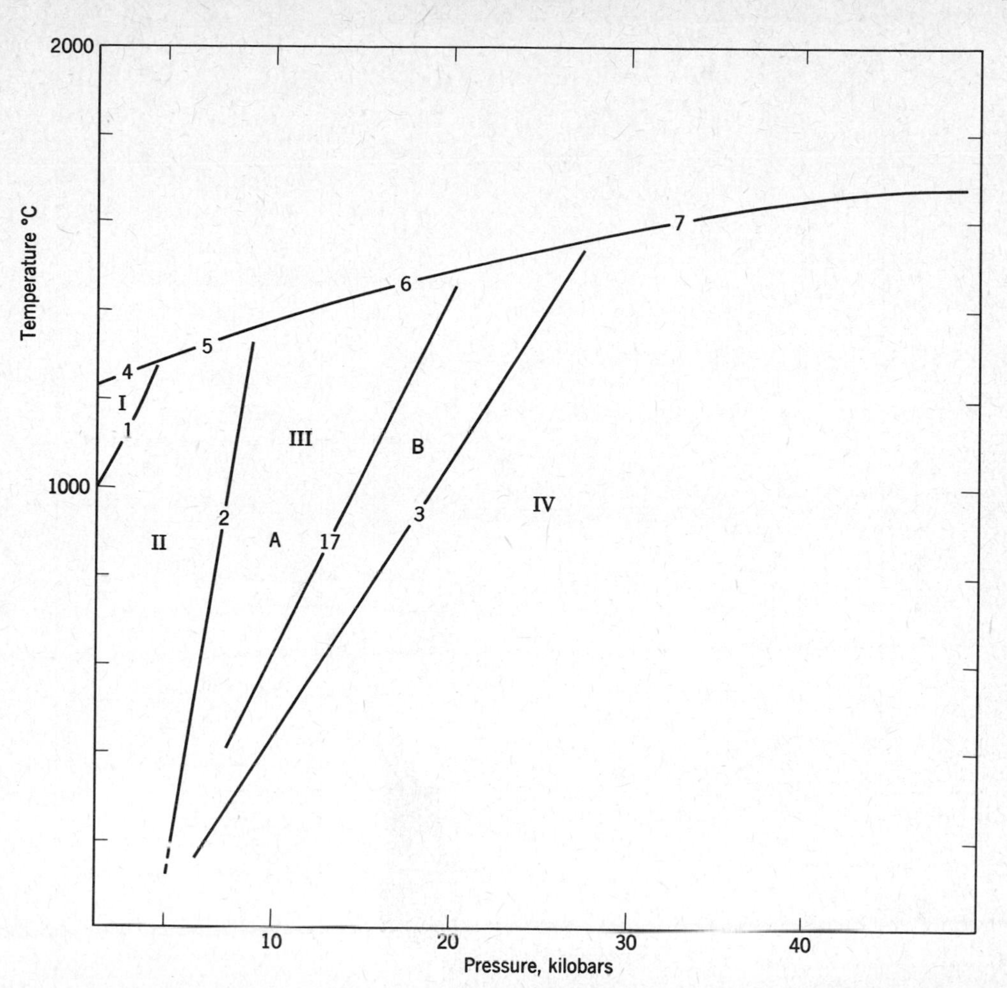

Fig. 1.3 Pressure-temperature relationships of certain equilibria numbered as in the text, based on data from sources cited in the text. The roman numerals indicate the pressure temperature fields occupied by particular mineral facies in ultrabasic materials, numbered as in the text. The precise relationships of many of these equilibria are poorly defined (cf. Fig. 12.2).

suitable basic rock compositions. These are distinguished as:

Seiland subfacies of spinel-lherzolite facies .... IIIA
(diopside + enstatite + anorthite + spinel, observed in rocks described by Oosterom, 1963).

Ariégite subfacies of spinel-lherzolite facies .... IIIB
(diopside + enstatite + garnet + spinel, described by Lacroix, 1900 and 1917).

When H_2O is considered as an extra component it must either dissolve in one of the phases already present, such as the liquid phase, or form an additional phase such as vapor, calciferous amphibole, chlorite, serpentine, talc, or anthophyllite. The solubility of H_2O in forsterite, pyroxenes, anorthite, spinel, and garnet may be ignored, and therefore the reactions 1, 2 and 3 in CMAS will not change significantly if they proceed in the presence of H_2O vapor in CMASH. The facies boundaries 1, 2, and 3 therefore hold in the presence of water vapor up to the beginning

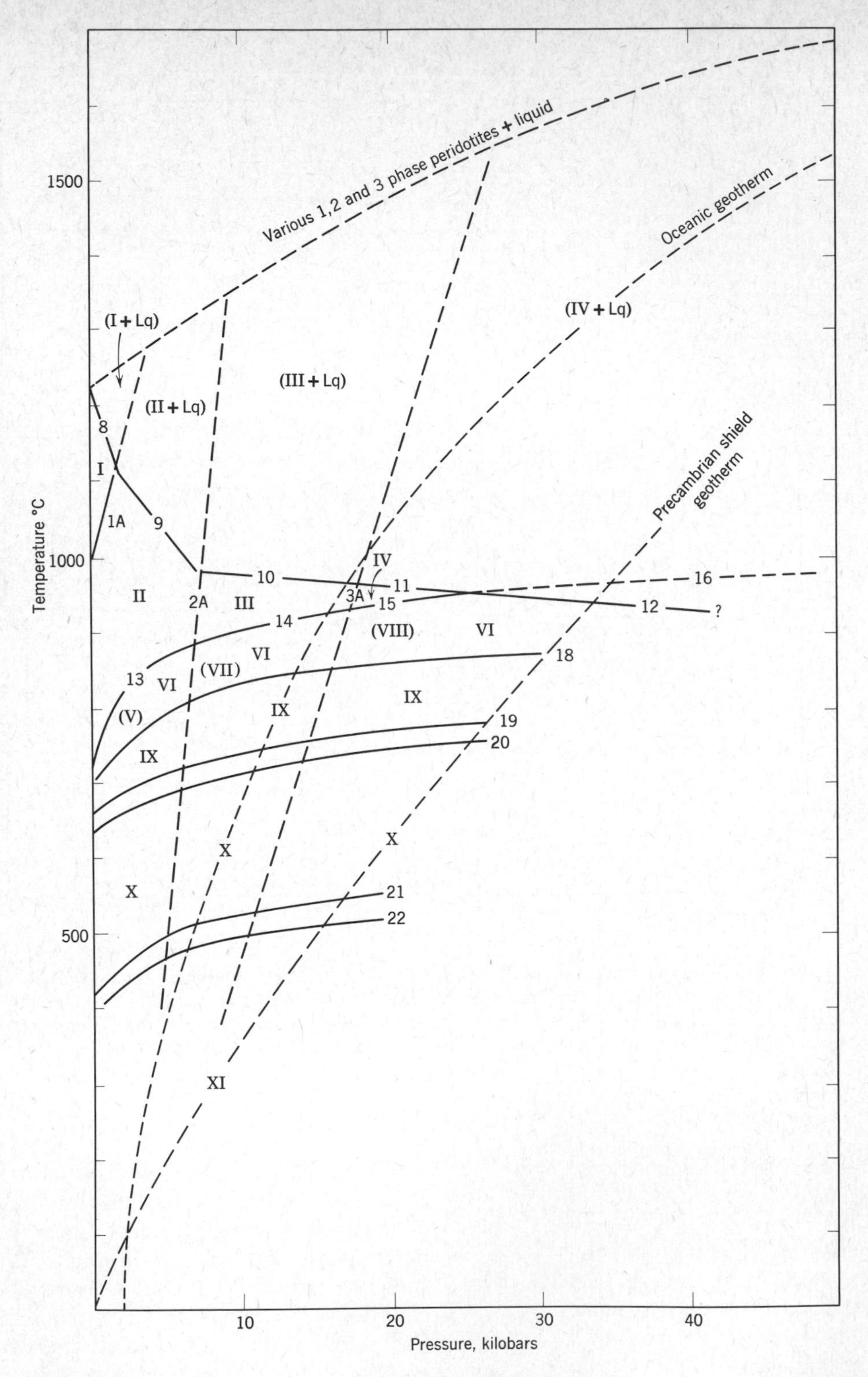

Fig. 1.4 Pressure-temperature relationships of equilibria involving water or water vapor and ultrabasic compositions, similar to Fig. 1.3 and subject to the same reservations. Curves for the equilibria involving hydrous phases have been extrapolated. Solid lines and roman numerals indicate equilibria and facies fields involving presence of a vapor phase. Dashed lines and numerals in parentheses indicate equilibria and facies field which are vapor deficient but which contain a water-bearing phase.

of melting, as reactions 1A, 2A, and 3A. Compare Figs. 1.4 and 1.3. When H_2O dissolves in the liquid phase, the equilibria 4–7 above became divariant equilibria in the system CMASH, and as more water is added the temperature at given pressure at which four anhydrous phases and liquid can coexist decreases. Eventually the liquid is saturated with water and vapor appears in univariant equilibrium with the four crystalline phases and liquid. The univariant equilibria of the system CMASH that represent the beginning of melting of four phase peridotite assemblages in the presence of excess water vapor are shown in Fig. 1.4 as the lines 8, 9, 10, and 11, which correspond to the reactions 4, 5, 6, and 7, respectively, occurring in the presence of a vapor phase. The melting curve 11 passes below the curve for the upper stability limit of amphibole, 15, producing a melting reaction that involves amphibole (12). The positioning of reactions 8–12 is based on a single item of information from Yoder and Chinner (1960a), giving the temperature of equilibrium 10 at 10 kb.

The temperature and pressure ranges of these equilibria also represent the conditions under which the appropriate four-phase peridotites might accumulate from water-saturated basaltic or andesitic melts, or yield these liquids by partial melting (O'Hara, 1965). The pressure range of equilibrium 11 may be very small. Four-phase peridotites may accumulate from water-bearing basic liquids, in the absence of water vapor, throughout the temperature range between the reactions 4–7 and 8–12, the residual liquids becoming progressively enriched in water.

*2. **Amphibole-bearing facies.*** At low-moderate pressures and moderate temperatures any water present can only appear as vapor. At low temperature, however, water may combine to form hydrated phases. The bounding univariant equilibria in the system CMASH involving the formation of amphibole are shown in Fig. 1.4:

Forsterite + amphibole = diopside + enstatite + anorthite + vapor 13

Forsterite + amphibole = diopside + enstatite + spinel + vapor 14

Forsterite + amphibole = diopside + enstatite + garnet + vapor 15

The positions of equilibria 13–15, as well as 16 in Fig. 1.4, are a guess guided by the stability curve of tremolite (in a silica-saturated environment) determined by Boyd (1959).

Two amphibole-bearing facies then arise from each facies existing at temperatures above the stabilization curve of the amphibole. One is vapor-deficient. Clinopyroxene also may be unstable in these conditions particularly when there is little CaO and excess vapor present. The following mineral facies arise:

Hornblende-plagioclase peridotite facies V
(forsterite + diopside + enstatite + anorthite + amphibole)

Hornblende-peridotite facics .. VI
(forsterite + enstatite + amphibole + vapor ± diopside)

Hornblende-spinel-peridotite facies VII
(forsterite + diopside + enstatite + spinel + amphibole) or an extension of VI with excess H_2O present.

Hornblende-garnet-peridotite facies VIII
(forsterite + diopside + enstatite + garnet + amphibole) or an extension of VI with excess H_2O present.

Dashed lines and numerals in brackets in Fig. 1.4 indicate reactions and facies fields that are vapor deficient, but contain a water-bearing phase.

Above a certain pressure, amphibole is stable to the beginning of melting (reaction 12 in Fig. 1.4) but no additional facies arise. However, in the presence of H_2O, facies I to IV have an extensive "igneous" portion in which liquid may be present with the critical subsolidus assemblage. At very high pressures in the presence of adequate water, facies VI also has an increasing "igneous" field. Figure 1.4 shows that the fields of the different facies overlap in the P-T projection.

It is apparent from Fig. 1.4 that once amphibole has become stable on the beginning of the melting curve, there will be another univariant equilibrium curve representing the beginning of melting of water-deficient peridotite at high pressure:

Forsterite + diopside + enstatite + garnet + amphibole + liquid 16

At very high pressures the univariant equilibrium 12 above may terminate in critical phenomena. At pressures above the critical pressure, partial melting or crystallization of lherzolite cannot be said to begin or terminate at any particular temperature, the solid four-phase peridotite assemblage being able to coexist with a dense fluid phase rich in water at all temperatures.

3. Serpentinites and other hydrous facies. At low temperatures and moderate to high pressures, forsterite and enstatite become unstable in the presence of excess water vapor and are replaced by serpentine group minerals, chlorites, talc, and anthophyllite, possibly accompanied by tremolitic amphibole when sufficient calcium is present. Studies on the stability of these minerals in the systems MASH and CMSH have been made by Bowen and Tuttle (1949), Greenwood (1963), Nelson and Roy (1958), Fawcett and Yoder (1963), Fawcett (1964) and Boyd (1959). An approximate transition zone of P-T conditions may be defined within which the olivines, pyroxenes, and Al_2O_3-rich phases will become totally replaced by the low-temperature hydrated phases. The serpentinite facies is defined by the stability of serpentine minerals + chlorite + talc + tremolite. The low temperatures at which the serpentinite facies exists, and the large temperature gap between this and the beginning of melting of ultrabasic compositions in the presence of excess water, throw grave doubt on the existence of serpentinite magmas at low pressures, but may not preclude the existence of fluid systems of serpentine + liquid (rich in sodium silicate for example) at low pressures.

The positions of four equilibria, estimated and extrapolated from the data of authors cited in this section are shown in Fig. 1.4.

Lower temperature limit of stability of an Al_2O_3-rich phase in the presence of olivine, orthopyroxene and vapor; formation of aluminous chlorite in its place 18

Lower limit of stability of magnesian orthopyroxene + vapor; its replacement by anthophyllite. Anthophyllite remains stable in the presence of forsterite and absence of vapor at temperatures down to equilibrium 21 19

Lower limit of stability of anthophyllite in the presence of vapor; replacement by the assemblage talc + forsterite. Between this equilibrium and the next is the field of conditions in which bastite pseudomorphs of orthopyroxene may form without serpentinization of olivine 20

Lower limit of stability of magnesian olivine with talc and vapor; replacement by serpentine 21

Lower limit of stability of olivine with vapor; its replacement by serpentine plus brucite. Onset of total serpentinization in presence of excess vapor 22

These reactions mark the approximate boundaries of a number of vapor saturated mineral facies in ultrabasic rocks, which may be distinguished as follows (Fig. 1.4):

Chlorite-amphibole-peridotite facies IX
(forsterite + enstatite + amphibole + chlorite + vapor)
Bastite-peridotite facies X
(forsterite + talc + chlorite + amphibole + vapor)
Serpentinite facies XI
(serpentine + talc + brucite + chlorite + ?amphibole? + vapor)

There are too few data to justify an attempt to subdivide vapor-deficient but hydrous mineral assemblages in the pressure temperature ranges covered by facies IX to XI at the present time, and interpretation of natural assemblages recrystallized in this low-temperature range is inevitably complicated by partial replacement of one assemblage by another, which introduces an element of subjective judgment as to which phases constitute the equilibrium assemblage.

Estimates of the normal geothermal gradient show it passing through the field of the serpentinite facies at shallow depths (Fig. 1.4). A peridotite upper mantle saturated with water and undergoing convectional cycling would be serpentinized, with a marked volume increase as it rose above a certain depth and deserpentinized in the descending current at a certain depth, precise depths depending upon the local geothermal gradient. These effects play an important part in the model of convection in the upper mantle and continental drift proposed by Hess (1955a).

4. Melilite and monticellite-bearing ultrabasics. Monticellite is found in rare ultrabasic rocks associated with alkaline rock provinces (Bowen, 1922; Buie, 1941) and has recently been reported from kimberlite (Janse, 1964a). Melilites or their alteration products are important constituents of similar ultrabasic rocks, but neither mineral is known from any alpine-type or xenolithic peridotite. These minerals crystallize only in systems that are exceptionally poor in silica, and they cannot coexist stably with orthopyroxene under any known conditions. At low pressures, magnesian melilites and forsteritic olivine may coexist with either diopside or monticellite but not both. Al_2O_3 present in such assemblages is generally accommodated in melilite solid solutions. Monticellite becomes unstable at moderate pressure, likely to be attained within the continental crust, and monticellite peridotites would be replaced by olivine + merwinite + melilite assemblages (Kushiro and Yoder, 1964b). Merwinite has not yet been confirmed from any natural peridotite. At slightly higher pressures corresponding to depths in the uppermost mantle, melilite also becomes unstable, and the assemblage in silica-poor ultrabasic rocks corresponding to the high-pressure part of the spinel-lherzolite facies (III) and the garnet-lherzolite facies (IV), will be a merwinite-diopside-forsterite rock (Kushiro and Yoder, 1964b), perhaps containing a spinel *in both facies.*

Kushiro (1964b) observed that Al_2O_3-poor melilites are unlikely to be found in ultrabasic rocks equilibrated on the normal geothermal gradient.

C. Generalized Facies Model

The model of mineral facies based on the system CMASH must be generalized to take into account the presence of FeO replacing MgO, Fe_2O_3 and Cr_2O_3 in part replacing Al_2O_3, and TiO_2 and Na_2O entering plagioclase, pyroxene, or amphibole. Each new component adds an extra degree of freedom and the univariant equilibria yielding lines separating mineral facies in the P-T diagram (Fig. 1.4) become multivariant transition zones. Because the amounts of other components are small, and vary relatively little, the transition zones between ultrabasic mineral facies will be relatively narrow and only slightly displaced in relation to the univariant equilibria of the system CMASH (cf. Fig.

12.4). The important changes introduced are the following:

1. The stability of Na_2O and TiO_2-bearing amphiboles to higher temperatures than CMASH amphiboles, leading to the elimination of equilibria 10, 11, 14, and 15 of Fig. 1.4 and the substitution of equilibria:

olivine + two pyroxenes + spinel or plagioclase + amphibole + liquid 23
olivine + two pyroxenes + amphibole + liquid + vapor 24

Reaction 24 is an extension to lower pressures of equilibrium 12. This change is a guess inspired by inspection of natural assemblages.

2. Lowering of the temperatures of equilibria 4–10.

3. Potential appearance of an additional phase, chromite, to accommodate Cr_2O_3 in the lower pressure facies, and a resulting rather broad high-pressure region of the orthopyroxene-plagioclase lherzolite facies (II) in which an Al_2O_3-bearing chrome spinel may coexist with olivine, plagioclase and two-pyroxenes. The stability or instability of olivine + plagioclase must be considered the critical distinction between facies II and III here. Chromite may also appear in Al_2O_3-poor bulk compositions in all the facies but Cr_2O_3 will normally be accommodated in Al_2O_3-rich spinel or garnet at higher pressures.

1. Correlation of mineral facies. Approximate correlations between the ultrabasic mineral facies we have suggested and those established by Fyfe, Turner, and Verhoogen (1958) in basic, pelitic, and calcareous rocks, are as follows:

I.	Protohypersthene-plagioclase-lherzolite	=	sanidinite
II.	Orthopyroxene-plagioclase-lherzolite	=	pyroxene hornfels
III.	Spinel-lherzolite	=	granulite
IV.	Garnet-lherzolite	=	eclogite
V.	Hornblende-plagioclase-peridotite	=	hornblende hornfels
VI.	Hornblende-peridotite	=	amphibolite
VII.	Hornblende-spinel-peridotite	=	hornblende granulite
VIII.	Hornblende-garnet-peridotite	=	(hornblende-eclogite?)
IX.	Chlorite-amphibole peridotite	=	parts of amphibolite, albite-epidote amphibolite and greenschist
X and XI.	Bastite-peridotite and part of serpentinite		
XI.	Part of serpentinite	=	glaucophane schist

2. *Ultramafic Rocks in Layered Intrusions*

I. INTRODUCTION

P. J. Wyllie

The gabbro-norite-peridotite association occurs in layered intrusions ranging in size from large, stratiform lopoliths to the small funnel-shaped Skaergaard intrusion, which is one of the most thoroughly studied igneous bodies in the world. A recent symposium volume (Fisher et al., 1963) describes several layered intrusions, and Turner and Verhoogen (1960) review the petrology of the association. Wager and Brown (1966) have treated the subject in detail, but unfortunately their book is not available at the time of this writing.

Most petrologists agree that the layered ultramafic rocks of this association developed in floored chambers as superposed accumulations of crystals formed during the fractional crystallization of a parent gabbroic magma of tholeiitic type. The influence of gravity in causing crystal settling is evident, but an additional process is required to explain the formation of cyclic units within the layers. Those proposed include the operation of convection cells in the magma chamber, and the intermittent intrusion of new magma into the chamber; both processes involve the flow of magma across the underlying cumulates.

In Section II Jackson outlines the geologic setting of the Stillwater, Great Dyke, and Bushveld intrusions and provides a detailed review of their ultramafic zones. He emphasizes that similarities between these intrusions have been obscured by differences in terminology used by previous authors. The ultramafic rocks in this association are essentially magmatic sediments with readily distinguishable cumulus and postcumulus crystals. Jackson stresses the importance of using the cumulus minerals to classify these rocks and indicates the confusion caused if they are classified in terms of total mineral modal content. He offers a standard nomenclature based on sedimentary terminology adapted for description of these magmatic sediments. With Jackson's classification and nomenclature, significant features of layering contacts become more evident. He notes essential differences between the three intrusions reviewed, where layers are generally bounded by a change in the single cumulus mineral, and those of Skaergaard and Rhum, where layers are generally bounded by changes in ratio of the several cumulus minerals. Jackson's nomenclature should facilitate studies of similar intrusions, and of the association as a whole.

In Section III Irvine and Smith describe the Muskox intrusion as a model example of the formation of ultramafic rocks by fractional crystallization of a basic magma. The layered series has 42 contrasting layers with areas of approximately 40 to 100 square miles. The recurrence of two distinct cyclic units in the layered series of ultramafic rocks is explained by the repeated intrusion of fresh magma which is presumed to flow gently over the full width of the undisturbed, underlying layers. The appropriate sequences of silicate phases in the two cyclic units can be simulated by fractional crystallization in the systems diopside-forsterite-silica and diopside-forsterite-anorthite. Evaluation of the distribution of nickel between olivine and liquid leads to the conclusion that each cycle was accompanied by the displacement of "old" magma by the inflow of "new" magma. They propose that the "old" magma is pushed on and erupted through volcanic fissures, which would explain why the intrusion now contains a disproportionate amount of ultramafic material compared to the composition of the chilled gabbroic margin. Irvine and Smith conclude that gravitational settling of mineral grains in plutonic basalt magma is almost inevitable, and this must be a prime consideration in studies of the origin of ultramafic rocks.

Although layering characterizes the ultramafic rocks of this association, it occurs also in other ultramafic rock associations. Layering occurs in many of the concentrically zoned ultramafic complexes reviewed by Taylor in Chapter 4-III. In one of these complexes, Duke Island (described by Irvine in Chapter 4-II), there is spectacular development of gravitational layering, with evidence of strong current action. The alkalic ultrabasic ring complexes referred to by Upton in Chapter 9-II also exhibit gravity-controlled layering. Tomkeieff (1961) compared the component rocks of the alkalic massifs of the Khibina and Lovozero Tundras of U.S.S.R. to the Skaergaard intrusion, because they are funnel-shaped, with ultrabasic layers of urtite, jacupirangite, and apatite-nepheline rocks stacked up like a pile of saucers. Layering of various kinds also occurs in the alpine-type intrusions described in Chapters 5, 6, and 7. According to Thayer (Chapter 7-IV) the layering or banding in alpine-type peridotites appears to be largely deformational in origin and more characteristic of metamorphic rocks than sedimentary cumulates. However, the preservation of layering that does appear to be gravity controlled indicates that some alpine-type intrusions could represent layered rocks of the gabbro-norite-peridotite association that became involved in the regional deformation, were metamorphosed, and subsequently emplaced tectonically (see Green, Chapter 7-III; O'Hara, Chapter 5-IV; Challis, 1965a).

II. ULTRAMAFIC CUMULATES IN THE STILLWATER, GREAT DYKE, AND BUSHVELD INTRUSIONS

Everett D. Jackson

A. Introduction

Of the eight or ten known major gabbroic intrusions, three—the Stillwater intrusion in the United States, the Great Dyke in Rhodesia, and the Bushveld intrusion in the Republic of South Africa—appear to be remarkably similar in bulk composition, internal form and structure, mineralogy, and texture. Each of them is of large areal extent and is undisputedly stratiform; each contains a considerable proportion of ultramafic rocks; and, fortunately, each has been the subject of comprehensive investigations in recent years. It has been agreed, moreover, by most of the modern investigators that the igneous rocks of these great bodies originated as superposed accumulations of crystals formed during the fractional differentiation of magma in floored chambers. The rocks of these three intrusions may therefore be regarded as a type plutonic assemblage of simple, self-seeded, magmatic sediments. The purpose of this section is to present a standard nomenclature adapted for use in describing the common features of these magmatic sediments; and, more especially, to enumerate, compare, and contrast the primary internal features of the ultramafic zones of the three intrusions. The Muskox intrusion in Canada, which has a number of features common to this group, is described in Chapter 2-III.

B. Nomenclature

Unfortunately, many of the similarities in texture, rock type, and stratigraphy in the Stillwater, Great Dyke, and Bushveld intrusions are obscured by differences in terminology used by the various authors who have described them. A consistent basis of comparison is needed, and definitions of terms used in this paper are summarized in Table 2.1. I take full responsibility for any errors made or misconceptions created in applying these terms to features described by other authors.

1. Components of rocks formed by crystal accumulation. When it is assumed that rocks are formed by crystal settling, it is implied that these rocks are divisible into two classes of material: 1) the grains or crystals that settled and became packed together to make the framework of the rocks; and 2) the material that later crystallized in place to cement the settled particles together. This distinction between grains and cement, so orthodox among sedimentary petrologists, has gained slow acceptance among workers in accumulative igneous rocks. Early attempts were made to distinguish the two classes of material (Wager and Deer 1939, p. 127; and Hess, 1939, pp. 430–432). Wager and Deer's terms "primary precipitate crystal" and "interprecipitate material" were widely accepted. These terms, however, as originally defined, failed to provide for what sedimentary petrologists would call "overgrowth" or "secondary enlargement," a process that plays an important part in the formation of magmatic sediments (Hess, 1939, p. 431; Brown, 1956, p. 37; Jackson, 1961a, pp. 52–61).

More recently, Wager, Brown, and Wadsworth (1960, p. 73) proposed the terms "cumulus crystal," "intercumulus liquid," and "intercumulus material," which are now coming into general use. Their definition of "intercumulus material," however, though it included material formed by secondary enlargement, failed to provide for material formed by partial replacement of "cumulus crystals," which is also an important process in the formation of certain kinds of accumulative rocks (Cameron and Emerson, 1959, pp. 1189–1191; Worst, 1960, p. 87; Jackson, 1961a, pp. 47–52).

An almost identical problem in classification of particulate matter in sedimentary rocks was recognized many years ago (Kalkowsky, 1880, p. 4), and modern usage in describing such rocks is unambiguous (Pettijohn, 1957, pp. 107–112). Wager, Brown, and Wadsworth's term "cumulus crystal" is therefore redefined in Table 2.1 to conform with sedimentary terminology. The term "settled crystal" is synonymous and self-explanatory, and I prefer to use it where it is not closely followed by or contrasted with the other terms for components. Wager, Brown, and Wadsworth's term "intercumulus liquid" is retained. To avoid parallelism their term "intercumulus material" is replaced by "postcumulus material," which is defined in accordance with sedimentary usage.

2. Names for rocks formed by crystal accumulation. Wager, Brown, and Wadsworth (1960, p. 73) proposed the term "cumulate" as a group name for rocks formed by crystal accumulation. Their definition is adopted in Table 2.1. The term "magmatic sediment" is synonymous and

TABLE 2.1 Terms Used to Describe Rocks Formed by Crystal Accumulation

I. Components of Rocks Formed by Crystal Accumulation
  A. *Cumulus crystal = settled crystal*—a crystal (mineral) that came into existence outside of, and previously to, the magmatic sediment of which it now forms a part.
  B. *Postcumulus material*—primary material that formed in the places it now occupies in the magmatic sediment.
  C. *Intercumulus liquid*—the liquid that occupied the interstices between the cumulus crystals before and during the growth of the postcumulus material.

II. Rocks Formed by Crystal Accumulation
  A. *Cumulate = magmatic sediment*—a group name for igneous rocks formed by crystal accumulation through the action of gravity.
  B. *Classification of rocks by cumulus minerals.*
    1. Semiquantitative—based on cumulus crystals only; cumulus minerals are listed in order of decreasing abundance; e.g., olivine-orthopyroxene cumulate.
    2. Quantitative—based on cumulus crystals only; the measured volume proportions of cumulus minerals are listed by subscript; e.g., the proportions of cumulus minerals in the cumulate are $ol_{75}opx_{25}$.
  C. *Classification of rocks by mode of all minerals.*
    1. Standard modal classification (such as Peterson, 1960, p. 33) based on all minerals of the rock, whether cumulus or postcumulus; e.g., the bronzite cumulate is dominantly bronzitite, but locally it is websterite or norite.

III. Horizons in Cumulates
  A. *Horizon*—a reference plane in a cumulate that marks a former surface of deposition.
    1. *Phase contact*—a horizon marked by the appearance or disappearance of a cumulus mineral.
    2. *Ratio contact*—a horizon marked by a sharp change in the proportions of two cumulus minerals.
    3. *Form contact*—a horizon marked by a sharp change in the physical properties of a cumulus mineral, such as size or habit.

IV. Layers in Cumulates
  A. *Lamina*—the smallest recognizable unit layer in a cumulate.
    1. *Planar lamination*—platy parallelism of one or more cumulus minerals in a cumulate.
    2. *Lineate lamination*—linear parallelism of one or more cumulus minerals in a cumulate.
  B. *Layer*—a continuous sheetlike cumulate that is characterized by uniform or uniformly gradational properties.
    1. Layering based on proportions of cumulus minerals.
      a. *Isomodal layer*—a layer characterized by a uniform proportion of one or more cumulus minerals.
      b. *Mineral-graded layer*—a layer characterized by a gradual stratigraphic change in proportions of two or more cumulus minerals.
    2. Layering based on physical properties or composition of cumulus minerals.
      a. *Size-graded layer*—a layer characterized by a gradual stratigraphic change of grain size of one or more cumulus minerals.
      b. *Chemical-graded layer*—a layer characterized by a gradual stratigraphic change in chemical composition of one or more cumulus minerals.

V. Groups of Layers in Cumulates
  A. *Zone*—an informal, mappable, rock-stratigraphic unit in a layered intrusion, characterized by lithologic homogeneity or distinctive lithologic features.
  B. *Member*—an informal subdivision of a zone.

self-explanatory, but longer; I use it only where a question of meaning or euphony is involved.

a. Classification of rocks by cumulus or postcumulus material. The necessity for special classification of cumulates arises from their particulate nature. Their composition does not approximate that of the magmatic liquids from which they crystallized, and the composition and character of cumulus crystals and postcumulus material are virtually independent. Hesitancy to use a cumulate classification has led to a chaotic jumble of rock names based on total modes (see Table 2.4). Classification of cumulates may be based either on the character of the cumulus crystals or on that of the postcumulus material. Wager, Brown, and Wadsworth (1960, pp. 74–79) presented a primary subdivision of cumulates based on the amount of postcumulus secondary enlargement of cumulus crystals. This classification indicates what sedimentary petrologists call milieu (Pettijohn, 1957, p. 108), and is akin to classifying sandstones by their cement. In this paper the self-evident terms "simple postcumulus space-filling," "postcumulus overgrowth," and "postcumulus replacement" will be used to describe the processes that occur to modify and cement the settled crystals after deposition.

However, Wager, Brown, and Wadsworth (1960, p. 85) also presented a classification based on the character and proportions of settled crystals in cumulates, and suggested that such rocks be named by prefixing the settled minerals in order of decreasing abundance. This system indicates provenance (Pettijohn, 1957, p. 108) and is therefore much more useful for purposes of mapping and description than one based on milieu. The classification is adopted in this paper, but I must emphasize that whereas the term "cumulate" alone refers to a whole rock formed by crystal accumulation, the named mineral modifiers refer only to the settled crystals that form the framework of the cumulate. Thus one would speak of an olivine cumulate in the same sense as one does of a quartz sandstone. A quantitative variant lists proportions of settled crystals directly as ratios (Jackson, 1961a, p. 90–91). The notations are summarized in Table 2.1.

b. Classification of rocks by total mode. If cumulates are clearly classified by the kinds of settled minerals they contain, then conventional igneous rock classifications may be used to express their total mineralogical composition (see Table 2.1). An ultramafic cumulate is not necessarily an ultramafic rock, any more than a quartz sandstone is necessarily a quartzite. In the Stillwater Complex, for example, a particular unit that contains only olivine as a settled mineral (an olivine cumulate) may be a dunite in one locality where postcumulus overgrowth has been the dominant cementing process. The same olivine cumulate unit, however, may be a gabbro in another locality along strike, where entrapment of intercumulus liquid has resulted in cementation by postcumulus plagioclase and pyroxene.

3. Kinds of horizons and layers in cumulates. The layering in cumulates is evidenced by stratigraphic changes in proportion, grain size, or composition of settled crystals. Such layering, which corresponds to bedding in sedimentary rocks, is caused by changes in supply or dispersal of settled crystals at the surface of deposition. Most petrologists have followed the layering nomenclature of Wager and Deer (1939, pp. 36–38), and have used their terms "rhythmic layering," "igneous lamination," and "cryptic layering." But while this nomenclature served in describing the tabular features of the Skaergaard intrusion, for which it was intended, it has several shortcomings in its applications to intrusions of the Stillwater–Great Dyke–Bushveld type. The terms "band" and "seam," for example, which designate layers caused by abrupt mineralogical changes, and which have no direct counterpart in Wager and Deer's classifications, are in common use among students of layered intrusions of Africa. For similar features in the Stillwater Complex, Hess (1960a, p. 51) proposed the term "phase layering," which he defined as "the abrupt appearance or disappearance of a precipitated crystalline phase or phases during the course of crystallization of a magma." Hess's "phase layer," however, is not a very useful mapping unit because it is primarily defined as an horizon rather than a stratigraphic unit of finite thickness.

The terms applied to horizons and layers in this paper are defined in Table 2.1. The term "phase contact" is suggested by Hess's "phase layering," but is redefined as a boundary plane. The terms "phase contact" and "ratio contact" are mutually exclusive; a "form contact" may or may not coincide with either one. The term "planar lamination" is equivalent to Wager and Deer's "igneous lamination," but modified in order to contrast with "lineate lamination." The layer types are newly coined. The overwhelming majority of layers seen in the field are visible by reason of changes in relative proportions of their settled minerals. The terms "isomodal layer" and "mineral-graded layer" apply to structures of this type. These two terms are mutually exclusive, and a particular layer must be one or the other. The terms "size-graded layer" and "chemical-graded layer" apply to less obvious structures caused by changes in size and composition of settled minerals. These terms are not mutually exclusive, and doubtless many other kinds of layers based on other physical properties of settled crystals could be added to this part of the list. Size-graded and chemical-graded layers may be present or absent in a sequence of layers due to changes of relative proportions of settled minerals; their contacts may or may not coincide with those of isomodal or mineral-graded layers.

4. Groups of layers in cumulates. Mappable groups of layers that are fundamental rock-stratigraphic units of local classification would ordinarily be called "formations." Workers in layered complexes, however, have called such units "zones," and have called subdivisions of zones "members." Definitions of these terms as used here are given in Table 2.1. Use of the term "complex" has been less uniform; perhaps it is best thought of in this paper as a group of zones and their chilled border rocks.

On a smaller scale, Wager and Deer's (1939, p. 37) term "rhythmic layering" describes a group of layers that could be redefined as "a sequence of 'right-side-up' mineral-graded layers." Similarly, Jackson's (1961a, p. 14, 91–93) "cyclic unit" consists of a sequence of particular isomodal and mineral-graded layers that are repeated a number of times. Both terms, however, were defined in some detail by their originators, and it seems better to use them as defined.

C. Geologic Setting of the Stillwater, Great Dyke, and Bushveld Intrusions

It is not within the scope of this presentation to compare and contrast all aspects of the character and origin of the Stillwater, Great Dyke, and Bushveld intrusions. Neither is an historical treatment attempted; complete bibliographies are contained in the principal references cited. The underlying assumption in what follows is that the layered rocks of all three intrusions are cumulates. All modern students of the Stillwater intrusion and the Great Dyke agree that their rocks are magmatic sediments, but there is no such unanimity of opinion regarding the origin of the Bushveld intrusion. While Cameron and Emerson (1959), Willemse (1959), Hess (1960a), and Cameron (1963) are convinced of the accumulative nature of part or all of the Bushveld rocks, S. van Biljon (1949) proposes the interesting hypothesis that this complex was formed by transformation of sediments of the Pretoria Series; Coertze (1958, 1960) and Coertze and Schumann (1962) hold that it was formed by repeated injections of heterogenous sills; and

Cousins (1959) is rather inclined to think it was formed by repeated extrusion of exotic lavas. In my opinion, the similarities of Bushveld rocks to those of the Stillwater and the Great Dyke, as later noted, are so fundamental that the three intrusions must be similar, though not necessarily identical, in origin.

1. Geologic age. Absolute age measurements of a number of minerals and rocks from the Stillwater intrusion are currently being made by the United States Geological Survey. Preliminary results on K-Ar ratios in the Ultramafic and Basal zones indicate an age of at least 3200 m.y. (million years) for the intrusion (J. Obradovich and R. Kistler, personal communication).

Rb-Sr and K-Ar measurements on biotites from the ultramafic rocks of the Great Dyke by Allsopp (1965) have indicated a lower age limit of 2530 ± 30 m.y.

Nicolaysen and others (1958) gave an age of 1950 ± 150 m.y. for the Bushveld intrusion, based on absolute determinations from a variety of minerals by several methods. Most of the determinations, however, were made on material from the Bushveld granites, whose relations to the mafic and ultramafic rocks of the intrusion are in doubt (Hess, 1960a, p. 164). But one Rb-Sr determination of 2050 ± 50 m.y. was made on biotite from a pyroxenite.

At the present state of knowledge, it seems best to regard the values for all three intrusions as minimum ages.

2. Primary magma type. Two methods of determining the primary magma type of each of the three intrusions have been tried: (a) chemical analysis of chilled border rocks, and (b) summation of the compositions of all the differentiated layers of the intrusion. Hess (1960a, pp. 151–167) has summarized the shortcomings of both methods, and, in addition, Smith and Kapp (1963, pp. 34–35) have emphasized the uncertainty introduced by differential movement of phenocrysts in the feeders during emplacement. Nevertheless, the two approaches permit some general conclusions about primary compositions to be made, particularly in the case of the Stillwater intrusion, whose chilled border rocks contain no intratelluric crystals.

Hess (1960a, p. 53) cites a chilled gabbro from the Stillwater intrusion as reasonably representative of its original magma composition. The analysis is within the normal range of basalts, but rather high in aluminum (17.64 per cent Al_2O_3). It is doubtful that Hess's analysis is representative. Three more recent analyses (Jackson, unpublished data) of chilled gabbros show a range of Al_2O_3 content from 13 to 15 per cent, which indicates a tholeiitic composition. A complete volumetric summation cannot be made for the Stillwater intrusion because the top is nowhere exposed; nevertheless the ratio of exposed gabbroic rocks to exposed ultramafic rocks in cross section is about 4:1, and Hess's (1960a, p. 102) composite analysis of the entire exposed section gives an average composition that could be that of a basalt.

No exposures of a lower chilled margin of the Great Dyke have been found (Worst, 1960, p. 155). Hess (1950, p. 169) has described what he regards as the remnants of an upper chilled margin, but Worst (1960, p. 82) doubts this interpretation on stratigraphic grounds. The thickest known section of gabbroic rocks in the Great Dyke is less than half as thick as the ultramafic rocks beneath it (Worst, 1960, Plate II). Hess (1950) does not regard this stratigraphic preponderance of ultramafic rocks as evidence of an unusually mafic magma, but suggests that a thin sheet of gabbroic rocks, since eroded away, may have extended a considerable distance beyond the present narrow outcrop of the Great Dyke, and Worst (1960, p. 168) agrees that this is likely.

The problems relative to the composition of the lower chilled margin of the Bushveld intrusion have been summarized by Willemse (1959) and by Hess (1960a, pp. 153–165). Both believe the original magma to have been basaltic, and Hess (1960a, p. 152) selects an analysis by Daly

(1928) as being most nearly representative of its average composition. The ratio of gabbroic rocks to ultramafic rocks in the Bushveld intrusion is about 6:1 (Hall, 1932; Cameron, 1963), and composite analyses, even excluding the controversial Bushveld granite, would probably be within the basaltic range of composition.

On the whole, then, there appears to be no necessity to call on preintrusion differentiation or exotic magma types to account for the bulk composition of the three intrusions. To judge from our present incomplete knowledge, the primary magma type of the Stillwater and Bushveld intrusions was almost certainly basalt, and the primary magma type of the Great Dyke could have been similar.

3. Gross structure and stratigraphy. The Stillwater is the best exposed of the three intrusions, but has by far the smallest area of outcrop. It has been completely mapped on a scale of 1:62,500 (Jones, Peoples, and Howland, 1960) and much of it has been mapped on scales ranging from 1:12,000 to 1:1,200 [Peoples and Howland (1940); Howland, Garrels, and Jones (1949); Peoples, Howland, Jones, and Flint (1954); Jackson, Howland, Peoples, and Jones (1954); Howland (1955)]. This mapping shows that the intrusion consists of a single complex that strikes northwest across the northern margin of the Beartooth Mountains over a distance of about 30 miles. The dips of the layered rocks range from steeply north to overturned, and the exposed portion is believed to be the edge of a much larger saucer-shaped body that is buried under the plains to the north. The southern (lower) contact of the complex is intrusive into and chilled against pelitic sedimentary rocks of Precambrian age, which were metamorphosed to cordiertite-hypersthene-biotite-quartz hornfels (Howland, 1954; Butler, 1964). Pyroxene-hornfels metamorphic facies extends as much as 3000 feet vertically below the lower contact of the complex. The northern (upper) contact of the complex is an erosional unconformity covered by Paleozoic sedimentary rocks.

Internally, the Stillwater Complex consists of a series of conformably interlayered magmatic sediments 18,000 feet in stratigraphic thickness, (Jones, Peoples, and Howland, 1960, p. 287); Hess (1960a, p. 104) estimates that another 10,000 feet of section has been eroded away. Although the complex has been divided into a number of zones and subzones by Peoples (1936) and Hess (1960a), its most important and persistent horizon is the phase contact that marks the lower limit of settled plagioclase. Below this horizon lies the Ultramafic zone (Jackson, 1961a, p. 4, 91), which has an average stratigraphic thickness of 3500 feet and is composed entirely of layered cumulates that contain settled olivine, orthopyroxene, and chromite. No settled plagioclase occurs within the Ultramafic zone, and no layers above the Ultramafic zone are free of it.

Geologic maps of the Great Dyke were compiled by Lightfoot as early as 1940. Since that time the Dyke has been completely mapped on a scale of 1:100,000 by Worst (1960). The Great Dyke trends a little east of north across 332 miles of Rhodesia, and varies in width from 3 to 7 miles. Worst (1958, 1960) describes the Dyke as consisting of four separate complexes: the Musengezi at the north end, 27 miles long; the Hartley, 195 miles long; the Selukwe, 60 miles long, and the Wedza, at the south end, 50 miles long. Each of the complexes is layered, and the layering in each forms a shallow, doubly plunging syncline. The elongate shape of the Dyke is partly a consequence of elongate feeders to these sheet-like complexes, and partly a result of the formation of longitudinal graben at the margins. The Dyke was intruded into crystalline rocks—Archean granite for the most part—and is bordered by a metamorphic aureole a few hundred feet wide (Worst, 1960, p. 128). Where the complex is in contact with more mafic rocks, pyroxene granulites and hornfels have been produced (Zealley, 1919, p. 24).

Large inclusions in the Dyke show high-grade thermal metamorphism (Tyndale-Biscoe, 1949, p. 40). Internally, each of the four complexes constituting the Dyke consists of remarkably similar sections of magmatic sediments ranging in stratigraphic thickness from 6000 to 12,000 feet. Neither the top nor bottom of any one of these complexes is known to be exposed, but gravimetric data (Weiss, 1940, Worst, 1960) indicate that their roots extend to considerable depths.

The internal stratigraphy of the Dyke complexes is described by Worst (1960, Plate II); its most striking feature is that each complex is divided by a phase contact that marks the lower limit of settled plagioclase. The minimum thicknesses of the ultramafic zones that lie below this horizon range from 5000 feet in the Selukwe complex to 11,700 feet in the Musengezi complex. The rocks of these zones appear to be cumulates that contain settled olivine, orthopyroxene, and chromite. No settled plagioclase occurs within the zones, and, apparently, no cumulates above the zones are free of it.

The Bushveld intrusion is by far the largest of the three, and structurally the most complex, but the South Africa Geological Survey had mapped it on a scale of 1:148,750 by 1931. More recently, Survey Sheet 4 (Rustenburg) has been remapped by Backström and others (1960), Sheet 3 (Middelburg) by Visser and others (1961), and Sheet 13 (Olifants River) by Schwellnus and others (1962), all on a scale of 1:125,000. A great many larger scale maps of parts of the Bushveld intrusion have been published, and Willemse (1959) has given a good summary of the results up to the end of 1958. Since that time the maps made by Cameron and Emerson (1959), Heckroodt (1959), Hiemstra and van Biljon (1959), and Cameron (1963) in the Eastern Bushveld; and by Fourie (1959), Coertze (1960), Coertze and Schumann (1962), and Coertze (1963) in the Western Bushveld, have been published.

The rocks of the Bushveld intrusion crop out over a great oval area 290 miles long and 170 miles wide. In a general way, the ultramafic and gabbroic rocks form an outer ring around a central basin that consists largely of Bushveld granite (Hall, 1932). The Bushveld intrusion has long been interpreted as a single complex—a vast lopolith intrusive into, and virtually conformable with, the rocks of the Pretoria Series. Wilson (1956) gave reasons for believing that the complex was not a lopolith, but funnel-shaped, the base dipping more steeply than the layering. A recent gravity survey of the Bushveld area has prompted Cousins (1959) and Smit (1962) to propose the hypothesis that the ring of outliers of ultramafic and gabbroic rocks is composed of narrow, curved, moatlike troughs with dikelike feeders, and that the layering in these troughs forms shallow synclines like those in the Great Dyke. Cousins (1959) concludes that at least four separate complexes are present, an idea previously advanced on other grounds by Truter (1955). The outer (lower) contact of the complex (or complexes) is intrusive into rocks of the Pretoria Series, and fine-grained, presumably chilled "norite" is exposed at the contact in some places (Hall, 1932, pp. 308–311; Hess, 1960a, pp. 158–161). Hall (1932, Plate 41) shows an aureole of progressive metamorphism around the outer circumference of the complex that affects as much as 13,000 feet of sedimentary strata. Metamorphosed argillites in the Pretoria Series range from the pyroxene-hornfels facies to greenschist facies, the rocks of higher facies being consistently closer to the footwall of the complex (Willemse, 1959). Along the inner (upper) contact, the stratigraphically highest gabbroic rocks of the Bushveld complex are in places chilled against highly metamorphosed sedimentary rocks of the Rooiburg Series (Hall, 1932, pp. 408–409; Hess, 1960a, pp. 161–164). The controversy regarding the origin of the Bushveld granite is not essential to this discussion.

Internally, the Bushveld complex consists of conformably interlayered magmatic sediments (Hall, 1932, pp. 264–265; Cameron, 1963, p. 101). The Eastern Bushveld section north of the Steelpoort River was divided by Hall (1932, Table XXII) into five major stratigraphic units totalling as much as 18,000 feet in stratigraphic thickness. In this area all the ultramafic cumulates (except the magnetitites, which have no counterparts in the Stillwater or Great Dyke intrusions) lie within his Transition and Critical Zones, that is, in the lower 7000 feet of the section above his Basal Zone. In the Western Bushveld, they lie within Hall's "Lower Portion," about 7000 feet stratigraphically above the diabasic quartz norite. Cameron and Abendroth (1956) further subdivided the Critical Zone in the Eastern Bushveld into a lower pyroxenite series and an upper anorthosite series. The pyroxenite series consists of cumulates that principally contain settled orthopyroxene, with lesser amounts of settled olivine, plagioclase, and chromite. The pyroxenite series differs radically from the ultramafic zones of the other two intrusions in that (a) settled plagioclase occurs within it, and (b) cumulates that contain settled chromite and orthopyroxene but no settled plagioclase occur above it, though in small quantities. Cameron's pyroxenite series as originally defined does not extend south of the Steelpoort River (E. N. Cameron, personal communication). But a unit of predominantly ultramafic rocks apparently does continue southward through the Lydenburg district (Lombaard, 1934), and pinches out around the southeastern part of the great Bushveld oval (Lombaard, 1950). In the Western Bushveld, a similar ultramafic zone, comprising the rocks between the Middle Chromite Group of Kupferbürger and Lombaard (1937) and the floor of the complex, appears near Brits (Lombaard, 1934), gradually thickens to the west and north (Backström, 1960), and reaches its maximum thickness of 5500 feet north of Pilandsberg (Coertze, 1958). Whether this western ultramafic section correlates with the pyroxenite series in the Eastern Bushveld, as Hess (1960a) believes, or whether it is part of a separate complex (Cousins, 1959), it clearly resembles the Eastern Bushveld section, and not the simpler section of the Stillwater and Great Dyke. The stratigraphic columns of Coertze (1958), Fourie (1959), Feringa (1959), and Coertze and Schumann (1962) show that some settled plagioclase occurs below the Middle Chromite Group, and that some chromite and orthopyroxene cumulates occur above it.

D. Ultramafic Zones of the Stillwater, Great Dyke, and Bushveld Intrusions

The Ultramafic zone of the Stillwater Complex was defined by Jackson (1961a, p. 4). In terms of settled minerals, it consists of the cumulates that lie between the lowest horizon at which settled olivine appears and the lowest horizon at which settled plagioclase appears.

The four complexes of the Great Dyke are extremely similar; for the purposes of brief comparison, the following discussion will be restricted to the ultramafic zone of the Hartley complex (Worst, 1960). In terms of settled minerals, it consists of the cumulates that lie below the lowest horizon at which settled plagioclase appears.

The ultramafic zones of the Eastern and Western Bushveld appear to be much alike, but those of the Eastern have been more thoroughly investigated. The ultramafic zone will therefore be taken as the pyroxenite series of Cameron (1963), which consists of the cumulates that lie stratigraphically below the top of his pyroxenite unit L. The ultramafic zone thus includes some cumulates with settled plagioclase. If it were defined to include only the rocks that lie below the lowest horizon at which settled plagioclase appears, the upper contact would lie at the top of Cameron's pyroxenite unit E. Such a definition, unlike the parallel one for the Stillwater and Great Dyke, does not seem warranted because it would place a considerable volume of cumulates that contain only settled orthopyroxene above the upper boundary.

Recent work by E. N. Cameron and by J. Willemse (unpublished) in the Eastern Bushveld has revealed previously unknown sections of olivine-rich ultramafic rocks that lie below the pyroxenite series (E. N. Cameron, personal communication). While the presence of these rocks will not affect the upper boundary problem, it should ultimately tend to increase the resemblance between the Eastern Bushveld ultramafic zone and those of the Stillwater and Hartley complexes.

The three ultramafic zones, as presently known, are compared and contrasted in the following section.

1. Mineralogy. A summary of available data on the mineralogy of the three ultramafic zones is given in Table 2.2. Although the striking similarities of mineralogy are obvious, there are some minor but significant differences. The proportion of settled olivine is much greater in the ultramafic zone of the Hartley complex (and in the other Great Dyke complexes) than in the Stillwater or the Eastern Bushveld zones. It is probably no coincidence that the Mg content of all the settled minerals, and the Cr content of the chromites, in the Hartley complex are significantly greater than in comparable Stillwater and Bushveld settled minerals. The proportion of settled olivine is greater in the Stillwater Ultramafic zone than in the Eastern Bushveld zone, but no significant differences in compositions of settled minerals are apparent. It is possible that settled clinopyroxene occurs in the uppermost part of the ultramafic zone of the Hartley complex (see descriptions by Keep (1930, p. 23) and Worst (1960, p. 67) but I am assuming that it does not. Only the Bushveld ultramafic zone contains settled plagioclase, and, as previously noted, this could technically be eliminated by a redefinition of stratigraphic units.

The proportions and compositions of the settled minerals suggest that the parent basalt of the Great Dyke was comparatively enriched in MgO and impoverished in SiO_2 compared to the Stillwater and Bushveld basalts. From the data of Table 2.2 it seems possible that the parent basalt of the Bushveld intrusion was somewhat richer in SiO_2 and Al_2O_3 than the Stillwater basalt, but this conclusion will be subject to modification when information on the mineralogy of the recently discovered olivine-rich Bushveld rocks becomes available.

2. Textures. Hess (1960a, pp. 113–114) and Jackson (1961a, pp. 11–81) have stressed the sedimentary-type textures of the rocks of the Stillwater Complex, and the fundamental importance of distinguishing between cumulus and postcumulus material. Although the general concept of "sunken crystals" has been familiar to workers in Africa for many years, only Hess (1950, 1960a), Cameron and Emerson (1959), and Guilbert (1962) have attempted to distinguish settled particles in individual rocks of the Great Dyke and Bushveld intrusions. A summary of the textural features of cumulates, based largely on the textures of the rocks of the Ultramafic zone of the Stillwater Complex, is given in Table 2.3. Where similar textures in the ultramafic zones of the Hartley and Eastern Bushveld complexes have been described, or where rock descriptions seem to disclose textural relations identical with those of the Stillwater Complex, they are cited in the table.

A rapid perusal of the articles cited, particularly those with photomicrographs, will convince the most dubious critic that the textures of the rocks in the three ultramafic zones are identical.

3. Kinds of cumulus minerals in cumulates. In most published reports the kinds and proportions of settled minerals in cumulates are concealed by the practice of classifying the rocks by total modal mineral content. Table 2.4 is (a) an illustration of the utter confusion produced by

TABLE 2.2 Mineralogy of the Three Ultramafic Zones

	Cumulus Crystals					
	Stillwater Complex		Hartley Complex of the Great Dyke		Eastern Bushveld Complex	
	Per cent of cumulus crystals[1]	Range of composition	Per cent of cumulus crystals[5]	Range of composition	Per cent of cumulus crystals[8,9]	Range of composition
Olivine	27	Mg_{80-90}[2,3]	64	Mg_{86-94}[5,6,7]	5	Mg_{86-89}[9]
Orthopyroxene	72	Mg_{77-88}[3]	34	Mg_{77-92}[5,6,7]	80	Mg_{75-89}[9,10,11]
Chromite	1	Mg_{30-59} $(Cr_{49-69}Al_{23-41})$[4,16]	2	Mg_{41-70} $(Cr_{66-77}Al_{19-26})$[5,16]	1	Mg_{30-56} $(Cr_{60-69}Al_{20-31})$[8,11,16]
Plagioclase	None	...	None	...	14	An_{77-86}[17]
Clinopyroxene	None	...	None(?)	...	None	...
	Postcumulus Material					
	Mineral	Range of composition	Mineral	Range of composition	Mineral	Range of composition
Postcumulus overgrowth	Same as cumulus crystals above	Same as cumulus crystals above	Same as cumulus crystals above	Same as cumulus crystals above	Same as cumulus crystals above	Same as cumulus crystals above
Postcumulus replacement	Orthopyroxene	Mg_{80-82}[12]	Orthopyroxene	Mg_{85-88}[5,6,7]	Orthopyroxene	Mg_{87-89}[9,11]
	Clinopyroxene	$Ca_{41-42}Mg_{46-53}$[3,12]	Clinopyroxene	$Ca_{30-41}Mg_{44-51}$[5,6,7]	Clinopyroxene	$Ca_{45}Mg_{50}$[9,11,15]
Simple postcumulus space-filling	Orthopyroxene	Mg_{80-82}[12]	Orthopyroxene	Mg_{85-88}[5,6,7]	Orthopyroxene	Mg_{87-89}[9,11]
	Clinopyroxene	$Ca_{41-42}Mg_{46-53}$[3,12]	Clinopyroxene	$Ca_{39-41}Mg_{44-51}$[5,6,7]	Clinopyroxene	$Ca_{45}Mg_{50}$[9,11,15]
	Plagioclase	An_{69-77}[13]	Plagioclase	An_{48-72}[5,6,7]	Plagioclase	An_{61-71}[9,11]
	Biotite	Mg-rich[1]	Biotite	Mg-rich[5,6,14]	Biotite	Mg_{60-63}[9,11]
	Quartz	...[1]			Quartz	...[9]
	Garnet	$Gr_{70}Py_{20}Al_{10}$[1]			"Myrmekite"	...[9]

Source of data:
[1] Jackson (1961a) [2] Jackson (1960) [3] Hess (1960a) [4] Jackson (1964) [5] Worst (1960) [6] Worst (1958) [7] Hess (1950) [8] Cameron (1963) [9] Guilbert (1962) [10] Kuschke (1939) [11] Cameron and Emerson (1959) [12] Jackson, unpublished data [13] Jackson (1961b) [14] Allsopp (1965) [15] Hess (1949) [16] Terminology of Thayer (1946) [17] Cameron and Desborough, unpublished data

TABLE 2.3 Comparison of Textures in the Three Ultramafic Zones

Textural Feature	Description	Citation		
		Stillwater	Hartley	Eastern Bushveld
	Cumulus Crystals			
Shape	Discrete crystals; euhedral where surrounded by simple postcumulus space-filling material; anhedral where surrounded by postcumulus overgrowth material; embayed where surrounded by postcumulus replacement material	[1] p. 13	[2] p. 161 [3] p. Pl. LIV (1, 3, 4) [4] p. 58	[6] p. 1187–1191 [7] p. 25–50, 68–111
Distribution	Cumulus crystals form the framework (50–80%) of the rocks and define the layering planes. Changes in presence, proportions, shape, or size cause horizons, laminae, and layers	[1] p. 13–15	[3] p. 310; Table 20 [4] p. 56–58	[5] p. 60 [6] p. 1191 [7] p. 68
Internal character	Unzoned, and usually unstrained	[1] p. 15–20	[4] p. 67	
Grain size	Olivines and orthopyroxenes are about the same size; chromites are much smaller. All three are subject to change in average diameter; such changes are perpendicular to the layering plane	[1] p. 20–28	[4] p. 52–57 Pl. VI (3)	[5] p. 60 [6] Fig. 42 [7] Table 2
Sorting	Generally excellent, but bimodal where two or more cumulus minerals are present in the same cumulate	[1] p. 28–37	[4] p. 53	[6] p. 1193 [7] Table 1, 2
Orientation	Simple apposition fabrics. Lineation: weak or absent	[1] p. 37–47	[3] p. 300 [4] p. 66	[5] p. 62 [7] p. 28, 70
	Interaction Between Cumulus Crystals and Postcumulus Material			
Postcumulus overgrowth	Cumulus crystals surrounded by postcumulus rims of the same mineral. Complete overgrowth produces mosaic textures and monomineralic rocks	[1] p. 52–58	[3] p. 300 [4] Pl. V(1)	[6] p. 1192 [7] Fig. 8
Postcumulus replacement	Cumulus olivine surrounded and embayed by postcumulus orthopyroxene. Cumulus orthopyroxene surrounded and embayed by postcumulus clinopyroxene. Poikilitic textures characteristic	[1] p. 47–52	[3] p. 304; Pl. LV(8) [4] p. 89; Pl. VI(2)	[6] p. 1189 [7] Fig. 38, 39, 40
Simple postcumulus space filling	Cumulus crystals surrounded by mesostasis of postcumulus material crystallized from trapped intercumulus liquid. (Initial porosity ranged from 20–50 per cent.) Intersertal to poikilitic textures	[1] p. 58–65	[3] Table 20 [4] Pl. IV(4)	[6] p. 1191, 1199 [7] Fig. 36
	Postcumulus Material			
Shape	Rims on cumulus crystals; interstitial; poikilitic	[1] p. 65–67	[3] p. 296–297 [4] p. 52, 53, 58	[6] p. 1187 [7] p. 25–50, 68–111
Distribution	Tend to be same assemblage regardless of kind of cumulus minerals. Poikilitic crystals cross laminae and layer boundaries	[1] p. 67–74	[4] p. 58	[6] p. 1191 [7] p. 28
Internal character	Zoned	[1] p. 74–77		[7] p. 35, 104
Size	Extreme size range, from tiny interstitial grains to poikilitic crystals 15 inches in diameter	[1] p. 77	[4] p. 53	[7] p. 99
Sorting	Poor	[1] p. 77–79	[4] p. 58	[7] p. 34–35
Orientation	Random	[1] p. 79		[7] p. 99

Citations:
[1] Jackson (1961a) [2] Hess (1950) [3] Worst (1958) [4] Worst (1960) [5] Kuschke (1939) [6] Cameron and Emerson (1959) [7] Guilbert (1962)

TABLE 2.4 Kinds of Cumulus Minerals in Rocks of the Three Ultramafic Zones

Association of Cumulus Minerals in Cumulates (based on kind and abundance of cumulus minerals)	Dominant Postcumulus Process	Rock Name Given in Literature (based principally on mode of all minerals in the rock)		
		Stillwater Complex[1,2,3]	Hartley Complex[4,5]	Eastern Bushveld Complex[6,7,8,9,10]
Olivine cumulate	Overgrowth	Dunite	Dunite	Dunite
	Replacement	Poikilitic harzburgite	Poikilitic harzburgite	Troctolite with bronzite nodules
	Space filling	Feldspathic poikilitic harzburgite	Picrite	Troctolite; mafic olivine norite
Olivine-orthopyroxene cumulate	Overgrowth	Granular harzburgite	Granular harzburgite	Granular harzburgite
	Replacement	Granular harzburgite	Granular harzburgite	Mafic olivine norite
	Space filling	Feldspathic granular harzburgite	Picrite	Mafic olivine norite
Orthopyroxene-olivine cumulate	Overgrowth	Olivine bronzitite	Olivine pyroxenite	Olivine pyroxenite
	Replacement	Olivine bronzitite	Does not occur	Olivine pyroxenite
	Space filling	Feldspathic olivine bronzitite	Does not occur(?)	Olivine norite
Orthopyroxene cumulate	Overgrowth	Bronzitite	Pyroxenite	Pyroxenite
	Replacement	Bronzitite	Pyroxenite; websterite	Pyroxenite
	Space filling	Feldspathic bronzitite	Feldspathic pyroxenite; websterite	Feldspathic pyroxenite; mafic norite; norite
Olivine chromite cumulate	Overgrowth	Chromite dunite	Chromite concentration in dunite	Chromite dunite
	Replacement	Poikilitic chromite harzburgite	Chromite concentration in harzburgite	Chromitiferous mafic olivine norite
	Space filling	Feldspathic poikilitic chromite harzburgite	Does not occur(?)	Chromitiferous troctolite
Chromite olivine cumulate	Overgrowth	Olivine chromitite	Chromite seam	Olivine chromitite
	Replacement	Olivine chromitite	Chromite seam	Olivine chromitite
	Space filling	Feldspathic olivine chromitite	Does not occur(?)	Olivine chromitite
Chromite cumulate	Overgrowth	Chromitite	Chromite seam	Chromitite
	Replacement	Does not occur	Does not occur	Does not occur
	Space filling	Feldspathic chromitite	Does not occur(?)	Feldspathic chromitite

Orthopyroxene chromite cumulate	Overgrowth Replacement Space filling	Does not occur	Does not occur	Chromiferous pyroxenite Chromiferous pyroxenite Chromiferous pyroxenite
Chromite orthopyroxene cumulate	Overgrowth Replacement Space filling	Does not occur	Does not occur	Impure chromitite Does not occur Does not occur
Orthopyroxene plagioclase cumulate	Overgrowth Replacement Space filling	Does not occur	Does not occur	Mafic norite; norite Mafic norite; norite Mafic norite; norite
Plagioclase orthopyroxene cumulate	Overgrowth Replacement Space filling	Does not occur	Does not occur	Anorthositic norite; norite Anorthositic norite; norite Anorthositic norite; norite
Plagioclase cumulate	Overgrowth Replacement Space filling	Does not occur	Does not occur	Anorthosite Does not occur Anorthositic norite
Chromite plagioclase cumulate	Overgrowth Replacement Space filling	Does not occur	Does not occur	Feldspathic chromitite Does not occur Feldspathic chromitite
Plagioclase chromite cumulate	Overgrowth Replacement Space filling	Does not occur	Does not occur	Chromitic anorthosite Does not occur Chromitic anorthosite
Olivine plagioclase and Plagioclase olivine cumulates		Do Not Occur in Ultramafic Zones		

[1] Jones, Peoples, and Howland (1960) [2] Hess (1960a) [3] Jackson (1961a) [4] Worst (1958) [5] Worst (1960) [6] Cameron and Emerson (1959) [7] Guilbert (1962) [8] Cameron (1963) [9] Schwellnus and others (1962) [10] Cameron (personal communication)

this practice; (b) an attempt to provide a link between settled mineral associations and total-mode rock names used in published reports; and (c) a comparison among the settled mineral associations that do occur in the three ultramafic zones. It is apparent from Table 2.4 that a cumulate having a particular settled mineral assemblage may have been given as many as three different total-mode names in the same complex, depending on how its postcumulus material (cement) happened to solidify. It is also apparent that different total-mode names have been applied to cumulates having the same settled mineral assemblage where such rocks occur in different complexes. Finally, it can be seen that the same total-mode names have sometimes been given to cumulates having different assemblages of settled minerals.

Once the rock names based on total modal mineral content have been deciphered (and I may not have done it correctly in every case), the similarities and differences of the settled mineral associations in the three ultramafic zones can be examined. These associations are important because they provide information about crystallization-supply of settled minerals, efficacy of mechanical sorting, strength of currents, rates of settling, and other depositional processes. For example, the complete absence of olivine-plagioclase cumulates in the three ultramafic zones almost surely indicates that the two minerals were never co-precipitates from the magmas during accumulation of the zones. Also, the presence of chromite-plagioclase and chromite-orthopyroxene cumulates in the Bushveld complex, but not in the other two, probably indicates two unique types of cotectic crystallization not present in the Stillwater and Great Dyke intrusions.

In stressing the importance of using the cumulus minerals to classify the rocks of the three zones, I do not mean to imply that the postcumulus material is not important. Indeed, a study of changes in the postcumulus material can provide information about the composition of the trapped magma, the rate of diffusion within it, the rate of burial, the original porosity of the mush of settled crystals, and other depositional and postdepositional processes. Some information is available on these processes in the Stillwater Complex (Hess, 1960a; Jackson, 1961a) and in the Bushveld complex (Cameron and Emerson, 1959) but present knowledge is insufficient to warrant a comparison between them.

*4. **Layers.*** A summary of the character and abundance of isomodal and mineral-graded layers in each of the intrusions is given in Table 2.5. Two striking features are (a) the high proportion of layers composed of only one settled mineral; and (b) the high proportion of phase contacts, even when mineral-graded layers are present. In these respects the typical ultramafic zone layers differ markedly from the layers in the Skaergaard intrusion (Wager and Deer, 1939) and the Rhum intrusion (Brown, 1956), which are mineral-graded (usually rhythmic) layers with ratio contacts. The layers in the ultramafic zones also differ from layers in the upper gabbroic zones of the same intrusions, which contain a much higher proportion of mineral-graded layers (Hess, 1960a).

I have presented evidence elsewhere (Jackson, 1961a, pp. 81–100) to show why I believe that phase contacts are, for the most part, caused by changes in crystallization supply, and that ratio contacts are the result of mechanical disturbances of the magma during crystal accumulation. The presence of mineral-graded layers with ratio contacts in most cumulates containing two settled minerals that differ in grain size and density (for example, olivine and chromite, or orthopyroxene and plagioclase), indicates that mechanical processes were operative. However, such processes cannot account for the thick cumulates composed of only one settled mineral, or of two settled minerals of the same grain size and density (for example, olivine and orthopyroxene). The dominant

TABLE 2.5 Relative Abundance of Isomodal and Mineral-Graded Layers in the Three Ultramafic Zones

Type of Layer	Type of Contact (at base of layer)	Number of Settled Minerals in Layer	Graphic Distribution of Minerals	Stillwater Complex[3] Volume Frequency	Hartley Complex[4] Volume Frequency	Eastern Bushveld Complex[5] Volume Frequency
Isomodal	Phase	One[1]	ooooooo ooooooo ooooooo xxxxxxx xxxxxxx xxxxxxx xxxxxxx xxxxxxx xxxxxxx ooooooo ooooooo ooooooo	88%	~90%	~70%
		Two	ooooooo ooooooo ooooooo oxoxoxo xoxoxox oxoxoxo xoxoxox oxoxoxo xoxoxox ooooooo ooooooo ooooooo	< 1%	Absent?	~ 5%
	Ratio	Two[2]	ooxoxoo ooxoxoo ooxoxoo xxoxoxx xxoxoxx xxoxoxx xxoxoxx xxoxoxx xxoxoxx ooxoxoo ooxoxoo ooxoxoo	< 1%	Absent?	~ 5%
Mineral-Graded	Phase	Two[2]	ooooooo ooooooo ooooooo oooxooo ooxoxoo oxoxoxo xoxoxox xxoxoxx xxxoxxx ooooooo ooooooo ooooooo	12%	~10%	~10%
	Ratio	Two[2]	xoxoxox xxoxoxx xxxoxxx oooxooo ooxoxoo oxoxoxo xoxoxox xxoxoxx xxxoxxx oooxooo ooxoxoo oxoxoxo	< 1%	< 1%	~10%

[1] Excepting 1–3% accessory chromite where present
[2] By definition
[3] Data from Jackson (1961a)
[4] Estimated from data by Worst (1960)
[5] Estimated from data by Cameron (1963)

process of layer formation, therefore, seems to have been sudden repetitive changes in supply of crystallization products (settled crystals).

The lateral continuity of the layers is astounding. A chromite cumulate 2 to 12 feet thick in the Stillwater Complex can be traced for nearly 30 miles (Jackson, 1963). Worst (1960) has mapped single layers of chromite cumulate less than a foot thick, and of orthopyroxene cumulate as little as 30 feet thick, more than 70 miles along strike. Cameron (1963) reports that layers which contain settled plagioclase and are 30 to 45 feet thick can be traced for 45 miles. Ratios of lateral continuity to thickness have a minimum range of 10^4 or 10^5 to 1. These figures are considerably larger than Hess's estimate (1960a, p. 127) of "several hundred to perhaps a thousand times" for the layers in the upper part of the Stillwater Complex. I suspect, however, that my estimate applies to phase-contact layers, and Hess's to ratio-contact layers. If this is correct, the processes that produced sudden changes in supply apparently affected enormous areas of the floors of the intrusions, whereas mechanical processes appear to have been more localized.

Size-graded layers are difficult to see in the field, and little systematic information is available on their development in the ultramafic zones of the three intrusions. In the Stillwater Complex, laboratory measurements of the grain size of settled crystals showed that size-graded layering, both from coarse to fine and fine to coarse, occurred within every layer studied (Jackson, 1961a, pp. 20–28). The work of Cameron and Emerson (1959, Fig. 42) and of Guilbert (1962, Table II) suggests similar pervasive grain-size changes in eastern Bushveld layers.

Chemical-graded layering in individual chromite cumulates of the Stillwater Complex is described by Jackson (1964). It is also developed in single orthopyroxene cumulate layers in the Eastern Bushveld ultramafic zone (Kuschke, 1939; Cameron and Emerson, 1959). So far as I know, chemical-graded layering has not been looked for in the Great Dyke. But it is my belief that both size-graded layering and chemical-graded layering will be found to be ubiquitous throughout both isomodal and mineral-graded layers in the ultramafic zones of all three complexes; further study of these changes should furnish much information on layering processes.

In the Stillwater and Eastern Bushveld complexes at least, planar lamination is developed wherever settled crystals are tabular or elongate, but lineate lamination is absent or weakly developed even where settled crystals are elongate (Jackson, 1961a, pp. 37–47; Hess, 1960a, p. 127; Berg, 1946; Cameron and Emerson, 1959, pp. 1187–1189). This fact has been used as an argument against current deposition, but details such as whether lineate lamination is better developed in layers with phase or ratio contacts have not been investigated.

5. Sequence of layers. The persistent repetition of sequences of cumulus minerals in the three ultramafic zones is perhaps their most obvious common feature. Recent work, however, has shown that the succession in at least two of the intrusions is repeated in a regular way.

The Stillwater Ultramafic zone is composed of about 100 mappable layers that contain only olivine, orthopyroxene, and chromite as settled minerals (Table 2.4). These layers, however, can be grouped in 15 regular repetitions that I have called "cyclic units" (Jackson, 1961a, pp. 14, 91–93). The base of each cyclic unit is a phase contact above which lies an isomodal olivine cumulate layer. The lower part of this layer contains a thin section of chromite and olivine-chromite cumulates in which the layering is variable—in part isomodal, in part mineral-graded. At the top of the olivine cumulate layer, another phase contact marks the appearance of settled orthopyroxene, and above this contact is a layer of olivine-orthopyroxene cumulate, usually mineral-graded, with the proportion of settled orthopyroxene increasing upward. Another phase contact marks the disappearance of olivine, and the uppermost layer of the cyclic unit contains only orthopyroxene as a settled mineral. The cyclic unit is not a "layer" in the sense defined in this paper, but rather an internally layered, mappable stratigraphic unit. In the lower part of the ultramafic zone, cyclic units are sometimes beheaded, olivine cumulates of a younger cyclic unit lying directly on olivine cumulates of the previous cyclic unit.

In the Hartley complex of the Great Dyke, Worst's (1960, Pl. II) sections show a very similar cyclic repetition in the ultramafic zone, although he does not call special attention to it. Olivine cumulates, containing chromite and olivine-chromite cumulates, are succeeded upward by olivine-orthopyroxene cumulates, which in turn are overlain by orthopyroxene cumulates. In the lower part of the succession, these units commonly are beheaded. From a study of Worst's sections and descriptions, I conclude that the exposed part of the ultramafic zone of the Hartley complex consists of 14 cyclic units virtually identical to those in the Stillwater succession.

The Eastern Bushveld ultramafic stratigraphy is distinctly different. Cameron's (1963) sections do not reveal the existence of any cyclic units of the Stillwater type; in fact no rational repetitive sequence has yet been discovered. The section is unique, moreover, in containing plagioclase cumulates interlayered with orthopyroxene and chromite cumulates.

Discovery of cyclic units in the Stillwater Ultramafic zone, and, apparently, also in the Hartley ultramafic zone, considerably simplifies the problem of explaining the repetition of cumulus minerals. In the Stillwater Complex, for example, the necessity of explaining 100 events repeated at random is reduced to explaining 15 regular repetitions. I have offered an explanation to account for this repetition in the Stillwater Ultramafic zone (Jackson, 1961a, pp. 91–100); Worst (1960, pp. 151–158) has given another for the Great Dyke; and Cameron (1963) has given a third to explain the different sequence in the Eastern Bushveld intrusion.

6. Sequence of variations in mineral composition. The overall sequences of variations in the compositions of individual minerals in the three ultramafic zones is not well known, but they appear to be extremely complicated. In the Stillwater Complex, for example, it was found that the within-layer variation (chemical-graded layering) of settled chromite compositions was of greater magnitude than the between-layer variation (Jackson, 1964). In order even to determine the overall variation, therefore, it was necessary to work out the chemical-graded layering and then compare chromite compositions at the footwalls of the various chromite cumulates. The overall pattern, when obtained, was not one of simple iron enrichment (Jackson, 1963). Other complicating factors are known: one is the variation of mineral compositions with amount of diffusion in the intercumulus liquid (Hess, 1960a, pp. 109–121); another is the sympathetic variation of settled minerals where two or more are present (Jackson, 1964).

The sequence of mineral variations in the Hartley complex seems more straightforward (Hess, 1950, Table I; Worst, 1958, Table 20; 1960, pp. 113–116): the minerals here apparently tend to show a uniform iron enrichment upward in the section. But there are local reversals of this tendency, and the extent of variation within layers has not been investigated.

In the Eastern Bushveld, very intricate variations in mineral compositions from layer to layer were discovered by Kuschke (1939) and confirmed by Cameron and Emerson (1959) and by Guilbert (1962).

7. Other primary structures. A good many examples of local unconformity, crosscutting relations, and other interruptions of the layered structures have been observed in the ultramafic zones of the three intrusions, and have been described by Hess (1960a, pp. 129–131), Worst (1960, pp. 95–97; 158–176), Cameron (1963, pp. 101–103), and Cameron and Desborough (1964). Although these irregularities have been cited by some authors as evidence of intrusion by ultramafic magmas, modern opinion generally agrees in ascribing them to sedimentary-type local unconformities, slump structures, mush intrusions similar to sandstone dikes, and local replacement.

E. Conclusion

The ultramafic zones of the Stillwater, Great Dyke, and Bushveld intrusions are similar in stratigraphic position, mineralogy, texture, mineral associations, and internal structure. Many of their similarities have been unrecognized because of semantic differences among workers. The rocks of the ultramafic zones are simple cumulates in which the cumulus crystals and postcumulus material can generally be readily distinguished. Differences in kinds, proportions, and compositions of settled minerals suggest slight differences in composition among their primary basaltic magmas. Differences in some settled mineral associations between the Bushveld ultramafic zone and the other two zones indicate some differences in crystallization paths during fractionation. The layers of all three ultramafic zones are predominantly cumulates that contain only one settled mineral, and they are disposed for the most part in isomodal layers with phase contacts. For this reason, they require a different explanation than the cumulates of the Skaergaard and Rhum intrusions, which for the most part have two or more settled minerals, and which are characterized by rhythmic layering with ratio contacts. In the Stillwater and Great Dyke ultramafic zones, the internal stratigraphic sequence is practically identical, but the sequence within the ultramafic zone of the Bushveld complex is different from the other two. Vertical variations in mineral composition in all three ultramafic zones are intricate and only partially known.

III. THE ULTRAMAFIC ROCKS OF THE MUSKOX INTRUSION NORTHWEST TERRITORIES, CANADA

T. N. Irvine and C. H. Smith

A. Introduction

The Muskox intrusion is a "stratiform" body of ultramafic, gabbroic and granophyric rocks situated in the Arctic barren lands of the Canadian Precambrian Shield, 90 miles east of Great Bear Lake, and 50 miles south of the settlement of Coppermine on Coronation Gulf (Fig. 2.1). It is significant to the study of ultramafic rocks because it is a model example of their formation by fractional crystallization of basaltic magma. The intrusion has been chilled locally along its margins, and is systematically differentiated into many contrasting rock types. Its feeder, roof, and lower walls or floor are all well exposed in surface outcrops; and aeromagnetic and gravity surveys, and diamond drilling, have provided information on its size and configuration at depth. A continuous drill core sample through the intrusion has been obtained for petrographic, chemical, and other scientific studies (Findlay and Smith, 1965).

B. Structural Setting and Age

The intrusion occurs within a basement complex of schists and gneisses (derived from Early Proterozoic sediments), and

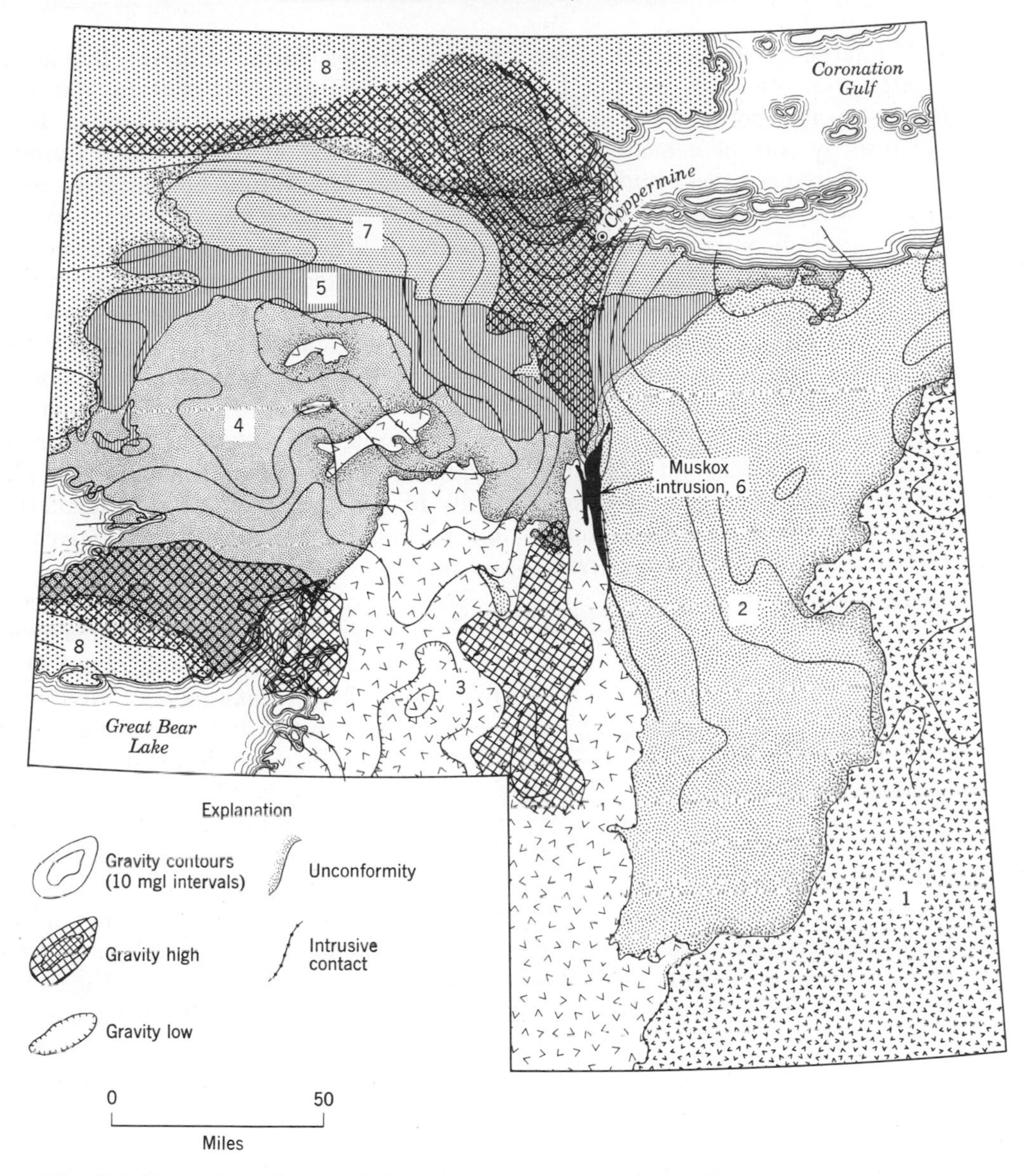

Fig. 2.1 Regional geology and Bouguer gravity map of the Coppermine region. Geology compiled from maps published by the Geological Survey of Canada. Gravity data from Hornal (1966). Legend, with K-Ar ages, as follows: 1. Archean granitic rocks, paragneiss, and volcanic rocks, 2300–2600 m.y. 2. Early Proterozoic sedimentary rocks. 3. Proterozoic granitic, rhyolitic and metamorphic rocks, 1700–1900 m.y. 4. Middle Proterozoic sediments. 5. Coppermine basalt. 6. Muskox intrusion, 1150–1250 m.y. 7. Late Proterozoic sediments. 8. Paleozoic sediments.

granitic rocks having K-Ar ages of 1700 to 1900 m.y. (Fig. 2.1). The basement is unconformably overlain by a 10,000-foot succession of Middle Proterozoic sandstone, dolomite and basalt (the Coppermine basalt) which dips to the north at 5 to 10°.

The intrusion is dike-like in plan, trending north-northwest, and has the cross section of a funnel (Figs. 2.1, 2.2; and Smith, Irvine, and Findlay, 1966). It is exposed for 74 miles, and aeromagnetic and gravity data show that it extends on to the north beneath its roof rocks for at least another

75 miles. The large gravity anomaly (Fig. 2.1) indicates that its cross section becomes larger to the north. The magma apparently rose by way of a near-vertical fracture in the basement rocks and spread along or near the unconformity beneath the sandstone roof. Room for the magma was largely made by depression or downwarping of the floor of its chamber rather than by elevation of its roof, and it seems probable that the larger northern part of the intrusion occupies a graben or rift type of structure.

K-Ar ages of 1155, 1220 and 1245 m.y. have been obtained from biotite, pyroxene and K-feldspar from the Muskox Intrusion. The intrusion and the Coppermine basalt are probably close in age, but since they are not in contact their relation is not unequivocally defined.

C. Internal Structure and Composition

The principal structural units of the Muskox intrusion are its feeder dike, two lower marginal zones, and a layered series (Fig. 2.2).

The feeder dike forms the southern 37 miles of the exposed part of the body and is inferred to project beneath the other units like the keel beneath a sailboat. It is vertically dipping and 500 to 1800 feet wide. Its southern end consists of bronzite gabbro, but as it is traced northward picrite is encountered, first as pods in the gabbro and then as a continuous central band. Still farther north two and locally three internal bands of picrite are present. The gabbro is chilled against its country rocks, but its contacts with picrite are gradational over short distances. The picrite is believed to have been formed by segregation of olivine grains. Smith and Kapp (1963) have suggested that the segregation was caused by flow differentiation, and the feasibility of this mechanism has been experimentally demonstrated by Bhattacharji and Smith (1964). (See also Chapters 3-III and 3-IV.)

The marginal zones occur along the two inward-dipping lower walls of the intrusion and are generally 400 to 700 feet thick. They typically grade inward from bronzite gabbro at the contact through picrite and feldspathic peridotite to peridotite, but at places this sequence is partly repeated (Fig. 2.3). The gradation is essentially marked by an increase in the concentration of olivine and is accompanied by an increase in the MgO/FeO ratios of the mafic silicates (e.g. olivine changes from Fo_{70} to Fo_{85}). Small amounts of pyrrhotite with Cu- and Ni-bearing sulphides occur sporadically along the walls of the intrusion and for small distances into the marginal zones and country rocks.

The layered series comprises 42 contrasting layers ranging in thickness from 10 to 1100 feet and totalling about 6000 feet (Fig. 2.3). Small scale, "rhythmic" layering is present but uncommon. The layered series has the form of a shallow syncline plunging northward at 4°. It is approximately comformable to the overlying sandstone, dolomite and basalt, and is discordant to the marginal zones. The layers resemble the "phase layers" of the Stillwater complex (Hess, 1960) and have similarly formed by gravitational accumulation of mineral grains. They have sharp contacts and are remarkable in their great lateral continuity. Most layers are continuous between the marginal zones, and insofar as the intrusion has been exposed by erosion or drilling, they are generally continuous down its plunge. Two chromitite layers, only a few inches in thickness, extend for more than 40 square miles, and many of the rock layers undoubtedly have areal extents greater than 100 square miles. The rock succession changes with much repetition from dunite at the base through peridotite, various pyroxenites and gabbros to granophyric gabbro and granophyre at the top.

The Muskox intrusion does not have a mafic unit along its roof comparable to the lower marginal zones, or to the upper border group of the Skaergaard intrusion

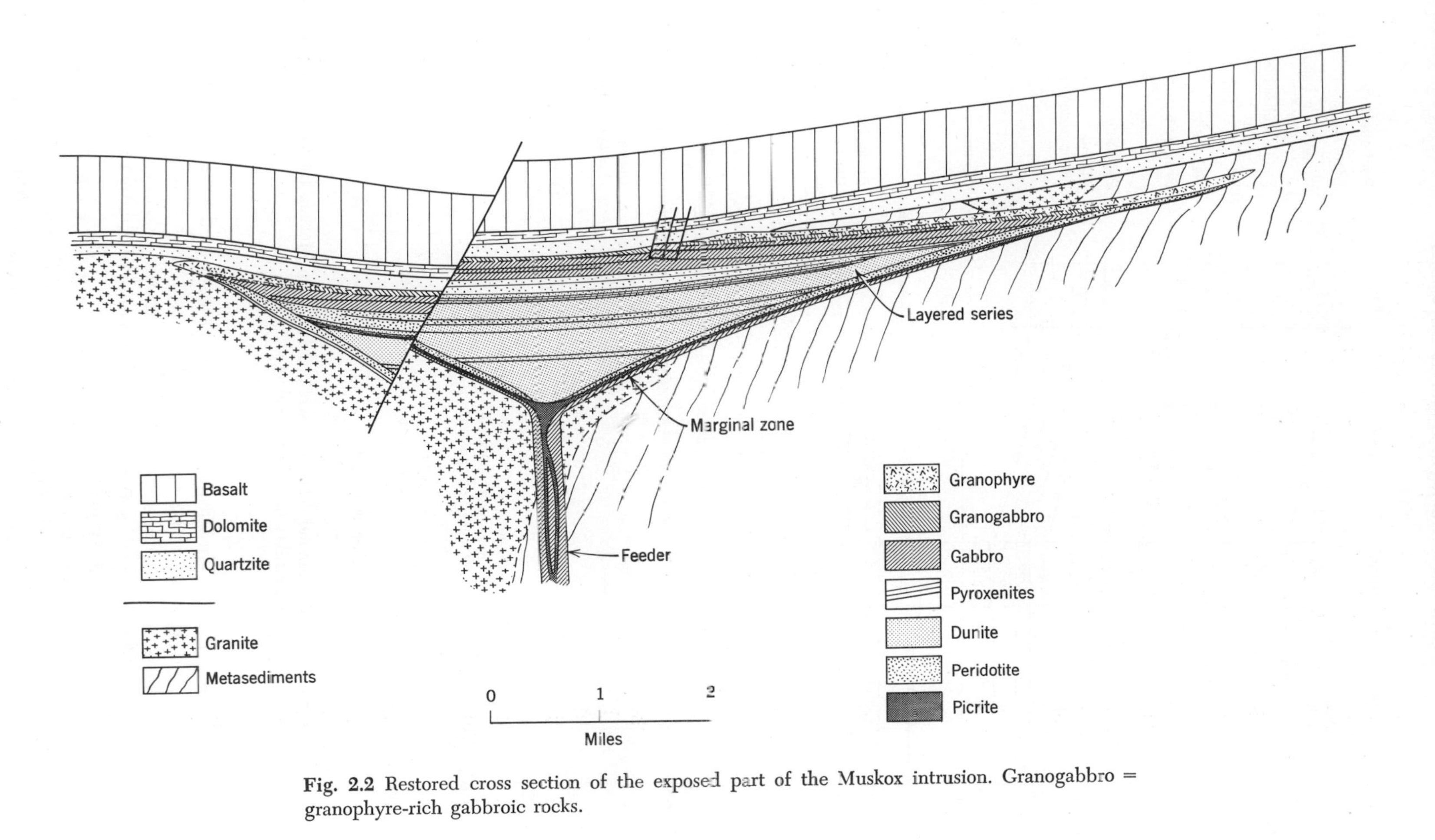

Fig. 2.2 Restored cross section of the exposed part of the Muskox intrusion. Granogabbro = granophyre-rich gabbroic rocks.

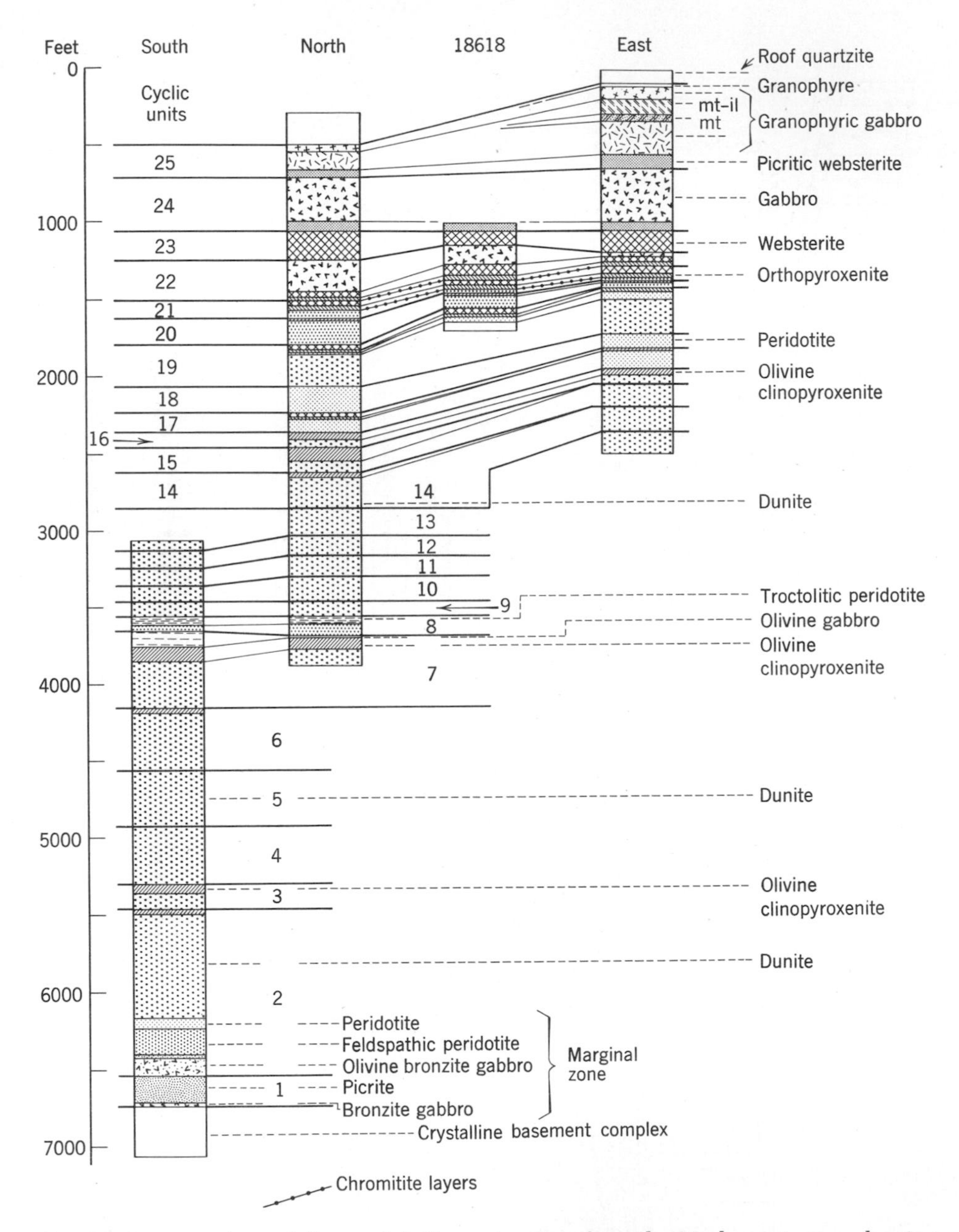

Fig. 2.3 Summary logs of diamond drill core sections from the Muskox intrusion showing the main cyclic units. Diabase dikes have been neglected.

(cf. Wager and Deer, 1939). The granophyre at its roof would appear to be the final member in the differentiation sequence developed in the layered series, although on the other hand, it typically contains fragments of the overlying country rocks and may therefore be partly due to assimilation along the roof contact.

Chemical analyses of the bronzite gabbro from the chilled margin of the intrusion show that it is equivalent to a silica-saturated basalt closely similar to the typical tholeiite of Kilauea volcano, Hawaii.

D. Origin of the Ultramafic Rocks in the Layered Series

1. Cyclic units and their origin. The layered series of the Muskox intrusion

(Fig. 2.4) is distinguished by a large proportion of ultramafic rocks, particularly the olivine-rich types, and by the repetition of layers in specific sequences or cycles. The 6000-foot section includes about 5000 feet of ultramafic layers of which almost 4000 feet contain 75 to 90 per cent olivine. As pointed out by Smith and Kapp (1963), this is a disproportionate amount of ultramafic material compared with the basaltic composition of the chilled margin.

The cycles of layer repetition, which are similar to the "cyclic units" recognized by Jackson (1961) in the Stillwater complex, are best illustrated by three examples.

a. Peridotite-orthopyroxenite-websterite. This sequence is repeated four times at the top of the main section of ultramafic layers (Fig. 2.4). The upper two units contain the chromitite layers, which occur in peridotite just at the base of orthopyroxenite layers and are thus an integral part of the systematic repetition.

The rocks are typical "cumulates" (see Wager and others, 1960), consisting of gravitationally settled (cumulus) grains of certain minerals cemented by the solidification products of intercumulus (trapped) magma. The cumulus minerals in the peridotite are olivine (now extensively altered to serpentine and secondary magnetite) and minor chromite. It is significant that virtually all the dunite and peridotite in the intrusion contains 1 to 3 per cent chromite. The mineral occurs as tiny subhedral crystals, either included in olivine grains or, more commonly, distributed around them. These features are believed to indicate that olivine and chromite coprecipitated in approximately the ratio 98:2, an inference that is supported by the liquidus relations of forsterite and chromian spinel in the system MgO-Cr_2O_3-SiO_2 (Keith, 1954).

The orthopyroxenite contains only one cumulus mineral, bronzite, while the websterite has settled grains of both augite and bronzite, approximately in the ratio 3:1. Chromite is generally absent from the pyroxenite units of the Muskox intrusion, suggesting that the pyroxenes were able to accomodate all the chromium the cooling magma could supply and thus suppressed formation of the spinel phase. The nature of this (peritectic) relation is further discussed by Irvine (1966).

All rock types in the layer sequence have plagioclase, ortho- and clinopyroxene, and minor biotite as intercumulus mate-

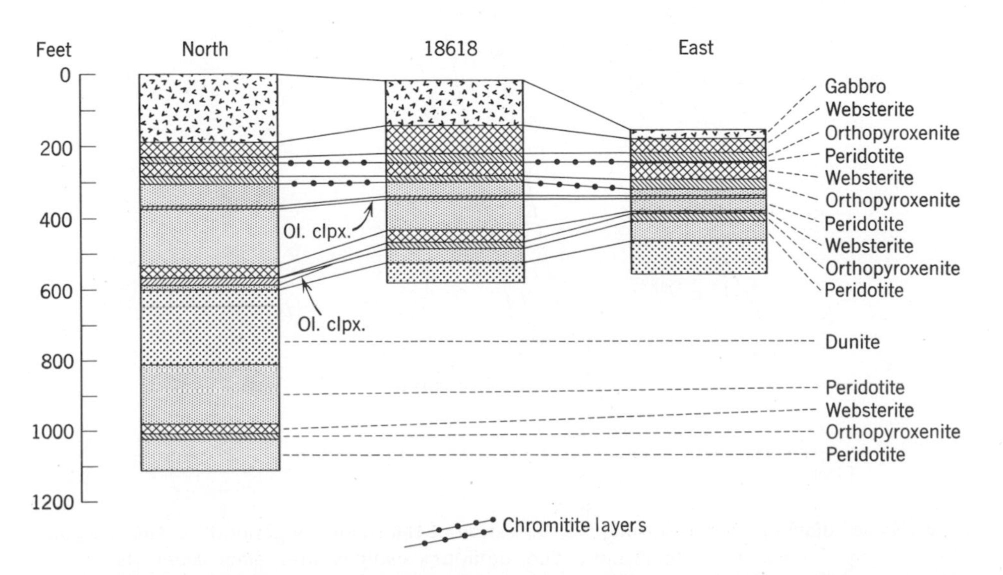

Fig. 2.4 Diamond drill core sections of part of the Muskox layered series showing repetition of the cyclic unit peridotite-orthopyroxenite-websterite. The upper peridotite layers are coarser grained and more feldspathic than the lower ones.

rials. The pyroxenite units commonly contain traces of interstitial quartz or granophyre.

The recurrent consistency of the sequence evidently reflects the order of mineral crystallization from the magma. The appropriate sequence of silicate phases can be obtained by fractional crystallization in the system $CaMgSi_2O_6$-Mg_2SiO_4-SiO_2 (Fig. 2.5) beginning with a melt just "saturated" in silica; and the modal proportions of the solids, as "predicted" from the phase diagram by assuming that the fractionated minerals trap 20 to 30 per cent of their parent liquid, are closely similar to the mineral proportions observed in the corresponding Muskox rocks (Fig. 2.6). (Note that the pyroxenites derived in the experimentally based diagram also contain minor free silica as a result of trapping liquid slightly oversaturated in silica.) This similarity, together with the sharpness of the contacts between layers, indicates that the natural process of crystal fractionation was extremely efficient. In effect, the cumulus minerals settled out as fast as they formed.

From what has been said to this point, it will be apparent that the repetition of cyclic units requires crystallization of separate batches of compositionally similar magma. This aspect is discussed in Sections D-2, 3, and 4.

The chromitite layers are apparently the result of both fractional crystallization and gravitational sorting of the cumulus minerals according to their grain size. Grain-size measurements have shown the following:

1. The settled olivine in the peridotite

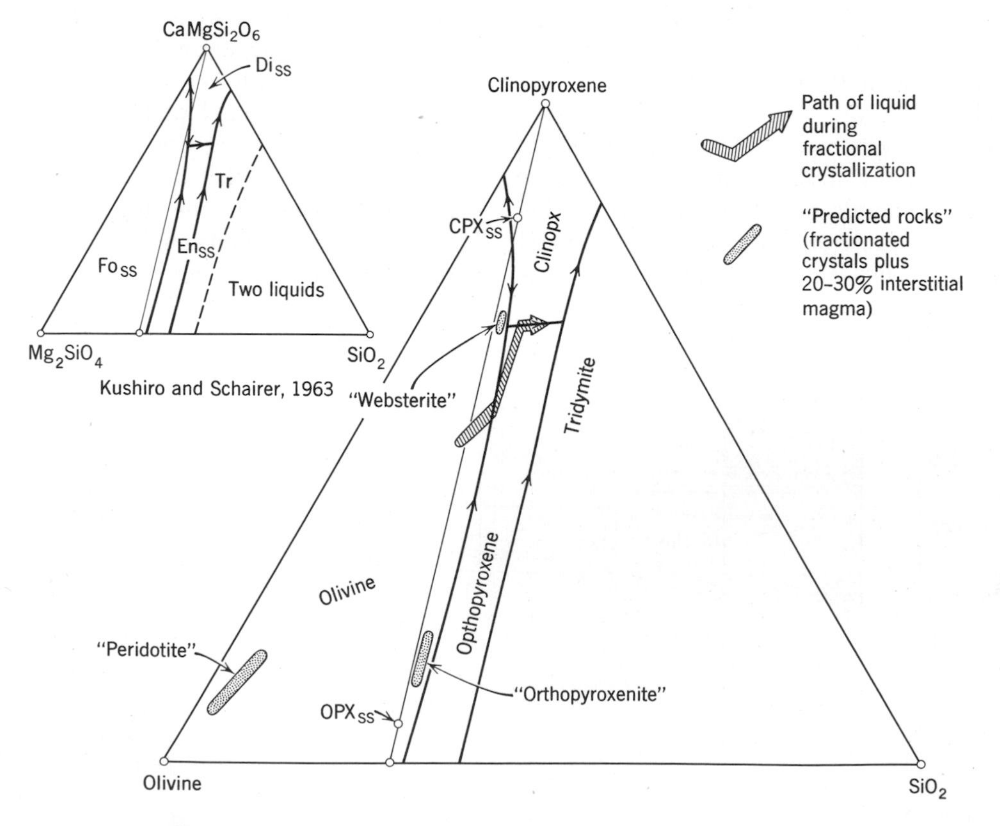

Fig. 2.5 Phase diagram model showing the derivation of the sequence peridotite-orthopyroxenite websterite by fractional crystallization. The liquidus relations are taken from the system $CaMgSi_2O_6$-Mg_2SiO_4-SiO_2 (inset). The compositions of the pyroxene solid solutions OPX_{ss} and CPX_{ss} are approximately those of the Muskox pyroxenes.

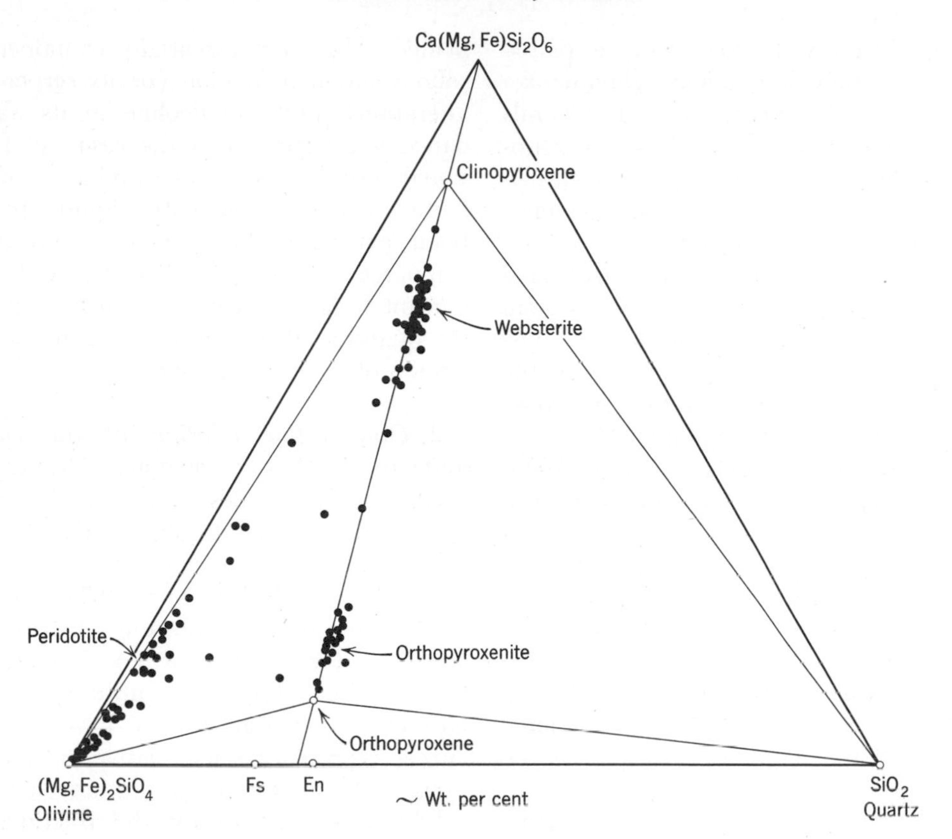

Fig. 2.6 Modal analyses of the peridotite, orthopyroxenite, and websterite layers shown in Fig. 2.4. The compositions of the pyroxene solid solutions are based on analyses of the Muskox pyroxenes. Compare with the "predicted rocks" in Fig. 2.5.

immediately below the chromitite layers is almost twice as coarse as the cumulus orthopyroxene above them. (In fact, it is the coarsest settled olivine in the intrusion.) Its grain size is 1.2–1.5 mm as compared to 0.6–0.8 mm for the pyroxene.

2. The cumulus olivine and pyroxene grains are so much coarser than the chromite crystals that they must have settled many times faster (roughly 10–100 times as fast on the basis of Stokes Law).

From (1) it may be inferred that during the accumulation of each of the cyclic units containing chromitite layers olivine outdistanced the orthopyroxene that followed it as they settled to the floor of the magma body and, accordingly, there was a pause in the accumulation of silicate materials. During this pause the tiny chromite grains that formed with the olivine but settled more slowly could have accumulated by themselves in thin layers. Sulfides in the chromitite may represent immiscible droplets concentrated in an analogous manner.

In the two peridotite-orthopyroxenite-websterite units that lack chromitite layers the cumulus olivine and pyroxenes have similar grain sizes. Apparently there was no hiatus in the accumulation of silicates during which chromite could have concentrated.

b. Dunite-olivine clinopyroxenite-olivine gabbro. Another cyclic unit in the Muskox layered series is the sequence dunite-olivine clinopyroxenite-olivine gabbro. The unit is fully developed only once (in the interval overlapped by the North and South drill holes in Fig. 2.4), but is partly developed at seven other levels as paired layers of dunite and olivine clinopyroxenite. In the main unit, the cumulus minerals occur in the order: olivine + minor chromite; olivine + clinopyroxene; olivine + clinopyroxene + plagioclase. The sequence and approximate proportions of the silicate phases can be simulated by a fractional crystallization model based on the system $CaMgSi_2O_6$-Mg_2SiO_4-$CaAl_2Si_2O_8$ (cf. Osborn and Tait, 1952). Chromite, as in the preceding example, ceased to form when pyroxene began to precipitate.

The order of crystallization is different from that indicated by the cyclic unit peridotite-orthopyroxenite-websterite in that orthopyroxene formed only as a minor interstitial (late) mineral rather than preceding clinopyroxene and plagioclase as a cumulus phase. The difference implies a change in the composition of the magma that cannot have been caused by fractional crystallization within the intrusion. If the different liquids were compared just as they began to crystallize their first pyroxene, that which precipitated peridotite-orthopyroxenite-websterite would be the richer in silica.

c. Cyclic units within layers. The cyclic units described above are identified by the repetition of layers that are visibly distinguished in the field. There are in addition repetitive units in thick layers of dunite that can only be distinguished by detailed chemical and petrographic studies. Examples are illustrated in Fig. 2.7, where the concentration of Ni is seen to define four cycles in a stratigraphic interval of 1700 feet. The uppermost cycle corresponds to the sequence dunite-olivine clinopyroxenite-olivine gabbro examined above, and the next coincides with a dunite-olivine clinopyroxenite pair. The lower two occur entirely in dunite. In each cycle, the concentration of Ni decreases upward with minor variations to about half its initial value in a stratigraphic interval of 300 to 350 feet. It then increases sharply, and the gradual decline is repeated. The Ni is essentially contained in solid solution in olivine (or its serpentine alteration), and the decline in its abundance is interpreted as the result of fractional crystallization of olivine from a finite amount of magmatic liquid, the Ni being partitioned in favor of the olivine as compared to the liquid. The decline is significant because it can be used to estimate the quantity of magma involved in the formtaion of each cyclic unit.

2. *Quantitative relation of the cyclic units to the Muskox magma.* The appropriate theory for describing the behavior of a trace element during fractional crystallization has been developed by Neumann, Mead and Vitaliano (1954). By assuming that the (equilibrium) distribution coefficient for the element K = (concentration in the solid)/(concentration in the liquid), is a constant, they have derived curves representing its relative concentrations in the solid and liquid at any stage of solidification. Curves for the fractionated solid for K-values greater than unity are shown in Fig. 2.8. Their trends are believed to correspond in principle to the upward decrease of Ni in the cycles in Fig. 2.7.

A K-value for the partitioning of Ni between dunite and magma in the Muskox intrusion can be estimated by comparing the maximum concentration in the cycles to the amount in the chilled margin (about 200 ppm). On this basis, K is not less than 10, and it probably does not exceed 15. Wager and Mitchell (1951, p. 154) have estimated that, during the early crystallization of the Skaergaard intrusion, the olivine/liquid distribution coefficient for Ni was about 12.

The application of the fractionation curves to the Muskox intrusion may be illustrated by considering the curve for $K = 10$. It is seen that when the concentration of the element has dropped to about half its original value (as in the Ni-cycles in Fig. 2.7), roughly 8 per cent of the liquid is solidified. Thus it could be

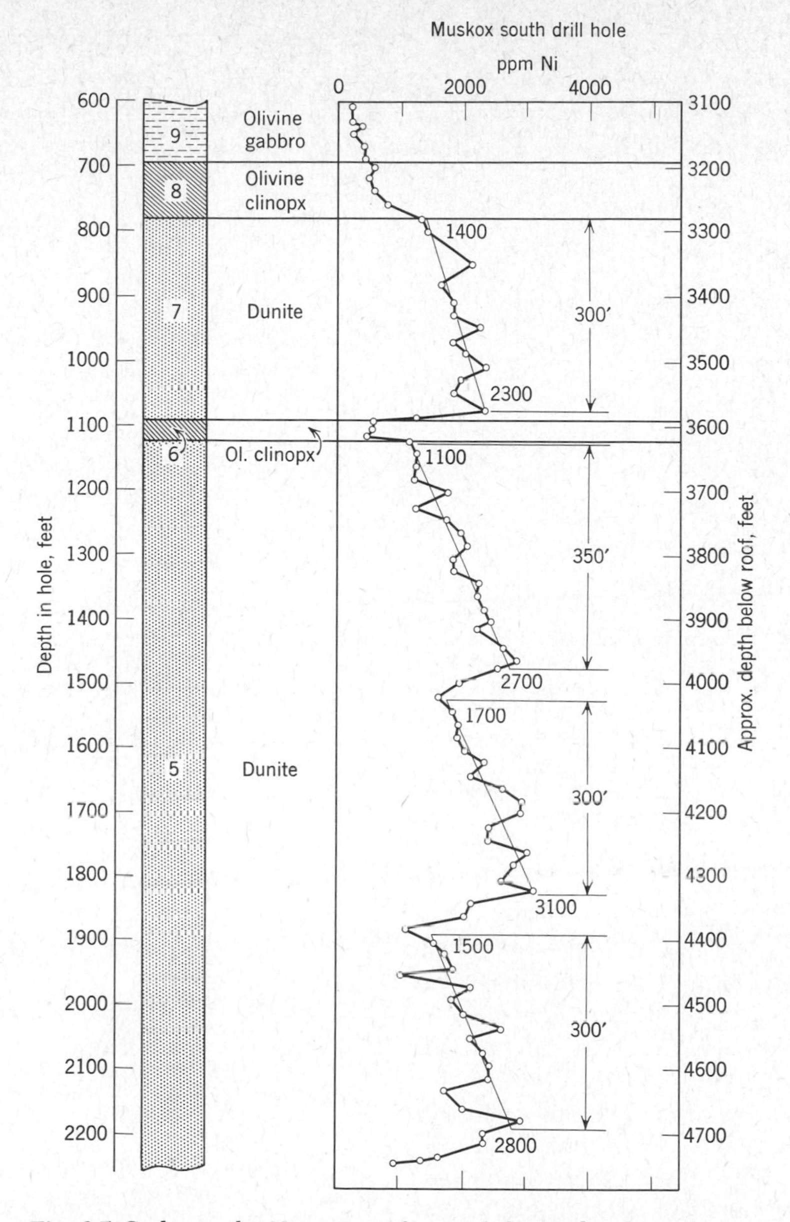

Fig. 2.7 Cycles in the Ni-content of part of the Muskox layered series.

inferred that a 300- to 350-foot dunite layer in the Muskox intrusion is about 8 per cent of an equivalent column of the liquid from which it formed.

More detailed calculations using *K*-values of 10–15 indicate that the dunite layers defined by the Ni-cycles probably represent 5 to 10 per cent of their parent liquid. Significantly, about 12 per cent olivine can be derived from a silica-saturated basalt (similar to the chilled margin) following liquidus relations like those in Fig. 2.5. Moreover, it can be inferred from the cross section of the intrusion that each of the dunite layers constitutes roughly 5 per cent of all the magma that was above it when it formed. Therefore each repetition of cycle must have involved displacement of most, if not all of the magma in the presently exposed part of the intrusion by "new"

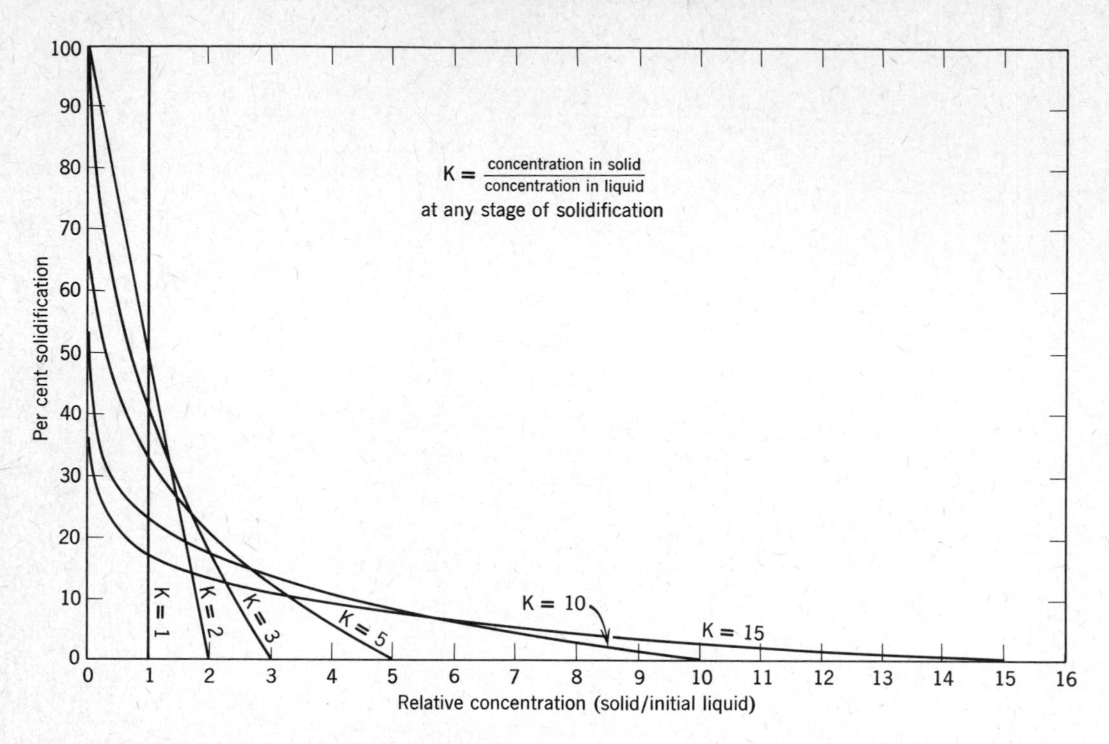

Fig. 2.8 Curves showing the variations in the trace element contents of fractionated solids (as compared to the concentration in the initial liquid) with per cent solidification of their parent liquid for distribution coefficients greater than unity.

magmatic liquid similar to that which originally preceded it.

3. Overall development and significance of the cyclic units. The development of cyclic units in the Muskox intrusion is shown in Fig. 2.3. At least 25 can be identified, of which 18 comprise two or more phase layers and seven are subdivisions of dunite layers. Notably, all but one of the units contain layers in which olivine is a principal cumulate mineral (i.e. layers of dunite, peridotite or picritic rocks); thus it is probable that each unit reflects a major renewal of the composition of the magma by a large introduction of fresh liquid in place of that which had partially crystallized. Herein is the reason for the large proportion of ultramafic rocks in the intrusion.

4. Mechanics of introduction of magma during solidification of the intrusion. The problem of introducing new magma into the intrusion after the layered series began to form will now be considered. At this stage, the exposed feeder dyke had probably solidified, as had the marginal zones. The exposed feeder does not penetrate even the lower layers, and no other dikes of appropriate composition and structural relations are found in surface outcrops.

The most probable access route for the magma introduced during the accumulation of the layered series was along the length of the intrusion in the space below the roof and above previously formed layers. The large gravity anomaly north of the exposed part of the intrusion (Fig. 2.1) is believed to indicate the position of the major feeder system and, possibly, a reservoir from which magma periodically flowed southward. The flow evidently occurred over the full width of the layered series inasmuch as the cyclic units typically have that extent. It must have been fairly gentle because the underlying layers were rarely affected.

The "old," partially crystallized magma

was probably pushed southward and then to the surface as volcanic fissure eruptions, although the evidence for this has since been removed by erosion. The possibility that it returned to the north by convection is precluded by considerations of the geometry of the space available to the magma as compared to the distance of flow involved. On the other hand, to infer a relation to volcanism is reasonable because the intrusion was close to the surface and the amount of magma displaced was evidently very large.

E. Conclusions

A point of principle that may be emphasized on the basis of the Muskox intrusion is that gravitational settling of mineral grains (particularly grains of mafic minerals) and, consequently, fractional crystallization are almost inevitable in the solidification of relatively fluid magmas such as basalt under plutonic conditions. These processes should therefore receive prime consideration in studies of the origin of ultramafic rocks, as Bowen (1915) pointed out long ago. Probably the best evidence of fractional crystallization within igneous intrusions is the presence of rock sequences which, like those in the Muskox intrusion, are mineralogically compatible with established or theoretically possible phase relations. The sequences within the Muskox intrusion are structurally consistent with a model of gravity-controlled fractional crystallization because they are stratigraphic successions, but this may not be an obvious feature in other intrusions depending on the physical conditions accompanying their crystallization and their subsequent tectonic histories. The usefulness of trace elements (particularly Ni in ultramafic rocks) as indicators of fractional crystallization is also noted.

The apparent direct relation of the Muskox intrusion to volcanism suggests the possibility that other ultramafic bodies have formed in subvolcanic reservoirs. Many ultramafic bodies are not visibly related to gabbroic differentiates, and it is commonly assumed that the differentiates either never existed or have been eroded away. Another possibility is that the feldspathic residuum of their parent magma has been removed by volcanism. Many volcanic series show chemical variations attributable to fractional crystallization, and we therefore should expect them to have related crystallization differentiates, such as ultramafic rocks, at depth.

Finally, the layers and cyclic units of the Muskox intrusion are similar to those in other stratiform igneous complexes, allowing differences in rock types. Therefore the evidence that the repetition of cyclic units is due to repeated introduction of fresh magma may have general application in this type of complex. The Muskox intrusion also provides a model for the formation of chromitite that may, with more or less modification, apply in other stratiform intrusions and perhaps to the origin of chromite concentrations in other types of ultramafic bodies.

3. *Olivine-Rich Rocks in Minor Intrusions*

I. INTRODUCTION

P. J. Wyllie

The ultramafic rocks produced in basic sills, dykes, sheets and laccoliths by concentration of mafic minerals provide striking examples of differentiation, and for many years the generally accepted mechanism for their origin was gravitative settling of early femic minerals from a basic magma. They have been widely cited as examples to support Bowen's (1928) thesis that fractional crystallization, produced largely by gravitative settling of minerals, is the dominant process in magmatic differentiation. More detailed work of recent years indicates that this simple explanation for the formation of ultramafic rocks in basic minor intrusions is inadequate.

In Section II Drever and Johnston compare and contrast the ultrabasic facies developed in association with alkaline dolerites and with tholeiitic dolerites. The petrographic variation in vertical sections through sills are summarized diagramatically for nine alkaline sills, and for four tholeiitic sills. They pay particular attention to mineralogical and textural features of the rocks, and consider also the chemical variation within and among sills. There is an abrupt discontinuity between many of the picrite layers and the overlying olivine-poor dolerite, rather than the gradational transition often claimed in earlier literature. Drever and Johnston conclude that concentration of olivine crystals in basic magma antedated emplacement of many of the alkaline sills, and that flow differentiation as well as gravity influenced the distribution of the ultrabasic facies. For some alkaline sills, they appeal also to the "concept of residual concentration of refractory minerals due to an upward transference of volatile-rich material." They suggest that whereas undifferentiated tholeiitic magma appears to be injected regionally, the upward migration of alkaline magmas appears to be arrested within the crust, where precipitation of olivine causes the formation of olivine-enriched fractions, which are then emplaced in minor intrusions at a higher level as liquid-solid systems.

In Section III Simkin outlines the results of a detailed study of a group of differentiated alkaline sills in north Skye. Although margins are olivine-poor, picrite constitutes from one half to three quarters of the thickness of these sills, with transition to surrounding olivine-poor rocks taking place abruptly at the top of the picrite and gradationally at the bottom. This is well illustrated in a series of detailed mineral profiles across a number of sills. The intruding magma carried olivine in suspension, but examination of two-dimensional sections provides conclusive evidence that gravitational settling of olivine crystals in place could not explain the distribution of picrite. Simkin considers the experiments of Bhattacharji and Smith (1964) simulating magmatic flow in a vertical conduit, and extends this to the sill situation. He concludes that hydrodynamic migration of particles away from the margins during flow would produce the observed olivine-poor margins while gravity would both complement (above) and oppose (below) this migration to produce the observed transitions between picrite and olivine-poor rocks. He suggests modifications of this process and also discusses the various flow patterns in solid-fluid systems that have been recognized in the hydrodynamic literature, citing possible geological examples of these.

Simkin's interpretation has been independently verified by Bhattacharji's model experiments which are described and illustrated in Section IV. These experiments, an extension of previous work with model pipes and dikes, simulate the emplacement of magma plus suspended crystals into a sill. The photographs of the experiments confirm that horizontal flow could produce a concentration of olivine crystals within the magma.

Finally, in Section V Drever and Johnston describe small dikes, sills and sheets that are composed almost wholly of picrite. Detailed petrographic and chemical studies indicate that these rocks cannot be explained as simple mixtures of basaltic magma plus suspended olivine crystals. Many of the marginal selvedges are picritic, containing skeletal or thinly tabular olivine crystals. Drever and Johnston suggest that the magma was a picritic liquid containing some suspended olivine crystals before emplacement. In a number of the picrite sills, removal of olivine by flow differentiation aided by gravity has yielded a non-porphyritic fraction which is significantly more calcic and richer in CaO/Al_2O_3 than basaltic liquids.

II. THE ULTRABASIC FACIES IN SOME SILLS AND SHEETS

H. I. Drever and R. Johnston

A. *Introduction*

The development of our knowledge and understanding of the ultrabasic facies which occurs in certain sills and sheets stems from the pioneer work, at the beginning of the century, of Lewis, Daly and Tyrrell, who convinced most petrologists that this facies, in the intrusions they investigated, had been derived from basaltic magma mainly by the gravitative settling of early formed femic minerals. That crystal settling (antedating, accompanying or postdating emplacement) was not only the principal mechanism responsible for this differentiation, but also for magmatic differentiation in general, became firmly established between 1915 and 1928 through the classical work of Bowen.

In discussing crystal settling Bowen paid particular attention to the evidence in the tholeiitic dolerite (diabase) of the Palisade sill in New Jersey, analogous evidence in alkaline dolerite sills apparently being overlooked, although his textbook (1928) did include a note by E. B. Bailey on the teschenite-picrite sills of the Midland Valley in Scotland. From the detailed work which has since been undertaken on the ultrabasic facies in sills and sheets, many differences and variations in mineralogy, texture, and chemistry have been discovered between the two types of sills. By highlighting these differences in this review it is hoped that the oversimplification of the problem that has tended to stultify interpretative thought may be avoided. All alkaline ultrabasic rocks in the present paper form part of the Alkaline-Olivine-Basalt Volcanic Association, and all tholeiitic ultrabasic rocks form part of the Tholeiitic Flood Basalt Volcanic Association (Kennedy, 1938; Turner and Verhoogen, 1960).

B. The Ultrabasic Facies Associated with Alkaline Dolerites and Teschenites

The occurrence of this facies in alkaline dolerite or teschenite sills is so common that the significance of the association may tend to be overlooked. Only very rarely do alkaline ultrabasic rocks of this type form the major part of the sills in which they occur, but examples have been found in Scotland (in northern Skye and on the island of Inchcolm in the Firth of Forth), and in west Greenland on the Nugssuaq peninsula (Drescher and Krueger, 1928). Typical alkaline picrites on the other hand do commonly occur as the sole or principal component of dikes whereas composite picrite-dolerite or picrite-teschenite intrusions do not form dikes. No counterparts are found as major intrusions and an association of picrite-teschenite sills with picritic lavas is exceptional.

Figure 3.1 compares the features of those sills and sheets (with an alkaline picrite facies) which have been investigated in

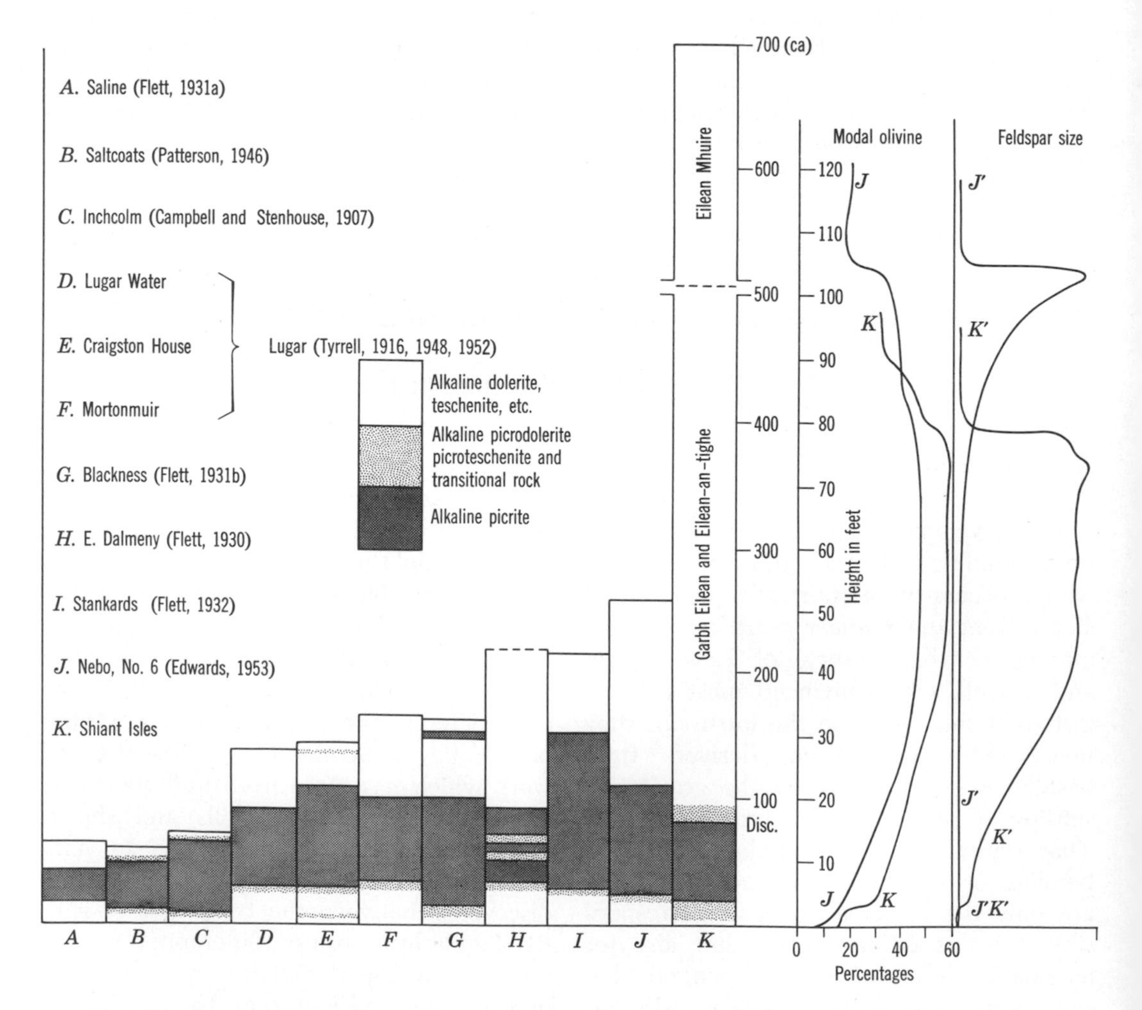

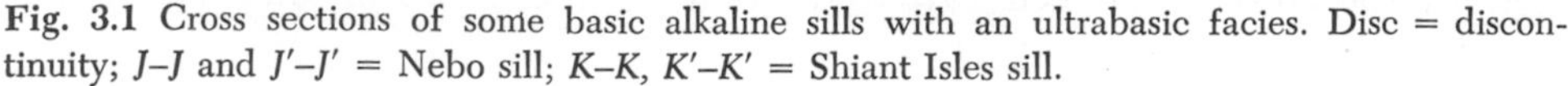

Fig. 3.1 Cross sections of some basic alkaline sills with an ultrabasic facies. Disc = discontinuity; *J–J* and *J′–J′* = Nebo sill; *K–K*, *K′–K′* = Shiant Isles sill.

fair detail, and permits an appraisal of the variations in the position of the picrite facies, its amount and its relationship with other facies. The Shiant Isles sill, being at the same time the largest and most thoroughly explored, will be reviewed here in greatest detail. The composite sills in northern Skye have been studied in great detail by T. E. Simkin as part of a St. Andrews University project, and a brief account is presented in Section III of this chapter.

The main features of the alkaline picrite facies include the following:

1. The amount of the ultrabasic facies bears no consistent relationship with the amount of the basic facies.
2. The bulk of the ultrabasic facies tends to be located in the lower half of the larger sills, but ultrabasic rock can also occur in a much higher position. In the smaller sills (Fig. 3.1A, B, C) it tends to occur in a central position and to exhibit, marginally, interbanded relations with teschenitic rocks.
3. The top of the ultrabasic facies is usually terminated by an abrupt discontinuity. However, above the distinctive discontinuity between picrite and picrodolerite in the Shiant Isles sill there is an upward gradation in the amount of olivine, with no significant change in its composition, between the picritic facies and the alkaline dolerite. This is anomalous.
4. The bottom of the main ultrabasic facies in these sills is characteristically gradational.
5. Sections through the same sill at different localities (e.g., Fig. 3.1D, E, F) reveal significant lateral variation. This emphasizes the incompleteness of the two-dimensional picture which is commonly presented.
6. The greatest thickness (123 feet) of ultrabasic rock in the sills illustrated is that in the Stankards sill (Fig. 3.1I). A thickness up to 400 feet has been found by Simkin (Section III) in northern Skye (Drever, 1964). The thickness of the ultrabasic facies in the Shiant Isles appears to increase toward the south. It is therefore conceivable that the thickness recently established by drilling (Drever and Johnston, 1965) is much less than the maximum.
7. In the Shiant Isles and Nebo picrites (and also in the Stankards and E. Dalmeny picrites) the plagioclase develops as large crystals poikilitically enclosing olivine, reaching a maximum size in the upper part of the picrite (Fig. 3.1, *J′-J′*, *K′-K′*). Reduction in the size of the plagioclase to the very much smaller dimensions typical of dolerites can coincide with a reduction in the amount of olivine, but it is quite evident from, for instance, the two Nebo graphs (Fig. 3.1) that this size change is not solely controlled by this reduction. Size variations that have been recorded in the case of olivines and pyroxenes will be referred to later.

Analcite occurs in variable amount in all these sills, its place being rarely taken by nepheline (e.g., Lugar), or by albite (e.g., Stankards). Especially in those sills in which teschenite forms the basic facies it is quite apparent that water must be regarded as a significant component. In contrast, the minerals are characteristically fresh and there is little analcite in the Dalmellington sill (Benbeoch-Benquhat Hill) in Ayrshire (Drever and MacDonald, 1967) where a distinctive "kylitic" picrite grades into "kylitic" rocks with less olivine. It was probably this freshness and relative lack of analcite that led Tyrrell (1912, 1923) to link these "kylites" closely with "crinanite." Between a "crinanitic" picrite (e.g., Shiant Isles) and a "kylitic" picrite (e.g., Dalmellington) the most distinctive difference is the crystallization in the latter of idiomorphic augite (in advance of plagioclase) with a highly zoned mantle like that of the augite phenocrysts in the Hocheifel ankaramites recently investigated by Huckenholz (1966).

Many of these sills have been intruded into marls or shales and a rheomorphic "teschenitic" facies (Drever and Johnston, 1959) may be developed marginally (e.g.,

Shiant Isles, Flodigarry in northern Skye, Inchcolm, Saltcoats). From the evidence of recent drilling it is probable that the top of the Shiant Isles sill is represented by the section exposed on Eilean Mhuire (Fig. 3.1K) which is capped by metamorphosed marl.

C. The Ultrabasic Facies Associated with Tholeiitic Dolerite

The tholeiitic or quartz dolerite sills and sheets in which this facies is found are commonly associated with the approximately contemporaneous eruption of tholeiitic flood basalts. As in the case of the alkaline ultrabasic facies, this facies is typically developed in sills and sheets, and not as a facies of dolerite dikes. But, in contrast, widespread picritic basalts of tholeiitic affinity do occur, and in major intrusions such as the Muskox intrusion there is a picritic facies of similar type (Chapter 2-III). The Uwekahuna laccolith (Murata and Richter, 1961) is small enough to be included in the present context. The principal occurrences of this ultrabasic facies are in association with certain of the Karroo dolerites of South Africa (Walker and Poldervaart, 1949) and the classical Palisade sill of New Jersey (Walker, 1940). It is to the work of F. Walker and A. Poldervaart that we owe much of our present knowledge of the tholeiitic dolerite sills. The picrite facies in the Elephant's Head dike (Poldervaart, 1944) is located where undulations have provided a floor of tholeiite sharply separated from the picrite. The hypersthene-rich zone in the Egerton sill, Antarctica (Gunn, 1963), is an ultramafic facies of much greater thickness than the olivine-rich picritic facies in other intrusions of this type. The Basistoppen "gabbro-picrite" (Hughes, 1956; Douglas, 1964) occurs in a sheet the relatively large dimensions of which represent an approach to the conditions obtaining in typical layered intrusions.

Comparison of the selected sills and sheets illustrated in Fig. 3.2, reveals the following points:

1. The sills (and sheets) in which a picritic facies occurs are relatively large and the width of this facies is relatively small. Even in thick sills or sheets it may be absent.
2. The unusual locations of the olivine-rich facies in the Jagersfontein sill have counterparts in some of the basic alkaline sills (e.g., Fig. 3.1G).
3. As in the alkaline type, the bottom of this facies in the Palisade sill is gradational into dolerite whereas at the top there is a very rapid transition or an abrupt discontinuity. In the Elephant's Head dike the picritic facies grades upward into dolerite (Poldervaart, 1944).
4. According to Truswell (1955) the size of the plagioclase in the Jagersfontein sill(s) shows "a marked increase associated with concentration of olivine." The amount of olivine also varies directly with the size of the plagioclase in the Calamity Hill section of the Elephant's Head dike (Poldervaart, 1944) and in the Palisade sill.
5. Where an Mg-rich facies develops to a thickness comparable with that of the Mg-rich facies in many basic alkaline sills, the dominant mineral is hypersthene.
6. Picritic rock is not found in close proximity to the contacts with country rock.

In general, the relations with the basic facies are much simpler than in the case of the alkaline ultrabasic facies. Where it has been possible to follow the picritic facies laterally some variation in its thickness is apparent, and it disappears in the case of the Basistoppen sill. This variation cannot be correlated with any corresponding decrease in the thickness of the sills or sheets. There is little evidence of significant hydrothermal effects.

D. Mineralogical and Chemical Variation

In both the alkaline and tholeiitic ultrabasic facies olivine, plagioclase and augite are normally the principal minerals, and

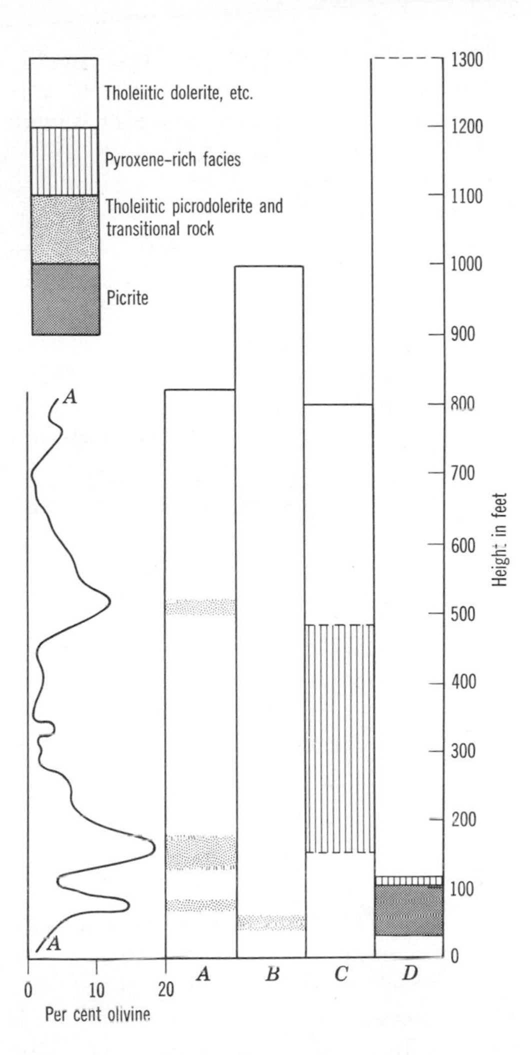

Fig. 3.2 Cross sections of some tholeiitic sills and sheets with ultrabasic, ultramafic, or olivine-rich facies. (*A*) Jagersfontein sill; (*B*) Palisade sill; (*C*) Egerton sill; (*D*) Basistoppen sheet; (*A-A*) Jagersfontein sill.

the amount of olivine may maintain its "maximum" over a considerable vertical range. This maximum is approximately 60 per cent over 60 feet in the Shiant Isles and about 50 per cent is typical of the sills to the south (northern Skye). In the Nebo sill, it is approximately 40 per cent, 35 per cent in the Dalmellington sill and in the Circular Head laccolith, and about 20 per cent in the Black Jack sill.

In the majority of sills investigated the amount of olivine in the picritic facies diminishes gradually downward from the maximum zone, whereas at the top of this zone it diminishes quite abruptly. In the picritic facies above the discontinuity (Fig. 3.1 and Drever, 1953) in the Shiant Isles sill the upward decrease is also gradual. Gradual upward decrease in olivine is also apparent in the Elephant's Head dike, the Uwekahuna laccolith, and the Black Jack sill.

Micrometric data for variations in the amount of pyroxene and plagioclase have established few distinctive distribution patterns. The amount of augite increases markedly at the top of the Nebo picrite, and a pyroxene-rich layer occurs immediately above the Basistoppen picrite. The olivine-free Egerton sill has a thick pyroxenic facies. A rapid decrease in the amount of augite, accompanied by an equally rapid decrease in its size and in the size of the plagioclase, occurs in the Shiant Isles picrite towards, and immediately below, the discontinuity. Also accompanying this change is a change in the plagioclase from large poikilitic crystals to relatively small laths some of which are in subophitic relation to the sparse pyroxene.

The distribution of analcite and other zeolites in the alkaline ultrabasic facies is probably of particular significance. In the Nebo sill these zeolites are concentrated at the top of this facies. In the Shiant Isles picritic facies, on the other hand, the zeolite concentration occurs in plagioclase-rich vertical veins and less commonly in small irregular patches about fifteen feet below the discontinuity. Another major component of these veins and patches in the Shiant Isles picrite is idiomorphic augite, but only a few contain olivine (Fig. 3.5). Some skeletal ilmenite is usually present and a few of the veins contain small amounts of alkali amphibole and nepheline. Similar zeolite-rich veins occur in some of the picrites in northern Skye (Walker, 1932).

Even in the relatively narrow tholeiitic picrodolerite layer in the Palisade sill (Walker, 1940), the maximum amount of olivine seems to be confined between definite limits (20 to 25 per cent) and both pigeonite and hypersthene are present in addition to augite. Only two pyroxenes (augite and hypersthene) have, however, been recorded from the picritic facies of other tholeiitic intrusions. The pyroxene-plagioclase ratio remains fairly constant at about 0.85 throughout the picrodolerite layer in the Palisade sill, and changes very little immediately above and below it. In the three chemically analysed picrites from Karroo dolerite intrusions (Walker and Poldervaart, 1949), the amount of pyroxene is slightly in excess of plagioclase and as the olivine decreases in amount the ratio, in the Calamity Hill occurrence, remains remarkably constant. The pyroxene-plagioclase ratio in the Uwekahuna laccolith (Murata and Richter, 1961) is similar and changes inappreciably with changes in the amount of olivine. In the anomalous Jagersfontein sill, hypersthene increases in amount with increase in the amount of olivine and the pyroxene-plagioclase ratio is variable. Hypersthene is the dominant mineral in the ultramafic facies of the Egerton sill (Gunn, 1963) and it varies in amount up to 70 per cent. The lack of any clearly defined femic maximum 'zone' in this sill contrasts significantly with the observed occurrence of such a zone in many picritic facies. Lenses of bytownite anorthosite occur within this hypersthene-rich facies.

Chemical analyses of picrites and related rocks are given in Table 3.1. In the analyses 3–5 of the alkaline ultrabasic facies the MgO percentage is fairly constant, thus reflecting the tendency for olivine to reach an optimum level: a tendency which has already been noted. The relatively high MgO values in the Shiant Isles picrites, and also in two from northern Skye (Walker, 1932), are due to their high olivine optimum. The richness in amphibole in the Lugar ultrabasic facies is mainly responsible for the high Na_2O and TiO_2. The relatively low H_2O content of the Shiant Isles picrite reflects the absence of serpentinization and analcitisation.

The high percentage of MgO in the Karroo ultrabasic facies (analysis 9) corresponds to a modal percentage of olivine of 60.2 (Walker and Poldervaart, 1949) which is similar to that of the olivine in the Shiant Isles picrite. There is, however, insufficient data from the ultrabasic facies of tholeiite sills and sheets, to permit detailed comparison with the serial modal and other determinations which have been made through this facies in many alkaline sills. Chemical analyses of the picritic rocks in the Uwekahuna laccolith (Murata and Richter, 1961) are all characterized by a relatively high percentage of TiO_2 (analysis 10).

E. Textural Contrasts

In these ultrabasic rocks there are three distinctive textures to which some references have already been made. They are illustrated diagrammatically in Fig. 3.3.

1. Large poikilitic unzoned bytownite and poikilitic unzoned pyroxene enclosing unzoned olivines. The pyroxene is moulded on the bytownite. Peripheral zoning of the plagioclase occurs in some rocks with this texture. In some sills this texture changes by gradation into texture (2). The inferred order of crysallization is olivine, bytownite, pyroxene (e.g., the Shiant Isles picrite). Relatively large poikilitic plagioclase also characterizes the following ultrabasic facies: Stankards, E. Dalmeny, Inchcolm, Nebo (at the top of this facies), Basistoppen, Calamity Hill, Palisade.

2. Unzoned olivines (or with peripheral zoning) associated with an ophitic intergrowth of plagioclase and pyroxene(s); i.e., a typical doleritic texture (which may grade into texture [1]). The inferred order of crystallization is olivine, plagioclase with pyroxene(s). Examples include most of the northern Skye picritic rocks, the picritic rocks above the discontinuity in the Shiant Isles sill, most of the Nebo picrite, the tholeiitic Middleburg picrite (Walker and Poldervaart, 1942).

TABLE 3.1 Selected Chemical Analyses

Wt. %	1	2	3	4	5	6	7	8	9	10
SiO_2	40.50	44.84	40.30	39.21	40.84	40.35	44.18	46.20	42.78	46.59
Al_2O_3	7.87	14.99	6.30	9.56	6.58	3.75	10.67	19.61	7.06	7.69
Fe_2O_3	2.08	1.43	4.12	5.00	2.59	3.53	0.97	2.74	0.51	2.20
FeO	12.00	9.85	10.83	9.53	11.61	9.86	10.03	4.16	12.48	10.46
MgO	27.19	14.32	24.95	23.13	23.72	25.69	17.77	3.90	31.02	21.79
CaO	5.36	9.36	3.99	5.07	4.46	4.64	9.75	6.69	3.84	7.41
Na_2O	1.20	2.38	1.52	0.64	0.91	3.14	2.37	7.08	0.51	1.33
K_2O	0.16	0.33	0.80	0.49	0.32	0.80	1.23	0.56	0.33	0.28
H_2O+	1.83	1.05	4.08	4.59	6.15	5.28	} 0.97	5.76	0.92	0.37
H_2O-	0.74	0.36	1.44	1.00	1.22	0.83	}	0.41	0.09	0.04
TiO_2	0.67	0.80	1.28	0.91	1.29	2.12	1.30	2.85	0.49	1.83
MnO	0.25	0.18	0.35	0.19	0.21	0.20	n.d.	0.11	0.20	0.18
P_2O_5	0.15	0.11	0.07	0.31	0.21	0.25	0.38	0.25	...	0.11
Other	...	...	0.02	0.47	0.16	0.06	...	...	0.58	0.25
Total	100.00	100.00	100.05	100.10	100.27	100.50	99.62	100.32	100.81	100.53

Legend:

1. Gabbroic picrite, Shiant Isles. Average of three analyses. Analysts: E. G. Radley (Walker, 1930), and E. J. Murray.
2. Picrodolerite, Shiant Isles. Average of two analyses. Analysts: E. G. Radley (Walker, 1930), and R. J. Murray.
3. Picrite at 323 feet, Nebo No. 6 bore. Analyst: G. C. Carlos (Edwards, 1953).
4. Picrite, Inchcolm. Analyst: T. C. Day (Day and Stenhouse, 1930).
5. Picrite 90 feet from top of Stankards sill. Analyst: B. E. Dixon (Flett, 1932).
6. Barkevikite-peridotite, Lugar. Analyst: A. Scott (Tyrrell, 1916).
7. "Kylite," Dalmellington. Analyst: Dittrich (Tyrrell, 1912).
8. Feldspathic patch in picrite, Shiant Isles. Analyst: R. J. Murray.
9. Picrite, Calamity Hill (Elephant's Head dike) (Poldervaart, 1944).
10. Picrite, Uwekahuna, Hawaii. Analyst: G. Steiger (Daly, 1911) (Murata and Richter, 1961).

3. Unzoned olivines partly or wholly enclosed in idiomorphic augite, both poikilitically enclosed in large bytownite (zoned peripherally). The inferred order of crystallization is olivine, augite, bytownite. An example is the Dalmellington picrite (Chalmerston Hill). Variolitic texture occurs in a picrite at one locality in the Mount Fred section of the Elephant's Head dike (Poldervaart, 1944), where it is partly surrounded by normal picrite with texture (2). This variolitic texture is of common occurrence in small picritic intrusions (Section V of this chapter). Figure 3.4 illustrates some textural variations in hand specimens.

The olivine in the massive picritic rocks exhibits little significant variation in its textural relations. In 1957 Drever and Johnston drew attention to the shapes of some of the olivines in the Shiant Isles picrite and also to the occasional occurrence of inclusions of special interest.

Unlike the olivine, the plagioclase and pyroxenes show remarkable and significant changes in their textural relations accompanied by a change in chemical composition of the plagioclase. The transition of the plagioclase from large unzoned poikilitic crystals to small zoned laths is either a rapid and uniform decrease in size (Drever and Johnston, 1959, 1965), or small laths may appear between the large crystals. This latter type of intermediate

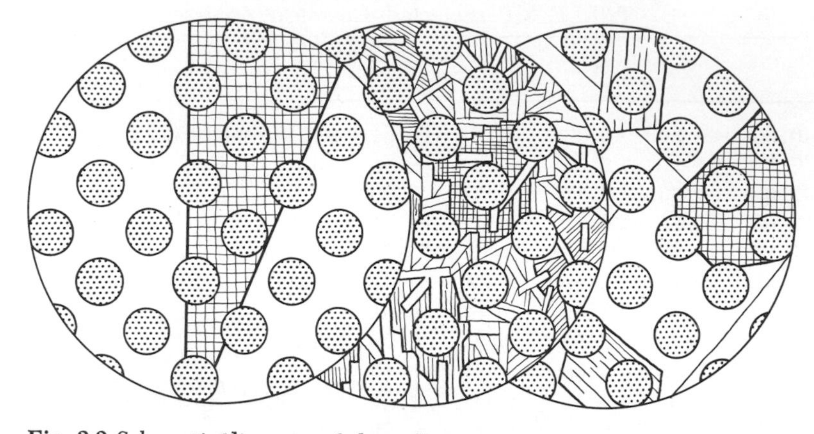

Fig. 3.3 Schematic diagrams of three distinctive textures in ultrabasic rocks: stipple–olivine; clear–plagioclase; lines–pyroxene.

stage is found above the picrite near the bottom of the Calamity Hill section of the Elephant's Head dike (Poldervaart, 1944). The picrite above the transitional zone has a doleritic texture, the textural relations of the pyroxenes having also changed. The poikilitic plagioclase and poikilitic augite of the Shiant Isles (Fig. 3.4) and Nebo picrites attain their largest dimensions near the tops of these facies.

Idiomorphic augite, with a composition little different from the poikilitic augite in the Shiant Isles picrite (Table 3.2), grows freely in the feldspathic veins and patches, at the margins of which this augite may be in optical continuity with the poikilitic augite in the picrite. Nor is plagioclase in these veins and patches significantly different in composition from that in the picrite; it is simply the textural relations of these two minerals which have changed, as illustrated in Fig. 3.5. The textural relations of the olivine, where it occurs in this feldspathic facies, have also changed, again without significant compositional change. The forsteritic olivine has crystallized (or recrystallized) as large crystals often assuming irregular skeletal shapes (Drever and Johnston, 1957. Fig. 18), and tongues from the skeletal units frequently

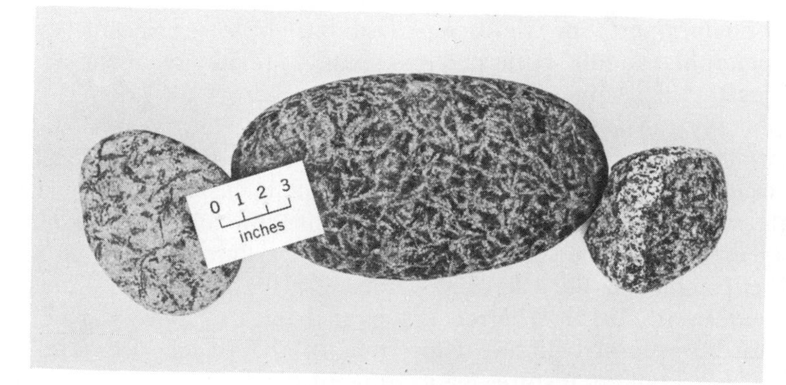

Fig. 3.4 Three boulders from Garbh Eilean, Shiant Isles. In the center is coarse-grained gabbroic picrite with large (white) bytownites and dark augite both poikilitically enclosing innumerable olivines (over 60 per cent of the rock). On the right is a feldspathic vein cutting picrite, and on the left is alkaline dolerite with branching poikilophitic olivines, zoned from Fa_{25-85}.

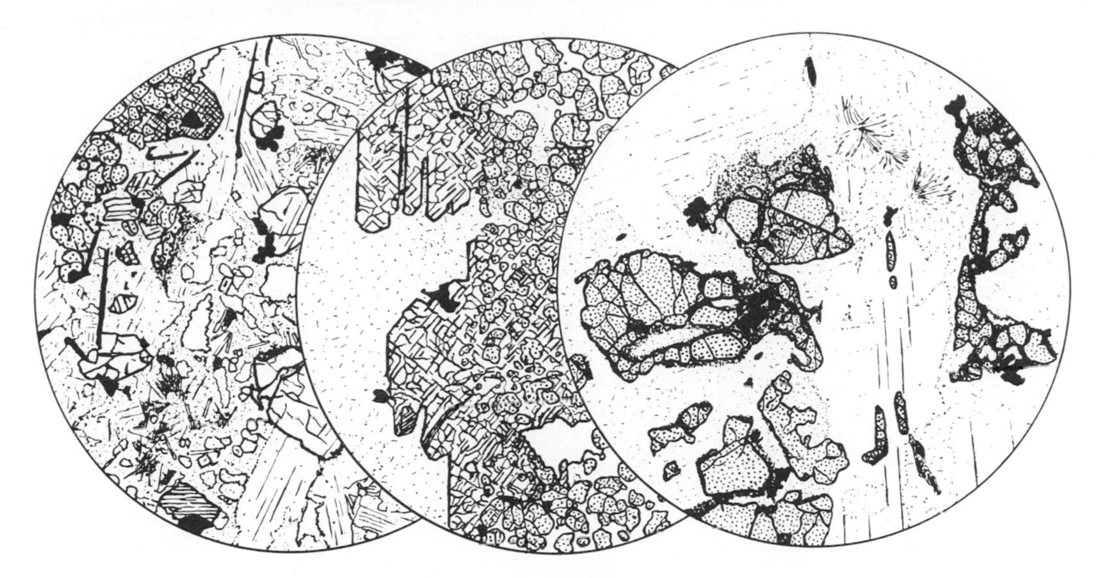

Fig. 3.5 (*Left*) Feldspathic vein in picrite. Olivine (stippled), augite, bytownite (considerably zeolitized), small nephelines, acicular ilmenite and arfvedsonite. Loc.: Eilean-an-Tighe, Shiant Isles. Scale: 2.35. (*Center*) Contact of Picrite with a feldspathic vein. A large augite crystal poikilitically enclosing olivines (stippled) has continued its growth freely into the zeolitized feldspar of the vein with the development of its crystal facies. Loc.: Garbh Eilean, Shiant Isles. Scale: 2.35. (*Right*) Irregular growth of a single crystal of olivine (stippled) in a feldspathic patch in picrite. The bytownite is partially zeolitized. Loc.: Garbh Eilean, Shiant Isles. Scale: 2.35.

extend between, and are moulded on, the large bytownites. Due to the presence in it of an abundance of analcite and other zeolites, this facies is rich in alkalis and water (analysis 8, Table 3.1).

The crystallization of augite in advance of plagioclase is particularly well displayed in the fresh rocks of the Dalmellington sill (Drever and MacDonald, 1967). This contrast in the order of crystallization of these two minerals, exemplified for instance by the Shiant Isles and Dalmellington sills, probably reflects differences in water pressure (Hamilton, Burnham and Osborn, 1964) rather than chemical differences.

F. Chemical Composition of Olivine, Plagioclase, and Pyroxenes

The data for the Shiant Isles picritic facies are more complete than for any other thick ultrabasic facies. They are presented in Fig. 3.6.

Data from other sills, sheets, small laccoliths, etc., are marshalled in Table 3.2, together with data from the Shiant Isles. This permits comparison and a reasonable representation of the overall compositional ranges. The olivines show a remarkable uniformity of composition, and a restricted compositional range (Fo_{77-85}) if we omit the exceptionally low average value of Fo_{71} in the Palisade picrodolerite. The large poikilitic plagioclase crystals also show a restricted compositional range (An_{74-72}) if we exclude those of the Palisade sill and Elephant's Head dike. The range of the peripheral zoning of the large plagioclase in the Dalmellington picrite is relatively wide, and the plagioclase in the Uwekahuna laccolith is relatively low in An. The augites of the alkaline picrite association have a very restricted range (Murray, 1954; Wilkinson, 1957) and hypersthene, except in the Palisade picrodolerite, also has a restricted compositional range (En_{75-85}).

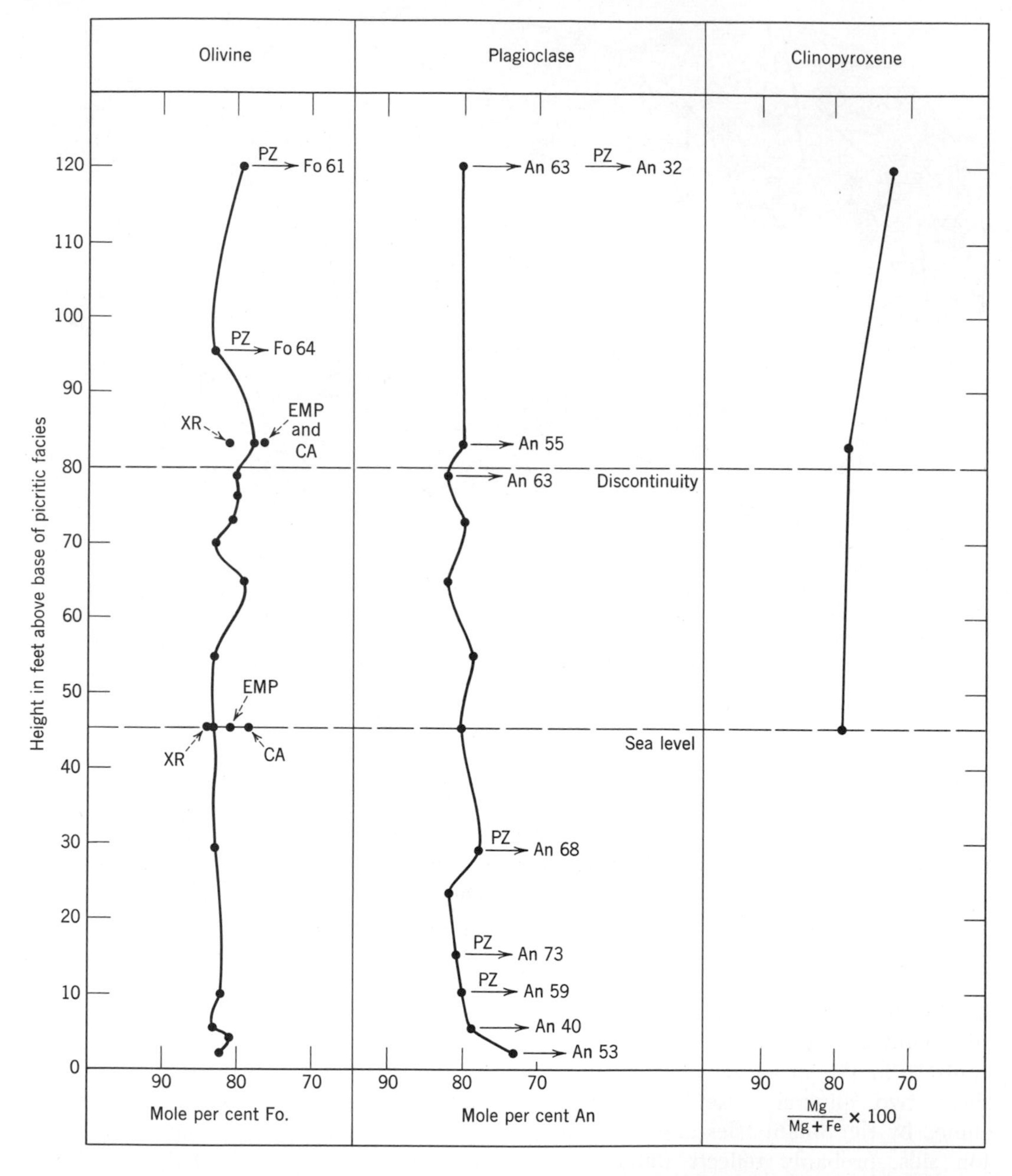

Fig. 3.6 Variation in the composition of olivine, plagioclase, and pyroxene in the bottom section (as developed at the southeast end of Garbh Eilean) of the Shiant Isles sill (data from Johnston, 1953; Murray, 1954; Drever and Johnston, 1965. Some new data have been added). PZ, peripheral zoning (range of zoning indicated by arrowed value); EMP, determination by electron microprobe; XR, determination by x-ray; CA, determination by chemical analysis; others by optical methods.

G. *Petrogenesis*

The relationships of the ultrabasic facies (Fig. 3.1) in a large number of the basic alkaline intrusions leave little room for doubt that concentration of olivine antedated emplacement. Before these olivine-enriched facies were intruded horizontally the way had been prepared by an earlier emplacement of more mobile and more

TABLE 3.2 Mineral Composition in Picrites from Basic Sills

Intrusions	Rock	Olivine Mol. % Fo.	Plagioclase Mol. % An.	Augite At. % Ca, Mg, Fe (from chemical analyses)	Hypersthene Mol. % En.
Shiant Is. (1)	Picrite	81(av)	*80	47, 42, 11	. . .
Shiant Is. (2)	Picrodolerite	77(av)	80(−55)	44.5, 43.5, 12	. . .
Shiant Is. (3)	Feldspathic vein in picrite	84	*76	†45, 40.5, 14.5	. . .
Shiant Is. (4)	Feldspathic patch in picrite	84	*77	†46, 40, 14	. . .
Northern Skye (5)	Picrite	78(av)	80(−60)	. . .	. . .
Inchcolm (6)	Picrite	81	*82(−75)	. . .	. . .
Dalmellington (7)	Kylitic picrite	78	*74(−45)	. . .	. . .
Black Jack (8)	Picroteschenite	80–77 79 (chemical analysis)	72–65	48, 37, 15	. . .
Palisade (9)	Picrodolerite	approx. 71 (over-all average)	*65	. . .	65(−60)
Elephant's Head (10)	Picrite	83–77	*70	. . .	⊕85
Basistoppen (11)	Picrite	83	*76	. . .	(+)75
Uwekahuna (12)	Picrite	85 (chemical analysis)	64–58	†39.5, 50, 10.5	†77.5 (chemical analysis)
Egerton (13)	Hypersthenite	. . .	81–80	. . .	†83–71

* Large poikilitic plagioclase.
† Idiomorphic or hypidiomorphic pyroxene. (−60) peripheral zoning.
(+)/⊕ Idiomorphic pyroxene at top/bottom of picrite zone.
(12) Nos. of intrusions refer to Fig. 3.7.

volatile-rich material: teschenite or alkaline dolerite (Drever and Johnston, 1959). In a minority of basic alkaline intrusions, there is some evidence that the ultrabasic facies was formed during or after emplacement, the two contending but not necessarily mutually exclusive hypotheses being on the one hand (a) the concept of gravitative differentiation (e.g., Bowen, 1928; Walker, 1930 and 1940; Poldervaart, 1944; Murata and Richter, 1961; Drever and Johnston, 1965), or flow differentiation (Bhattacharji and Smith, 1964) aided by gravity (Bhattacharji, 1965; and Section IV of this chapter)—and on the other hand (b) the concept of a residual concentration of refractory minerals due to an upward transference of volatiles and liquid (cf. Drever 1952, Hess 1956, Wilkinson 1958, Wilshire 1963, Hamilton, 1965).

In many cases there is convincing evidence in support of gravitative differentiation, and the new concept of flow differentiation would seem to be applicable to the ultrabasic facies in the sills of northern Skye, which is the subject of Section III of this chapter. It will be more rewarding here, therefore, to review the evidence in support of the mechanism or mechanisms in the second concept.

The simple model of a rapidly emplaced homogeneous magma settling down quietly to fractionate *in situ* is, in basic alkaline sills, probably exceptional. Rapid emplacement, however, seems likely to have been operative in the case of thick tholeiitic sills of great lateral extent and lateral uniformity (Hess, 1956). To slower injection, and injection at varying rates, of a magma already partly differentiated, the variable distribution patterns of the picritic facies in many basic alkaline sills can be attributed (cf. Jaeger, 1958). The interplay of differing rates of emplacement with different rates of differentiation after emplacement may account for other variations.

Although the relatively rare upward gradational decrease in the amount of olivine [e.g., the Shiant Isles sill (above the discontinuity), the Elephant's Head dike, and the Uwekahuna laccolith] is readily explicable in terms of gravitative accumulation superimposed on flowage differentiation, the more common upward gradational increase in the amount of olivine from the bottom of these sills has, in the past, received too little attention. This more common variation pattern (Fig. 3.1) which is very well demonstrated in the Shiant Isles and Nebo sills can now be interpreted in terms of flow differentiation (Section III).

In both these sills the plagioclase crystals increase in size, as the olivine increases in amount, and they reach a maximum size near the top of the picrite. At approximately the same levels the plagioclase becomes the unzoned poikilitic bytownite which we regard as a mineral (with characteristic textural relations) of crucial significance in any interpretation of the origin of all of the olivine-rich rocks in which it occurs (cf. Fig. 3.4, center, and Fig. 3.13*b*). More than 35 years ago Flett (1930) wrote that the picrite in the Easter Dalmeny sill "is not a teschenite enriched by precipitation of olivine but a bytownite-augite-olivine rock of distinct character." Yet Walker and Poldervaart (1949), when referring to this type of picrite (gabbroic picrite), affirm that it is simply a variant of cumulative picrite formed under tranquil conditions (i.e., without intervention of magmatic flow). The present authors suggested (Drever and Johnston, 1965) that the lack of zoning in the plagioclase was probably the result of crystallization with a steep solidus slope (Wyllie, 1963), and they rejected the idea that this type of picrite could be explained by a mechanism of intercumulus plagioclase growth by two-way diffusion. Such an interpretation (Douglas, 1964) of the gabbroic picrite at the base of the Basistoppen sill is probably justifiable since this sill has obvious affinities with layered intrusions; but there must be another factor, common to both large and small intrusions to be taken into account before the range in occurrence of this phenomenon can be adequately explained.

What might now be considered is the location in any particular intrusion, and the paragenetic mineral relationships, of this distinctive picrite. It is relatively coarse-grained and is associated (notably in the Nebo sill) with a concentration of zeolites. Taken as a whole, the evidence suggests that consolidation, from the bottom upward, was accompanied by an early magmatic, vertical migration (in the picritic facies) of volatile-rich material. Where this volatile-rich material is mainly concentrated will be the location of highest liquidity. The chemistry of this migration, however vaguely conceived at present, seems effectively to stabilize Mg-rich olivine and Ca-rich plagioclase with relation, respectively, to iron and sodium, and these minerals retain their refractory compositions even in the alkali-rich feldspathic patches and veins (see Fig. 3.15). Volatile-enrichment has also retarded the nucleation and crystallization of augite, its growth at lower temperatures coinciding with the crystallization of zeolites. The richness in the veins and patches of bytownite, its textural relations with augite, the crystal shapes and textural relations of the olivine, all suggest that in the hydrous liquid, from which the minerals in these veins and patches crystallized, the primary liquidus phase was anorthitic plagioclase. The occurrence of large unzoned, relatively anorthite-rich plagioclase in association with high concentrations of olivine is consistent with an interpretation of this concentration as a residual fraction, due to the removal of some constituents and the closer packing of olivines, probably by flow differentiation in an environment of relatively reduced viscosity. The common occurrence of an optimum amount of olivine over a wide horizontal range in these sills is also consistent with the operation of flow differentiation.

This alternative concept of residual concentration of refractory minerals due to an upward transference of volatile-rich material is not presented as a serious challenge to the validity of the concepts of gravitative accumulation and flow differentiation as the *principal* mechanisms responsible for the distribution of olivine in the ultrabasic facies of many of these sills. The suggestion is made, however, that it played a part in the concentration of olivine in some sills. More importance is attached to this alternative mechanism as a factor in any explanation of the growth and composition of the plagioclase (and the pyroxene), to which neither gravitative accumulation nor flowage differentiation could have contributed directly. Enrichment in MgO and CaO in the Egerton sill (see Fig. 3.15) has been interpreted by Hamilton (1965) in terms of "liquid fractionation."

Attention might also be drawn to the marked disparity in the composition of the plagioclase in the ultrabasic facies of (a) basic alkaline intrusions, such as that of the Shiant Isles, and (b) intrusions of tholeiitic affinity, such as that of the Uwekahuna laccolith and the Palisade sill (respectively, 12 and 9, Fig. 3.7). This disparity, shown in Fig. 3.7, indicates firmly that the simple explanation in terms of gravitative settling of olivine in a *basaltic* magma, however applicable to the differentiation in these two tholeiitic intrusions, cannot be applied to the origin of the Shiant Isles picrite (1, Fig. 3.7).

The evidence outlined suggests that the parent basaltic (or picritic) magma, after generation at depth, became arrested at crustal levels corresponding to a pressure-

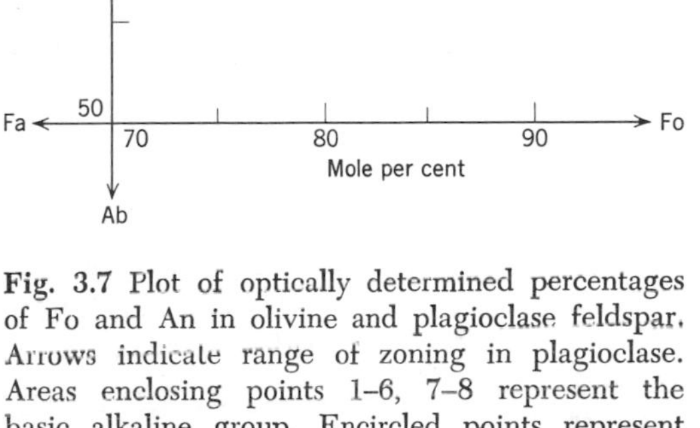

Fig. 3.7 Plot of optically determined percentages of Fo and An in olivine and plagioclase feldspar. Arrows indicate range of zoning in plagioclase. Areas enclosing points 1–6, 7–8 represent the basic alkaline group. Encircled points represent the tholeiitic group. Numbers refer to intrusions, etc., listed in Table 3.2.

temperature environment in which the magma became supersaturated with olivine. Following the precipitation of olivine, the increase in water-vapor pressure would contribute the energy necessary for the final injection as sills and sheets. Relatively heavy olivine-enriched fractions could, under these circumstances, be squeezed into well "lubricated" subsurface locations but would not normally be erupted as lava flows. The water-rich basic alkaline magma appears to have been accommodated in relatively small and localized magma chambers where in many cases it differentiated, before intrusion as sills and sheets at higher levels. The sills and sheets of water-poor tholeiitic magma, on the other hand, represent a regional expression of crustal injection of relatively undifferentiated magma from greater depths.

III. FLOW DIFFERENTIATION IN THE PICRITIC SILLS OF NORTH SKYE

Tom Simkin

A. Description

The north end of the Isle of Skye (northwest Scotland) is dominated by a series of early Tertiary sills, up to 400 feet thick and strongly differentiated, which intrude Jurassic sedimentary rocks. These subhorizontal sills are well exposed on the three coastal sides of the Trotternish peninsula, but are covered by flood basalts to the south. The central plutonic complex of Skye lies about 30 miles south and the Shiant Isles 15 miles north.

Olivine content in the sills ranges from 0 to 67 per cent with plagioclase (An_{70-40}), augite, and magnetite making up the balance of the rock in relatively constant proportions. Alkaline affinities are indicated by the presence of zeolites and the absence of orthopyroxene; biotite and amphibole are also absent. Mineral variation is illustrated in Fig. 3.8—a generalized sequence showing an olivine-poor lower margin followed by a rapid, but gradational, increase in olivine to the picrite that constitutes one-half to three-fourths of the sill thickness. Picrite is succeeded abruptly by olivine-poor rock which continues to the upper margin.

These discontinuities between rocks relatively rich and poor in olivine were observed in all sills and were sharp enough to be seen in a single petrographic thin section in all those illustrated in Fig. 3.8 (except 3.8*f*, where pegmatite occurs at the discontinuity). Where the olivine-poor unit is less than 20 feet thick (Fig. 3.8*d,e,f*), the discontinuities separate dolerite bearing approximately 10 per cent small ($\leqslant \frac{1}{2}$ mm) subophitic olivine ($Fo_{50\pm5}$) from picrite containing more than 30 per cent subhedral olivine phenocrysts (Fo_{82-77}) that are at least twice the size of the dolerite olivine. There is no evidence of interior chilling at these discontinuities and columnar joints cross them unbroken. However, where the overlying olivine-poor unit is thick (Fig. 3.8*c,i*) its base carries a higher proportion of olivine (to 29 per cent) consisting largely of phenocrysts. Discontinuities also occur at the base of some of the picrite units (Fig. 3.8*e,g,h*).

B. Differentiation Hypotheses

Choice of the magma, or magmas, that might have produced these sills is limited to a single liquid, successive liquids, or combinations of liquids and suspended phenocrysts.

A single homogeneous liquid should yield a chilled margin representative of the bulk composition of the sill. Inspection of cross sections such as Fig. 3.8*d,e,f* shows bulk compositions containing $2\frac{1}{2}$ to 6 times the volume of olivine present in and near their chilled margin.

Multiple intrusion of liquids of differing compositions would require initial intrusion of basaltic liquid (basaltic chilled margins) followed, with no significant time lag (absence of interior chilling), by a more basic, perhaps ultrabasic, liquid at the base of each sill. A rather delicate mixing of these two liquids would seem necessary to explain the gradational dolerite-to-picrite transitions at the base (Fig. 3.8*a,b*), a relatively cool part of the sill where abrupt, if not chilled, junctions would seem more likely. However, in the upper central, and presumably hottest, part of the sill the junction is invariably sharp. Addition of a third pulse of basaltic liquid might explain the upper discontinuities, but would require three separate intrusions in the same time and space sequence throughout all north Skye sills.

These objections to nonporphyritic magmas leave the third possibility of magma

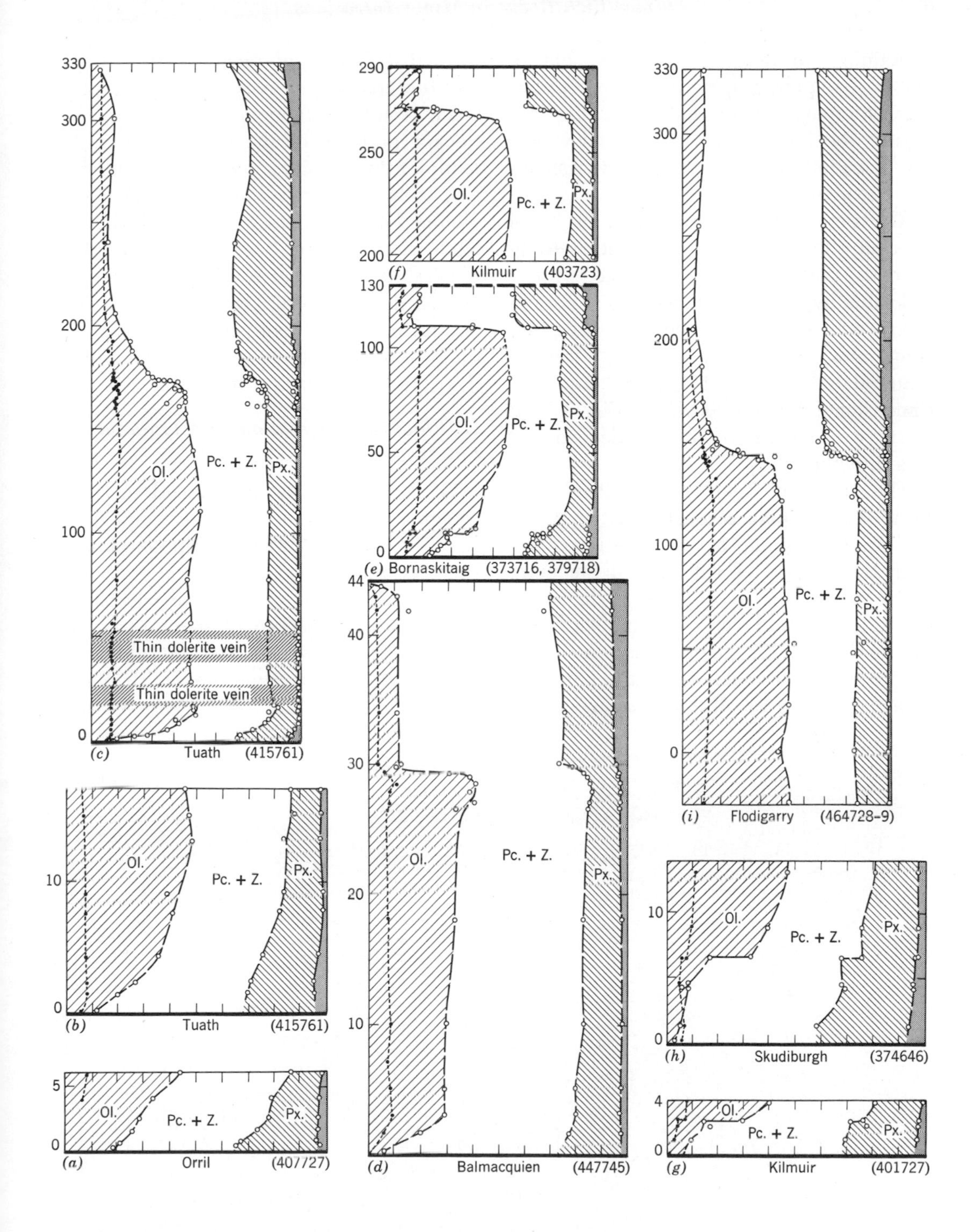

Fig. 3.8 Mineral variation in north Skye sills. Vertical dimensions in feet above lower contact or sea level (note that lower, wider sections are more detailed). Horizontal dimension is cumulative modal per cent of olivine, plagioclase (and zeolite), clinopyroxene, and magnetite (total = 100 per cent). Dotted lines indicate average grain intercept of olivine (1.0 mm ≅ 20 modal per cent on these graphs). Contacts are shown by thick lines. Sections are located by sill names and National Grid Reference (in parentheses).

containing intratelluric olivine phenocrysts. The petrographic evidence supports this alternative and indicates that the liquid was essentially basaltic; however, the distribution of the phenocrysts remains to be explained.

The time-honored explanation for basal concentration of olivine is gravity settling of early olivine crystals in place. This is a flexible hypothesis and, as long as parameters such as viscosity, cooling rates, settling rates, and supply of crystals can be manipulated, it might explain any one-dimensional section shown in Fig. 3.8. At least two dimensions are needed to test this hypothesis.

The cliffs at Sgeir nan Eather Bàna (Fig. 3.9) display a local variation of 40 feet in the height of the Flodigarry sill roof. Truncation of flat-lying sedimentary rocks marks this as a primary change in the sill roof, and vertical columnar joints in the lower cliff suggest that the unexposed floor is subhorizontal. Given a primary change in sill thickness and a uniform distribution of phenocrysts throughout the magma, gravity settling in place must result in more phenocrysts in the thicker portions of the sill. However, the mapping in Fig. 3.9 shows that the olivine-rich unit is neither thicker nor richer in olivine below the higher roof of the sill. Sgeir nan Eather Bàna is but the best illustrated of several north Skye examples of absence of picrite thinning under low points in the sill roof; clearly gravity settling in place cannot explain the olivine distribution pattern in these sills.

C. Flow Differentiation—Background and Sill Model

G. P. Scrope, who introduced the word "magma" to petrology, strongly emphasized ". . . its analogy to those compound liquids such as mud, paste, milk, blood, honey, etc., which consist of solid particles deriving a certain freedom of motion amongst one another from their intimate admixture, in greater or less proportion, with one or more perfect fluids, which act as their

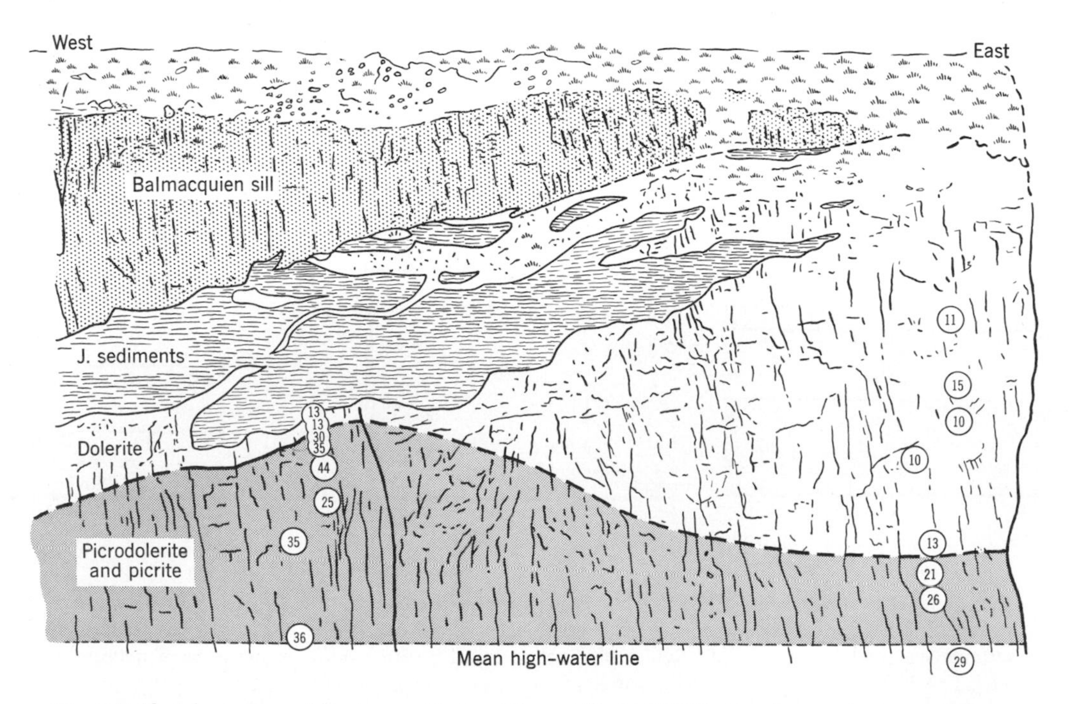

Fig. 3.9 Sketch section of Sgeir nan Eather Bàna cliffs (447745). Numbers indicate modal per cent olivine where sampled. Younger Balmacquien sill (above) is chilled against both underlying rock types. Cliff height is approximately 130 feet.

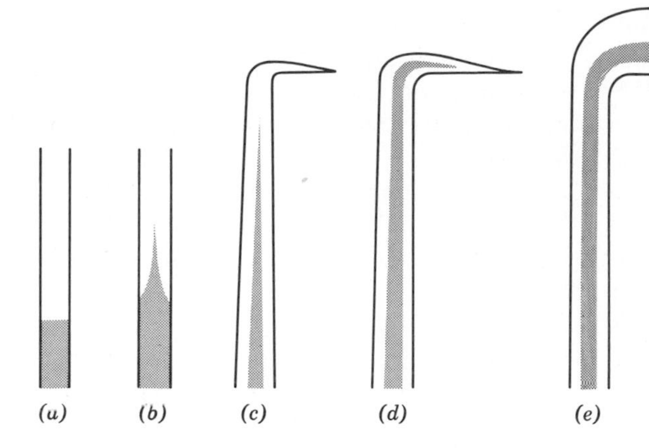

Fig. 3.10 Schematic model: flow differentiation at progressive stages of intrusion. Basaltic liquid carrying olivine phenocrysts (stipple). (*a*) and (*b*) from Bhattacharji and Smith (1964); experimental concentration of particles at rest (*a*) and after initiating flow (*b*).

vehicle" (Scrope, 1825, p. 19). During the following 140 years many investigators have studied the hydrodynamic behavior of most of the above "compound liquids" as well as others such as printing ink, coal slurries, and melted chocolate, but these studies were not applied to magmas until Baragar (1960) noted the similarities between fiber concentration in flowing wood pulp and plagioclase phenocryst distribution in sills of the Labrador trough. Bhattacharji and Smith (1963, 1964) recognized the importance of this concept and scaled models to simulate porphyritic magma in a vertical dike. They noted concentration of "phenocrysts" toward the center of the "dike" during flow and went on to explain the olivine-rich center of the Muskox feeder dike by this mechanism.

The differentiation model favored for the north Skye sills (Simkin, 1964, 1965) is based on the movement of particles away from margins during flow as demonstrated over a wide range of conditions by many hydrodynamicists since 1836. In Fig. 3.10, *a* and *b* are from Bhattacharji and Smith's (1964) experiments simulating magmatic flow, and clearly show concentration of phenocrysts away from the margins during flow. Extending this to the sill situation, liquid would be expected at the thin end of the intruding wedge (*c*) and would chill there as basaltic margins. The central concentration of phenocrysts, when spreading laterally (*d*), would be affected by gravity and move in the lower part of the sill. Particles near the base would experience upward hydrodynamic forces (decreasing away from the margin) and the constant downward force of gravity, the conflict of forces producing the gradational transition from basaltic margin up into olivine-rich picrite. At the top of the picrite unit (essentially the interface between crystal mush and overlying liquid) both gravity and flow concentration work together producing the abrupt discontinuity observed in the Skye sills. Crystallization of the surrounding liquid then yields the remaining minerals in relatively constant proportions, plus the small, subophitic olivine grains (about 10 per cent) in the dolerite. By this model, then, the major features of mineral distribution in these (see Section III-A) and other sills (see Section II) may be explained. Bhattacharji (1965, and Section IV) has produced this pattern (typified by Fig. 3.8*d*) in recent scale-model experiments of sill formation.

This basic pattern may be modified in several ways. Should the phenocryst suspension lag appreciably behind the intruding wedge of liquid, its lower margin would be previously consolidated, but still hot, dolerite, resulting in a discontinuity at the *base* of the picrite (Fig. 3.8*e,g,h*). Another modification would be caused by post-intrusion settling of stray phenocrysts caught in, or crystallizing from, the overlying liquid. Coming to rest on the underlying mush, these phenocrysts would diminish the abruptness of the discontinuity (Fig. 3.8*c,i*), but they would quickly decrease upward and their number would probably be insignificant in thin "liquid" units (Fig. 3.8*d,e,f*). Within the suspension itself, however, the greatly increased viscosity of the concentration (Bhattacharji, 1964, Shaw, 1965) suggests that postintrusion settling has little effect on the phenocryst distribution pattern imposed during flow.

D. Flow Differentiation—Theory and Illustrations

The hydrodynamics of flow concentration are complex and not yet fully understood, but useful guides to the extensive literature of this field are the reviews by Goldsmith and Mason (1964, 1967) and Scott Blair (1958). Three basic patterns have been described for radial migration of suspended particles during flow. In simple *axial migration* (Poiseuille, 1836; Vejlens, 1938; Starkey, 1956), particles move toward an equilibrium position at the tube axis during flow. *Plug flow* (Coulter and Pappenheimer, 1949; Forgacs et al., 1958; Bhattacharji and Savic, 1965), an extension of this process, concentrates particles in a central plug within which there is little or no velocity gradient, radial migration, or rotation. In the *tubular pinch effect,* only recently recognized (Segré and Silberberg, 1961, 1962, 1964; Oliver, 1962), central particles are moved toward the wall while axial migration is moving marginal particles away from the wall, thereby concentrating particles at an equilibrium position approximately midway between tube axis and wall. Of these three patterns, only axial migration in the special case of nonrigid particles (e.g., blood corpuscles) ". . . has been explained with any degree of completeness" (Karnis et al., 1963, p. 160), and the conditions separating them have not been established.

Probable examples of all three patterns, however, can be found in the petrologic literature. In addition to the sills of north Skye (above) and the Labrador trough (Baragar, 1960), those described by Edwards (1952), MacGregor (1948, p. 66), and many others show the essential phenocryst distribution of plug flow. Some picritic lava flows also show these features (Walker, 1959; Fuller, 1939). But it is in vertical dikes, where gravity effects can be discounted, that the results of flow concentration are best seen. The Muskox feeder dike (Bhattacharji and Smith, 1964) has already been mentioned, and the picritic dikes of Skye (Bowen, 1928; Drever and Johnston, 1958) provide excellent illustrations. Several Skye dikes (e.g., Lynedale dike, Wilson, 1938), show the homogeneous picrite core with rapid marginal gradation to chilled basalt that is characteristic of plug flow. Drever and Johnston (1958) describe several thin picritic dikes in which size and abundance of olivine phenocrysts increase to the very axis (simple axial migration) and one (their Fig. 11a; see Fig. 3.12 in this chapter) showing clear concentration of phenocrysts midway between center and both margins (as in the tubular pinch effect).

Flow differentiation, however, would not be expected during intrusion of all porphyritic magmas. Goldsmith and Mason (1961, and 1962) have shown that rigid particles undergo no axial migration under flow conditions of very high viscosity or low velocity, or both (particle Reynolds numbers less than 10^{-6}); and examples may be found in quartz monzonite porphyry sills with apparent high magmatic viscosity (e.g., Tweto, 1951), yet no reported decrease of phenocryst abundance at margins. Some north Skye sills illustrate magmas of sufficiently low viscosity (or high velocity or both) that margins were free of phenocrysts during intrusion, while others illustrate intermediate conditions in which up to 19 per cent phenocrysts were trapped in the chilled margin. As might be expected from the great increase in viscosity accompanying increased crystal loads (Shaw, 1965), the marginal phenocryst abundance in each sill reflects the total phenocryst concentration in that sill (compare sections *d* and *e* in Fig. 3.8). Some picrite dikes in the area show little or no marginal decrease in olivine and may represent the "high viscosity-low velocity-no flow concentration" end member in this series (analogous to the quartz monzonite porphyries).

IV. SCALE MODEL EXPERIMENTS ON FLOWAGE DIFFERENTIATION IN SILLS

Somdev Bhattacharji

It is only recently that the specific mechanisms operating during flowage which are capable of producing crystal and chemical differentiation in ultramafic-mafic complexes have begun to be investigated by geologists (Bhattacharji, 1964, 1965; Bhattacharji and Smith, 1964). In order to verify the hypothesis that the phenocryst-rich central core of a sill might be formed by the concentration of intratelluric crystals towards the center of the flowing magma, experimental scale models were devised using solid-fluid mixtures. Dimensional analyses were made and experimental quasi-scale models were constructed for ultramafic-mafic sills 5 to 2000 feet in thickness, with feeder dikes. Model analysis differs little from that employed by Bhattacharji and Smith (1964) and details are discussed in a separate paper in preparation. This paper describes a few significant results from the experiments, which tend to confirm the interpretation of Simkin for the Skye sills (Section III of this chapter).

Viscous fluids (coconut oil, motor oil, turpentine) were selected that, with temperature variation, resemble in prototype magma viscosities of 100 to 30,000 poises; an average viscosity of 3000 poises was considered for most of the models (Hess, 1960; MacDonald, 1963). Solids (lucite, paraplex plastic, bakelite, calcium chloride) of various sizes, shapes and densities were used to reproduce properties of olivine (Fo_{40-85}), pyroxene, and plagioclase (labradorite-anorthite). Models using parallel plates of lucite plastic were constructed to represent the sill. Cross sections are shown in Fig. 3.11. Rectangular parallel plates, representing a vertical fracture or dike, were connected at the top with a horizontal rectangular box with walls one inch apart. A floatable rectangular box was fitted inside the horizontal box; this was weighted to represent the superincumbent load. Sill formation was reproduced when the solid-fluid mixtures were pushed up through the vertical conduit. The upward pressure of the solid-fluid mixture raised the inner box, allowing the solid-fluid mixture to make its way into the horizontal box as a sill. Magma chilling at the margins of the sill and gradual crystallization towards the interior were simulated by circulating cold water through the jackets surrounding the horizontal box. The flow of solid-fluid mixtures was studied with different thermal and shear gradients.

Figure 3.11 shows that separation of solids (crystals) from the walls and their concentration at or near the center of both vertical and horizontal conduits is observed in experiments. Figure 3.11*a* illustrates the behavior of a mixture of Paraplex plastic representing olivine (Fo_{78-80}) and coconut oil representing melt. 50 per cent by volume consisted of solid. The average

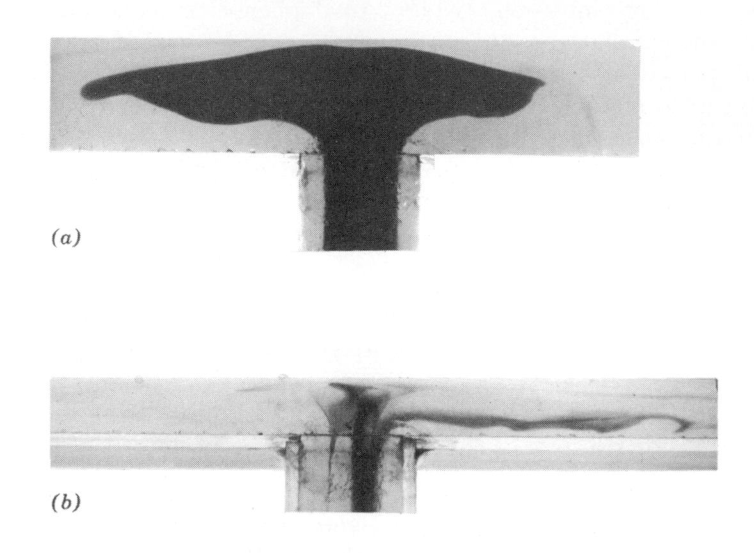

Fig. 3.11 Flowage differentiation in model sills containing solid-fluid mixtures representing olivine phenocrysts and basic melt. These photographs show a vertical feeder connected to a horizontal "sill." The feeder is 1 inch in width. The solid particles (black) become concentrated near the central parts of the feeder and "sill" during flowage. (*a*) 50 per cent by volume of solid; flow rate 4 mm/sec. (*b*) 15 per cent by volume of solid. Flow rate 3.5 mm/sec. dropping to 1.8 mm/sec.

flow rate of the solid-fluid mixture was 4 mm/sec. Central concentration of solid in the vertical feeder and in the horizontal "sill" is shown. Figure 3.11*b* illustrates the behavior of the same components, with the solid concentration 15 per cent by volume, and with an initial flow rate of 3.5 mm/sec dropping suddenly to 1.8 mm/sec. The maximum concentration of the solid (representing olivine) is visible just below the median line of the sill in the flow of the solid-fluid mixture. Note also the tendency of solid settling which developed as the flow rate dropped. Thus, gravity settling becomes significant below certain flow rates. However, chilling of the lower margin and increased crystallization, which produce an increase in the viscosity of the magma, tend to hinder crystal settling close to the margin. The segregation effects of the solids, simulating olivine or plagioclase phenocrysts, to form the equivalent of central picrite, anorthosite, or peridotite in the model sills has been found to be largely influenced by the segregation pattern of the phenocrysts in the dikes during flowage (Fig. 3.11).

There is considerable difference of opinion as to the relative importance of the various differentiation processes involved in the formation of ultramafic-mafic sills (Walker, 1956; Jaeger and Joplin, 1956; Hess, 1956; this chapter, Section II) and the mechanisms involved require careful consideration. Flowage differentiation has been invoked to account for certain features of the Muskox intrusion (Chapter 2-III) and the fractionation of mafic-ultramafic sills in Skye and elsewhere (this chapter, Sections II and III). The process may provide an explanation for some of the features illustrated in Fig. 3.12. The effect of flowage differentiation in the formation of different magma compositions during their transport from the mantle to the crust and surface of the earth is probably more significant than is generally realized.

V. PICRITIC MINOR INTRUSIONS

H. I. Drever and R. Johnston

A. Introduction

Unlike the picritic rocks that characteristically occur as a facies of thick doleritic sills, the picritic rocks dealt with in this chapter constitute the whole or almost the whole of the intrusions. In addition, the majority of these rocks form relatively small dikes, sills, or sheets varying from less than a foot to about 30 feet in width. Only rarely do they exceed 30 feet. These minor intrusions are termed "picritic" owing to their richness in olivine, and no attempt will be made to compare them with rocks rich in augite phenocrysts such as augite-picrites, monchiquites, ankaramites, fourchites, limburgites or nepheline basalts. Attention will be directed simply to a natural and distinctive assemblage of olivine-rich minor intrusions, the petrogenetic status of which has yet to be defined and related to the tholeiitic, the alkaline basalt, or to any other type of "primitive" magma.

The finest development of these picritic minor intrusions is in association with other Tertiary igneous rocks in the Cuillins of Skye in Scotland and on Ubekendt Ejland in west Greenland. No other type of igneous rock containing abundant olivine is more consistently free from late-magmatic replacements, and in no other can the crystal growth of this mineral be more readily and profitably studied. Textural and other variations can also be examined with unusual thoroughness in many fine glaciated exposures that are continuous both across and along the strike.

The picritic minor intrusions of the Cuillins were given special prominence by Bowen (1928) as evidence of olivine accumulation. Among other things, he drew attention to the absence of aphanitic selvedges of ultrabasic composition. But further and much more detailed investigations of these intrusions, and the discovery and thorough investigation of the other particularly fine development in west Greenland, have now greatly extended our knowledge and have stimulated a revival of interest in the possible existence of natural magnesium-rich liquids (picritic magma). In addition, this detailed inquiry has disclosed the natural occurrence with these picritic rocks of silicate liquids more calcic than basalt.

Certain petrographical observations seem to the authors to be more likely than others to retain a fundamental significance. This is the basis on which they have made their selection, emphasis and comments.

B. Regional Distribution and Geologic Setting

It is appropriate here to refer almost entirely to the two principal and best known areas, in the islands of Skye and Ubekendt. The picritic minor intrusions of the Cuillins in Skye are associated with the major intrusive complex composed mainly of peridotitic, picritic, eucritic, gabbroic and granitic rocks (Harker, 1904; Bowen, 1928); but minor intrusions of similar type also occur at considerable distances from this intrusive complex (Drever and Johnston, 1958), and they may occur as members of the regional swarm (Allison, 1936). The picritic minor intrusions of Ubekendt Ejland cut zeolite-rich picritic lavas (Drever, 1956, 1958) and a few of these intrusions are demonstrably lava feeders. They are not associated with the major intrusive complex in the south of this island.

In the Cuillins an early picritic group, approximately contemporaneous with the plutonic ultrabasic rocks, can be distinguished from a much later group. It is preferable, however, to adopt here the following more general and more petrographical groupings, the main criteria being the size and textural relations of the plagioclase:

1. A group comprising relatively thick (and rarely thin) dikes and sheets most of which have large poikilitic plagioclase and, in the Cuillin area, often contain an assemblage (as xenoliths) of other ultrabasic rocks.

2. A group comprising relatively small intrusions which are, typically, without large poikilitic plagioclase and seldom contain ultrabasic xenoliths.

In addition, two relatively large sills (with feeder dikes), one in the Cuillins (Weedon, 1960) and one on Ubekendt Ejland (Drever, 1958), have distinctive feldspathic banding near their upper margins.

Some picritic rocks which are found elsewhere (such as the olivine-rich Mauritius dikes) have yet to be investigated in sufficient detail to warrant comparison with those in the two areas with which this account is concerned. It seems probable that the extensive development of Karroo picritic rocks in the Nuanetsi Igneous Province (Cox, *et al.*, 1965) in Rhodesia will yield information of critical significance.

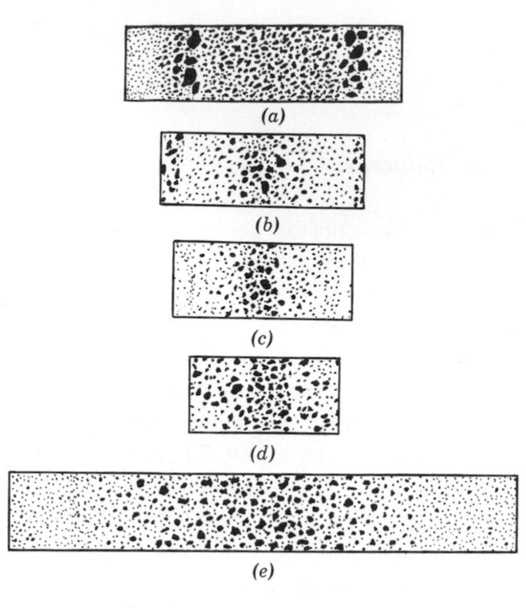

Fig. 3.12 Sketches (Drever and Johnston, 1958) from large microsections illustrating variation in the size and amount of olivine phenocrysts in some complete cross sections of narrow or attenuated picritic dikes in the Cuillins, Skye, Scotland. Scale: ×½.

C. Petrography

1. Variation in the amount, size and habit of the olivine. The most common variation pattern is an increase in the amount of olivine from the margin of these intrusions towards the center, but in some this increase is only very slight. An increase downward has been observed in one dike but another, when followed upward in continuous exposure for more than a thousand feet, showed no marked variation. The average amount of olivine (usually equidimensional) in these intrusions varies from 25 to 60 per cent. An increase in its amount is often accompanied by an increase in its size, and this is particularly well displayed in some small dikes in the Cuillins (Fig. 3.12), offshoots of dikes on Ubekendt Ejland, picritic veins in the Ingia intrusion (Ubekendt Ejland) and veins in olivine dolerite at Kranskop in S. Africa (Frankel, 1942). The nonporphyritic facies in one of the Soay sills (Fig. 3.16*a*), in the Igdlorssuit intrusion (Drever, 1956, 1958), and in a sill on the island of Scalpay (Fig. 3.13) passes downward into the facies rich in olivine through a transitional zone in which there is a downward increase in the size and amount of the equidimensional olivines (Fig. 3.16*c*). Decrease in size of the olivines toward the margins of some examples in Scotland, and many in Greenland, is accompanied by a change to a thinly tabular or lamellar habit (Fig. 3.14); in some of the small intrusions, crystals with this habit are common even in the center.

2. Variation in texture and mode. In the group of relatively small intrusions, the textures most commonly developed are variolitic and doleritic (subophitic to ophitic), and textures transitional between these two types can be referred to as subvariolitic. Feldspar and pyroxene inter-

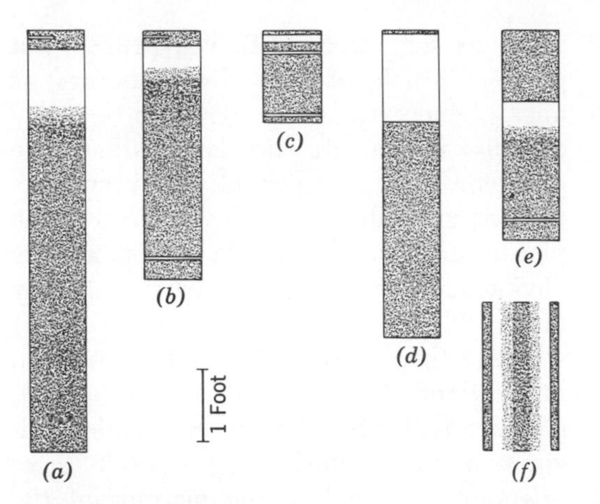

Fig. 3.13 Vertical sections of five sills (*a–e*) and a horizontal section of a dike (*f*). White: nonporphyritic facies (gradational relations with picrite as indicated). (*a*) Igdlorssuit intrusion (Sheet 2), Ubekendt Ejland, west Greenland; (*b*) Sill 2, Soay. (*c*) Sill C2, Soay; (*d*) Sill, Cuillin ridge (data from F. G. F. Gibb); (*e*) Sheet on northeast coast of Scalpay (data partly from C. M. Thomas); (*f*) Dike 2, Coire Lagan, Cuillins. (*b–f*) in Skye, Scotland.

grown as thin elongated crystals, arranged in sheaves and radiating groups, typify the variolitic textures which in some intrusions extend from near the marginal contacts to the center without any marked change in crystallinity. In some olivine-rich central zones the size of the groundmass crystals may even be slightly reduced. The texture in the nonporphyritic facies is always doleritic, and even where there is no discontinuity between this facies and the variolitic picrite the textural change is fairly abrupt. Very small olivines can be detected in the groundmass of most of these small intrusions, except in globules within the nonporphyritic faces of the Igdlorssuit intrusion (Drever, 1960). A few small brown chrome spinels are ubiquitous components in the Scottish picritic rocks.

In the group of relatively large intrusions, all stages can be traced from fine-grained doleritic or subvariolitic marginal textures through increasingly coarser doleritic textures until the plagioclase develops as large tabular, and occasionally branching, crystals poikilitically enclosing olivines (Fig. 3.16*b*). In an inclined sheet on Sgurr Dearg in Skye large arborescent growths of bytownite enclose hundreds of olivines. Small zoned plagioclase crystals in one intrusion may change gradationally to large unzoned (or peripherally zoned) poikilitic plagioclase crystals over a distance of about a foot from the margin, whereas in another intrusion the change takes place over a much longer distance from the margin, there being no apparent relation between the rapidity of this change and the size of the intrusion.

The evaluation and comparison of modes in the members of the group of small intrusions has not been recorded in much detail. One of the reasons for this is the difficulty in accurately measuring the amounts of pyroxene and feldspar in the commonly developed variolitic intergrowths. Detailed micrometric measurements across some of the thicker intrusions and the large banded intrusions are still in progress. Wyllie and Drever (1963) determined the modal variation across a small sill (Sill 1) in Soay which exhibits the

Fig. 3.14 Skeletal olivines and parallel growths drawn from microsections of picritic minor intrusions. Scale: ×17 (top row), ×12 (bottom row). Loc.: Ubekendt Ejland, west Greenland.

usual concentration of olivine centrally. In spite of this increase in olivine from about 40 to 60 per cent, the amounts of plagioclase, and of olivine plus pyroxene, remain remarkably constant. The ratio of pyroxene to plagioclase shows, accordingly, a steady decrease toward the sill center. In another Soay sill (Fig. 3.13*b*), the non-porphyritic facies has a ratio of pyroxene to plagioclase of 39.0/40.5 and in the olivine-rich central picrite it is 32.7/48.9.

3. Ultrabasic xenoliths. Ultrabasic xenoliths are very common in the group of thicker dikes in the Cuillins. Their distribution patterns are very variable; they may disappear in a dike for some distance and then reappear, and they show no marked tendency to be concentrated along a middle zone in any intrusion. In some places they may be so numerous as to constitute about 60 per cent of a dike and in some instances are rounded like boulders in a conglomerate. Their composition is equally variable and may range from a highly feldspathic olivine-bytownite rock to peridotite (with less than ten per cent plagioclase) and dunite. A few exhibit layering and igneous lamination. The junction between these xenoliths and the enclosing picrite is almost invariably sharp without any indication of reaction or assimilation.

One of the rare occurrences of ultrabasic xenoliths in the group of relatively small picritic intrusions (without poikilitic plagioclase) is in the sill on the island of Soay (Sill 1) described by Wyllie and Drever (1963). In this sill, peridotitic and allivalitic xenoliths are concentrated in a remarkable zone at the margin of the sill where its emplacement has been arrested by a vertical dolerite dyke. Their transitional relationships with the picrite indicate some assimilation and the olivine is partly replaced by augite intergrown with plagioclase.

4. Marginal selvedges and the growth of olivine. In many of these minor intrusions the marginal selvedges are not basaltic, as suggested by Bowen (1928), but picritic. Much of the olivine occurs as microphenocrysts; there may also be many crystals which are no larger than the pyroxene and feldspar of the very fine-grained groundmass. In the majority of the picritic intrusions on Ubekendt Ejland, the olivines in the marginal facies are thinly tabular and skeletal (Drever, 1956) whereas this phenomenon is less common in Scotland (Wyllie and Drever, 1963). Characteristically, the thinly tabular olivines all have their large (010) faces orientated parallel to the margins of the intrusions whether these are horizontal, inclined or vertical.

A comparison of the habit and shape of the olivines in many of these contact selvedges, with those known to have been developed as a result of rapid skeletal or dendritic crystallization (Drever and Johnston, 1957), has substantiated the view that the tabular olivines of these selvedges were very rapidly precipitated (Drever, 1952). In addition to a tabular habit, irregular shapes, embayments, inclusions of groundmass, and parallel growth can also be ascribed to rapid crystallization (Fig. 3.14). Analogous shapes have been observed in Rhodesian limburgites (Cox et al., 1965) in which there is the same correspondence between the rapidity of congelation and the development of olivine with such growth features. In South Africa, Frankel (1942) has described magnesium-rich glassy veins containing olivine with embayments and inclusions, which could be the result either of rapid crystallization or of corrosion.

Dactylitic growths of clinopyroxene (and occasionally a little brown amphibole) are not uncommon as inclusions (Drever and Livingstone, 1948) in the olivines of some of these picritic rocks, and also in alkaline picritic rocks such as those of the Shiant Isles. These inclusions are not confined to skeletal or tabular olivines. They may have originated at high pressure as nuclei around which the olivines crystallized at depth.

5. Two banded intrusions. According to Weedon (1960), the 250-foot-thick sill on the south slope of Gars-bheinn in Skye is mainly feldspathic peridotite except for the top 50 feet which is banded. This sill is demonstrably connected with a feeder dike of feldspathic peridotite below it and the banded top of what may be an upper extension of the same sill occurs in a much smaller outcrop higher up. The bands, which are relatively rich in feldspar, increase in number and thickness upward until they form the main component at about one foot from the upper contact. A notable feature of this sill is the fact that the very thin lower bands (about 0.5 inches thick) remain remarkably constant in width and horizontal direction for at least 50 feet.

The Ingia sill on the northeastern tip of Ubekendt Ejland, which also has feldspathic bands toward the top, is only 50 to 60 feet thick. The bands, although horizontal, may have wavy (not flat) planar margins and may increase in number but decrease in thickness upward. They disappear at six feet below the fully exposed upper margin. In spite of these differences, the banding in the two sills is very similar in other respects. All contacts of the Ingia sill and its feeder dyke can be examined. Some vertical feldspathic veins occur toward the bottom.

Near the picritic margins of both intrusions there is a reduction in the amount of olivine. This olivine, particularly in the Ingia intrusion, becomes elongated and skeletal, the contact rock being indistinguishable from that of many small sills. The texture when traced from the margins toward the center changes from variolitic or microdoleritic to coarsely doleritic, and the feldspar finally becomes larger and poikilitic in the bulk of both intrusions. The augite in the center of these intrusions is also poikilitic, the enclosed olivines being well rounded grains in contrast to the olivines within the plagioclase which tend toward idiomorphism (Drever, 1956). The feldspathic bands contain little or no olivine and where it does occur it develops, like the augite, as irregular growths between, or intergrown with, the feldspars, the resulting texture being quite distinct from typical poikilitic or intercumulus textures. In addition, the feldspar in the feldspathic bands in both sills has wide zoned mantles and its average composition is more sodic than the unzoned (or peripherally zoned) poikilitic feldspar in the picrite (or feldspathic peridotite). The textural change from the feldspathic bands into the ultramafic rock is typically abrupt but occasionally transitional.

6. Contact metamorphism. The thermal effects at the contacts of these picritic minor intrusions with xenoliths and country rocks vary from the usual low-temperature metamorphism to high-temperature fusion in some cases; and the same intrusion may effect high-temperature metamorphism at one locality and only slight metamorphism at another. There seems to be no relation between the degree of metamorphism and the size of the intrusion responsible for it.

A considerable degree of thermal metamorphism of siliceous sediments has been observed in association with a 3-foot-thick picritic intrusion in Scalpay (Drever, Johnston and Thomas, 1961) and with a small sill in Soay (Sill 1) intruded into arkose and containing xenoliths of both arkose and ultrabasic rock (Wyllie, 1961; Wyllie and Drever, 1963). The Soay sill is also the only picritic minor intrusion, containing ultrabasic xenoliths, that has demonstrably transformed and partially assimilated them. Fused arkose xenoliths in a picritic dike on the island of Scalpay have been recorded by Drever, Johnston and Thomas (1961), who also refer to a conspicuous zone of contact metamorphism and partial fusion below the 11-foot-thick picritic sill near Igdlorssuit in west Greenland. This zone has been developed in zeolite-rich picritic lava.

Wyllie's research (1961) on the thermal transformation of an arkose by the small picritic sill in Soay (Sill 1) is one of the most detailed investigations of contact metamorphism by minor intrusions. He records that up to 92 per cent of the original minerals of the arkose were fused, with tridymite, cordierite and magnetite crystallizing from the liquid and the remaining liquid congealing as a glass. Reaction between the picrite and the sediment resulted in the following: (a) the replacement of olivine by antigorite, (b) the development of orthopyroxene mantles around olivine, and (c) the isolation of olivine pseudomorphs and picrite inclusions within fused sediment (Fig. 3.16*d*). In spite of the isolation of these pseudomorphs, the junction between fused sediment and picrite is sharp, but some mixing of acid and basic liquids is indicated by the brown coloration of the glass in the endogenous contact zone.

D. Petrogenesis

The variation in the size and amount of the olivine in these picritic intrusions has been discussed in detail by Drever and Johnston (1958), who came to the conclusion that they were due to a differentiation process operating, during emplacement, on a liquid in which olivines of different sizes were carried in suspension. A valid and definitive explanation of such a mechanism has now been achieved, by way of an experimental approach, in terms of "flowage differentiation" (Bhattacharji and Smith 1964; Bhattacharji 1965; Section IV). To this mechanism the formation of the facies free from olivine phenocrysts can be ascribed, the removal of suspended olivines (in the sills) being assisted by gravity. The finest example of this process, uncomplicated by successive intrusive impulses, is the Igdlorssuit intrusion (Fig. 3.13*a*, and Drever 1956, 1958) in which the occurrence of the nonporphyritic facies can be examined over a relatively great distance. In this intrusion it can be observed that, where it assumes a sill- or sheet-like orientation, the thickness of the nonporphyritic facies varies directly with the thickness of the parent body. The variation in position of this facies in the other sills (Fig. 3.13*c*–*e*) could be attributed to displacement of the facies before consolidation. In the dike (Fig. 3.13*e*) flowage differentiation has effected the removal of olivine phenocrysts in the two symmetrically disposed nonporphyritic zones. Those intrusions which exhibit little differentiation may have been emplaced less rapidly. Attention has been drawn to the fact that the characteristic texture of all nonporphyritic facies is doleritic and a change to variolitic texture may accompany the appearance, and gradational increase in the size and amount, of olivine. The variolitic texture is probably due to an increase downward in viscosity.

In the more quickly cooled facies of these intrusions the frequent occurrence of olivine in shapes that can only be attributed to very rapid skeletal growth seems open to only one interpretation—they crystallized virtually *in situ*. Many of the rocks in which this occurs are picritic, not basaltic, in chemical composition. It then follows that the intrusive liquid was a picritic one in which olivines crystallized very rapidly as it became emplaced at a relatively low-pressure level. There is little doubt, however, that much of the crystallization in the bulk of these intrusions antedated emplacement, and some of the olivine is xenocrystic. It can, however, be inferred [see the micrometric analysis of Sill 1 in Soay (Wyllie and Drever, 1963)], from the constancy in the amount of olivine plus augite, that even the large olivine phenocrysts have continued their crystallization *in situ*.

The crystallization in these picritic minor intrusions of large poikilitic bytownites, identical with intercumulus bytownites in layered intrusions, implies that such bytownites either owe their formation to more than one process, or the diffusion mechanism employed in the interpretation of intercumulus bytownite may require some revision (Section II).

One of the exceptions to the rule that these intrusions have not metamorphosed the country rocks to any marked degree is Sill 1 in Soay. The temperature of this intrusion was estimated by Wyllie (1961) to be at least 1175°C on the assumption that it was emplaced at a depth of 1.7 km, and if it was emplaced at a shallower level the minimum intrusion temperature would be between 1175 and 1460°C. It seems unlikely that it was emplaced much nearer to the surface than 1.7 km and the intrusion temperature therefore was probably in the range 1175 to 1200°C. In the light of more recent experimental work on the solubility of water in mafic magmas (Hamilton, Burnham and Osborn, 1964), a water saturated picritic liquid under high pressure could exist in this temperature range. Harris (1962) has focussed attention on the release of gravitational energy as a source of magmatic heat. In particular, the partial assimilation of ultrabasic xenoliths in this Soay sill might be attributed to superheat from this source.

The compositions of olivines and plagioclase feldspars in these picritic minor intrusions are shown in Table 3.3. Most of the olivines have compositions ranging from Fo_{88} to Fo_{90}. The average in the associated picritic lavas on Ubekendt Ejland, according to Game (1942), is slightly less (Fo_{85}). These compositions are closely equivalent to those of olivines in the picritic lavas of the Hawaiian Province (Muir and Tilley, 1957) and olivines in lavas of the mid-Atlantic ridge (Muir and Tilley, 1964). The composition of xenocrystic olivines in these Atlantic lavas, and in ultrabasic nodules (Ross, Foster and Myers, 1954), is $Fo_{90\frac{1}{2}}$, and the composition of the olivines in the Cyprus ultrabasic pillow lavas (Gass, 1958) is Fo_{92-93}. The difference between these olivine compositions

TABLE 3.3 Composition of Olivine and Plagioclase from Picritic Rocks

Source of Data	Olivine*
Average at, or near, the center in nine members of the group of small intrusions.	$Fo_{88\frac{1}{2}}$
Average at, or close to, the contacts of five members of the group of small intrusions.	Fo_{90}
Average from two nonporphyritic facies	Fo_{87}
One of the group of relatively large intrusions (Sgurr Dearg)	Fo_{90}
Average from three ultrabasic xenoliths in three members of the group of small intrusions	$Fo_{85\frac{1}{2}}$
Gars-bheinn "feldspathic peridotite" (Weedon, 1960).	Fo_{89}
Ingia picrite	Fo_{89}
	Plagioclase
Average from seven members of the group of small intrusions	[An_{83}–An_{54}] sp.
Average from two nonporphyritic facies	[An_{85}–An_{43}] sp.
One of the group of relatively large intrusions (Sgurr Dearg)	[An_{83}] lpp.
Allivalite xenolith in Sill 1 (Soay)	[An_{83}] lpp.
Average from six feldspathic bands in the Gars-bheinn sill (Weedon 1960)	An_{75} core An_{79} in one band; zoned in upper band
Main part of the Gars-bheinn sill (Weedon, 1960)	[An_{78}–An_{75}] lpp.
Feldspathic band in the Ingia sill	An_{71}–An_{43}
Ingia picrite (main part of sill)	[$An_{82\frac{1}{2}}$] lpp.

* Olivines in some other picritic minor intrusions (Scotland and west Greenland) are peripherally zoned.

sp: small plagioclase; lpp: large poikilitic plagioclase.

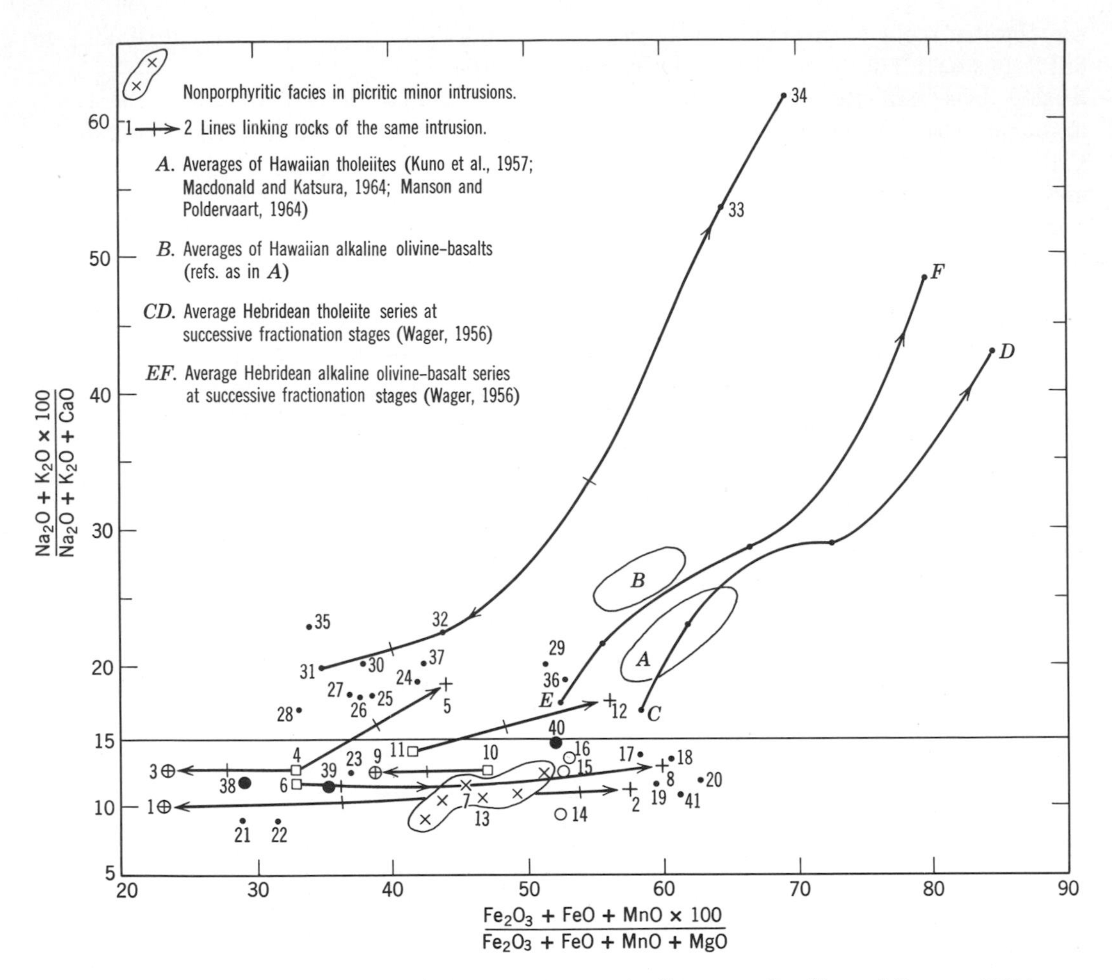

Fig. 3.15 Comparative variation diagram. 1. Center of Sill 1, Soay (Wyllie and Drever, 1963). 2. Fine-grained apophysis of Sill 1, Soay (Wyllie and Drever, 1963). 3. Peridotite, Gars-bheinn sill (Weedon, 1960). 4. Chilled margin of feeder dike, Gars-bheinn sill (Weedon, 1960). 5. Feldspathic band, Gars-bheinn sill (Weedon, 1960). 6. Bottom contact, Igdlorssuit intrusion (Sheet 2), Ubekendt Ejland (Drever, 1956). 7. Nonporphyritic facies, Igdlorssuit intrusion (Sheet 2), Ubekendt Ejland (Drever, 1956). 8. Globular zone, nonporphyritic facies, Igdlorssuit intrusion (Sheet 2) Ubekendt Ejland (Drever, 1956). 9. Center of fine-grained picritic sill, southeast coast, Scalpay*. 10. Margin of fine-grained picritic sill, southeast coast, Scalpay. 11. Top contact of Ingia intrusion, Ubekendt Ejland*. 12. Feldspathic band, Ingia intrusion, Ubekendt Ejland*. 13. Average of the five (x) analyses of nonporphyritic facies in picritic minor intrusions. 14. Aphanitic dike cutting small picritic dike, Coire Lagan, Cuillins*. 15. Very fine-grained aphanitic offshoot from margin of central member of the multiple picritic dike, Coire a Greadaidh, Cuillins*. 16. Aphanitic dike (18 inches thick) cutting picritic dike, Coire a Greadaidh, Cuillins*. 17. Average Skjaldbreid basalt, Iceland (Wager, 1956). 18. Basalt (III), Iceland (Tryggvason, 1943). 19. Basalt (VI), Iceland (Tryggvason, 1943). 20. Calculated groundmass of vitrophyric pillow lava, Cyprus (Gass, 1958). 21. Peridotite xenolith in Sill 1, Soay*. 22. Picrite-basalt lava, Igdlorssuit, Ubekendt Ejland*. 23. Picrite-basalt lava (ankaramitic), Mauna Kea, Hawaii (Muir and Tilley, 1963). 24. Liquid formed by 28 per cent partial fusion of synthetic peridotite (Reay and Harris, 1964). 25. Picrite-basalt dike, Nugssuaq, west Greenland (Drever and Livingstone, 1948). 26. 1840 picrite-basalt lava, Kilauea, Hawaii (Macdonald, 1944). 27. Picrite, Uwekahuna laccolith, Hawaii (Murata and Richter, 1961). 28. Oceanite lava, Svartenhuk, west Greenland (Noe-Nygaard, 1942). 29. Warner high-alumina basalt (re-analysis, Yoder and Tilley, 1962). 30. Average Hawaiian picrite-basalt (Macdonald and Katsura 1964). 31. Picrite, Shiant Isles*. 32. Picrodolerite,

(Fo_{88-90} and Fo_{90-93}) is not so critical as to justify an assertion that only the slightly more magnesian olivines can have originated in the mantle. Significantly less magnesian, however, is the average composition of olivines, Fo_{81}, in the picrite facies of such alkaline dolerite sills as that of the Shiant Isles. In general, the olivines of all ultrabasic facies in doleritic (or gabbroic) sills tend to be less magnesian (Section II, Table 3.2) than in the picritic intrusions dealt with here; whereas the plagioclases where developed poikilitically are, with some notable exceptions (such as the Dalmellington sill and the Uwekahuna laccolith), closely comparable bytownites with a composition An_{78-83}. Xenocrystic plagioclase in basalts from the mid-Atlantic ridge is more anorthitic (An_{88}).

There is little evidence to suggest that the ultrabasic xenoliths which occur in some of these picritic minor intrusions represent the rock from which these intrusions were derived. Their presence may only mean that the picritic rocks containing them used the same channel, the xenoliths corresponding to an earlier, intracrustal, consolidation of ultrabasic rocks which have suffered disruption during subsequent transit upward of ultrabasic material generated at a much deeper level. This interpretation is consistent with observed compositions of the minerals in the xenoliths (olivine—$Fo_{85\frac{1}{2}}$; and plagioclase—An_{83}).

The natural removal of olivine by flowage differentiation aided by gravity has yielded from a picritic parent a fraction which proves on analysis to be significantly more calcic, and higher in CaO/Al_2O_3 ratio, than common basaltic liquids. Further differentiation in the Igdlorssuit intrusion yielded a residuum which crystallized in globules (Drever, 1960). Other late fractions are represented by the horizontal feldspathic bands near the top of both the Gars-bheinn and Ingia intrusions, and the vertical feldspathic veins that occur toward the bottom of the Ingia intrusion. The horizontal banding is probably due to flowage after concentration of less refractory material near the top of these intrusions. The relations of these rocks and trends are contrasted with other rocks and trends in Fig. 3.15, in which an alkali index is plotted against a mafic one (Simpson, 1954). Chemical analyses of picritic and related rocks are given in Table 3.4.

It is apparent that the chemical diversity of these picritic minor intrusions and associated facies is characterized by differences in the iron ratio which are unaccompanied by a change in the alkali/lime ratio; whereas in the differentiation of the well-established basaltic and doleritic associations the iron ratio does not tend to change independently. The variation diagram also demonstrates the calcic chemistry (below the boundary line at 15 per cent alkali/lime ratio) of these picritic minor intrusions, which distinguishes them from most of the better known picrite-basalts and the fusion fraction derived from average peridotite (24, Fig. 3.15). Only two of the plotted picritic lavas (22, 23, Fig. 3.15) are fairly closely equivalent. Chemical variation in the Ingia and Gars-bheinn intrusions, leading to the formation of the horizontal bands, is in accordance with the more normal trends.

The rapid precipitation of olivine (with little compositional change) could be explained by its primary crystallization on a liquidus surface where the inclination of

---

Shiant Isles*. 33. Feldspathic patch in picrite, Shiant Isles*. 34. Feldspathic vein in picrite, Shiant Isles*. 35. Olivine-enriched basalt lava, mid-Atlantic ridge (Muir and Tilley, 1964). 36. Olivine-basalt lava, Achtalean, Skye (Tilley and Muir, 1962). 37. Oceanite lava, Mauritius (Walker and Nicolaysen, 1954). 38. Hypersthene-rich zone at 200 feet above bottom of Mt. Egerton sill, Antarctica (Gunn, 1963). 39. Hypersthenite, Mt. Harmsworth dike, Antarctica (Gunn, 1963). 40. Average gabbro, basement sill, Antarctica (Hamilton, 1965). 41. Average composition of parental tholeiite of Japan and Korea (Kuno, 1960).

* Analyses with no reference have not yet been published.

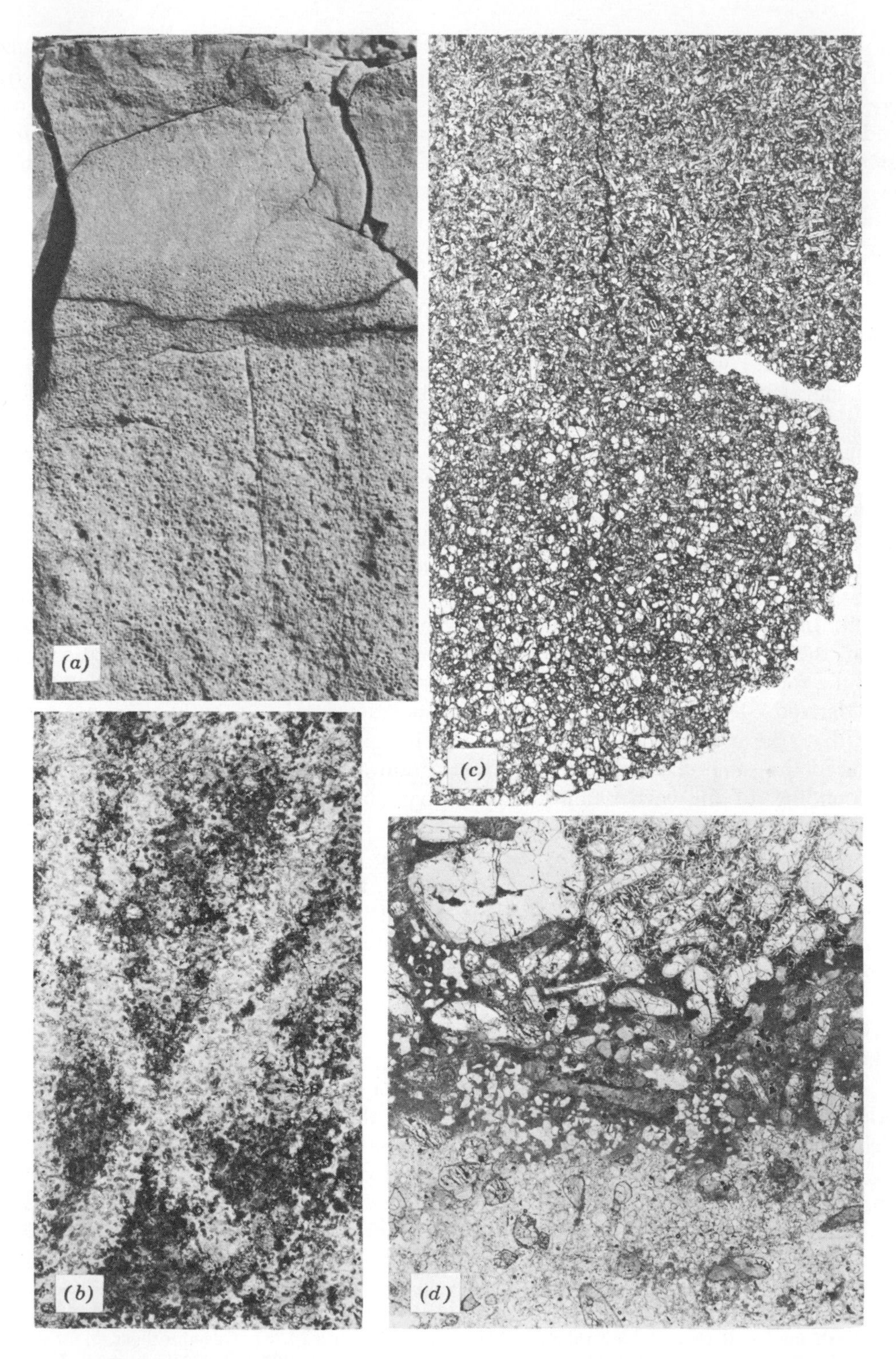

Fig. 3.16 (*a*) The nonporphyritic facies near the top of Sill 2 (Soay, Skye). Differential weathering of the olivines demonstrates the gradational increase in the size and amount of olivine in the picrite below. The width of the nonporphyritic facies is 6 to 8 inches. (*b*) Thin section from a picritic minor intrusion (inclined sheet) with large poikilitic by-

TABLE 3.4 Selected Chemical Analyses

	1	2	3	4	5	6	7	8	9	10
SiO_2	44.32	44.92	43.57	41.86	46.94	45.64	45.91	44.89	47.44	47.88
Al_2O_3	10.29	12.25	10.29	8.82	15.42	12.62	17.19	17.38	14.71	17.81
Fe_2O_3	1.88	2.02	3.77	1.46	2.65	6.29	2.33	1.55	0.16	1.93
FeO	8.93	9.19	6.50	8.14	8.29	7.72	7.67	8.73	9.98	4.55
MgO	22.07	16.12	20.99	31.56	12.83	9.44	7.48	9.39	8.21	8.34
CaO	8.06	9.93	7.47	5.38	11.45	11.73	13.54	13.89	13.22	13.71
Na_2O	0.94	1.54	1.01	0.56	1.36	1.34	1.63	1.35	2.41	3.10
K_2O	0.10	0.10	0.04	0.04	0.04	0.38	0.14	0.15	0.48	0.13
H_2O+	1.41	1.55	4.84	1.62	...	1.47	1.78	1.59	1.48	1.83
H_2O-	0.92	0.79	0.40	0.28	...	1.03	1.26	0.29	0.59	0.14
TiO_2	0.78	1.15	0.58	0.29	0.81	1.96	0.94	0.72	1.08	0.95
MnO	0.11	0.28	0.14	0.14	0.17	0.25	0.22	0.15	0.21	0.10
P_2O_5	0.12	0.14	0.03	trace	0.04	0.18	0.04	0.01	0.05	0.03
CO_2	0.15	0.28	n.d.	...	...	0.03	...	...	trace	n.d.
Other	...	...	0.39	...	...	0.27	...	...	...	0.02
Total	100.08	100.26	100.02	100.15	100.00	100.35	100.13	100.09	100.02	100.52

Legend:

1. 0.5–2.5 cm above bottom contact of Igdlorssuit intrusion (Sheet 2) Ubekendt Ejland, Analyst: W. H. Herdsman. Quoted from Drever, 1956.
2. Top contact of Ingia intrusion (Sheet 4), Ubekendt Ejland. Analyst: W. H. Herdsman.
3. Chilled margin of feeder dike, Gars-bheinn, Skye. Analysts: E. A. Vincent and R. Hall. Quoted from Weedon, 1960.
4. Center of Sill 1, Soay, Skye. Analyst: W. H. Herdsman. Quoted from Wyllie and Drever, 1963.
5. Average of 5 analyses of the nonporphyritic facics in picritic sills, Ubekendt Ejland and Skye (Soay and Scalpay). Calculated to 100%, H_2O and CO_2 free.
6. Zone of relatively large globules 14–15 cm below the top contact of the outcrop in the stream gorge, Igdlorssuit intrusion, Ubekendt Ejland. Quoted from Drever, 1960.
7. Fine-grained apophysis of Sill 1, Soay, Skye. Analyst: W. H. Herdsman. Quoted from Wyllie and Drever, 1963.
8. Aphanitic dike cutting small picritic dike, Coire Lagan, Skye. Analyst: W. H. Herdsman.
9. Feldspathic band in the Ingia intrusion (Sheet 4), Ubekendt Ejland. Analyst: W. H. Herdsman.
10. Feldspar-rich band in Gars-bheinn sill, Skye. Analysts: E. A. Vincent and R. Hall. Quoted from Weedon (1960).

this surface decreases abruptly (Wyllie, 1960), and the trends leading to increase in the iron/magnesia ratio in the residual liquid could be interpreted in terms of crystal fractionation. On the other hand, one cannot ascribe the relative enrichment in lime, without a parallel enrichment in alumina, to an early and rapid precipitation of diopsidic pyroxene. In this case, a mechanism may have to be invoked which

townites enclosing large numbers of olivines. Scale: ×2. Loc.: Sgurr Dearg, Cuillins, Skye. (*c*) Thin section of the bottom part of the nonporphyritic facies of the Igdlorssuit intrusion (Sheet 2), Ubekendt Ejland. The doleritic texture of this facies changes downward into the variolitic texture associated with the increase in size and amount of olivine (cf. *a*). Scale: ×2. (*d*) Thin section of lower margin of Sill 1 (Soay, Skye) where it is in contact with arkose. Uncontaminated picritic rock (above) with olivine phenocrysts, is followed downward by a contaminated zone in which olivines are associated with a dark glass containing numerous small relicts of quartz (white). Below this zone, rounded olivine relicts are entirely enclosed in partially fused arkose. Scale: ×10.

will effectively and independently eliminate alkalis so as to leave a residual high-lime liquid fraction.

In his attempt to interpret the basification of the gabbro facies in a thick Antarctica sill, Hamilton (1965) envisaged a separation of fractions in the liquid state, the process being termed "liquid fractionation." More extreme enrichment in magnesia, represented by the hypersthene-rich facies in neighboring Antarctica intrusions (Gunn, 1963) is also, according to Hamilton, the result of this process. In these intrusions, the more basic section of the differentiation trend corresponds closely with the other trends below the line representing an alkali/lime ratio of 15 (Fig. 3.15, 38–40).

Unlike the Antarctica intrusions, the picritic minor intrusions are relatively rich throughout (i.e., from margin to center) in magnesia and lime. It is therefore conceivable that, before intrusion, magnesia and lime-rich liquids (in the Hebridean and west Greenland provinces) were not residual but original. Recent experimental work, and discussions on its implications (Hamilton, Burnham and Osborn, 1964; Green and Ringwood, 1964; Kushiro and Yoder, 1964a; O'Hara, 1965a) have led to the proposition that, from an ultrabasic source in the mantle, derivative liquids of a greater compositional range than hitherto realized may be formed. This means that the evidence for the existence of picritic liquids and calcic liquids (relatively poor in alumina) can no longer be regarded as contrary to experimentally based prediction. It is therefore possible that they may represent liquids formed at high pressures by the partial fusion of ultrabasic source rock in which the factors determining the relative amounts of Mg, Ca and Al are the degree of fusion or precipitation of aluminous pyroxenes.

4. *Zoned Ultramafic Complexes*

I. INTRODUCTION

P. J. Wyllie

Among the ultramafic rock types occurring in orogenic belts are the small concentrically zoned intrusions (half a mile or so in diameter) recently recognized and described in some detail from Alaska (Noble and Taylor, 1960; Taylor and Noble, 1960). They have features distinguishing them clearly from the alpine type of ultramafic intrusion, as discussed by Thayer in Chapter 7-IV, and by Taylor in Section III-A of this chapter. Most of the bodies are hornblende pyroxenites or hornblendites, but if they contain dunites a range of ultramafic rock types forms a crude zonal arrangement. A core of dunite is surrounded by successive shells of peridotite, olivine pyroxenite, magnetite pyroxenite, and hornblende pyroxenite. Gravitational layering is present in some of the complexes indicating the operation of crystal fractionation. However, the rocks are readily distinguished from the stratiform peridotite-gabbro complexes (Chapter 2) by their structure, mineralogy and chemistry. The ultramafic complexes are usually emplaced in gabbro that has been strongly saussuritized near the ultramafic contacts.

There is good evidence that most of the ultramafic rocks described in Chapters 2 and 3 were derived from a parent gabbroic magma, but it is almost certain that the rocks in these zoned complexes are not differentiation products of a gabbroic magma. The most likely interpretation is that they were formed by the successive intrusion of ultrabasic magmas in the order: magnetite pyroxenite, olivine pyroxenite, peridotite, and finally dunite (Taylor, Section III-E-6).

In Section II Irvine describes the ultramafic complex at Duke Island. This complex is notable for its unique and spectacular development of gravitational layering resembling graded bedding in clastic sediments. Most of the rocks in the zoned complex are cumulates but there are no gabbroic or feldspar-bearing rocks to suggest the presence of a gabbroic magma from which mafic minerals might have settled. Irvine compares the petrography and chemistry of the ultramafic rocks and the gabbros into which they are emplaced, and concludes that they were not formed from the same magma. From the textural, modal, chemical, and mineralogical features of the rocks, Irvine produces a detailed crystallization model for the intrusion. The complex is the product of at least two intrusions of liquid magma that crystallized *in situ*, with the various rock types being products of crystal fractionation through gravity settling of minerals. The structures indicate rather violent physical activity in the magma chamber, probably accompanied by convective overturn. The layering and associated structures, and the history of repeated intrusion and disturbance suggest that the Duke Island complex could have developed in a reservoir beneath a volcano.

In Section III Taylor reviews the zoned ultramafic complexes of Alaska and the Ural Mountains of the U.S.S.R., giving descriptions of eight Alaskan complexes, including Duke Island. He too concludes that although the ultramafic rocks are invariably associated with gabbros there is no evidence aside from their juxtaposition that they were derived from a common magma. Taylor cites considerable field evidence to support the intrusion of ultrabasic magmas with approximately the same compositions as the rocks. Examination of the phase relationships in the system forsterite-diopside-iron oxide, (Presnall, 1966) at various oxygen fugacities reveals crystallization paths that can produce mineral assemblages closely analogous to the three most important rock types in the ultramafic complexes; dunites, olivine pyroxenites, and magnetite pyroxenites. Temperatures of crystallization of the equivalent natural magmas would probably lie in the range 1200 to 1300°C. Taylor presents a detailed discussion of the origin of these ultramafic complexes, with particular attention to the problem of zoning, and careful consideration of the various hypotheses of origin that have been proposed. He favors the sequence of multiple intrusions of essentially liquid, ultramafic magmas following earlier intrusions of gabbro.

Gass describes the rocks of the Troodos massif, Cyprus, in Section IV. The core of the massif is formed of a plutonic complex ranging outwards from dunite and peridotite through pyroxenite and olivine-gabbro to gabbro and granophyre. Gass (IV-B-2) compares the complex with Thayer's (1960) alpine-type complexes, and Thayer (Chapter 7-IV) questions earlier structural interpretations that this was a "pseudostratiform complex." Taylor (III-A) cites the Troodos plutonic complex as one with a zoning pattern similar to the others described in this chapter, so it is included here to provide a transition from the zoned ultramafic complexes to the alpine-type ultramafic rocks described in the next chapter. Gass suggests from geological and geophysical evidence that the Troodos plutonic complex might represent upper mantle material lifted up when the African continent was thrust under the Eurasian continent during the Alpine orogeny.

II. THE DUKE ISLAND ULTRAMAFIC COMPLEX, SOUTHEASTERN ALASKA

T. N. Irvine

A. Introduction

Duke Island is situated at the southern end of southeastern Alaska. Its coordinates are 55°55′N, 131°20′W, and its area is 59 square miles. The ultramafic complex exposed on the island is a member in a belt of 35 or more bodies of distinctive ultramafic rocks occurring along the 350-mile length of the Alaskan panhandle. A general discussion of the belt is given in Section III by H. P. Taylor, Jr. The Duke Island complex is given specific attention here because it shows a unique and spectacular development of gravitational layering resembling graded bedding in clastic sediments. The layering has been particularly valuable as a basis for interpreting the history of emplacement and crystallization of the ultramafic bodies.

The geology of part of Duke Island is shown in Fig. 4.1. The oldest rocks are metamorphosed volcanic and sedimentary units, probably of late Triassic or Jurassic age (Buddington and Chapin, 1929, p. 134). The remainder of the island is under-

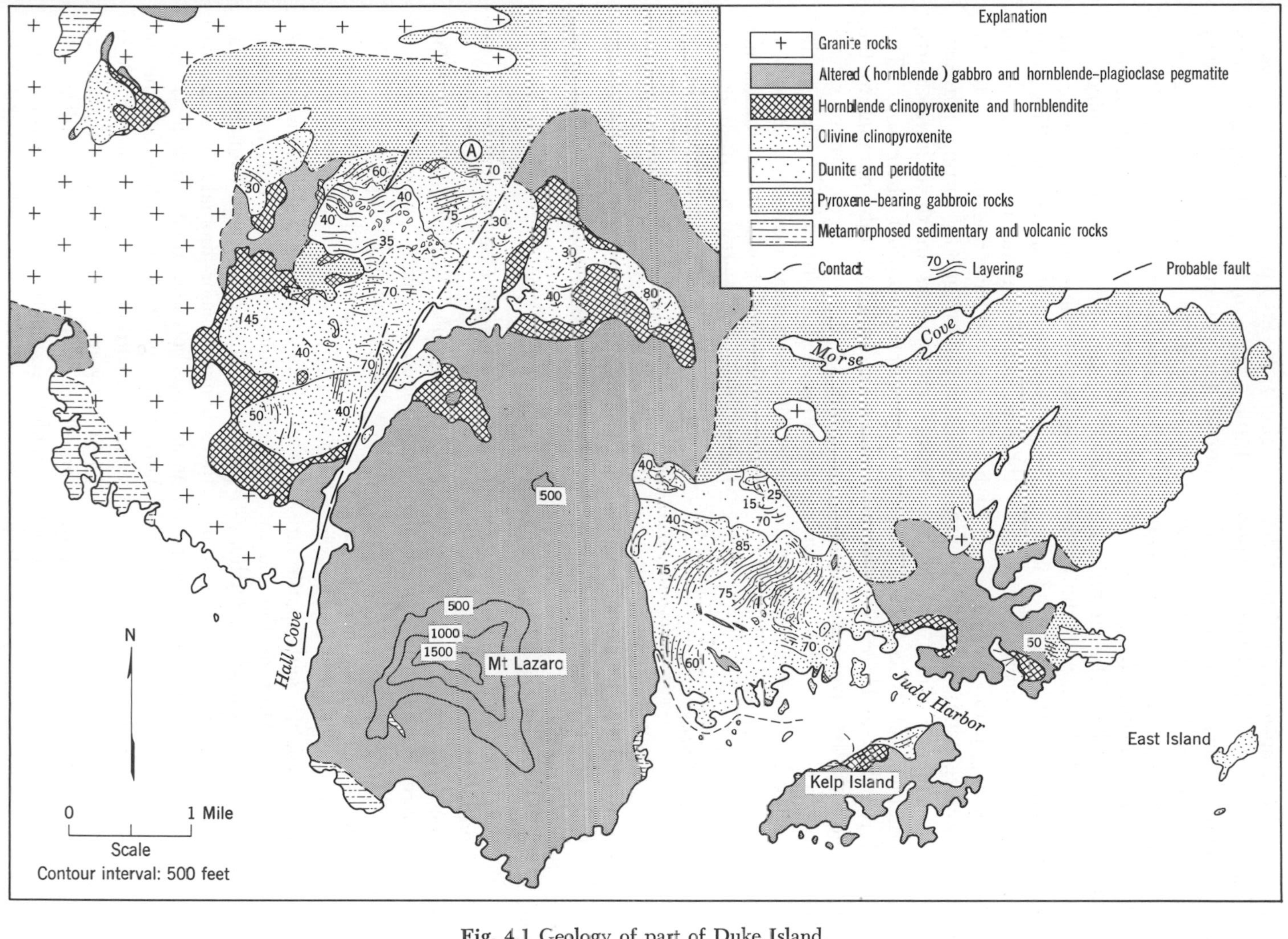

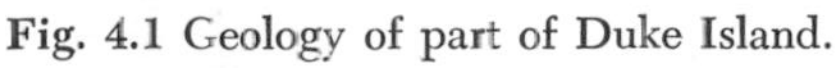

Fig. 4.1 Geology of part of Duke Island.

lain by plutons of gabbroic, ultramafic, and granitic rocks that are indicated by field relations to be emplaced in that order. M. A. Lanphere and G. D. Eberlain (personal communication) have recently obtained K-Ar ages of 173 m.y. for biotite from the gabbro, and 108 m.y. for hornblende from a pegmatitic differentiate of the ultramafic complex. The granitic intrusions are probably a part of the extensive granitic plutonism that occurred in the northern coast ranges during Cretaceous and early Cenozoic times.

In the following pages, descriptions are given of the gabbroic rocks, and of the ultramafic complex and its associated pegmatitic differentiates and contact effects. The gabbroic rocks are given consideration because their relation to the ultramafic complex is critical in its petrogenetic interpretation.

B. The Gabbroic Rocks

The gabbroic rocks are abundant, underlying almost two thirds of Duke Island. Where they have not been appreciably altered, they comprise a variety of pyroxene-bearing types, but near the ultramafic complex, they have undergone an extensive, and rather distinctive amphibolitization (to be described in Section E).

The less altered gabbroic rocks contain 40 to 50 per cent plagioclase, 20 to 35 per cent pyroxene, and 5 to 25 per cent hornblende. Olivine and biotite are present locally; ilmenomagnetite and apatite are common accessories. Most of the plagioclase is in the range An_{50}–An_{75}. Orthopyroxene and clinopyroxene (augite) are generally both present, but either may predominate. Some rocks contain orthopyroxene as reaction rims on olivine; other noritic types are evidently "cumulates" of orthopyroxene and plagioclase. Compositionally, the orthopyroxene ranges from En_{47} to En_{76}, and the clinopyroxene, from about $Ca_{37}Mg_{53}Fe_{10}$ to $Ca_{38}Mg_{29}Fe_{33}$. The Fe/Mg ratio of each pyroxene increases as its coexisting plagioclase becomes more sodic (Irvine, 1963, Fig. 3), and the composition of olivine shows similar variation, ranging from Fo_{82} to Fo_{27}.

Little is known about the overall structure of the gabbroic rocks because they occur in areas of low relief and are generally massive. However, small scale "rhythmic" layering is well developed at two localities, and one of them (denoted "A" in Fig. 4.1) is close to the ultramafic complex and particularly significant. The layers there are continuous and regular for several tens of feet and have thicknesses up to one foot. Many show gravity sorting, pyroxene being concentrated in their lower parts, and plagioclase toward their tops. The layering is approximately parallel to the boundary of the ultramafic complex, and dips toward it at 70°. The grading in the layering shows that the gabbroic rock is "stratigraphically" beneath the ultramafic rocks. This same relation is indicated, both for this locality and several others, by the graded layering in the ultramafic complex. It is one line of geological evidence that the gabbroic and ultramafic rocks are not differentiated from the same intrusions of magma.

C. The Ultramafic Complex

1. Petrography and Mineralogy. The Duke Island ultramafic rocks occur mainly in two areas—one of 5.4 square miles; the other of 3.6 square miles, including part of Kelp Island on the south side of Duke Island—believed to be the exposure of one large body at depth. This interpretation is principally based on aeromagnetic data, there being a major anomaly over the two areas and between them, but it is supported by geological evidence, some of which is mentioned below. It is the single large body of ultramafic rocks that is referred to as the Duke Island ultramafic complex; the two principal areas of outcrop will be called the Hall Cove and Judd Harbor *parts* of the complex. The ultramafic rocks forming East Island (at the southeast corner of Duke Island) are probably also part of the same body, and the small occurrence in the granitic pluton northwest of Hall Cove appears to be a portion that foundered in this younger intrusion.

The ultramafic rocks are essentially composed of olivine, clinopyroxene (diopsidic augite), and hornblende. Their modal range and the scheme of their classification are shown in Fig. 4.2. The principal units are dunite, peridotite (wehrlite), olivine clinopyroxenite, and hornblende clinopyroxenite. The dunite typically contains accessory chromite, and hornblende clinopyroxenite commonly contains 15 to 20 per cent ilmenomagnetite and traces of hercynitic spinel. Orthopyroxene and plagioclase are absent.

The olivine and clinopyroxene show slight increases in their Fe/Mg ratios in the rock sequence from dunite to hornblende clinopyroxenite. The range of olivine is Fo_{85}-Fo_{78}, and that of the pyroxene is $Ca_{45}Mg_{48}Fe_7$-$Ca_{50}Mg_{38}Fe_{12}$. A similar

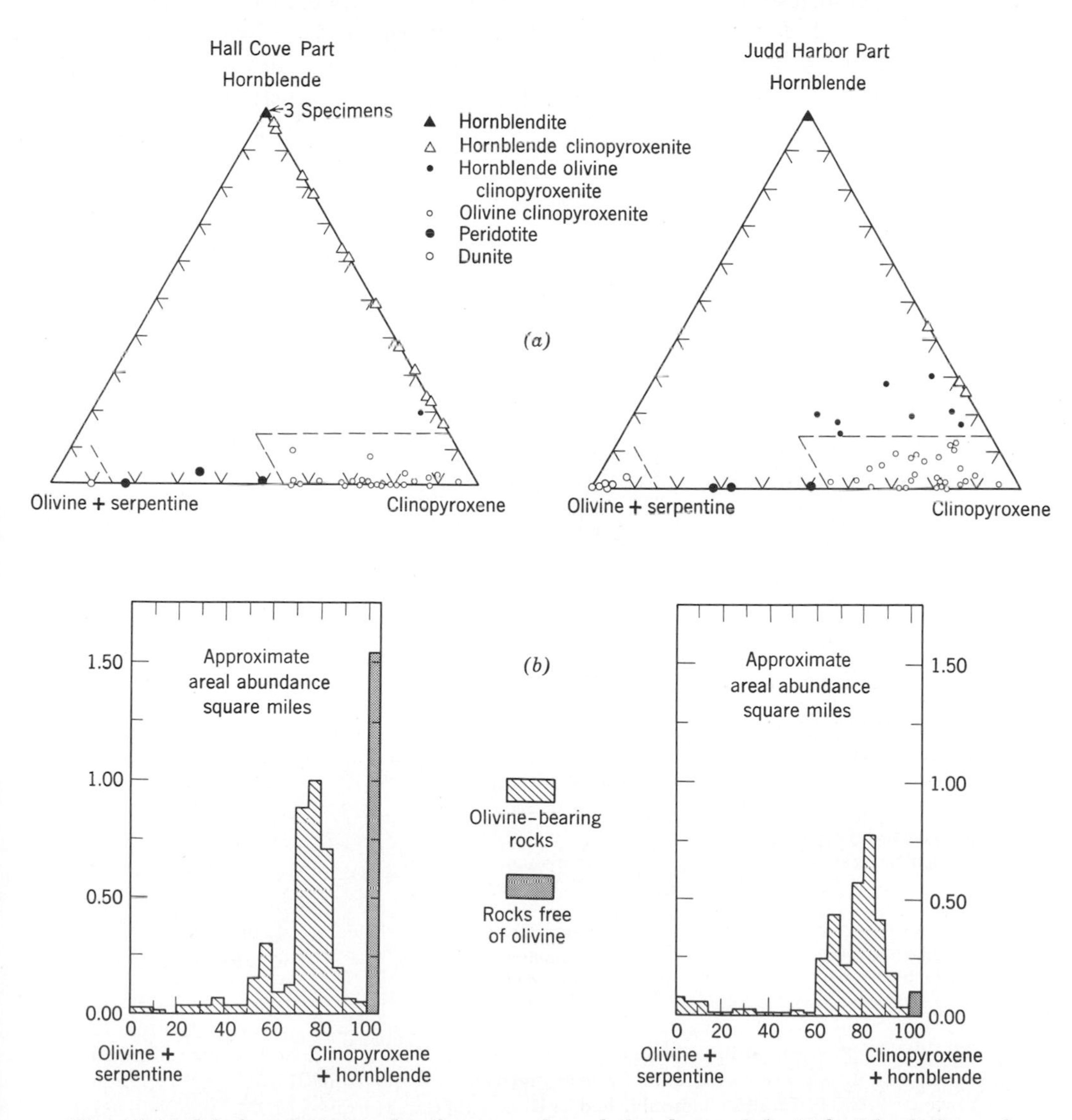

Fig. 4.2 Modal characteristics, classification and areal abundance of the Duke Island ultramafic rocks in their two main areas of occurrence.

composition has been found for clinopyroxene in ultramafic bodies of the same type occurring at Union Bay in southeastern Alaska and near Tulameen in southern British Columbia (Fig. 4.3). The proportion of Ca is relatively large (and distinctly greater than that in the clinopyroxene in the Duke Island gabbroic rocks), and the mineral is well removed from the apparent solvus boundary defined by analyses of augite coexisting with orthopyroxene or pigeonite in other igneous intrusions. The latter relation implies that the pyroxene is undersaturated in (Mg, Fe)-SiO_3, which is also indicated by the absence of orthopyroxene from the ultramafic rocks; and in those rocks containing olivine, it reflects the silica content of the parent magma, suggesting that the magma was markedly "undersaturated."

Chemical analyses of the principal ultramafic rocks are given in Table 4.1 together with their CIPW norms. Note that the rocks are also markedly undersaturated in silica as indicated by the nepheline, leucite and larnite in the norms.

2. ***Layering in the ultramafic rocks.*** The distribution of the layering in the ultramafic rocks and its overall structure are shown in Fig. 4.1 by trend lines with dip symbols. Its appearance in outcrop and some typical local structures are shown in Figs. 4.4 to 4.6 (see also Irvine, 1963, 1965). The more distinctive layers are 2 inches to 4 feet thick. Many have been

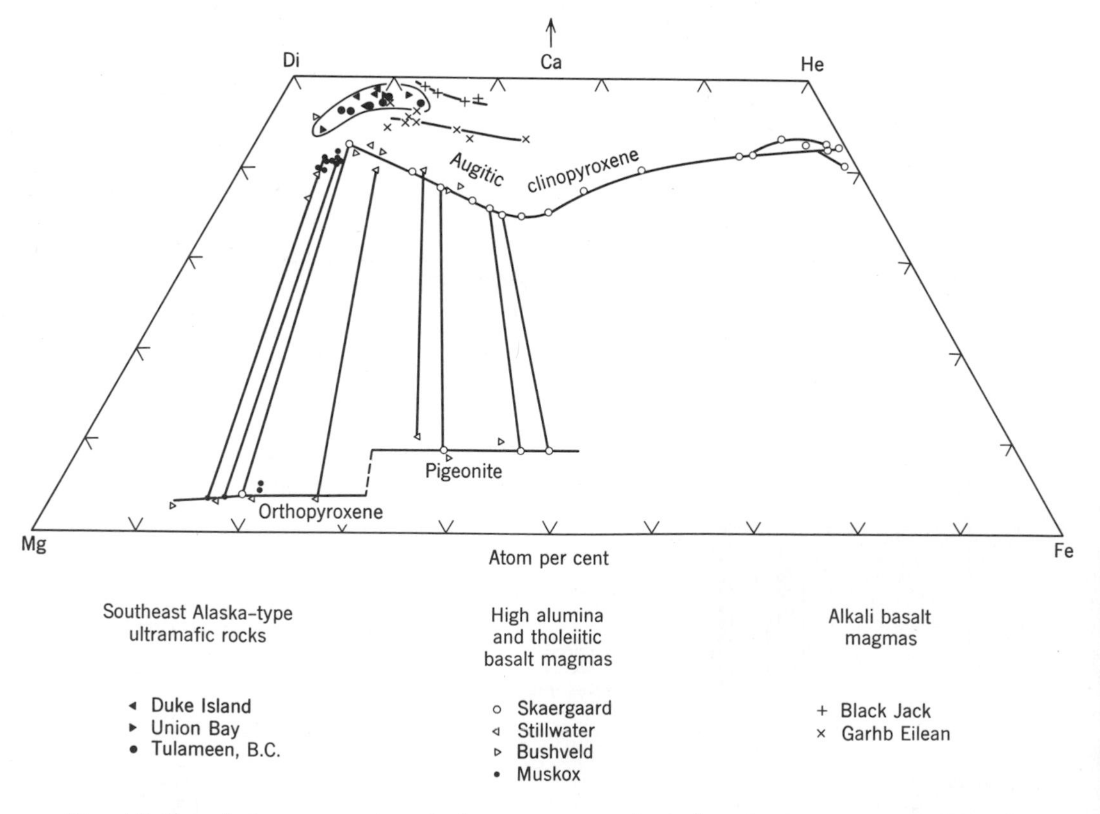

Fig. 4.3 Plot of the composition of clinopyroxene in the Duke Island and similar ultramafic rocks compared to pyroxenes in other igneous intrusions. Data from Brown (1957), Brown and Vincent (1963), Findlay (unpublished), Hess (1960), Murray (1954), and Wilkinson (1956). Muskox data unpublished. Coexisting pyroxenes (joined by tie lines) define a solid solution miscibility gap for their temperatures and depths of crystallization.

TABLE 4.1 Chemical Analyses of the Principal Ultramafic Rock Types at Duke Island, and Their CIPW Norms (percentages by weight)

	Dunite*	Olivine Clino-pyroxenite	Hornblende Clino-pyroxenite
SiO_2	39.23	47.55	37.37
Al_2O_3	1.48	4.77	15.34
Fe_2O_3	1.52	2.93	9.48
FeO	13.73	5.58	7.64
MgO	42.30	18.46	13.00
CaO	0.89	18.66	11.80
Na_2O	0.30	0.45	1.74
K_2O	0.02	0.03	0.49
H_2O+	*	0.70	1.24
H_2O-	*	0.20	...
TiO_2	0.13	0.52	1.47
Cr_2O_3	0.28	0.23	...
MnO	0.12	0.03	0.10
P_2O_5	...	0.04	0.00
CO_2	trace	nil	0.02
	100.00	100.15	99.69
CIPW Norms			
fo	73.13	13.78	17.31
fa	18.54	2.19	2.33
di	0.68	57.60	17.67
he	0.13	7.24	1.88
la	0.23	...	0.48
an	2.61	11.00	33.12
ab	...	0.47	...
or	...	0.18	...
ne	1.38	1.83	8.10
lc	0.09	...	2.31
ap	...	0.09	...
mt	2.56	4.28	13.96
il	0.25	1.00	2.84
cr	0.40	0.34	...
	100.00	100.00	100.00

* The dunite analysis has been corrected for effects of serpentinization by making the MgO/FeO ratio of the normative olivine equal to that of the modal olivine. The original analysis shows 8.85 per cent H_2O+, 0.55 per cent H_2O-, and has an Fe_2O_3/FeO ratio of 0.85.

traced for 300 feet, and some may extend for 900 feet. The layering occurs mainly in olivine clinopyroxenite, peridotite, and dunite and has two distinct ages as a result of having formed in at least two separate intrusions of magma. The thickest continuously layered section is in the Hall Cove peridotite (part of the younger intrusion) and is about 1500 feet thick, but layering is intermittently developed through a total (exposed) section of about 2 miles.

As may be seen in the photographs of Figs. 4.4 to 4.6, many layers grade from coarse to fine upward. In most cases, the graded particles are grains of olivine and clinopyroxene, but in the Hall Cove peridotite, there are about 50 layers resembling conglomerate or breccia beds in which rock fragments (broken from the olivine clinopyroxenite of the older intrusion) are

Fig. 4.4 Graded layering in olivine clinopyroxenite. The scale is 6 inches. Note the thin laminae of coarser pyroxene in the upper part of the layer on which the scale rests.

Fig. 4.5 A local angular unconformity in layered peridotite. The rock is cut by closely spaced joints parallel to the hammer handle.

sorted by size. The sorting undoubtedly reflects the relative settling velocities of the grains and fragments in a liquid magma. Some mineralogical sorting also occurs, clinopyroxene being concentrated in the lower parts of layers, and olivine toward their tops, but this is an effect of size sorting as the pyroxene is generally the coarser mineral.

The base of a graded layer is sharp; the top may coincide with the base of the next but more commonly is transitional into a series of thin layers of relatively fine, but sharply contrasting grain sizes. The latter sequence, it might be noted, is common in graded-bedded turbidity current deposits (e.g., Kuenan, 1952). The direction of grading is generally consistent and is therefore a useful indicator of the tops of layers in areas of complicated structure.

There is one variant of layering, particularly characteristic of the Judd Harbor olivine clinopyroxenite, that rarely shows grading. It is marked by a vague alternation of olivine and pyroxene (on a scale of inches), and by thin discontinuous bands of dunite. The pyroxene commonly shows pegmatoid textures and a faint preferred orientation normal to the stratification. The overall grain size of the rock is much greater than that of the graded layering, and there is some evidence that the vague stratification is due to pervasive "diagenetic" recrystallization of better developed layering shortly after its accumulation.

The only appreciable layering in hornblende clinopyroxenite is on Kelp Island. It appears as alternate bands of magnetite and hornblende. Some of the magnetite bands are sharply bounded on one side and gradational on the other. The layering is now folded and steeply dipping, but the direction of grading is consistent from band to band and is believed to reflect the settling velocities of the cumulus minerals as principally controlled by their specific gravities; thus, the magnetite layers are considered to grade "upward." The occurrence is significant as evidence that this kind of rock can be a cumulate. Magnetite is certainly a settled mineral, and hornblende may be, although it more probably replaces settled clinopyroxene.

Many remarkable depositional structures occur in the graded layering, particularly in the Hall Cove peridotitic rocks where the structures are closely associated with the fragmental layers and commonly involve larger fragments and blocks of olivine clinopyroxenite. Some typical features are: loading and impact structures; scour and fill; local angular unconformities; streamlining of layers over irregularities; and slump structures. In view of these, there can be no doubt that the layering formed

Fig. 4.6 A slump structure in olivine clinopyroxenite showing an alternation of regular and deformed layers.

during extremely unstable conditions by sedimentation from magmatic currents. The currents were probably density flows (consisting of magma with an appreciable content of solid materials) that descended in surges from the walls of each magma body and spread across its floor of accumulating layers. The flows are believed to have been generated by slumping of unconsolidated accumulations of mineral grains that repeatedly build up along inward-dipping parts of the walls. In the younger intrusion, the slumping must have been accompanied by crumbling or partial collapse of the sides and roof of the magma chamber as evidenced by the inclusions of olivine clinopyroxenite in the peridotite (see also Section C-3).

3. ***Structure of the ultramafic complex.*** In several of the ultramafic bodies in southeastern Alaska the distribution of rock types is systematic in a roughly concentric pattern. In the idealized case, a core of dunite is successively ringed by peridotite, olivine clinopyroxenite, clinopyroxenite and hornblendite. At Duke Island the pattern of rock units in the Hall Cove part of the ultramafic complex is vaguely concentric in approximately the above sequence, but mainly because of an apparent marginal zone of hornblende clinopyroxenite. In the Judd Harbor part, the principal occurrences of hornblende clinopyroxenite are also peripherally located, but the overall zoning is not concentric. Except for the position of the hornblende clinopyroxenite, which is discussed in Section F-2 of this chapter, the rock distribution is essentially the result of the two intrusions of magma previously mentioned.

The younger intrusion in the Hall Cove part of the complex is largely represented by the peridotite zone. Its northern (stratigraphically lower) boundary cuts sharply across the layering in the older olivine clinopyroxenite, and the layering in the peridotite is generally flatter by 20 to 30° so that the contact resembles an angular unconformity. Elsewhere, the olivine clinopyroxenite has been folded and faulted, probably by the emplacement of the younger magma body. The inclusions of olivine clinopyroxenite in the peridotite zone are further evidence of two intrusions. These are typically angular and commonly layered. They range from fragments measurable in inches to blocks tens to hundreds of feet on a side. The larger type occur both individually and in jumbled piles, particularly in the lower part of the peridotite layered series where their distribution resembles a talus fan.

The Judd Harbor dunite-peridotite zone

also represents the younger intrusion. It too truncates olivine clinopyroxenite layering and is discordant in terms of its own layering. The large folds in the main area of olivine clinopyroxenite (Fig. 4.1) appear to be an effect of crowding by the younger intrusion, and the occurrences of this rock in the dunite-peridotite zone may be very large inclusions, comparable to those in the Hall Cove peridotite. The similarities in the structures and histories of the Judd Harbor and Hall Cove ultramafic rocks is further reason to believe that they are parts of a single body.

Scattered through the olivine clinopyroxenite in both parts of the complex are small irregular bodies of "impure" dunite ranging in dimensions from inches to about 300 feet. Where the pyroxenite is layered, these bodies transgress the layering without displacing it, and traces of the layering usually can be followed through the dunite. The bodies are believed to have been formed by volume-for-volume replacement of the olivine clinopyroxenite by olivine and are thought to be a metasomatic effect of the younger intrusion of magma. They are commonly associated with pegmatoid clinopyroxene veins, and with zones of coarse recrystallized textures that are similarly transgressive to the layering.

D. Pegmatitic Rocks

One of the most remarkable rocks at Duke Island is a pegmatite of hornblende and extremely calcic plagioclase (An_{90-98}). It forms innumerable dikes and veins in the gabbroic rocks between and to the south of the two main areas of ultramafic rocks, and it is present as a swarm of dikes cutting Judd Harbor olivine clinopyroxenite and hornblende clinopyroxenite zones. The dikes range in width from less than an inch to 200 feet and extend as far as 1200 feet. The grain size of the pegmatite is commonly 1 to 6 inches and locally much coarser, prisms of hornblende being as long as 4 feet. In most dikes, plagioclase and hornblende occur in about equal amounts, but close to and within the ultramafic complex, there are associated pegmatitic segregations consisting almost wholly of hornblende. Extensive zones of hornblende-magnetite alteration occur along the dikes in the Judd Harbor olivine clinopyroxenite.

The very calcic nature of the plagioclase in the pegmatite is considered to preclude the possibility that the rock is a differentiate of the gabbroic intrusions. Plagioclase in magmatic pegmatite bodies typically is more sodic than that in the plutonic units from which they are apparently derived, whereas the primary plagioclase in Duke Island gabbro is generally An_{50-75}. Most probably the pegmatite magma evolved within the ultramafic complex from interstitial magma that reacted with Ca-rich clinopyroxene (presumably producing hornblende within the complex). If this interpretation is correct, then the great abundance of the pegmatite in the southern part of Duke Island is another indication of the presence of more ultramafic rocks at depth in that area.

E. Contact Effects of the Ultramafic Complex

The gabbroic rocks around the ultramafic complex in the same general areas invaded by hornblende-plagioclase pegmatite have undergone extensive alteration and metamorphism to hornblende and secondary plagioclase. The rocks have uneven textures ranging from hornfelsic to porphyroblastic and pegmatoid, and they commonly fade into pegmatite. Relicts of olivine and pyroxene, and of primary gabbroic textures are not uncommon in the altered rocks, and therefore their gabbroic parentage is generally certain, but where the alteration is complete, other materials could be involved. Much of the plagioclase produced by the alteration is more calcic than that in the original gabbro, and compositionally approaches the anorthite in the hornblende-plagioclase pegmatite (Fig.

4.7). On this basis, the alteration is believed to be caused by heat and water-rich calcic fluids derived along with the pegmatite magma from the ultramafic complex. In other words, the amphibolitic rocks constitute the metamorphic-metasomatic aureole of the ultramafic complex.

F. Further Petrogenetic Considerations

1. Crystallization differentiation. The graded layering in the ultramafic rocks is evidence that gravity-controlled crystal fractionation was operative during their formation, and therefore the role of crystallization differentiation in producing the various rock types must be examined.

Layering is widespread in the ultramafic complex, and the layered and unlayered facies of each rock type are texturally and modally similar except for the effects of grain-size or gravity sorting. Thus it can be inferred that the bulk of the ultramafic rocks are cumulates (some of which have recrystallized). Dunite can be shown to consist largely of settled or cumulus grains of olivine and (minor) chromite set in sparse intercumulus clinopyroxene. Peridotite and olivine clinopyroxenite are commonly granular aggregates of settled olivine and clinopyroxene cemented together by intercumulus overgrowth. Hornblende clinopyroxenite generally appears to consist of cumulus clinopyroxene and magnetite surrounded by intercumulus hornblende that partly replaces the pyroxene; and the Kelp Island rock showing magnetite layers has magnetite and, possibly, hornblende as settled minerals.

By piecing together the overall textural, modal, chemical and mineralogical features of the rocks, one may arrive at the crystallization model illustrated in Fig. 4.8. Thus the series dunite-olivine clinopyroxenite-hornblende clinopyroxenite-hornblendite can be attributed to successive fractionation of olivine + minor chromite; olivine + clinopyroxene; and clinopyroxene + magnetite, together with a gradually increasing crystallization of in-

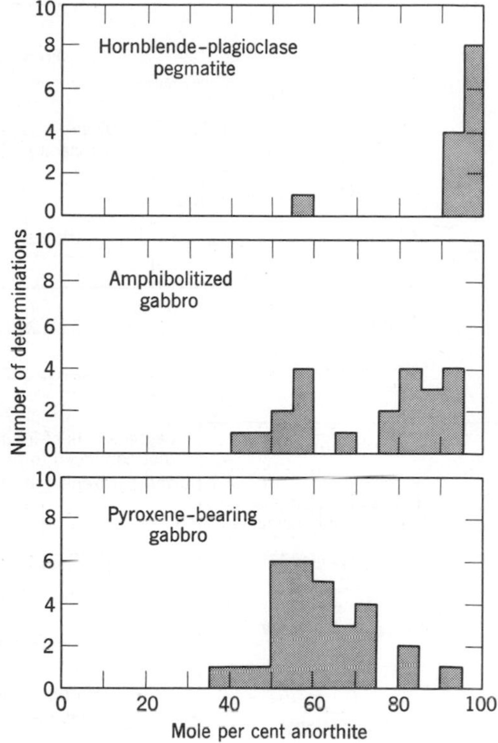

Fig. 4.7 Histograms of the composition of plagioclase in the Duke Island gabbroic rocks and hornblende-plagioclase pegmatite.

tercumulus hornblende. The increase in the Fe/Mg ratios of the olivine and pyroxene in the series is consistent with the model. Chromite probably ceased to form because of a peritectic relation to clinopyroxene (Irvine, 1966); and olivine may have had a similar relation to clinopyroxene, or to magnetite and its associated spinel. The spinel probably exsolved from the magnetite (cf. phase relations determined by Turnock and Eugster, 1962), and ilmenite intergrown with the magnetite probably formed by the oxidation-exsolution process proposed by Buddington and Lindsley (1964). Hornblende was certainly a reaction product of clinopyroxene. In olivine clinopyroxenite, the relatively constant ratio of olivine to clinopyroxene (Fig. 4.2*b*) suggests that the rock is a cotectic precipitate of these minerals, and the ratio is comparable to the eutectic proportions of forsterite and diop-

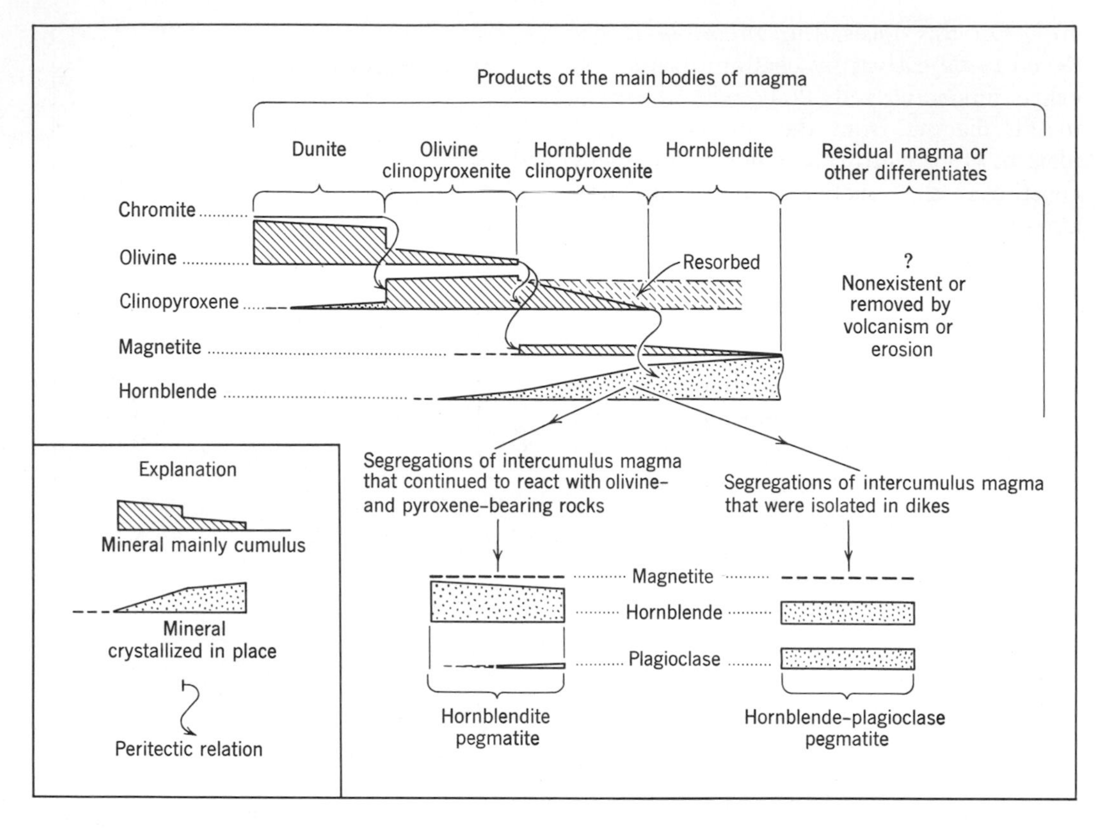

Fig. 4.8 Crystallization model for the Duke Island ultramafic complex and its related pegmatitic differentiates. The approximate concentration of each mineral is represented, but the relative abundances of the different rocks are not (e.g., hornblendite is rare compared to the other rocks). See text for further discussion.

side in the system Mg_2SiO_4-$CaMgSi_2O_6$ (Kushiro and Schairer, 1963). Similarly, the ratio of clinopyroxene to magnetite in hornblende clinopyroxenite is about that in which these phases co-precipitate in the system Mg_2SiO_4-$CaMgSi_2O_6$-iron oxide for an appropriate range of oxygen fugacity (Section III-D-4; Presnall, 1966).

In the "granular" peridotite the ratio of olivine to clinopyroxene has a broad range departing greatly from the cotectic ratio apparent in olivine clinopyroxenite, but in this respect, it may be significant that the peridotite is typically well layered. Possibly, the currents that produced the layering mixed products of different stages of crystallization. Thus the peridotite may be a combination olivine from one stage and olivine + clinopyroxene from another.

Figure 4.8 also schematically portrays the derivation of the pegmatitic rocks from the intercumulus magma of the ultramafic complex. As indicated, where the pegmatite magma was isolated in dikes, it crystallized both plagioclase and hornblende; where it could continue to react with olivine and clinopyroxene, potential plagioclase was consumed by the formation of hornblende.

2. Fractional crystallization and rock distribution. If gravity-controlled fractional crystallization is primarily responsible for the rock series present in the ultramafic complex, then it should also account for their physical distribution, remembering that the complex has formed from at least two intrusions of magma.

At the present erosion surface the younger intrusion is mainly dunite and peridotite, but in its Hall Cove part, some olivine clinopyroxenite overlies the peridotite with stratigraphic continuity—as it should if the suggested crystallization-differentiation model is applicable.

The exposed sections of the older intrusion are largely olivine clinopyroxenite bordered by hornblende clinopyroxenite. The main occurrences of hornblende clinopyroxenite are around the stratigraphic top of the olivine-bearing rock, and in view of the magnetite layering at the Kelp Island locality, they would seem to be succeeding differentiates formed by gravitational crystal fractionation. However, the narrow zones adjacent to (and beneath?) the olivine clinopyroxenite layered series cannot be explained this way. Their continuity suggests that they are reaction rims, and they may possibly represent an approach to local equilibrium between water-rich parental magma in the ultramafic complex and relatively anhydrous gabbroic country rocks. A similar reaction is evidenced by the hornblende-magnetite alteration along the pegmatite dikes in the Judd Harbor olivine clinopyroxenite.

3. *Relation of the ultramafic and gabbroic rocks.* In stratiform intrusions, ultramafic rocks that are known to have formed by crystal fractionation have precipitated from basaltic magmas and are commonly associated with "later" gabbroic differentiates. As noted previously, the Duke Island gabbroic rocks are older than the ultramafic complex; therefore they cannot be differentiated from the same *intrusions* of magma. A comparison of the petrography and chemistry of the ultramafic and gabbroic rocks suggests that they are not formed from even the same *type* of magma.

In this regard the concept of the "critical plane of silica undersaturation" developed by Yoder and Tilley (1962) is pertinent. The "plane" is apparently a thermal barrier that basaltic liquids cannot cross by fractional crystallization at relatively shallow crustal depths. In terms of normative constituents it is approximately the "join" *ol-cpx-pl,* where *ol* = forsterite + fayalite, *cpx* = diopside + hedenbergite, and *pl* = anorthite + albite. Tholeiitic basalts (which classically show hypersthene in reaction rims on olivine) and high alumina basalts typically contain normative hypersthene and plot on the side of the plane richer in silica. Alkali basalts distinguished by normative nepheline plot on the other side. The "barrier" character of the plane applies, strictly speaking, only to the liquid composition and not necessarily to the composition of its crystallization products. However, augitic pyroxenes do seem to indicate the composition of their parent liquid fairly reliably. Tholeiitic types generally show normative hypersthene, whereas most alkali basalt clinopyroxenes have normative nepheline and larnite because they are undersaturated in $(Mg, Fe)SiO_3$ and relatively rich in the silica-poor end members $NaAlSi_2O_6$ and $CaAl_2SiO_6$.

The unaltered gabbroic rocks at Duke Island have tholeiitic affinities because they contain orthopyroxene, commonly in reaction rims around olivine. The Ca-content of their clinopyroxene is similar to that in augite from intrusions of tholeiitic and high alumina basalt magmas such as the Muskox, Stillwater and Skaergaard intrusions. By contrast, the ultramafic rocks are devoid of orthopyroxene, and the $Ca/(Mg + Fe)$ ratio of their clinopyroxene is more like that of alkali basalt clinopyroxene. The ultramafic rocks and their clinopyroxene both show nepheline, leucite, and larnite in their CIPW norms. Thus as the evidence stands, it is improbable that the ultramafic and gabbroic rocks are closely related in other than their physical setting.

4. *Chemical characteristics of the parent magma of the ultramafic complex.* Fine-grained rocks that might constitute a chilled sample of the parent magma of the ultramafic complex have not been found, and the composition of the magma cannot be calculated from rock analyses without information on the volumes of each differentiate. The best indications of the composition of the magma are (a) the type of minerals in the ultramafic complex, and their sequence of formation; (b) the compositions of those minerals belonging to solid solution series; and (c) the concentrations in cumulative differentiates of those elements which can be inferred to be largely derived from intercumulus magma. None of these can be applied quantitatively at present; they are only useful qualitatively or in a comparative way.

The most distinctive characteristic of the magma was undoubtedly its poverty in silica (see Sections C-1 and F-2). It must have been relatively rich in MgO and CaO because it crystallized so much olivine and clinopyroxene, and its FeO/MgO ratio was apparently comparable to those of the Stillwater and Muskox magmas inasmuch as the olivine in Duke Island dunite is similar in fayalite content to the early olivine precipitated from these liquids (Hess, 1960, p. 61; and unpublished data). One can also infer that the magma had a larger content of Fe_2O_3 than most basaltic liquids because of the "early" magnetite in the hornblende clinopyroxenite. The large amount of primary hornblende in the ultramafic complex points to a considerable water content, as does the abundance of related pegmatitic differentiates. The overall concentrations of alumina and alkalies in the complex are not large, but they should not be if most of the rocks are cumulates of olivine and clinopyroxene. The pyroxene and hornblende are rich in Al_2O_3 (they respectively contain 3.5 to 7.0 and 14 to 16 per cent by weight), and although the ultramafic rocks lack plagioclase, they would appear to contain enough alumina and alkalies to be crystallization differentiates of an essentially basaltic liquid. For example, Duke Island olivine clinopyroxenite contains 3.5 to 4.8 per cent Al_2O_3 and 0.3 to 0.7 per cent Na_2O as compared to 2.0 to 4.0 per cent Al_2O_3 and 0.1 to 0.5 per cent Na_2O in olivine clinopyroxenite differentiated from the basaltic magma of the Muskox intrusion. The absence of plagioclase in the Duke Island rocks is evidently due to the low silica content of the magma, which would encourage Na and Al to enter clinopyroxene, and to the formation of hornblende as a result of an abundance of water in the magma.

The above considerations indicate that, if the formation of the ultramafic rocks was in any way related to a basaltic liquid, it must have been an alkalic type, in which case one would expect to find related gabbroic differentiates with alkalic characteristics. No such rocks have been recognized at Duke Island or in association with the other ultramafic bodies in southeastern Alaska (unless they be hornblendite, which is chemically equivalent to an alkali gabbro), but the ultramafic complex near Tulameen, British Columbia, is adjacent to a large body of syenogabbro and syenodiorite (Findlay, 1964) that might be petrogenetically related. In Alaska, alkalic gabbro could have been eroded away, or possibly, the residual magma after the formation of the ultramafic rocks was removed by volcanism. The history of repeated intrusion and disturbed crystallization evident in the Duke Island ultramafic complex might well have developed in a reservoir beneath a volcano.

G. Conclusions

Although the chemical composition of the magma represented by the Duke Island ultramafic complex is not wholly established, the complex has, by virtue of its layering, provided critical information on the nature and history of the magma that should be applicable to the same type of ultramafic body at other localities. The more important points are:

1. The complex is the product of at least two intrusions of liquid magma that were forcibly emplaced and crystallized *in situ*.
2. The various rock types in the complex (which are typical of this kind of ultramafic body) are largely products of crystal

fractionation effected by gravitational settling and accumulation of minerals.

3. During emplacement of the complex, large bodies of partly layered but otherwise massive ultramafic cumulates have been folded, and the folding appears to have greatly influenced the distribution of rock types at the present erosion surface.

4. Processes of intercumulus reaction and recrystallization have strongly affected the textural characteristics of the ultramafic rocks, and pyroxene-rich rocks are locally replaced by secondary dunite (i.e., by secondary olivine).

In regard to the origin of small-scale "rhythmic" gravitational layering in igneous rocks, the structures in the Duke Island ultramafic complex indicate that rather violent physical activity in magma bodies is both conducive to, and necessary for the formation of such layering.

III. THE ZONED ULTRAMAFIC COMPLEXES OF SOUTHEASTERN ALASKA

Hugh P. Taylor, Jr.

A. Introduction

The Duke Island ultramafic complex described in Section II is one of a series of zoned ultramafic complexes with associated gabbros and diorites that lie along a belt at least 350 miles in length in southeastern Alaska. This belt has a maximum width of 30 miles and includes 35 of the 39 known ultramafic occurrences in the region (Fig. 4.9). Four bodies lie along a poorly-defined, parallel belt some 60 to 70 miles west of the main zone. The main ultramafic belt has been described by Taylor and Noble (1960), and geologic and petrographic studies have been made by various investigators on six of the larger complexes in the belt (Walton, 1951; Taylor and Stebbins, 1956; Taylor and Nielsen, 1956; Ruckmick and Noble, 1959; Stebbins, 1957; Irvine, 1959).

The ultramafic bodies in the main belt have enough characteristics in common to indicate they were formed by similar mechanisms. Most of the bodies are magnetite-bearing hornblende pyroxenites or hornblendites of small size (one-half square mile or less in outcrop area), but two large hornblende pyroxenite intrusions occur at Klukwan and at Snettisham (Fig. 4.9). Eight of the larger complexes contain olivine-bearing rocks; these are the complexes at the Blashke Islands, Union Bay, Kane Peak, the Sukoi Islands, Annette Island, the Percy Islands, and two on Duke Island. Most of the above complexes contain peripheral zones of hornblende pyroxenite in addition to olivine pyroxenite, peridotite, and/or dunite. If dunite is present, essentially the entire range of ultramafic rock types commonly is present in a crude zonal arrangement. A core of dunite, generally about one mile in outcrop diameter, is surrounded by successive shells of peridotite, olivine pyroxenite, magnetite pyroxenite, and hornblende pyroxenite. Any one of the ultramafic zones may be present in only a small extent or may be missing altogether in any given occurrence, however, and frequently the various zones are not completely continuous. The ultramafic complexes are themselves generally enveloped by gabbro that has been strongly saussuritized near the ultramafic contacts.

The ultramafic belt trends parallel to the major structural features of southeastern Alaska, and the ultramafic bodies were intruded after the folding and metamorphism of the Paleozoic and lower Mesozoic

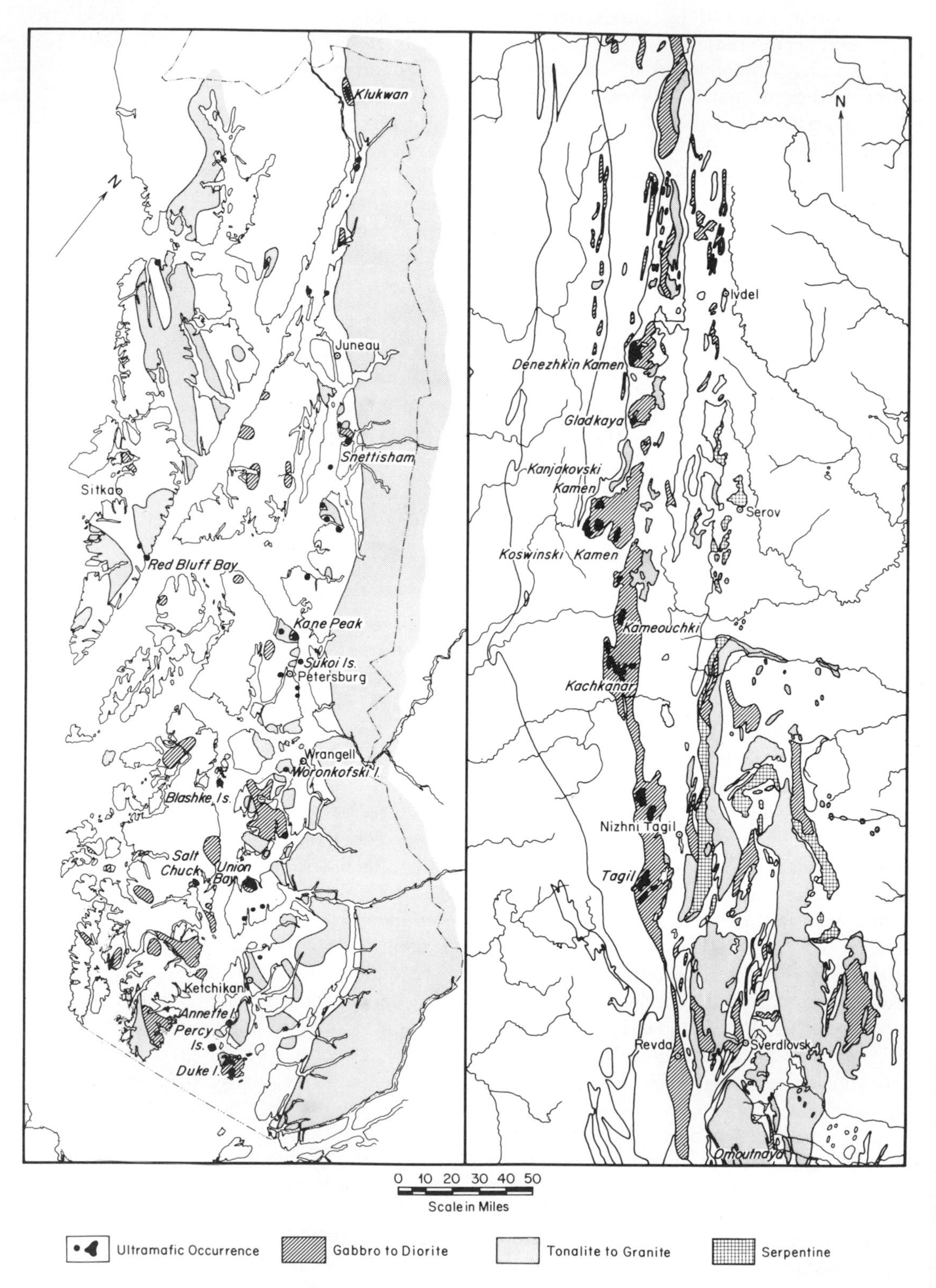

Fig. 4.9 Distribution of ultramafic complexes in southeastern Alaska and the Ural Mountains, U.S.S.R., after Buddington and Chapin (1929) and the Geologic Atlas of the Soviet Union.

rocks of the orogenic belt. In some of the complexes granitic rocks of the Coast Range batholith (Cretaceous to early Tertiary?) cut the ultramafic rocks or their associated gabbros. Hence, if all the ultramafic bodies are of the same age, they were emplaced after regional metamorphism but before the major batholithic intrusions. Lanphere and Eberlein (1966) have made detailed geochronologic studies on the ultramafic bodies and have obtained minimum potassium-argon ages of 100 m.y. for hornblende and/or biotite from the pyroxenite, hornblende pyroxenite, and gabbroic pegmatite units in six separate complexes. Their data suggest that the ultramafic bodies in the main belt were intruded between 100 and 110 million years ago, or in the early middle Cretaceous period. Bodies of the western belt are apparently much older than this, and in addition they show few of the mineralogical or structural characteristics of bodies in the main belt.

A belt of ultramafic rocks in the Ural Mountains, U.S.S.R., has so many features in common with those of southeastern Alaska that most of the descriptions are interchangeable (Duparc, 1920; Zavaritsky and Betekhtin, 1937; Noble and Taylor, 1960; Vorobyeva, 1961). There are 15 large ultramafic bodies (10 of which have dunite cores) distributed within a long, narrow, nearly continuous belt of gabbroic rocks along the north-trending axis of the Ural Mountains. The Ural Mountains belt is compared with the southeastern Alaska ultramafic belt in Fig. 4.9. These two belts include the best known examples of zoned ultramafic complexes in the world, although other occurrences have been described. The complex at Tulameen, British Columbia (Camsell, 1913; Findlay, 1964) is of this type, as is the Pacific Nickel body near Hope, B.C. (Aho, 1956). Several other bodies in British Columbia have similar characteristics, but more detailed descriptions are necessary before they can be included with certainty (Armstrong, 1949; Little, 1949; Roots, 1954). The Troodos massif on Cyprus (Wilson, 1959) shows a similar zoning pattern, and is described in detail in Section IV. Some ultramafic rocks from Japan, particularly the Miyamori and Tagozu groups (Onuki, 1965) bear a strong petrographic resemblance to the southeastern Alaska ultramafic bodies. Other examples of zoning in ultramafic bodies have been reported (Noble and Taylor, 1960), but most are clearly not of the type under discussion.

The Ural-Alaskan type of zoned ultramafic complex is distinctive enough in its mineralogy, structure, and genesis to warrant classification separate from the alpine-type and stratiform peridotite-gabbro complexes discussed by Thayer (1960). The zoned complexes are similar to the alpine-type ultramafic bodies in their confinement to eugeosynclinical orogenic belts, but they differ in their *concentric* zoning, in the absence or rarity of orthopyroxene, and in the pronounced contact metamorphic and metasomatic effects at their margins. This section considers in detail only the southeastern Alaska ultramafic belt, but obviously a theory of origin must explain the zoned complexes in the Ural Mountains and other parts of the world as well. We shall therefore attempt to compare chemical and mineralogical observations on ultramafic bodies in the Ural Mountains with analogous features in the southeastern Alaska bodies that seem critical to any theory of origin.

B. General Characteristics of the Zoned Ultramafic Complexes

1. Southeastern Alaska. The following generalizations can be made about the ultramafic intrusive rocks in southeastern Alaska:

1. A consistent zonal arrangement is a constant feature of those complexes that contain olivine-bearing rocks. This is shown in Fig. 4.10, where we present generalized geological maps of the most important ultramafic complexes in southeastern Alaska (Taylor and Noble, 1960). It

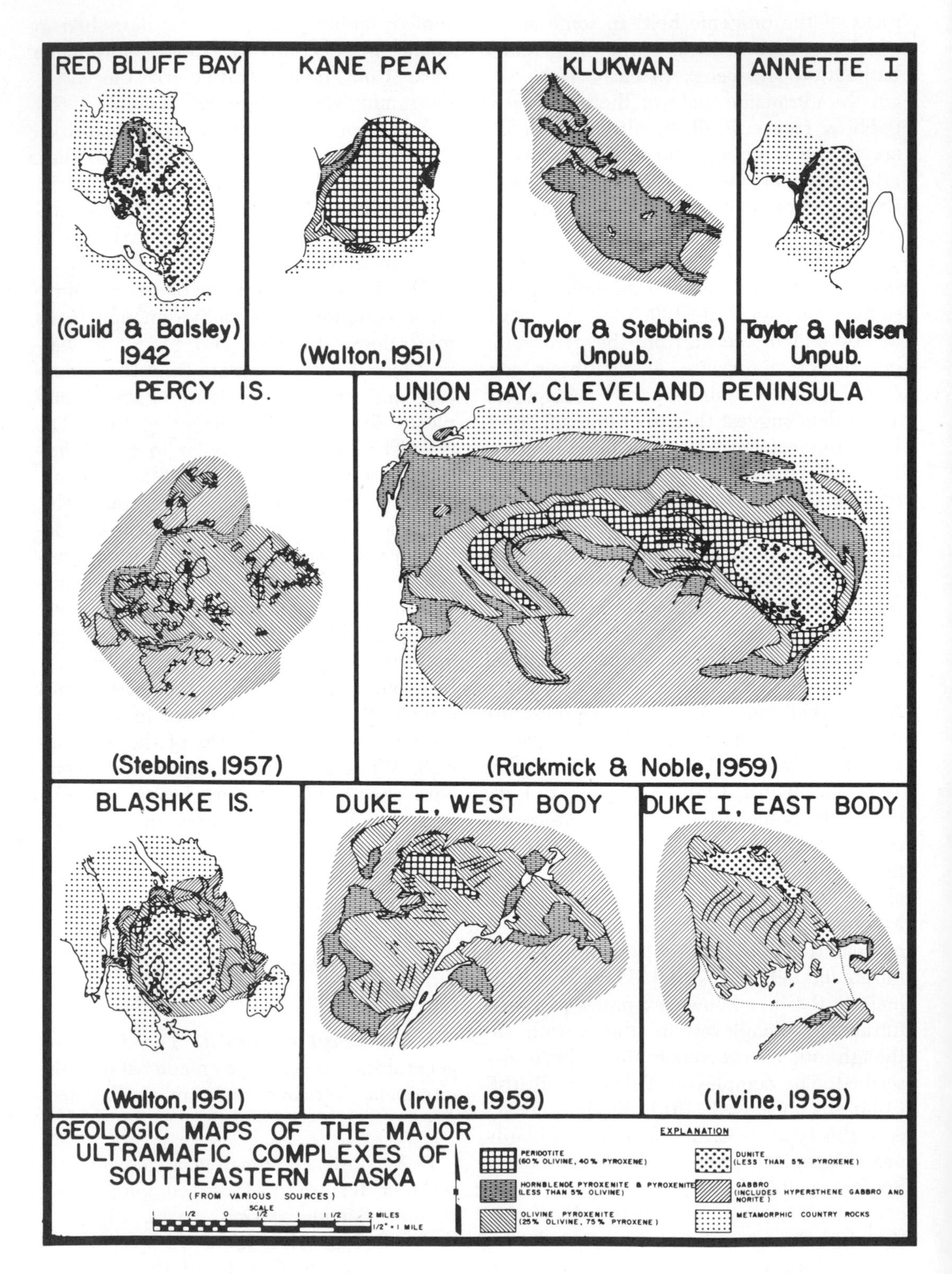

Fig. 4.10 Generalized geologic maps of the major ultramafic complexes in southeastern Alaska (from various sources).

should be pointed out that the Red Bluff Bay complex shown in Fig. 4.10 does not belong to the main ultramafic belt.

2. The following are distinctive mineralogical and textural features common to all the occurrences: (a) The clinopyroxene is exclusively a diopsidic augite, with a composition relatively close to the diopside-hedenbergite join, varying from $D_{70}H_{30}$ in the magnetite-hornblende pyroxenites to $D_{99}H_1$ in the dunites (Fig. 4.11). The pyroxenes are relatively high in alumina compared to clinopyroxene from the average gabbro, commonly containing 4 to 7 weight per cent Al_2O_3. No orthopyroxene has been identified from any of the ultramafic rock types. (b) No plagioclase occurs, even interstitially, throughout the great volumes of these ultramafic rocks, except in the late-stage gabbroic pegmatites and in the peripheral hornblendite zones. The plagioclase in the latter rock types is exceptionally calcic, An_{90}-An_{98}, except where it has been saussuritized to an aggregate of albite, clinozoisite, and epidote. This type of alteration is very common, particularly at the margins of the ultramafic bodies. (c) Olivine is highly magnesian, varying from Fo_{75} in the olivine pyroxenites to Fo_{93} in the dunites. (d) Serpentinization, where present, occurred after emplacement; much of the olivine is unaltered, and evidence of strain or of mortar texture is extremely rare. (e) Magnetite is commonly present in greater than accessory amounts in the pyroxenite and hornblende pyroxenite units, averaging a remarkably constant 15 to 20 per cent of the rock over large areas of outcrop. A few of the smaller hornblendite bodies contain only 5 to 10 per cent magnetite, with only local enrichment. Ilmenite is a ubiquitous accessory in all these rock types, generally forming 5 to 10 per cent of the opaque grains, both as "exsolved" blades in magnetite and as separate grains peripheral to the magnetite. (f) Minor amounts of hercynite spinel are invariably present in the hornblende pyroxenites. (g) Chromite is a ubiquitous (but rare) constituent of the dunites and occurs both in irregular veins and segregations and as individual grains. (h) Minor amounts (1 to 2 per cent) of hornblende occur interstitially and as an alteration of the pyroxene in the olivine pyroxenite zones. (i) Much of the hornblende and pyroxene is extremely coarse-grained, locally pegmatitic. Hornblende crystals up to a foot long are not uncommon in the late-stage gabbroic pegmatites and in the marginal zones of the hornblende pyroxenites.

3. Chemical compositions of the various minerals generally vary in a consistent

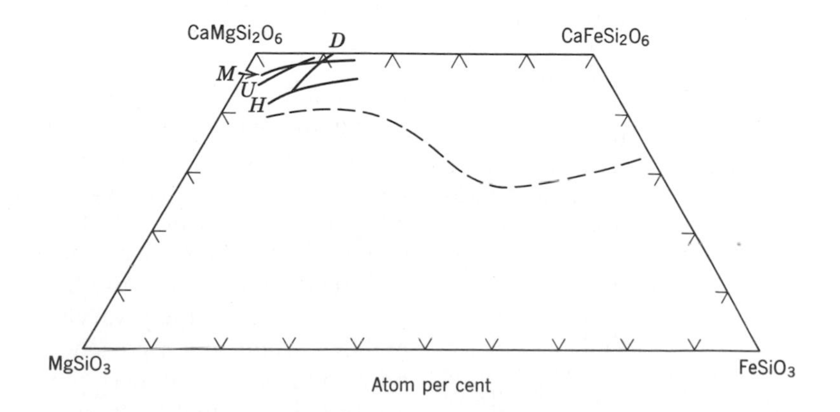

Fig. 4.11 Compositional variations in pyroxenes from some ultramafic complexes. *U*—Union Bay (Ruckmick and Noble, 1959); *D*—Duke Island (Irvine, 1959); *M*—Miyamori; and *H*—Horoman intrusives, Japan (Onuki, 1965). The dashed line is the trend of clinopyroxene variation in common mafic magmas (Hess, 1941).

manner from pyroxenite through olivine pyroxenite, peridotite, and dunite in any given complex. These variations include an increase in the Mg/Fe ratio of olivine and pyroxene, and a decrease in the Al/Si and Fe^{III}/Si ratios in pyroxene. Chemical compositions of hornblendes from the late-stage gabbroic pegmatites and the hornblende pyroxenites are very similar, as shown in Table 4.2. These hornblendes are unusual in their high Al_2O_3 and low SiO_2 contents relative to normal igneous hornblendes.

4. Each ultramafic rock unit tends to be mineralogically and chemically quite uniform throughout the entire ultramafic belt, as well as within a given complex. Dunite is generally 95 to 98 per cent olivine (ignoring the serpentine alteration) with accessory chromite, diopside, and magnetite. Olivine pyroxenite usually contains 15 to 20 per cent olivine, 70 to 75 per cent clinopyroxene, and accessory hornblende and magnetite. Magnetite-hornblende pyroxenite carries widely varying proportions of hornblende and pyroxene, from almost pure pyroxenite to almost pure hornblendite, but the magnetite content of the large bodies is relatively constant at 15 to 20 per cent. Peridotites (rocks intermediate between olivine pyroxenite and dunite) are more variable in their mineralogical com-

TABLE 4.2 Chemical Compositions of Hornblendes from Hornblende Pyroxenites and Gabbroic Pegmatites in Southeastern Alaska, the Ural Mountains, and Kitakami, Japan

Wt. %	1	2	3	4	5	6
SiO_2	39.8	41.2	42.5	39.9	40.1	40.8
Al_2O_3	16.6	16.2	14.6	15.2	15.0	14.5
Fe_2O_3	4.4	4.1	3.9	3.4	4.5	2.4
FeO	8.9	7.0	9.5	8.5	6.6	12.4
MgO	12.6	14.0	11.6	13.5	15.1	10.6
CaO	12.1	12.6	12.4	12.1	12.4	11.6
Na_2O	1.6	2.3	2.5	1.1	1.5	2.6
K_2O	1.0	0.6	0.4	0.8	0.8	0.1
TiO_2	1.2	1.4	1.4	1.2	1.7	2.1
MnO	0.2	0.0	0.3	0.1	0.1	0.3
H_2O+	1.4	0.4	0.9	3.4	...	2.0
H_2O-	0.3	0.3	0.2	0.5	...	0.1

1. Union Bay, pyroxene hornblendite (Ruckmick and Noble, 1959, Table 1, No. 95)
2. Duke Island, hornblendite (Irvine, 1959, Table 8, p. 67, sample I-31-4)
3. Duke Island, gabbroic pegmatite (Irvine, 1959, Table 8, p. 67, No. I-27-1)
4. Sinyaya massif, average of 3 specimens from gabbroic pegmatites (Andreyeva, 1959, Table 2)
5. Kachkanar massif, hornblende pyroxenite (Andreyeva, 1959, Table 2)
6. Miyamori intrusive, pyroxene hornblendite (Onuki, 1964, Table 1, sample M-4)

TABLE 4.3 Chemical Analyses of Representative Samples of Olivine Pyroxenite from Ultramafic Bodies in Southeastern Alaska, the Ural Mountains, and Kitakami, Japan

Wt. %	1	2	3	4	5	6
SiO_2	47.6	49.2	48.3	50.7	48.4	49.5
Al_2O_3	4.8	2.4	3.0	1.6	2.9	2.0
Fe_2O_3	2.9	2.0	3.1	1.6	2.5	3.1
FeO	5.6	6.8	6.0	3.9	6.1	2.2
MgO	18.5	19.1	18.1	20.2	19.1	19.2
CaO	18.7	18.9	20.2	20.9	20.1	20.2
Na_2O	0.5	0.2	...	...	0.3	0.2
K_2O	0.0	0.1	...	...	0.1	0.1
TiO_2	0.5	0.2	0.4	0.3	0.5	0.2
Cr_2O_3	0.2	...	0.2	0.5	...	0.4
MnO	0.0	0.2	0.2	0.1	...	0.1
H_2O+	0.7	0.6	0.2	0.3	0.8	2.4
H_2O-	0.2	0.2	0.3	0.2		0.3

1. Duke Island (Irvine, 1959, Table 8, p. 66, sample R-38-2)
2. Union Bay (Ruckmick and Noble, 1959, Table 1, sample 9)
3. Kanjakovski-Kamen (Vorobyeva, 1961, Table 2, specimen 3)
4. Kanjakovski-Kamen (Vorobyeva, 1961, Table 2, specimen 5)
5. Average olivine pyroxenite in Urals (Duparc, 1920, p. 83, analyses of 9 samples)
6. Least serpentinized olivine clinopyroxenite, Miyamori intrusive, Kitakami Mountains, northeastern Japan (Onuki, 1965, Table 7, p. 233, sample MY-31)

position, but they are much less abundant than the rock types just described. Much of the peridotite zone in the Union Bay complex, shown in Fig. 4.10, is the "structural peridotite" of Ruckmick and Noble (1959) which is actually interlayered dunite and olivine pyroxenite. In addition, the large zone shown as peridotite at Kane Peak (Fig. 4.10) has been mapped in only reconnaissance fashion; it is poorly exposed, but is known to contain appreciable dunitc. Chemical compositions of "typical" specimens of dunite, olivine pyroxenite,

TABLE 4.4 Chemical Analyses of Representative Samples of Dunite from Ultramafic Bodies in Southeastern Alaska and the Ural Mountains

Wt. %	1	2	3	4	5	6	7
SiO_2	38.9	40.2	40.0	39.9	39.0	40.1	40.0
Al_2O_3	1.5	1.7	1.1	0.5	...	0.5	...
Fe_2O_3	1.8	0.9	1.1	1.9	2.0	...	...
FeO	14.1	9.3	8.7	11.8	10.4	8.8	8.3
MgO	42.0	47.5	48.7	45.4	44.9	49.9	48.9
CaO	0.9	...	0.2	...	...	...	...
Na_2O	0.3	0.0	...	...	...	...	...
K_2O	...	...	...	...	...	...	...
Cr_2O_3	0.3	...	...	0.1	0.3	0.5	0.5
MnO	0.1	0.2	0.2	0.2	...		...
H_2O+		0.3		0.7	3.5		1.3
H_2O-		0.1		0.1	0.1		0.1

1. Serpentinized dunite, Duke Island (Irvine, 1959, Table 9, p. 68, sample H-4-4, recalculated on an anhydrous basis to eliminate 9.4% water)
2. Union Bay (Ruckmick and Noble, 1959, Table 1, sample 231)
3. Union Bay (Ruckmick and Noble, 1959, Table 1, sample 183a, recalculated on an anhydrous basis to eliminate 3.6% water)
4. Kanjakovski-Kamen (Vorobyeva, 1961, Table 2, specimen 71)
5. Denezhkin Kamen (Vorobyeva, 1961, Table 1, specimen 1)
6. Average dunite in Urals (Duparc, 1920, p. 62, analyses of 25 samples, recalculated to remove water and ferric iron)
7. Tagil massif at 500 meters depth (Vorobyeva, 1961, Table 1, specimen 4)

TABLE 4.5 Chemical Analyses of Representative Samples of Magnetite-Hornblende Pyroxenites from Ultramafic Bodies in Southeastern Alaska and the Ural Mountains

Wt. %	1	2	3	4	5	6	7
SiO_2	38.3	37.5	39.5	35.1	40.0	36.9	39.5
Al_2O_3	7.2	5.4	...	8.0	10.6	8.6	6.0
Fe_2O_3	13.3	15.5	...	...	...	17.5	13.7
FcO	9.7	9.6	...	...	...	8.0	8.1
Total Fe	16.8	18.3	17.4	18.6	14.5	18.4	15.9
MgO	11.7	11.9	...	9.6	...	11.9	12.2
CaO	16.7	17.4	...	16.1	13.8	18.2	19.5
Na_2O	0.9	...	...	...	...	...	0.3
K_2O	0.2	...	...	...	...	...	...
TiO_2	1.8	2.2	2.1	2.7	1.9	...	0.5
MnO	0.1	0.2	...	...	...	...	0.2
P_2O_5	...	...	0.2	0.6	0.5	...	
S	...	...		0.3		...	
H_2O+	0.2	0.3				0.2	
H_2O-		0.3					

1. Duke Island (Irvine, 1959, Table 10, p. 85)
2. Union Bay (Ruckmick and Noble, 1959, Table 1, Specimen 32a)
3. Klukwan (Wells and Thorne, 1953, Table 1, Samples 1 and 4 averaged together)
4. Snettisham (Thorne and Wells, 1956, Table 3), composite sample of drill core, recalculated on an anhydrous basis
5. Percy Islands (Stebbins, 1957), composite of chip samples along 8000 feet of shoreline on west half of Percy Island
6. Koswinski Kamen (Duparc, 1920, I, p. 76)
7. Kachkanar (Duparc, 1920, I, p. 77)

and magnetite-hornblende pyroxenite from the complexes at Union Bay, Duke Island, Percy Islands, Klukwan, and Snettisham are given in Tables 4.3, 4.4, and 4.5.

5. Contact relationships between the various ultramafic units are similar in all occurrences. Contacts are generally gradational on a large scale, particularly between hornblende pyroxenite and pyroxenite, and between pyroxenite and olivine pyroxenite, even though in detail the contacts between rock types may be sharp. This is well shown by the zone of "struc-

tural peridotite" at Union Bay, which consists of discrete masses of dunite interlayered with and containing inclusions of olivine pyroxenite, the whole zone being gradational between the olivine pyroxenite and dunite zones. Apparently conflicting age relationships are observed, in that dikes and veins of most of the ultramafic units can be found cutting one another. The pyroxenite veins that cut dunite and olivine pyroxenite, however, bear no chemical similarity to the main hornblende pyroxenite or magnetite pyroxenite zones, and they presumably originate in a different manner. Giant blocks of olivine pyroxenite occur in the dunite and peridotite zones at Union Bay and at Duke Island, suggesting that the dunite was formed after at least part of the olivine pyroxenite had crystallized. Gabbroic pegmatite dikes and veins are the youngest rock types in the ultramafic complexes, sharply transecting all other rock units except for the dunite cores.

6. A zone of gabbro more or less completely envelops each of the ultramafic complexes, and only rarely are the ultramafic bodies in direct contact with metamorphic country rocks. In most complexes the gabbro is definitely older than the ultramafic complex, and the gabbro is almost invariably saussuritized or hornblenditized for some distance away from the ultramafic contact. Contacts between the ultramafic rocks and the gabbro are generally very sharp and intrusive in appearance, although locally they may be obscured by saussuritization or by late-stage gabbroic pegmatite. The early-formed gabbros are generally medium-grained and even-textured, except where they are strongly altered to hornblende, epidote, or clinozoisite. The most widespread type is a hypersthene gabbro containing calcic labradorite, but variations are observed through normal gabbro and norite to hornblende gabbro and diorite. Olivine gabbros are very rare. The gabbros are chemically and mineralogically very different from the much more calcic gabbroic pegmatite associated with the ultramafic complexes, but in the field distinction between the two types may be difficult in areas of strong alteration. This has led to reports of conflicting age relationships between gabbro and ultramafic, but as far as is known to the author all the gabbro bodies that can be shown to transect ultramafic rock types are of the highly calcic gabbroic pegmatite variety. Well-defined dikes of hornblende pyroxenite or hornblendite can be observed cutting gabbro at the margins of several of the ultramafic complexes, notably at Union Bay and at Klukwan.

7. Impressive contact metamorphic and metasomatic aureoles have been formed around the ultramafic complexes. High-rank epidote amphibolite or amphibolite facies metamorphism may be observed for a distance of several hundred feet away from the contacts between the hornblende pyroxenite units in the larger complexes and either gabbro or metamorphic country rock. At Union Bay, regionally metamorphosed phyllites have been deformed and recrystallized to biotite-garnet schists and gneisses in an aureole over 1000 feet wide. At the Blashke Islands, which contain no distinct magnetite-hornblende pyroxenite zone, the country rock has been converted into a pyroxene granulite of gabbroic composition for at least 100 feet outward from the contact with the complex. Recognizable contact metamorphic effects are observed for several hundred to a thousand feet outward from the intrusion (Walton, 1951).

2. Ural Mountains, Soviet Union. The most complete discussion of the minerals and rocks of the zoned ultramafic intrusives in the Ural Mountains is still that of Duparc (1920). More recently, Romanov (1949) and Vorobyeva (1961) have presented data on the entire gabbro-ultramafic belt, but most of the later investigations have been detailed studies on portions of individual bodies. A fairly clear picture of the similarities and differences between the ultramafic rocks in southeastern Alaska and the Ural Mountains can be obtained from these descriptions. Generalized geologic maps of the major zoned intrusives in the Urals are given in Fig. 4.12, and comparison with Fig. 4.10 emphasizes the striking similarities these bear to the ultramafic bodies in southeastern Alaska.

The dunites in both ultramafic belts are very similar, as shown by the chemical analyses in Table 4.4, but the Uralian dunites are on the average somewhat higher in Mg/Fe ratio. Chromite is also more abundant than in the Alaskan bodies, and clinopyroxene is less abundant. Orthopyroxene is of rare occurrence, whereas in the Alaskan ultramafic rocks it is completely absent.

The magnetite pyroxenites in the Ural Mountains commonly contain olivine (to the extent of 5 to 10 per cent), and were termed koswites by Duparc (1920). Hornblende is apparently much less common than in the Alaskan occurrences. Nevertheless, chemical compositions of the magnetite pyroxenites are very similar throughout both regions, as shown in Table 4.5.

Olivine pyroxenites are mineralogically and chemically very similar to one another throughout the Ural and southeastern Alaska belts (Table 4.3), and rocks intermediate between olivine pyroxenite and dunite (i.e., peridotites) are rare in the Urals, just as in Alaska. The zoning of ultramafic rock types in a given intrusive is almost identical in both belts, but the dunite cores from the Urals are generally larger and more elongate or elliptical in outcrop pattern (Fig. 4.12). The olivine pyroxenite outer zones may be very narrow or nonexistent, a feature which is only observed in one occurrence in southeastern Alaska, namely at Annette Island.

The ultramafic bodies in the Ural belt are almost invariably intruded into gabbros that are part of a gabbroic complex that forms a long, narrow, nearly continuous belt extending along the Ural Mountains axis. This is very different from the isolated stock-like masses of gabbro that are associated with the ultramafic bodies in southeastern Alaska. The Uralian ultramafic bodies commonly occur near the western edge of the long gabbro belt (Fig. 4.9), and in at least one example (at Gladkaya) the ultramafic body has been intruded along the gabbro-metasediment contact.

Late-stage gabbroic pegmatite bodies containing anorthite and hornblende are practically ubiquitous in the Uralian ultramafic complexes (Yefimov and Kuuspalu, 1962; Andreyeva, 1959) and are identical in their occurrence and mineralogy with those associated with the complexes in southeastern Alaska. Chemical analyses of hornblendes from these rock types are given in Table 4.2. These dikes cut the hornblende pyroxenite and olivine pyroxenite zones in the Uralian complexes.

Dike rocks of a variety of types are very abundant in the Uralian complexes, and these show apparently conflicting age relationships. Unique to the Urals, however, is the relatively common occurrence of dunite dikes cutting pyroxenite and gabbro. Some of the dunite dikes are identical with the dunite of the larger bodies, but some are finer-grained and some are porphyritic, with large olivines enclosed in a groundmass of smaller ones. Other dike and vein relationships are essentially identical to those observed in the Alaskan bodies.

Platinum has been found in place in the Ural ultramafic rocks but not in those of southeastern Alaska, although the Salt Chuck body on Prince of Wales Island has produced appreciable amounts of palladium. Most of the platinum from the Ural Mountains is of placer occurrence, and no placers have escaped glacial erosion in southeastern Alaska; hence, this may be why platinum is apparently absent in the latter region. The zoned ultramafic body at Tulameen, B.C., is accompanied by platiniferous placers, however.

The Uralian ultramafic complexes are Paleozoic in age, probably Devonian. They also differ from the southeastern Alaska

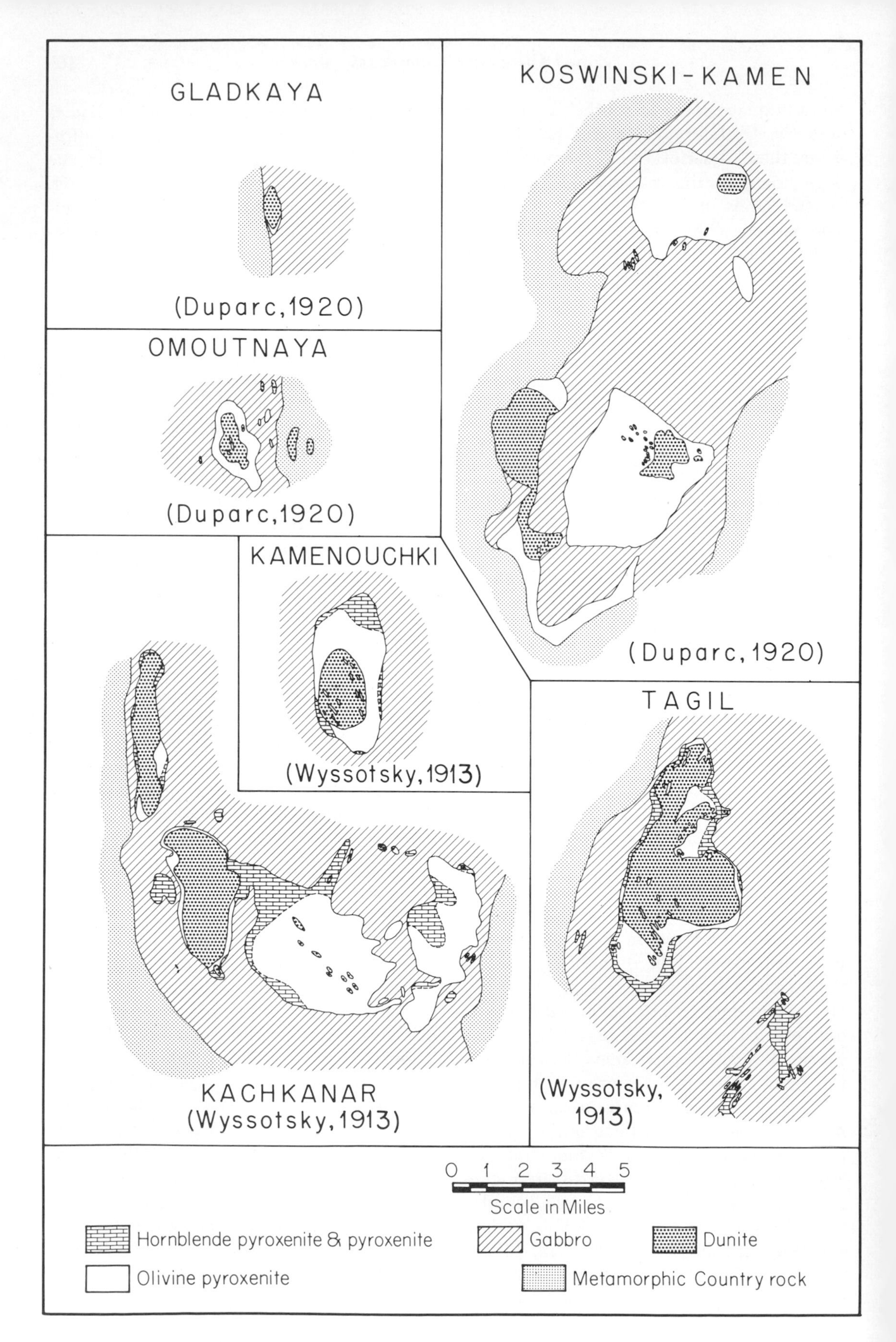

Fig. 4.12 Generalized geologic maps of the major ultramafic complexes in the Ural Mountain region, U.S.S.R. (after Wyssotsky, 1913, and Duparc, 1920).

bodies in that they are more highly serpentinized, more sheared, and more deeply weathered. This is largely because the Urals have not been glaciated, except in the far north.

C. Descriptions of Individual Ultramafic Complexes in Southeastern Alaska

General features common to the ultramafic bodies in southeastern Alaska were just summarized. In the following section, further details are presented for the major complexes. In these brief descriptions, emphasis is placed upon the critical and distinctive features of each complex that are pertinent to a theory of origin.

1. Duke Island. Two major bodies and three minor ones occur in the Duke Island area, and just to the west another major complex crops out in the Percy Islands. This represents the heaviest concentration of ultramafic rocks in southeastern Alaska. The features of the two major bodies have been described by Irvine (1959, 1963; and in Section II). The olivine-bearing rocks show a remarkable layering consisting of graded beds of olivine and clinopyroxene, which is in almost all respects analogous to graded bedding in sandstones. These features are best interpreted as the result of convection currents in a crystallizing olivine pyroxenite magma. Large areas in the western body show this layering; the total thickness of beds is at least 5000 feet, and probably is as much as 10,000 to 15,000 feet. Very little variation in chemical composition occurs from the base upwards, although a slight enrichment in iron does take place.

Layers of fragments of graded olivine pyroxenite occur in a matrix of graded peridotite, and these are analogous to conglomerate beds. These layers are abundant above the base of a major angular unconformity in the bedded sequence, interpreted to be the result of a second intrusion of a magma more olivine-rich than olivine pyroxenite. These peridotitic layers grade continuously upward into a thick section of the more common graded olivine pyroxenite.

The eastern ultramafic body shows grading only locally, but what appears to be a primary interlayering of dunite and olivine pyroxenite is common. This layering is tilted and folded, apparently by a later intrusion of dunite in the northern portion of the complex (Fig. 4.10). The dunite itself locally shows graded layering. The graded layering at Duke Island is a unique feature not observed in any other ultramafic complex in southeastern Alaska or the Ural Mountains, and it is of enormous importance because it indicates that the olivine pyroxenite definitely crystallized from liquid magma.

Both ultramafic bodies on Duke Island are intrusive into a large gabbroic mass that has been altered to hornblende gabbro in the vicinity of the ultramafic contact. The feldspar in the gabbro is commonly altered to bytownite, as well. Little or no saussuritization is observed either at the contact or in the late-stage gabbroic pegmatite dikes. An almost continuous zone of magnetite-hornblende pyroxenite envelops the western body, appearing to lie structurally above the olivine pyroxenite zone (Irvine, 1963). The eastern intrusive shows this zone only locally. In the latter area this zone shows graded layering of clinopyroxene and magnetite.

In many of the areas of graded layering in the western body, irregularly shaped dunitic bodies transect the layering without noticeably deforming it. These are interpreted by Irvine (1959) to be replacement bodies formed by metasomatic emanations from periodotitic magma that is in equilibrium with olivine but not pyroxene. The olivine in these replacement bodies is more magnesian than the olivine in the olivine pyroxenite.

A few inclusions of milky white vein quartz in the graded bedding of the western body are the only foreign materials within either ultramafic body, and these are unique to the Duke Island ultramafic complex. The inclusions have reaction borders of clinopyroxene. Presumably, inclusions of more complex mineralogy contained low-melting fractions that facilitated their assimilation by the olivine pyroxenite magma. Pure quartz would not melt and could be preserved by the armouring reaction rim of pyroxene.

2. Percy Islands. The Percy Islands complex, studied by Stebbins (1957), is similar to the two large complexes on Duke Island in size and in outcrop pattern. It is principally olivine pyroxenite with a border zone of magnetite-hornblende pyroxenite. Because of the islands, only discontinuous outcrops are exposed, but the hornblende pyroxenite zone appears to be invariably present between olivine pyroxenite and gabbro. It is, however, quite narrow, commonly 500 to 1000 feet wide at most. Stebbins (1957) sampled the hornblende pyroxenite zone along more than a mile of shoreline on the largest island in the Percy group, and found this zone to be remarkably uniform in chemical composition. A partial chemical analysis of this average sample is given in Table 4.5.

No dunite core or graded layering is exposed on the Percy Islands, but a clear-cut layering similar to that in the eastern body at Duke Island is observed, and these layers are folded and tilted from 45° to vertical. Dunite-rich layers as much as 200 to 300 feet thick occur within the olivine pyroxenite unit, and one passes both downward and upward from these layers into normal olivine pyroxenite.

Locally, near the ultramafic body, the Percy Island gabbro is impregnated with large concentrations of magnetite (15 to 20 per cent), and saussuritization of the gabbro is common. Gabbroic pegmatite dikes are numerous and cut all other rock types.

3. Annette Island. Yellow Hill on Annette Island is a dunitic plug intrusive into high-rank metamorphic rocks, partially surrounded by younger Coast Range granodiorite. The plug is almost identical in size and shape to the dunite cores at Union Bay and at the Blashke Islands, but the Annette Island body is unique in that ultramafic rock types other than dunite are almost completely lacking.

This complex has been mapped by Taylor and Nielsen (1956), but detailed petrographic and chemical studies have not been made. Serpentinized olivine makes up at least 98 per cent of the ultramafic body, with only very minor amounts of clinopyroxene and chromite. Only locally at the margins of the dunite plug does clinopyroxene make up as much as 5 per cent of the rock. Based upon index of refraction measurements on only two specimens, the olivine has a composition of $Fo_{90}Fa_{10}$; commonly, more than half the olivine in a given specimen is serpentinized. An unusual feature is the very coarse grain size of much of the olivine, crystals 1 cm or more in diameter being abundant.

A narrow selvage of hornblende pyroxenite (with accessory magnetite), no more than 5 to 10 feet wide, borders the dunite plug on the west, but exposures of the contact are so poor that this zone was seen in only two places. The hornblende is in clear-cut reaction relationship to the clinopyroxene, and minor amounts of interstitial clinozoisite are present. Some apparently discontinuous bodies of pyroxene gabbro and hornblende gabbro occur on the western periphery of the dunite plug, but they are poorly exposed and their relationship to the ultramafic body is unknown.

4. Union Bay. The largest single complex in southeastern Alaska, and the one which shows the most significant and best developed zonal structure, occurs just east of Union Bay in the vicinity of Mt. Burnett. Every ultramafic zone is present in considerable abundance, and a distinctive feature is the large zone of magnetite-hornblende pyroxenite that forms the northern and western portions of the complex. This zone generally contains less than 10 per cent hornblende, but hornblende increases in abundance toward the margins of the ultramafic body, forming a border zone of hornblende pyroxenite and hornblendite (with interstitial clinozoisite). The interior portions of the magnetite pyroxenite zone commonly contain 5 to 10 per cent olivine, and through an increase in olivine content this zone grades inward to normal olivine pyroxenite. The complex as a whole shows both a vertical and a lateral zoning, the zones extending completely around a central portion which contains interlayered dunite and olivine pyroxenite. Ruckmick and Noble (1959) have interpreted this to be a lopolithic offshoot from a pipelike dunite core at the extreme eastern end of the complex.

The dunite core has the shape of a plug that appears to have intruded the ultramafic rocks that surround it. Giant blocks of olivine pyroxenite are embedded in the marginal parts of the dunite plug. In places small areas of crude graded layering occur in the core, indicated by minor amounts of size-graded pyroxene grains. The Union Bay complex is almost completely enveloped by gabbro, except in the vicinity of the dunite core, where pyroxenite and olivine pyroxenite abut directly against metamorphic country rock. Above the ultramafic body and to the south of it are quantities of gabbro as large as the ultramafic complex itself. The gabbro is strongly saussuritized at the contacts with ultramafic rocks, and the relatively narrow zone of gabbro which borders the ultramafic body on the north and west is completely saussuritized.

Serpentinization is less pervasive at Union Bay than in any other ultramafic body in southeastern Alaska, and better exposures of olivine-bearing rocks are found here, as well. Some dunite in the core is completely free from serpentine, and such specimens are also free of strain shadows and mortar texture. Structurally, the most significant feature of the complex is the thick zone of magnetite pyroxenite that *underlies* the olivine-bearing rocks of the lopolith (Ruckmick and Noble, 1959). This zone is 1000 to 2000 feet thick in the bottom part of the lopolith, and it has a much thinner counterpart that forms the upper border zone of the intrusive. In other complexes in southeastern Alaska there is no definite evidence that a magnetite-hornblende pyroxenite zone lies beneath olivine pyroxenite, although such an arrangement is likely both at Duke Island and at Kane Peak. The magnetite pyroxenite zone at Union Bay is remarkably uniform in chemical composition. Partial analyses of 5- and 10-foot composites from 4100 feet of drill core showed little variation and averaged 18.03 per cent total Fe and 1.36 per cent TiO_2 (Stebbins, 1957). These figures may be compared with the values given in Table 4.5.

*5. **Blashke Islands.*** The ultramafic complex at the Blashke Islands, studied by Walton (1951), is the most symmetrically arranged complex in southeastern Alaska. It consists of almost concentric, vertical, cylindrical zones of the different ultramafic rock types. A circular core of dunite 6000 to 9000 feet in diameter is encircled by a continuous ring of olivine pyroxenite 500 to 2000 feet wide, outside of which is a nearly complete ring of gabbro, locally absent but elsewhere up to 1400 feet wide. There is no magnetite-hornblende pyroxenite zone in this complex, but hornblendite dikes and gabbroic pegmatite occur sporadically in the outer portions of the olivine pyroxenite zone. The gabbro is very irregular in composition and texture, but where the gabbro zone is wide the rock generally changes from olivine-augite gabbro near its inner contacts with olivine pyroxenite into a hornblende gabbro at the outer margins (Walton, 1951).

Well-defined dikes of pyroxene dunite cut both the dunite core and the olivine pyroxenite ring and thin veins of clinopyroxenite cut the outer parts of the dunite core. A group of fine-grained dikes ranging from olivine gabbro to hornblendite cut both the olivine pyroxenite and the gabbro. Xenoliths of country rock in the olivine pyroxenite and gabbro are texturally and compositionally similar to these fine-grained dikes. One very unusual dike-like rock, crosscutting olivine pyroxenite, consists of diopsidic augite and andradite garnet (Walton, 1951).

The enclosing metamorphic country rocks have undergone intense contact metamorphism that diminishes outward from the complex and disappears within 500 to 1000 feet. The ultramafic body is strongly transgressive, cutting across structures in the enclosing rocks, but it has also had a doming or upward-dragging effect on these rocks. Contacts with the enclosing rocks are steep to vertical.

6. Kane Peak. The Kane Peak complex, briefly studied by Kennedy and Walton (1946) and by the author, is principally peridotite and dunite (all shown as peridotite on the map in Fig. 4.10), with discontinuous outer zones of olivine pyroxenite and pyroxene hornblendite. Exposures in the peridotite-dunite zone are very poor. Discontinuous bodies of gabbro occur peripherally to the complex; some of the original gabbro border has apparently been cut out by a later intrusion of monzodiorite that may be related to the Coast Range batholith. The olivine pyroxenite zone dips steeply beneath the dunite-peridotite zone, giving this intrusion a funnel-shaped appearance. A distinctive feature is the sporadic occurrence of phlogopite in the olivine pyroxenite.

7. Snettisham. A brief report on the magnetite-hornblende pyroxenite body at Port Snettisham is given by Thorne and Wells (1956). Based upon magnetic anomalies it appears to be an oval-shaped intrusion about 2 miles long and 1.5 miles wide. Only the southern third of the body is exposed above sea level, and this portion is intrusive into hornblende gabbro and diorite except in its eastern portion where it is in direct contact with metasedimentary rocks in the vicinity of Sentinel Point. Dikes of pyroxenite are intruded into the metasedimentary rocks. Exposures are good only along the shoreline, but several holes have been drilled into the pyroxenite and the drill core is described by Thorne and Wells (1956). Based upon this drilling, the southeast margin of the pyroxenite has a steep, outward-dipping contact against gabbro.

No olivine-bearing rocks are exposed in the Snettisham complex. The pyroxenite contains widely varying amounts of hornblende and is texturally highly variable. Gabbroic pegmatite, largely altered to epidote and clinozoisite, occurs sporadically throughout the body. Nevertheless, the chemical composition and magnetite content of the pyroxenite are relatively constant, as shown by analyses of sections of drill core for total Fe by Thorne and Wells (1956). A partial chemical analysis of a composite sample from 6500 feet of core is given in Table 4.5. This body is in almost every respect identical to the magnetite-hornblende pyroxenite zone at Union Bay.

8. Klukwan. The northernmost body in the ultramafic belt is located at Klukwan, 20 miles north of Haines. Here a body of hornblende pyroxenite about 3 miles long by 1 mile wide is intrusive into a gabbro-diorite body at the margin of the Coast Range batholith. The gabbro is foliated and the pyroxenite crosscuts this foliation along contacts which are steep and very sharp. Dikes of pyroxenite cut the gabbro, and the gabbro is epidotized in the vicinity of the ultramafic body.

The Klukwan ultramafic body is texturally and mineralogically almost identical with the magnetite-hornblende pyroxenite at Snettisham and the corresponding zone at Union Bay. Large portions of the body contain less than 5 to 10 per cent hornblende, but the magnetite content is relatively uniform at 15 to 20 per cent. Wells and Thorne (1953) have made partial chemical analyses of several composite samples of the ultramafic body, and the intrusion is shown to be quite uniform in its content of SiO_2, TiO_2, and total Fe (see

Table 4.5). Some large segregations of magnetite do occur, however, in which the magnetite content reaches 60 to 80 per cent of the rock.

The body has been mapped by Taylor and Stebbins (1956), and their generalized geological map is given in Fig. 4.10. Because of a vertical relief of more than 5500 feet and absence of vegetation, this is the best exposed ultramafic complex in southeastern Alaska. Much of the pyroxenite is 100 per cent exposed over a vertical distance of more than 3000 feet; no significant mineralogical changes could be observed in that interval. Two large xenoliths or septa are exposed in the central portions of the body, one of gabbro and one of a metasediment. Numerous *en echelon* anorthositic dikes transect both the ultramafic body and the gabbro in the eastern portion of the complex; these are more feldspar-rich than the corresponding gabbroic pegmatites of the other complexes but are otherwise identical. Many are strongly altered to clinozoisite.

9. Others. Two other ultramafic bodies in the belt contain olivine-bearing rocks; these are located in the Sukoi Islands and on Woronkofski Island, but these bodies have not been studied in any detail. All other bodies are magnetite-bearing hornblende pyroxenites or hornblendites of small size. In Fig. 4.9 the size of these bodies is exaggerated for purposes of clarity. Hornblende is generally much more abundant than pyroxene in these small bodies, whereas the reverse is true in the large hornblende pyroxenite bodies at Klukwan, Snettisham, and Union Bay. The only unusual features of some of these bodies are the sporadic occurrence of large amounts of biotite or pyrite. They are almost invariably associated with gabbro and gabbroic pegmatite. Clinozoisite and/or epidote are also common.

D. Evidence for Ultramafic Magmas

1. General statement. Two major conclusions can be obtained from the above discussion (and will be elaborated upon in subsequent sections):

1. Differentiation in place by crystal fractionation of gabbroic magma is not an adequate explanation of the origin of the zoned ultramafic complexes, and they therefore must be the result of crystallization of ultramafic magma.
2. Magmas with approximately the composition of the several ultramafic rock types must have existed, and it is suggested that the zoned complexes were formed by a combination of fractional crystallization and multiple intrusion of these ultramafic magmas.

2. Relation between the gabbros and the ultramafic bodies. The evidence against the zoned ultramafic bodies having formed by fractional crystallization of the same magma which formed the adjacent gabbros can be summarized as follows:

1. The late-stage hornblende-anorthite pegmatite bodies are markedly more basic than the massive gabbro bodies associated with the ultramafic complexes; hence, the pegmatites could not be direct magmatic differentiates of the gabbro. The pegmatites almost certainly crystallized from a H_2O-rich residual magma, and their common association with the hornblende pyroxenite zones indicates they are probably related to this rock type.
2. Orthopyroxene has crystallized abundantly in the gabbros, but it is completely absent in the ultramafic rocks.
3. The gabbros are principally hypersthene gabbro, clinopyroxene gabbro, norite, and hornblende gabbro or hornblende diorite; olivine gabbro is only a rare variant and exhibits no spatial connection with the ultramafic rocks except at the Blashke Islands. In the latter occurrence, olivine pyroxenite abuts directly against gabbro and there has presumably been some olivinization of the gabbro by the ultramafic body.
4. No plagioclase occurs in any of the ultramafic rocks except in the marginal

portions of the hornblende pyroxenite zones. Even here it is very calcic or completely replaced by clinozoisite. This is evidence against there having been any interprecipitate gabbroic liquid.

5. Wherever age relationships can be clearly established, the gabbro is clearly older than the ultramafic body. These relationships are commonly obscured by saussuritization and by the presence of gabbroic pegmatite, which is invariably younger than either the gabbro or the ultramafic rocks.

6. Abundant evidence exists for metamorphism and metasomatism of the gabbro by the ultramafic body. This may include the introduction of H_2O, Ca, Fe, and Mg into the gabbro in the vicinity of the ultramafic contact. The gabbros have undergone anorthitization, hornblendization, and/or saussuritization from these emanations; they have been converted to epidote amphibolites (as at Union Bay and Klukwan) or to amphibolites (as at Duke Island), presumably depending upon the temperature and the activity of H_2O that prevailed during contact metasomatism.

7. Usually gabbro completely surrounds the ultramafic complexes, and at Duke Island gabbro forms the floor of the divine pyroxenite unit. These structural considerations are incompatible with the ultramafic complex having formed by crystal settling from gabbroic magma.

8. In several of the complexes in southeastern Alaska the quantity of gabbro is negligible compared to the volume of ultramafic rocks. This is not true of the zoned bodies in the Ural Mountains, which are embedded in very large gabbro massifs; nevertheless, the Uralian occurrences are the only ones which show clear-cut dikes of dunite cross-cutting gabbro (Vorobyeva, 1961).

9. The contacts between the ultramafic rocks and the gabbros are invariably sharp except where obscured by saussuritization; no real gradations between ultramafic rocks and gabbro are recognized, and no intermediate rock types exist. The magnetite-hornblende pyroxenite border zones are radically different in chemical composition (Table 4.5) from the gabbros, which are relatively common types.

10. The trend of chemical variation in the clinopyroxenes of the ultramafic complexes is shown in Fig. 4.11 and is very different from the trends observed during crystallization of gabbros. Also, the hornblendes (Table 4.2) are chemically distinct from those found in most diorites and gabbros.

11. Finally, direct evidence for the existence of ultramafic magmas can be cited, and such magmas could not have formed by fractional crystallization from gabbroic melts. This evidence is summarized below.

In conclusion, the ultramafic complexes in southeastern Alaska and in the Ural Mountains are invariably associated with relatively normal types of gabbros or gabbro-diorites. These gabbros appear to be older than the ultramafic bodies, and they were partially or largely consolidated before emplacement of the ultramafic rocks. The constant association of these rock types is obviously no accident, but there is no evidence, aside from the fact of their juxtaposition, that they were derived from a common magma. It is, however, conceivable that they are related to one another at depth, and they were clearly emplaced along similar zones of weakness in the crust during the early stages of the orogenic cycle. They represent a sequence of multiple intrusions in which the gabbros are seemingly always emplaced ahead of and earlier than the ultramafic bodies.

A further indication that the gabbros are essentially unrelated to the ultramafic bodies is given by the zoned complex at Tulameen, B.C. (Findlay, 1964). Here, the gabbroic complex into which the ultramafic rocks were emplaced includes mainly syenogabbro and syenodiorite. These are much more alkalic than the gabbros adjacent to the zoned ultramafic bodies in southeastern Alaska, but the ultramafic rock types and the zoning pattern are nearly identical in both areas. It is highly unlikely that such different gabbroic suites could give rise to ultramafic rocks that are so similar (Findlay, 1964).

3. Field evidence for magmatic emplacement. The best field evidence for the existence of a magma lies in demonstrating that minerals have accumulated from a liquid phase. The presence of structures and textures in an igneous rock that are elsewhere known to form only in a fluid medium provides almost unequivocal proof of magmatic crystallization. Just such structures are beautifully developed in the western ultramafic body on Duke Island (Irvine, 1959). The graded layering in olivine pyroxenite and peridotite, the fragments of earlier crystallized layered material, the unconformity separating the crystal accumulates of two compositionally distinct magmas, the basal conglomerate of olivine pyroxenite fragments above this angular unconformity, and the cross-bedding are all features that are indicative of sedimentation in a fluid medium (see Section II).

The olivine pyroxenite at Duke Island must therefore have formed by crystal settling from a silicate melt that was undergoing current motions of some type, perhaps convective overturn. What was the nature of this silicate melt? Reasons have just been given for dismissing the possibility that the olivine pyroxenites formed from a gabbroic melt, so the only suitable candidate would seem to be an ultrabasic melt of some kind. Rhythmically layered gabbros are common throughout the world, and they are thought to result from crystallization of gabbroic melt; so it is natural melt of some kind. Rhythmically layered olivine pyroxenite represents an accumulation from olivine pyroxenite magma. It should be noted here that a probable 12,000 feet of layered olivine pyroxenite at Duke Island exhibits very little change in chemical composition from bottom to top (Irvine, 1959). This is best explained by a process of simultaneous crystallization of olivine and pyroxene to form a rock with a chemical composition nearly identical to the magma itself.

Not only is the olivine pyroxenite at Duke Island relatively constant in chemical composition, it is very similar to the olivine pyroxenite units in other complexes (Table 4.3). The only suitable control for the constant mineralogical association in this rock type (15 to 20 per cent olivine, 70 to 80 per cent clinopyroxene) is a cotectic crystallization of these minerals. Even without the evidence of graded layering this would imply a magmatic origin for the olivine pyroxenites.

These arguments apply with equal force to the magnetite-hornblende pyroxenites. The similarity in chemical composition of this rock type throughout southeastern Alaska and the Ural Mountains (Table 4.5) suggests an origin by simple crystal-melt equilibria. The relatively constant ratio of abundance of magnetite to diopsidic augite (+ hornblende) suggests that these rocks were formed by cotectic crystallization of magnetite and pyroxene. Hornblende is almost invariably late to crystallize in these rock types, and it may in large part be deuteric in origin. Where hornblende is very rare, this rock type contains small amounts of olivine, suggesting simultaneous crystallization of diopsidic augite, magnetite, and olivine in the general proportions 75:20:5. This is a particularly common rock type (koswite) in the ultramafic bodies of the Ural Mountains.

Graded layers of magnetite-hornblende pyroxenite, with magnetite concentrated at the bottom of each layer, occur locally at Union Bay and at Duke Island. These are poorly developed, but they can reasonably be interpreted as having formed in the same manner as the graded layering in the olivine pyroxenite, namely by crystal settling from a magma that was simultaneously crystallizing magnetite and diopsidic augite. Such graded layers may have been common within the magnetite pyroxenite units at one time, but they would have been largely destroyed during the large-scale deuteric recrystallization that occurred in this rock type.

Other observations suggest a magmatic origin for the magnetite-hornblende pyroxenites.

1. Clear-cut dikes of this rock type can be seen to forcibly intrude gabbro; these are particularly well exposed at Klukwan, and there can be little doubt that they crystallized from a magma of roughly the same chemical composition as the dike rock itself.

2. The ultramafic bodies represent the only suitable source for the large amounts of H_2O that have been added to their adjacent gabbros during saussuritization and/or amphibolitization. It would be expected that H_2O might be liberated in large quantities during the later stages of crystallization of hornblende pyroxenite magma.

3. The late-stage gabbroic pegmatite dikes have all the attributes of a H_2O-rich, residual magmatic differentiate. Their common association with the hornblende pyroxenite zones suggests that they might be late differentiates of a pyroxenitic magma, as does the similarity in chemical composition of hornblendes from both rock types (Table 4.2).

It would be difficult to distinguish between rocks formed from peridotitic magma and rocks formed from dunitic magma, because any peridotitic melt would crystallize only olivine until the cotectic curve separating the fields of crystallization of clinopyroxene and olivine was reached. Large quantities of olivine crystals could accumulate at the bottom of a peridotitic magma chamber, thereby forming an almost pure dunite body. This may in fact be what has occurred in the parts of the dunite cores that exhibit graded layering of small amounts of pyroxene grains. However, it is also possible that the dunite cores represent emplacement of relatively pure dunite magma, perhaps with a high ratio of olivine crystals to liquid.

Cylindrical, pipe-shaped cores of dunite, all of very nearly the same size, occur at Union Bay, Annette Island, and the Blashke Islands. These may well represent the "feeders" through which the ultramafic magmas were transported. They contain the most magnesian olivine in the southeastern Alaska occurrences—Fo_{90}-Fo_{93}. Structural relationships indicate that these bodies are intrusive into the ultramafic complexes, and the occurrence of relatively unserpentinized, unstrained olivine indicates that they were intruded as a solid mass. Olivine in the dunite and peridotite from Duke Island and the Percy Islands is more iron-rich than the above, Fo_{80}-Fo_{85}, and these are more likely to be crystal accumulates from a peridotitic magma. Nonetheless, the dunite body in the eastern ultramafic complex on Duke Island cuts across folded layers in the adjacent olivine pyroxenite, and Irvine (1959) suggests that the intrusion of dunite may have caused this folding.

Replacement bodies of dunite transect olivine pyroxenite at Duke Island and these are explained as the result of emanations from a magma that is crystallizing olivine but not pyroxene (Irvine, 1959). Coarse-grained pyroxenite veins are interpreted to be material liberated from olivine pyroxenite by the dunitic replacement process. These veins are abundant in the olivine-bearing rocks of all the zoned complexes.

Irregular, cross-cutting bodies of dunite are common in all the large ultramafic complexes in southeastern Alaska. These may have been formed by a replacement process such as that just described, but this cannot be conclusively demonstrated because of the absence of primary graded layering. The alternating layers of nongraded dunite and olivine pyroxenite at Duke Island, the Percy Islands, and Union Bay could be of replacement origin, or they may represent crystal accumulates from a peridotitic magma that was periodically crystallizing on the olivine side of the olivine-clinopyroxene cotectic. The layers of dunite in the "structural peridotite" zone at Union Bay can also be interpreted as sills of dunite, however (Ruckmick and Noble, 1959).

Well-defined dikes of pyroxene dunite and peridotite cross-cut olivine pyroxenite in most of the zoned complexes, but this doesn't necessarily imply that magmas of such compositions existed. Some of these dikes at Duke Island contain highly deformed graded layering and were apparently intruded as plastic solids (Irvine, 1959), and others conceivably are of metasomatic origin. In any event these must have been derived ultimately from magmas that were richer in olivine than the olivine pyroxenite units. This is also suggested by the dunite dikes which are observed to cross-cut gabbro in the Uralian complexes.

4. Experimental phase equilibria on the join forsterite-diopside-iron oxide. In view of the field evidence for ultramafic magmas, it is useful to inquire into experimental studies of phase equilibria in chemical systems that are most analogous to the ultramafic rocks of the zoned complexes. The most useful recent study that is applicable here is that of Presnall (1966), and much of the following discussion is based upon this work. Presnall investigated the join forsterite-diopside-iron oxide at various oxygen fugacities under anhydrous conditions. This join is part of the five-component system CaO-MgO-FeO-Fe_2O_3-SiO_2, portions of which were previously studied by Bowen (1914), Bowen and Schairer (1933, 1935), Muan and Osborn (1956), Phillips and Muan (1959), Osborn and Muan (1960), and Kushiro and Schairer (1963).

The phase relations determined by Presnall (1966) at 0.21 atmospheres pressure of oxygen (i.e., in air) are given in Figs. 4.13 and 4.14. Note that the cotective curve separating the fields of primary crystallization of olivine and diopside trends across the diagram of Fig. 4.13 from a point where diopside and olivine form in the proportions of 89:11 (at 1389°C) to a reaction point where diopside, magnesioferrite (the magnetite equivalent), and olivine coexist in the proportions 76:22:2 (at 1299°C). The above proportions are given in weight per cent. These assemblages correspond very closely to two of the major rock types in the zoned ultramafic complexes, namely the olivine pyroxenites and the magnetite pyroxenites. The proportions of olivine are somewhat greater in the olivine pyroxenites than in the assemblage deduced from the equilibrium diagram, but Kushiro (1964a) has shown that crystallization at higher pressures shifts the olivine-diopside cotectic toward the olivine corner of the diagram. In addition, the natural assemblages probably formed at high H_2O pressures, and this would also change the shape of the diagram. Presnall (1966) has studied this system at oxygen fugacities down to 10^{-6} to 10^{-8} atmosphere, and the position of the cotectic curve shows almost no change from that given in Fig. 4.13.

Presnall (1966) traces the fractional crystallization path of a typical ultramafic magma, represented by the point *m* in Fig. 4.14. This point lies on the diopside-olivine-iron oxide join and has the chemical composition: SiO_2, 46.2 per cent; FeO, 13.0 per cent, MgO, 22.4 per cent, and CaO, 18.4 per cent. It would be analogous to a melt composed of about three parts olivine pyroxenite and one part magnetite pyroxenite (see Tables 4.3 and 4.5). Presnall (1966) states:

"Upon cooling, olivine rich in magnesium starts to precipitate at the liquidus temperature, about 1450°C. Olivine continues to precipitate as the composition of the liquid travels along the curved path *m-n* through the olivine primary phase volume. At point *n* (about 1330°C), diopside starts to crystallize along with olivine. With continued cooling and continuous removal of the crystalline phases, the composition of the liquid moves on the olivine-diopside boundary surface along the curved path *n-o* toward the univariant line *b-d*. At the same time, the compositions of the precipitating olivine and diopside become slightly

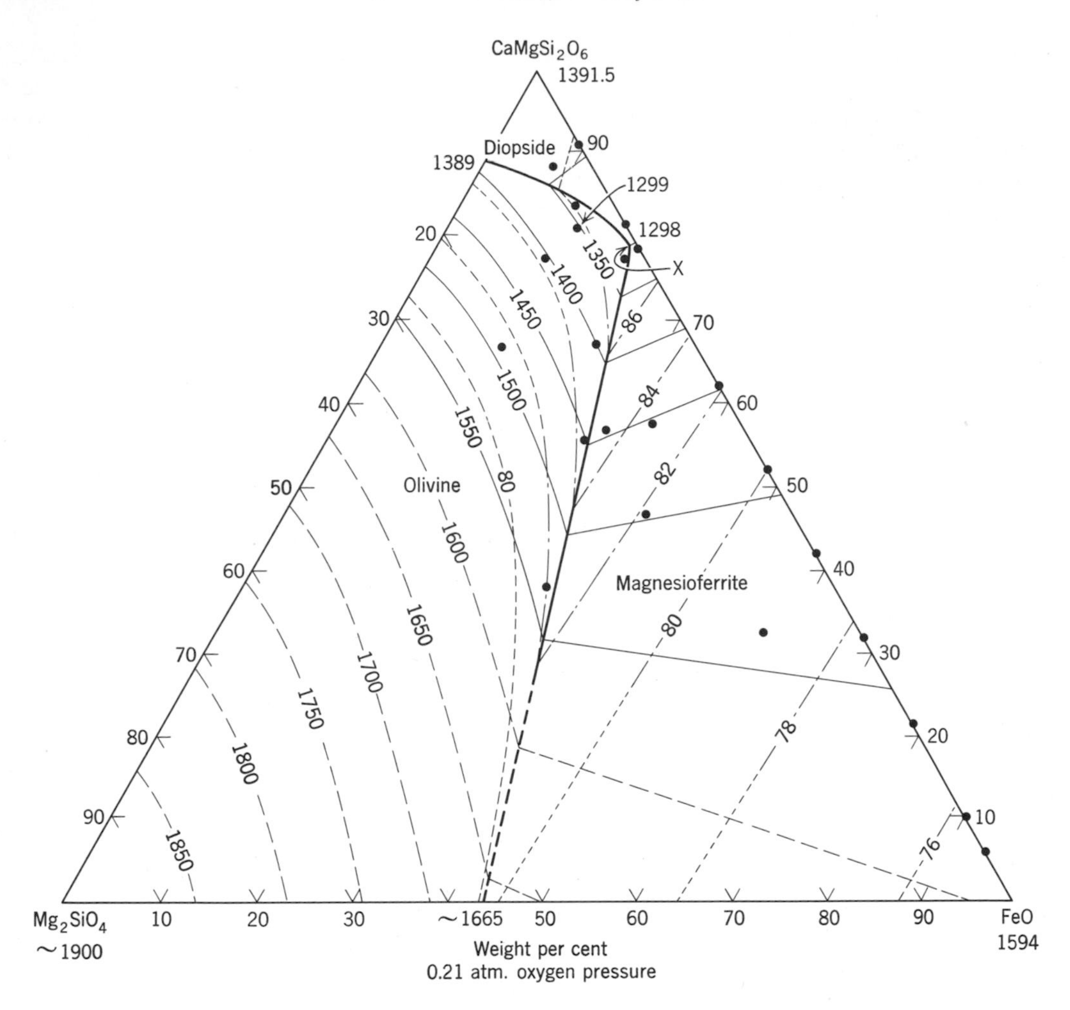

Fig. 4.13 The join forsterite-diopside-iron oxide at 0.21 atm. oxygen pressure. Medium lines separate the three primary phase fields, but they are not univariant lines, as the system is not ternary. Light lines are liquidus isotherms at intervals of 50°C. Light long and short dashed lines are contours of the quality $(Fe_2O_3)(100)/(FeO + Fe_2O_3)$ on the liquidus surface. This diagram is taken from Presnall (1966).

richer in iron. Just as the liquid reaches point *o* at about 1300°C, the composition of the precipitating olivine is close to point *y*. The composition of the diopside is unknown but it contains a small amount of iron and lies near the join $CaMgSi_2O_6$-$CaFeSi_2O_6$. Now, in the vicinity of point *x*, the line *b-d* is a reaction line along which olivine dissolves during equilibrium cooling, so with perfect fractional crystallization the liquid will not travel along this line but instead will move out along the path *o-p* in the surface *b-d-e* as diopside and magnesioferrite precipitate together. On continued cooling, the composition of the liquid moves beyond *p* to parts of the diagram in which no data have been collected.

If the precipitating crystals are assumed to acccumulate layer on layer at the bottom of a chamber without retaining any of the liquid phase in the pore spaces, then three mineral assemblages would be observed. Going from the bottom to the top of the sequence, these three assemblages and the approximate proportions of phases would be: olivine; 10 per cent olivine, 90 per cent diopside; and 20 per cent mag-

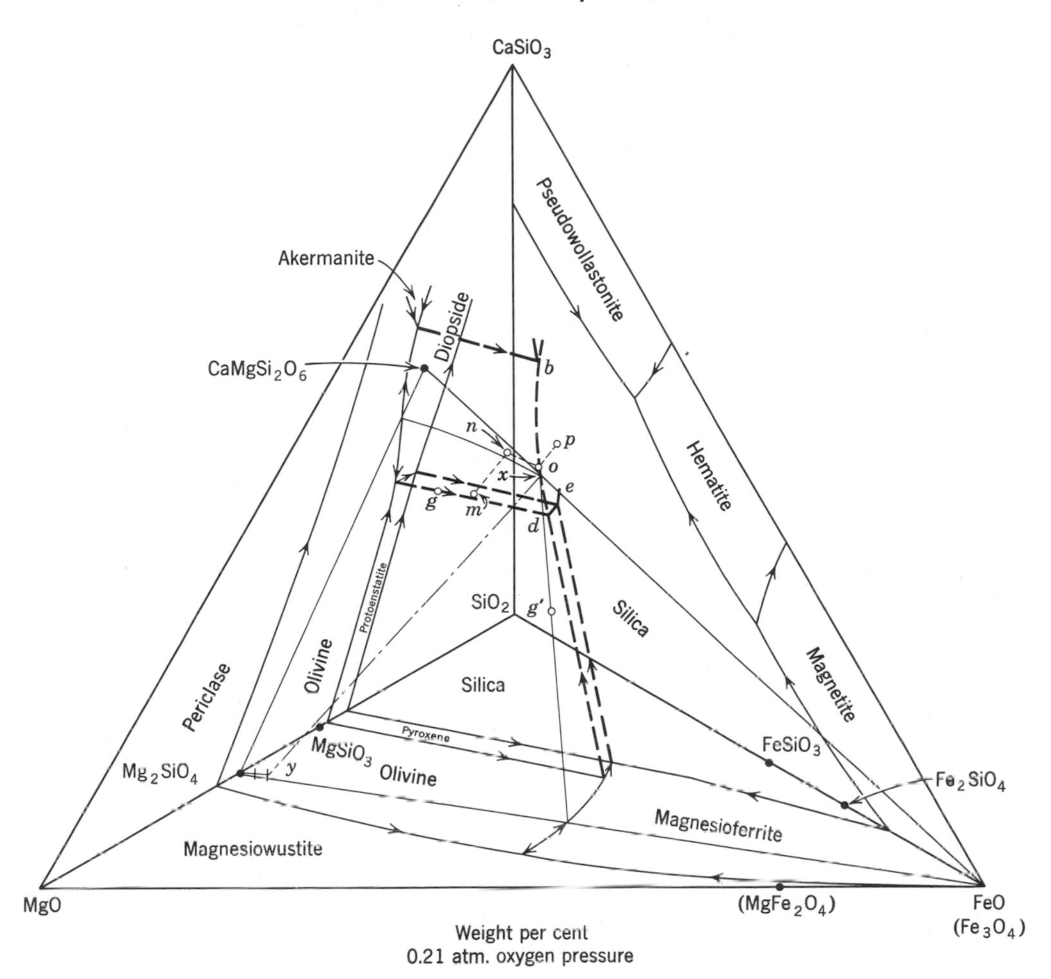

Fig. 4.14 The join $CaSiO_3$-MgO-iron oxide-SiO_2 at 0.21 atm. oxygen pressure. Medium lines in the faces of the tetrahedron are boundary curves on the liquidus surfaces with arrows pointing in directions of decreasing temperature. The join Mg_2SiO_4-$CaMgSi_2O_6$-iron oxide, outlined by light solid lines, is shown in detail in Fig. 4.13. Heavy dashed lines are univariant lines in the interior of the tetrahedron with arrows indicating directions of decreasing temperature. The dashed line *m-n-o-p* is a crystallization path described in the text. This diagram is taken from Presnall (1966).

nesioferrite, 80 per cent diopside. If 20 or 30 per cent of interprecipitate liquid is trapped and crystallized with the settled minerals, some transitional assemblages would be found."

This crystallization path was deduced for a system in which the oxygen fugacity is buffered. If the system is not buffered, the iron contents of olivine and pyroxene increase greatly as crystallization proceeds (Muan and Osborn, 1956), and this suggests that the lack of appreciable Fe-enrichment upward in the layered olivine pyroxenite at Duke Island might be due to crystallization at buffered values of the oxygen fugacity. Presnall (1966) suggests that buffering of the oxygen fugacity at a relatively constant H_2O/H_2 ratio might occur in a H_2O-rich magma by diffusion of hydrogen outward into the country rocks. Oxidation of the magma would then occur, magnetite would crystallize, and extreme iron-enrichment of the silicate minerals would be prevented.

The evidence of phase equilibria studies of appropriate silicate systems thus reinforces the field and mineralogical evidence that ultramafic magmas are responsible for the formation of zoned complexes in the ultramafic belts of the Ural Mountains and southeastern Alaska. The crystallization path outlined above can produce mineral assemblages that are closely analogous to the three most important rock types in the ultramafic complexes: dunites, olivine pyroxenites, and magnetite pyroxenites. The gabbroic pegmatites presumably would represent the latest differentiates in the above sequence, but there is no experimental study yet available which deals with the phase equilibria in ultramafic systems at the high H_2O pressures necessary to stabilize hornblende on the liquidus. The temperatures of crystallization quoted above probably would be lowered by at least 100°C in an ultramafic melt containing some Al_2O_3, TiO_2, and Na_2O which crystallized at high water pressures. Temperatures of 1200 to 1300°C are not unreasonable in the light of the pronounced contact metamorphic and metasomatic effects produced in the country rocks adjacent to the ultramafic complexes.

E. Origin of the Ultramafic Complexes

1. Problem of the zoning. If it were not for the unusual zonal arrangement of ultramafic rock types, a rather straightforward hypothesis of fractional crystallization would probably be accepted as an explanation of the chemical and mineralogical variations in the ultramafic bodies in southeastern Alaska and the Ural Mountains. We are faced with the problem of explaining why the ultramafic complexes appear to have crystallized from the center outwards. This obviously requires an unusual set of circumstances, and yet the mechanism must have been operative in essentially all of the zoned complexes. Various proposals have been made to solve these difficulties, and these are summarized in the following sections.

2. Reaction rim hypothesis. Wyssotsky (1913) and Zavaritsky (1928) proposed that the zoned complexes in the Urals were formed by intrusion of dunite magma into the earlier gabbro. The pyroxenites which surround the dunites were envisioned as gigantic reaction rims formed by the action of dunite magma on the gabbro, and the gabbro was thought to be partially melted by the dunite magma. In the light of the evidence given that the olivine pyroxenites and magnetite pyroxenites represent magmas of ultramafic composition, this hypothesis appears to be untenable. It is inconceivable that the dunite magmas contained enough superheat to liquify amounts of pyroxenite that are in some instances much greater in volume than the associated dunite. In addition, the ultramafic rocks are not always in contact with gabbro, yet the pyroxenite zones are still present.

3. Diffusion along temperature gradients in an ultramafic magma. Walton (1951) advocated intrusion of an H_2O-rich peridotitic magma to explain the formation of the Blashke Islands complex. Transfer of chemical constituents is supposed to have occurred along the temperature and concentration gradients set up between this magma and the surrounding rocks. Diffusion is thought to be rapid enough in the supercritical gas phase permeating the interstices of the nearly crystallized magma to allow large-scale transfer of Si, Ca, and H_2O outward and Mg inward. In addition, outward migration of volatiles to cooler regions of lower vapor pressure is thought to cause a bulk migration of dissolved solids. A quasi-steady state is envisioned in which olivine is stable in the hot core and crystallizes outward with cooling, while augite becomes the stable phase at the margins and crystallizes inward, replacing early-formed olivine.

This mechanism is essentially analogous

to the one suggested by Jahns (1955, 1956) and Jahns and Burnham (1961) to explain zoned granitic pegmatites that have monomineralic quartz cores and feldspar mantles. It is attractive because it would be operative in all the ultramafic complexes, as it is to a large extent independent of the attitude and structure of the complex and of its contacts with enclosing rocks. It provides a centripetal control rather than a gravity control on the magmatic differentiation. Nevertheless, this mechanism is considered untenable as a general explanation of the ultramafic zoning because:

1. It does not account for the existence of olivine pyroxenite and magnetite pyroxenite magmas, as the olivine pyroxenite zone would represent a replacement unit largely formed by solid-gas reactions.
2. Convective overturn is very likely in these magma chambers, and there is significant evidence of widespread current action in the olivine pyroxenite at Duke Island. These would upset the delicate gradients that are necessary for diffusion to proceed.
3. The chemical and mineralogical variations in the ultramafic rock types seem explicable in terms of simple crystal-melt phase equilibria. Note that in zoned granitic pegmatites the rock types *do not* correspond to plausible silicate melts, whereas in the zoned ultramafic complexes they certainly do.
4. There is much evidence that the ultramafic rock types accumulated in layers on the floors of their magma chambers, rather than crystallizing in the manner suggested by Walton (1951). Gravity has apparently played an important role.
5. If Walton's proposed mechanism is generally applicable, one wonders why no zone of magnetite pyroxenite is found at the Blashke Islands.

Although the major zoning of the ultramafic bodies probably cannot be explained by this hypothesis, it is likely that the distribution of hornblende in these complexes is controlled by some such mechanism. Hornblende is late to crystallize and the prevalence of pegmatitic textures suggests that an H_2O-rich gas phase had separated from the magma during these late stages. The H_2O would accumulate in the cooler portions of the ultramafic body (Kennedy, 1955) where it could deuterically interact with the magnetite pyroxenite unit to form hornblende, thus explaining the enrichment in hornblende that is observed at the margins of these complexes.

*4. **Flowage differentiation.*** The bronzite gabbro feeder dike of the Muskox intrusion (Smith, 1962a) contains a central zone that is highly enriched in olivine. Bhattacharji and Smith (1963) have suggested this may have been brought about by mechanical segregation of suspended olivine crystals away from the walls of the feeder simply as a result of upward movement of magma along the feeder. They have shown that this mechanism is effective in scale-model experiments, and such segregation is known to take place during the transport of solid-fluid mixtures in pipe lines (see Chapter 3-IV).

It is conceivable that this type of flowage differentiation could have been operative in the formation of zoned ultramafic bodies of the Ural-Alaskan type, but it clearly cannot be responsible for the major zoning pattern. If it has any applicability it might be in a situation such as occurs in the Blashke Islands, where a thin, cylindrical shell of olivine pyroxenite magma may have served as a lubricating layer between the walls of the pipelike feeder conduit and the central core of suspended olivine crystals. It is doubtful that the major zoning pattern at the Blashke Islands, however, is properly explained by a mechanism different from that invoked for the other ultramafic complexes.

*5. **Fractional crystallization.*** Simple fractional crystallization of ultramafic magma is the probable explanation of the late-stage hornblende-anorthite pegmatites, and it also obviously applies to features such as the upward gradation from peridotite through olivine pyroxenite in the western body at Duke Island. Any ultramafic complex in which presumed later differentiates lie structurally above the early ones (as the magnetite-hornblende pyroxenite zone in the western body at Duke Island) is readily explained by magmatic differentiation *in situ*.

A major problem exists, however, in a situation such as in the lopolithic portion of the Union Bay complex, where the supposed later differentiates (i.e., the magnetite pyroxenite unit) lie underneath olivine pyroxenite and peridotite. This is clearly at odds with normal mechanisms of fractional crystallization where crystals accumulate upward from the floor of a magma chamber, unless unusual phenomena are invoked. One very unusual feature of these complexes is the extreme Fe-enrichment in the hypothetical magnetite-pyroxenite magmas. These contain total Fe contents almost as high as the late-stage fayalite ferrogabbros of the Skaergaard intrusion (Wager and Deer, 1939). The average density of the magnetite pyroxenites is 3.6 to 3.7 g/cm^3, and the corresponding liquids must also have been quite dense. It is possible that such dense liquids could migrate to the bottom of a magma chamber and crystallize there, but it must be admitted that there is no independent evidence that this has happened. We can only speculate that dense, late-stage liquid differentiates might behave in unusual ways.

6. Multiple intrusions. The arrangement of ultramafic rock types in the zoned complexes is difficult, if not impossible to explain by any simple mechanism of fractional crystallization in place. This has led several workers to invoke a sequence of multiple intrusions to explain the ultramafic complexes and their associated gabbros (Ruckmick and Noble, 1959; Irvine, 1959; Taylor and Noble, 1960). Essentially all the observed field, chemical, and mineralogical relationships in these ultramafic bodies can be explained by successive intrusions of magma in the order: magnetite pyroxenite–olivine pyroxenite–peridotite and/or dunite. These magmas must be related to one another at depth, either through fractional crystallization in a deeper magma chamber or in the conduit itself, or by primary fractional fusion in their source region, presumably the upper mantle. It would be essentially impossible to distinguish between the results of fractional crystallization and fractional fusion by means of chemical or mineralogical data alone, as both processes can produce similar relationships among rock types.

On first consideration it might seem unlikely that a sequence of multiple intrusions would form in the same order in so many different localities, and this is in fact the only real argument that can be advanced against such a hypothesis. However, if the ultramafic magmas were formed by fusion in the upper mantle it is plausible that they might be generated in the above order, the lowest-melting fractions first. Also, it is not unreasonable to suppose that the magmas would find their way upward through the same conduit system. Several other lines of evidence form the basis for the multiple intrusion hypothesis:

1. The evidence for at least two separate intrusions in each of the complexes, namely of a gabbroic magma first, followed by ultramafic magma, is almost unequivocal. Gabbro would, in fact, be a likely early-melting fraction to form during fractional fusion in the mantle.

2. As already stated, the unconformity in the graded layering at Duke Island and the deformed layering surrounding the dunite core are practically indisputable evidence for at least a partial sequence of multiple intrusion of ultramafic magma. An olivine pyroxenite magma was injected, crystallized for an extended period of time, and then the magma chamber was invaded by a more magnesian, peridotitic magma (Irvine, 1959).

3. There is a marked variation in the

relative sizes of the ultramafic zones in the various complexes. Such variations are to be expected with a multiple intrusion origin, but are less easy to reconcile with a process of fractional crystallization of a single magma-type.

4. The different zones are rarely completely continuous and in some instances occur only sporadically or are missing altogether, even though their spatial arrangement is relatively constant. This can be explained as resulting from the irregularities that must accompany any sequence of multiple intrusion.

5. The macroscopically gradational contacts, commonly sharp and intrusive in detail, are readily explained by a process of successive intrusions of new magma into a chamber already occupied by another magma that is not completely crystallized. Contradictory age relationships among zones might be expected.

6. It seems unlikely that magnetite-hornblende pyroxenite (the most abundant and ubiquitous rock type) would all have formed by fractional crystallization of a more mafic magma. The large abundance of this rock type is better explained by its being the magma-type earliest and most readily formed (except for gabbro, of course) during fractional melting in the upper mantle.

7. The most magnesian olivine always seems to occur in the dunite cores. It is likely that the ultramafic magmas were transported up these pipelike conduits which are now almost wholly filled with dunite. The last magma to fill the conduit apparently was peridotitic or dunitic in composition, and structural relations generally indicate that it was intruded into the other olivine-bearing rocks of the ultramafic complex.

IV. THE ULTRABASIC VOLCANIC ASSEMBLAGE OF THE TROODOS MASSIF, CYPRUS

I. G. Cass

A. Introduction

Cyprus, an island of 3572 square miles lying in the northeast corner of the Mediterranean, is structurally divisible into three roughly parallel, east-west belts. These belts are gently convex to the south (Fig. 4.15) and from north to south are the Kyrenia range, the Mesaoria plain, and the Troodos mountains.

The Kyrenia range runs parallel to the north coast at an average distance of 5 miles inland and rises to elevations of over 3000 ft. This range, a segment of the outermost arc of the alpine chain, is markedly elongate, rarely more than 3 miles wide, and consists mainly of thrust slices of Permian to Cretaceous limestone. It is flanked by concurrent flysch deposits of Oligocene to Middle Miocene age.

The Mesaoria plain extends east-west across Cyprus and separates the upland areas of the Kyrenia range and the Troodos mountains. It is underlain by horizontally disposed Pliocene, Pleistocene and Recent sediments that completely mask the junction between the deformed flysch deposits of northern Cyprus and the undeformed contemporaneous sediments that flank the Troodos massif.

The Troodos mountains occupy a roughly oval area of some 900 square miles in the southern part of the island and rise to a maximum height of 6401 feet at Mount Olympus. The massif has a threefold, roughly annular structure: (a) the basic

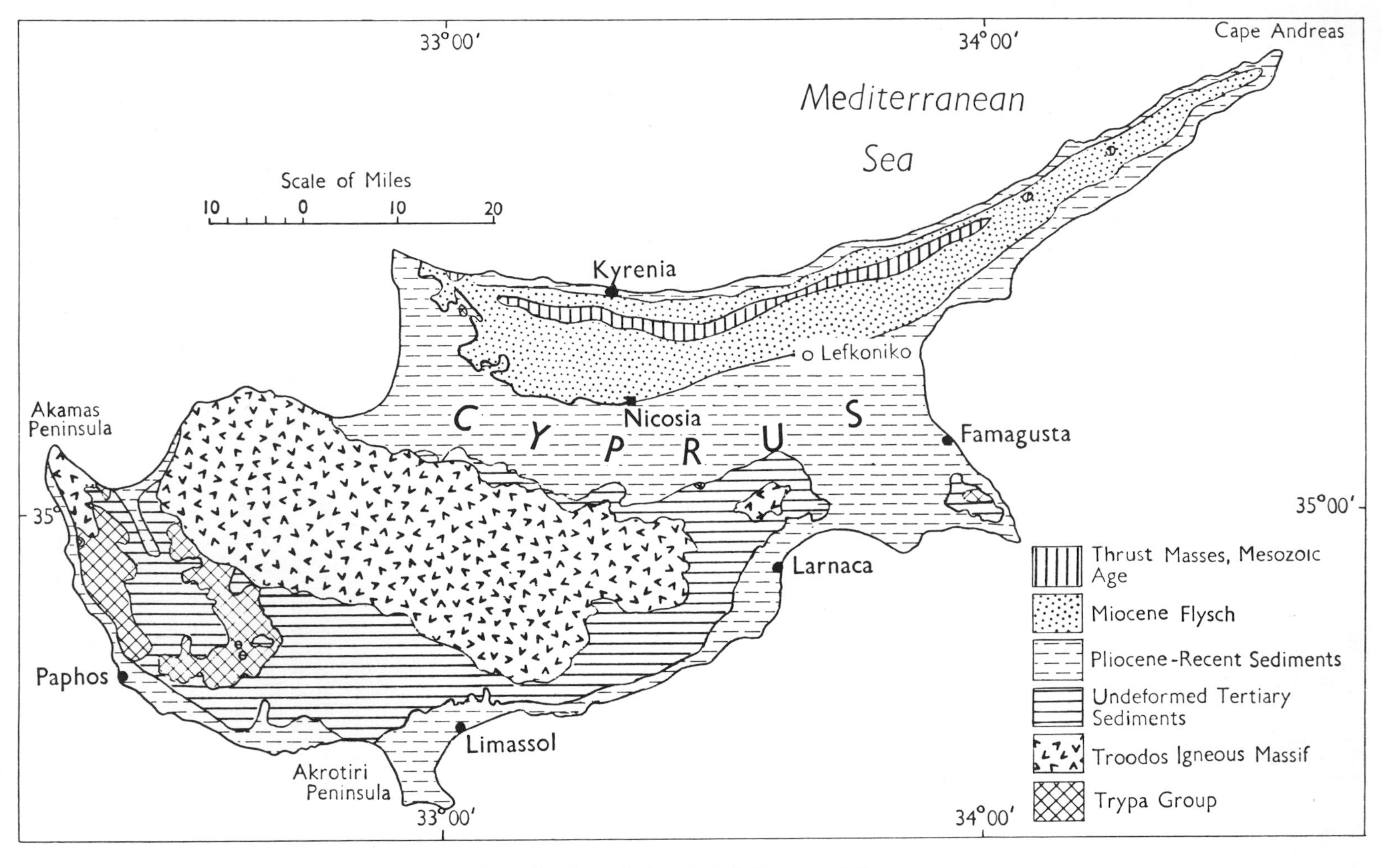

Fig. 4.15 The main lithological divisions of Cyprus.

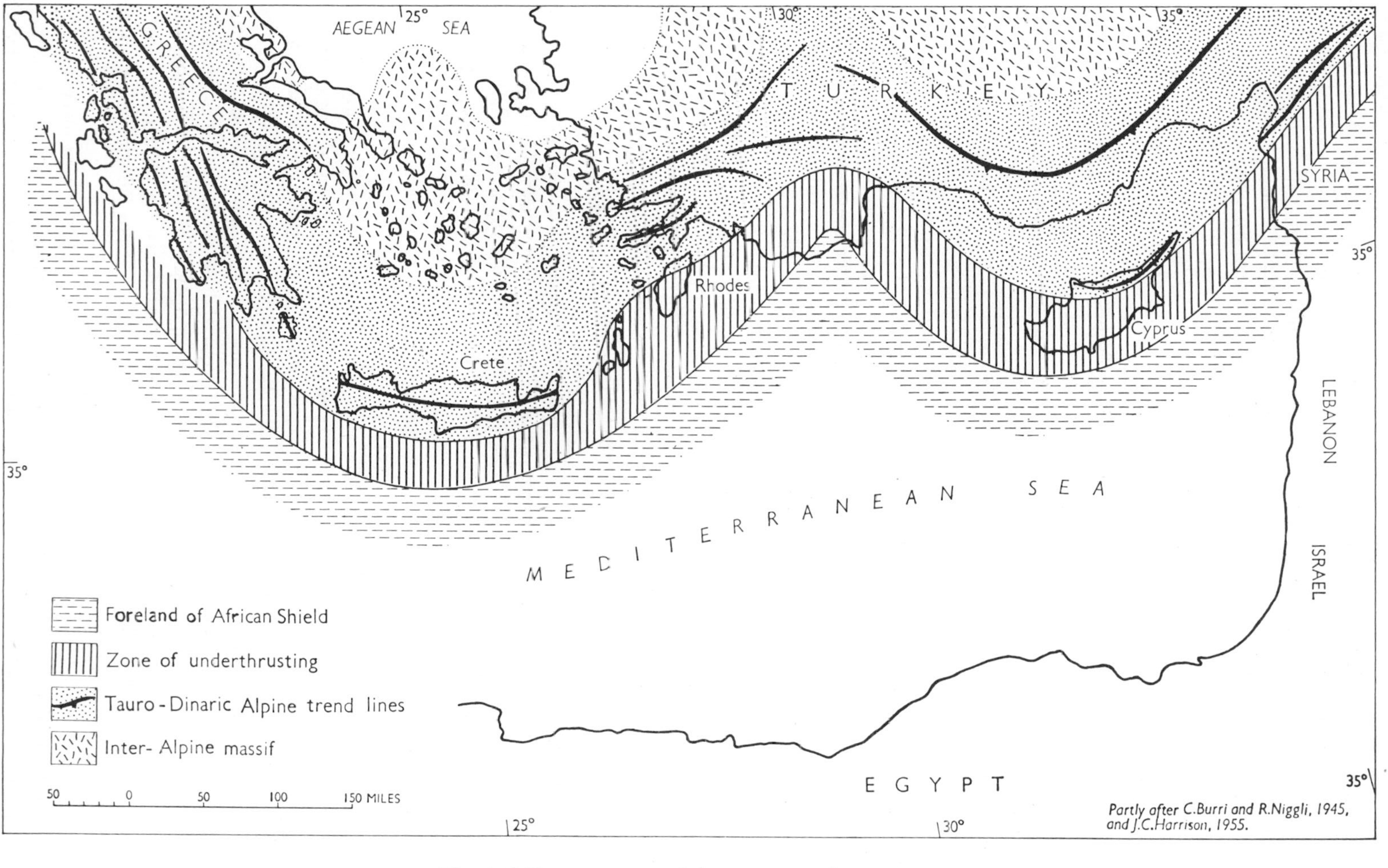

Fig. 4.16 Tectonic zones of the eastern Mediterranean.

and ultrabasic plutonic rocks which occur mainly in the centre of the range; (b) the Sheeted Intrusive Complex of basic, north-south dykes that forms the main part of the range; and (c) the peripheral lavas of the Troodos Pillow Lava Series (see Fig. 4.17). Partly surrounding the igneous massif are hills of Cretaceous to Miocene chalks; to the south this chalk cover has been partially removed to expose the structurally complex Triassic to Lower Cretaceous rocks of the Trypa group.

Excluding the tectonically complicated, and as yet mainly unsurveyed Trypa group, the overall structural picture of Cyprus is relatively simple. Broadly speaking, the Troodos igneous massif has acted as a rigid block against which the rocks of northern Cyprus were compressed by strong southerly alpine earth movements. The position of the Kyrenia range within the Tauro-Dinaric arc is depicted in Fig. 4.16. Both the Pliocene-Recent sediments of the Mesaoria plain and the extensive erosion surface formed during the Upper Miocene (Pontian) marine regression are undeformed, indicating that the latest orogenic movement in Cyprus was during the Lower and Middle Miocene.

One of the largest recorded positive gravity anomalies occurs over Cyprus. This anomaly is confined to Cyprus and the adjacent sea areas, the axis of maximum anomaly lying over the Troodos massif. Investigation of the anomaly indicates it to be due to an extensive slab of high-density rock, at least 7 miles thick, that underlies the Cyprus area at shallow depth.

Geological and geophysical evidence suggests that this slab was once part of the upper mantle underlying an oceanic area between the African and Eurasian continents. It will be suggested that when the continental shields approached each other during the Alpine orogeny, this slab of mantle was underthrust by the edge of the African shield and raised to its present level in the upper part of the crust by subsequent isostatic readjustment.

The following descriptions of the geology and gravity anomalies of the Troodos massif are based on an account by Gass and Masson-Smith (1963) which, in turn, drew heavily on official publications of the Cyprus Geological Survey.

B. The Geology of the Troodos Massif

The Troodos range is an igneous massif composed of basic and ultrabasic rocks of plutonic and extrusive character that fall into three main units: *the Sheeted Intrusive Complex; the Troodos Plutonic Complex;* and *the Troodos Pillow Lava Series.* The Sheeted Intrusive Complex forms the major part of the massif and consists of a swarm of steeply dipping, altered basic dykes with a dominant north-south trend. These near-vertical intrusions form over 90 per cent of the complex and are separated in places by thin screens of basic lava host rock. Emplaced into the Sheeted Intrusive Complex are rocks of the Troodos Plutonic Complex that range from dunite, through peridotites and olivine-gabbros to granophyres. The Troodos Pillow Lava Series appears to lie with marked unconformity on both the Sheeted Intrusive Complex and the Plutonic Complex. Throughout the series, which must be several thousands of feet thick, the extrusive rocks are all of basaltic composition and all show well-formed pillow structure.

1. The Sheeted Intrusive Complex. This complex is a huge series of near-vertical, basic dykes of regular attitude that are so closely packed that they present, in good exposures, a striking sheeted structure. The original host rock, which is of similar basic composition to the dykes, has been so disseminated by the intrusives that it now forms less than 10 per cent of the complex.

Intrusions of the complex vary in width from 1 to 15 feet and belong to two major phases; those genetically related to the complex and those that were feeder dykes to the overlying Pillow Lava Series. Two types of host rock are present: structureless lava in the lower levels of the complex and pillow lavas in the upper portion. Owing to the subsequent differential uplift centered on Mount Olympus, the lower portions of the complex are now exposed in the center of the massif, whereas the upper part occupies the periphery.

All rocks of this complex have been altered by saussuritization and attendant uralitization to a series that ranges with increasing alteration from keratophyres to epidosites. This alteration does not affect the feeder dykes of the Pillow Lava Series within the outcrop of the Sheeted Intrusive Complex.

Earlier workers, notably Bishopp (1952), considered the Sheeted Intrusive Complex to be a series of basic lava flows that had been compressed into isoclinal folds, undergone low-grade metamorphism and had subsequently been intruded *lit-par-lit* by numbers of basic dykes. Later, more detailed investigation revealed that the host rock has a near-horizontal disposition, that chilled margins are abundant, that volcanic features such as slaggy tops, flow structures, and lateritic boles are absent and that features such as cleavage and schistosity, expected in a series of tightly folded competent lavas, are lacking. These factors leave little doubt that the Sheeted Complex is intrusive in origin.

The Sheeted Intrusive Complex is therefore a north-south dyke swarm of unusual density in which the intrusions display a striking parallelism. Although repeated intrusive activity could be solely responsible for the unusual dyke density, there is evidence that the massif has suffered much erosion during and since its evolution. It is suggested, therefore, that this intense erosion has exposed the lower levels of the Troodos volcanic area in which intrusive material might be expected to predominate over extrusive rocks. It is perhaps significant that the only area known to me in which there is a dyke swarm of similar type and density is within a rift zone on Oahu, Hawaii (Stearns and Vaksvik, 1935).

2. The Troodos Plutonic Complex. Rocks of the Troodos Plutonic Complex range from dunite and peridotite through pyroxenite and olivine-gabbro to gabbro and granophyre. Field evidence suggests that this complex was emplaced after the formation of the Sheeted Intrusive Complex but before the extrusion of the Troodos Pillow Lava Series. No floor to the complex has been identified, there are no compositional changes towards the margins and the surrounding host rocks are not metamorphosed.

The largest outcrop of these rocks occupies a roughly oval area of about 200 square miles in the highest part of the mountains surrounding Mount Olympus. A further large area of basic and ultrabasic rocks crops out in the Limassol forest about 15 miles southeast of Mount Olympus (Fig. 4.17). Throughout the rest of the massif small isolated bosses of gabbro and granophyre belonging to this suite have been identified. A broad regional pattern can be discerned in that the rocks become more acidic proportionally with increasing distance from the central ultrabasic outcrop.

Ultrabasic rocks are well exposed on the summit of Troodos, where Wilson (1959), whose work is the most detailed so far published, divided them into three main groups: the *dunite,* the *enstatite-olivinite* and the *harzburgite-wehrlite* group. The dunites occupy a narrow, semicircular outcrop some 12 miles long and transgress the boundaries of the other members of the ultrabasic assemblage. They are markedly equigranular rocks, consisting of subhedral to anhedral grains of forsterite (Fa_8) between 1.0 and 2.0 mm in diameter that are invariably partly altered to antigorite. Enstatite-olivinite and its serpentinized equivalent bastite-serpentine are the most common rock types; there is no marked contact between the two, and serpentinization gradually increases from west to east. All have an allotriomorphic texture and contain between 70 and 85 per cent olivine and serpentine, the remainder being enstatite or bastite. The harzburgite-wehrlite group forms an incomplete transition zone between the central dunite and the surrounding gabbros; harzburgite forms the inner part, whereas wehrlite is more common nearer the gabbros. Olivine forms between 60 and 70 per cent of both rock types and occurs as poikilitic inclusions in a pyroxene host; in the harzburgites the host is enstatite, in the wehrlites it is diopside.

The main gabbro outcrop surrounds the ultrabasic rocks of Mount Olympus and extends eastwards, flanking the watershed for 12 miles. These rocks are also a common type in the plutonic complex of the Limassol forest. For descriptive purposes the gabbros have been divided into melagabbro, olivine-gabbro, gabbro and uralite-gabbro. No clear boundaries can be drawn between these types in the main outcrop and Wilson (1959) suggests that there is "a gradual transition outwards and upwards from the ultrabasic rocks through the more basic gabbros to the uralite-gabbro."

Developed locally within many of the ultrabasic rocks and the adjacent olivine and pyroxene-gabbros is a vertical or near-vertical mineral banding with a north-south orientation. On examination, this banding can be seen to be a vein-like concentration of olivine and pyroxene, the long axes of these minerals being in the direction of banding; individual bands vary in width from half an inch to a foot. The banding is especially prominent near the contact of the dunite with the other rock types of the ultrabasic assemblage. It is suggested that the banding was originally a mineral layering formed during a gravity differentiation process and that the subsequent reorientation was due to large-scale flowage of quasi-solid magmas, possibly when the area was tapped to provide the extrusive material of the Troodos Pillow Lava Series.

The distribution of the outcrops of this complex indicates that these plutonic rocks belong to a differentiated ultrabasic mass of batholithic dimensions. Differentiation has led to the upward and outward gradation from dunite and peridotite through melagabbro and olivine-gabbro to gabbro and granophyre. Field evidence suggests that the proportion of dunite and peridotite to the more acid differentiates increases markedly with depth and that the gabbros and more acidic members of the complex, although abundant at the surface, are, in fact, minor differentiates of a vast mass of ultrabasic material underlying Troodos.

In composition, and in the nature of the main rock types present, the Troodos plutonic complex is closely comparable to Thayer's (1960) "Alpine" type complexes. This comparison, it is suggested, indicates a similar parent magma, but not necessarily a similar tectonic setting. Many workers [Hess (1938, 1955), Noble and Taylor (1960) and others] have proposed that ultrabasic complexes within orogenic zones derive their parent magma from the upper mantle and that stresses present in these zones enable this ultrabasic material to be injected into the earth's crust. There is no evidence that orogenic forces were present during the evolution of the Troodos massif, but all evidence points to the upper mantle as the source of the Troodos Plutonic Complex magma.

3. The Troodos Pillow Lava Series. Forming an incomplete ring at the periphery of the massif is the Troodos Pillow Lava Series, a sequence of basaltic pillow lavas and their related intrusives. Wilson (1959) and Carr & Bear (1960) initially divided this series into an upper and lower division because of the presence of a partial unconformity and petrological differences in the rock types of the two units. It is not possible to estimate the thickness of the series with any degree of accuracy, but the Upper Pillow Lavas are between 200 and 1000 feet thick, whereas the lower division is probably between 2000 and 3000 feet thick.

In the Lower Pillow Lavas, extrusive and intrusive rocks are present in roughly equal proportions, extrusives consisting mainly of pillow lavas with very subordinate flow agglomerates, whereas intrusions include dykes, sills and irregular masses. Although they are mainly of basaltic composition, difficulties have been encountered in defining these rocks as the majority have a silica content of about 52 per cent, are low in alumina and high in magnesia. Mineralogically, the feldspars are about An_{50} in composition, the phenocrysts usually being labradorite, but the groundmass microlites are calcic andesine. Diopside is the main femic mineral and usually forms less than 40 per cent of the rock.

Dykes in the Upper Pillow Lavas form between 5 and 15 per cent of the outcrop and the extrusions are dominantly pillow lavas with occasional flow breccias and very rare tuff horizons. The rock types present are more basic than those in the lower division, with basalts, olivine-basalts and mugearites the most common; more basic lavas ranging from limburgites to oceanites exceptionally rich in forsterite (Fa_{8-10}) form up to 5 per cent of the sequence locally (Gass, 1958).

The evolution of the Pillow Lava Series was characterized by the gentle effusion of basaltic lava in a subaqueous environment. Treating the Pillow Lava Series as a whole and regarding the partial unconformity between the two units as a relatively localized phenomenon, it would appear that the series becomes progressively more basic with decreasing age. The general relationship can be well shown on a silica/oxide variation diagram of the pillow lava series on which the time relationship of the various rock types has been superimposed (Gass & Masson-Smith, Fig. 5, p. 438, 1963). It is postulated that partial fusion of an ultrabasic rock at low pressures would produce a liquid fraction of basaltic composition which would become increasingly basic as fusion became more complete.

Cutting the Pillow Lava Series and representing the final phase of volcanic activity associated with the Troodos massif, are minor intrusions of noritic affinities that are petrologically unlike the rocks of the series they invade.

Finally, serpentinites occur both within the Troodos massif and emplaced into the Lower Triassic rocks of the Trypa group of southwest Cyprus. It is evident from the field data that within the massif there are two types of serpentinite: one type originating from the alteration, *in situ*, of ultrabasic rocks by deuteric waters; the other type emplaced as serpentinite. The post Lower Triassic serpentinite of the Trypa group is associated with radiolarian sediments and sodic pillow lavas and represents the initial episode of igneous activity that accompanied the geosynclinal phase of the Alpine orogeny.

In considering the chemistry of the Troodos igneous rocks (analyses recorded in the Annual Reports of the Cyprus Geological Survey, 1955–1960) it is evident that the entire assemblage has a markedly tholeiitic character. For, although hypersthene is not a common modal mineral, it is present in the norms of all but three of the 33 analyses available, and two of these are rich in normative quartz. On the basis of their normative composition and using the divisions proposed by Yoder and Tilley (1962) the rocks are dominantly oversaturated tholeiites with olivine and saturated tholeiites common in the Plutonic Complex and the Upper Pillow Lavas. The tholeiitic character of the assemblage is substantiated when analyses are plotted on an alkali/silica diagram; 26 of the 33 specimens plot well within the tholeiite field found for Hawaiian rocks (Macdonald and Katsura, 1965). The seven analyses lying in the alkali basalt field all contain normative hypersthene and their position in the alkali field is undoubtedly due to secondary enrichment in alkalis, particularly soda. The tholeiitic affinity of the assemblage is emphasized further by the fact that the acid differentiates of the plutonic complex are of rhyolitic rather than trachytic or phonolitic composition.

The Troodos massif with a core of layered basic and ultrabasic plutonic rocks surrounded by dyke swarm of remarkable density and unconformably overlain by basic pillow lavas, represents a pre-Triassic volcanic pile of tholeiitic character that evolved in a subaqueous environment. Exceptional differential uplift centerd on Mount Olympus and resultant deep erosion have revealed the plutonic core and the deeper part of the volcanic mass where intrusive material predominates markedly over extrusive rocks. The extrusive pillow lavas, which once covered the whole of the mass, are now preserved as a relatively thin periphery where uplift and erosion have not been so intense. The plutonic complex is considered to have been formed from peridotitic material that was fused sufficiently so that gravity differentiation could operate to form the gradational layering exhibited and to provide the liquid phase to be extruded as the pillow lava series. In this connection, and recalling the markedly tholeiitic character of the assemblage, it is particularly significant that both Yoder and Tilley (1962) and Kushiro and Kuno (1963) indicate that tholeiitic magmas are generated at low pressures, a proposal endorsed by Reay and Harris (1964) who have produced tholeiitic liquids experimentally by the partial fusion of synthetic peridotite at atmospheric pressures.

C. Gravity Anomalies in Cyprus

Gravity measurements were first made in Cyprus by Mace in 1939. In 1946 a gravity survey of the eastern half of the island was undertaken for the Iraq Petroleum Company, and in 1958 the Overseas Geological Survey extended this to the rest of the island. The regional Bouguer anomaly map constructed from these surveys (Fig. 4.17) shows that Cyprus is covered with strong east-west positive anomaly mainly between 100 and 250 mgal, whose axis lies over the Troodos massif. This main anomaly falls off all round Cyprus to less than 100 mgal; elsewhere in the eastern Mediterranean the anomaly does not differ much from zero. Local smaller anomalies are superimposed upon the main anomaly.

A Bouguer anomaly is the difference between observed gravity and the value expected on the model earth which most closely represents the actual earth. In continental areas the mean density at the surface is about 2.7 g/cm^3. Non-zero Bouguer anomalies are therefore expected over areas where there are appreciable departures from this density in the near surface rocks. The present-day environment of Cyprus is intermediate between typical continental and oceanic conditions in that the surrounding Mediterranean is between 500 to 1000 fathoms deep. In this situation isostatic theory requires the crust to be sialic with a density of about 2.7 g/cm^3, but to be thinner than under typical continental areas. On this basis, the Sheeted Intrusive Complex and the Pillow Lava Series which make up most of the Troodos massif at the surface would not produce large anomalies unless present in very great thicknesses. It is assumed in the following interpretation that unaltered ultrabasic rocks of the Troodos Plutonic Complex with a mean density of 3.3 g/cm^3 produce positive anomalies and that the sediments (ρ = 2.40) and fully hydrated serpentine (ρ = 2.50) produce negative anomalies, whereas the Sheeted Intrusive Complex (ρ = 2.77) and Pillow Lava Series (ρ = 2.65) produce no anomaly.

Interpretation of a local negative anomaly over Mount Olympus indicates that under this highest part of the massif, where the ultrabasic rocks of the Troodos Plutonic Complex crop out, there exists a mass of low density material at least 6.5 miles thick (see shaded area on Fig. 4.18*a*). The density contrast between the low density mass and its surroundings required to produce the observed anomaly is 0.85 g/cm^3. In this geological setting, both the low- and the high-density rocks must be igneous. Although granite could be the low-density material, fully hydrated serpentine with a density of about 2.5 g/cm^3 seems more likely, both on geological grounds and also as the enclosing material would have the more acceptable density of 3.35 g/cm^3. Further, it is suggested that at

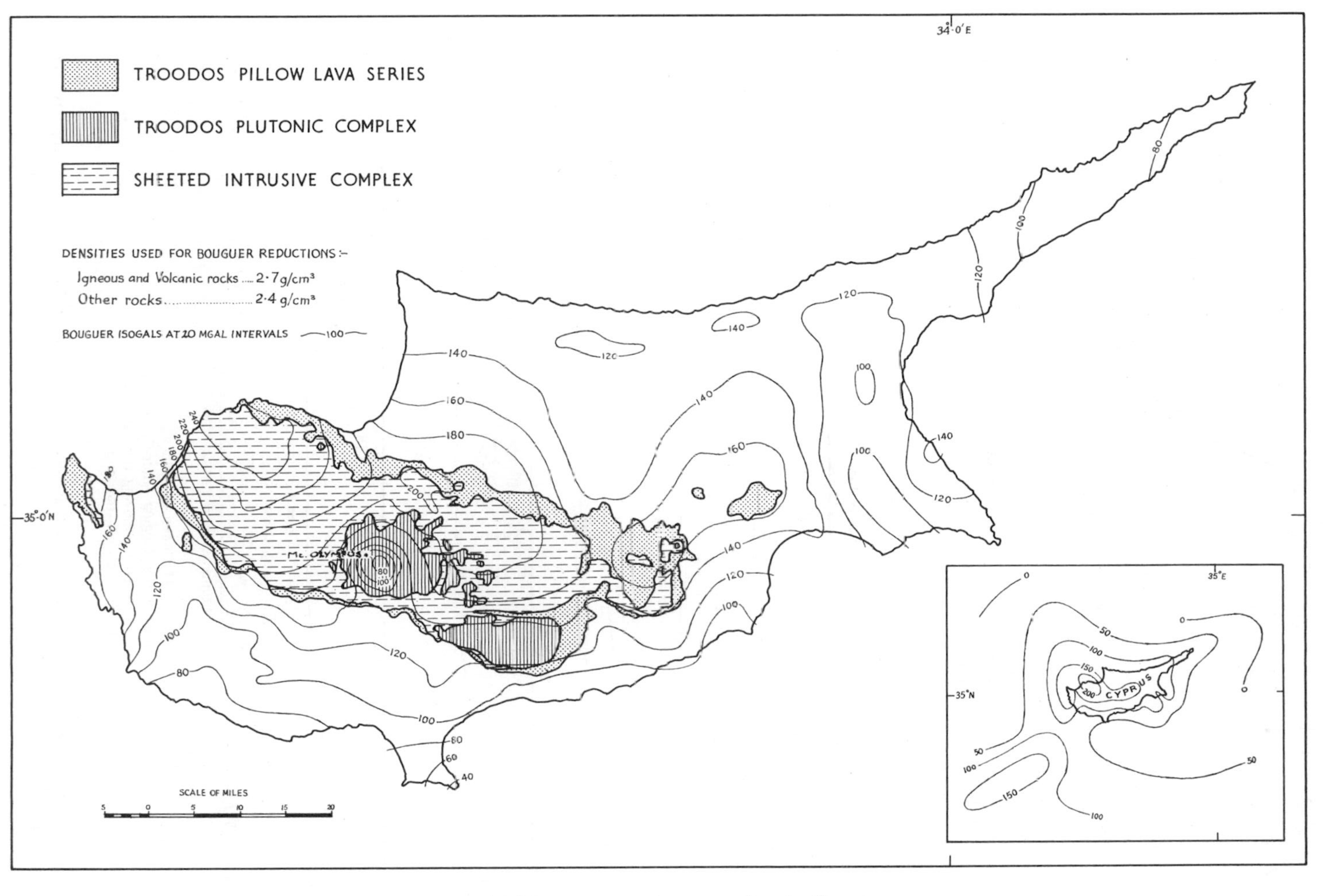

Fig. 4.17 Bouguer gravity anomalies in Cyprus.

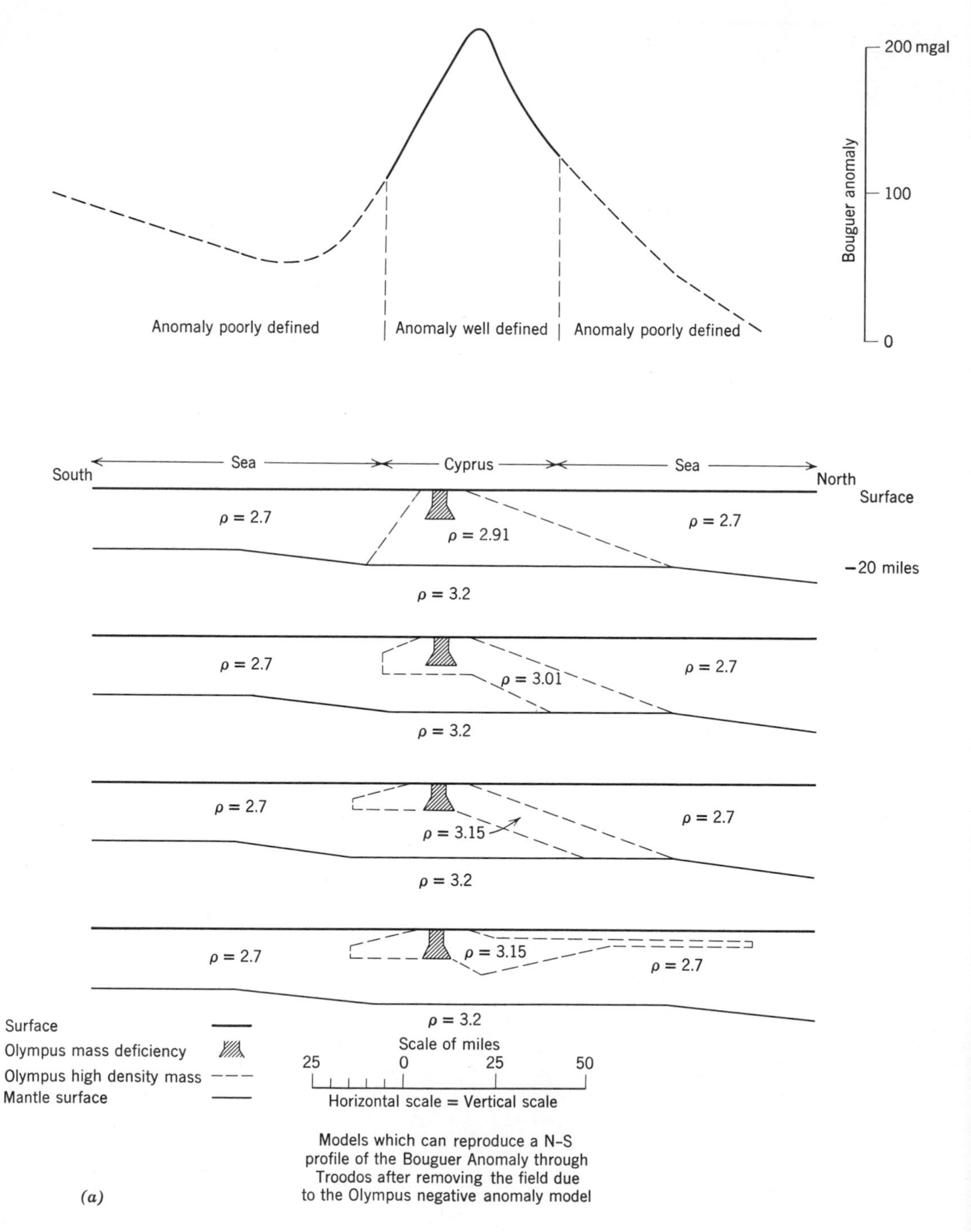

Fig. 4.18 Diagrammatic representation of stages in the underthrusting of Cyprus by the African shield.

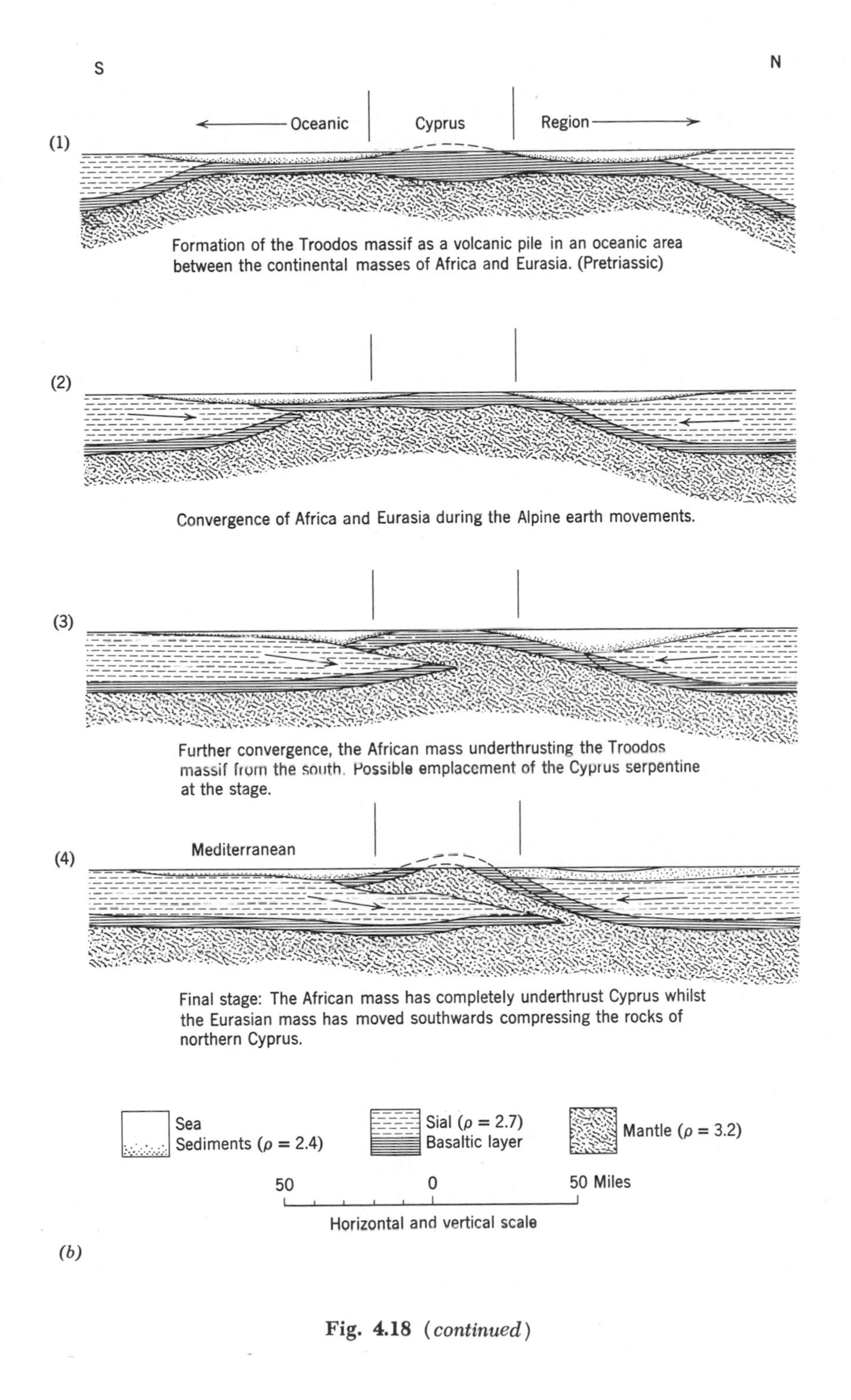

Fig. 4.18 (*continued*)

a depth of 7 miles the serpentine becomes unstable (Bowen & Tuttle, 1949; Yoder, 1952), thereby determining the lower limit of the low-density mass. This anomaly also shows that under Mount Olympus between 0.5 and 7 miles of the surface, there must be a layer of material whose density is greater than 3.3 g/cm^3; this layer may be thicker than 6.5 miles, but is certainly not thinner.

The high-density mass that causes the main positive anomaly is probably thickest about 20 miles northwest of Mount Olympus where the Bouguer anomaly reaches a maximum of over 250 mgal. In this area, the ultrabasic layer is not exposed, although it is probably within 2 miles of the surface, the lower surface of the high-density slab is calculated to be at a depth of 22 miles. The thickness of 20 miles assumes that the mean density of the ultrabasic slab is 3.3 g/cm^3 and that the enclosing crustal rocks have a density of 2.7 g/cm^3.

The limits imposed by the Olympus negative anomaly show that the slab is close to the surface around Olympus and at least 7 miles thick. The steady east-west trend of the isogals suggests that this thickness and depth is maintained for considerable distances to the east and west of Olympus. Figure 4.18*a* shows four models which could produce a north-south section of the main anomaly through Troodos. Although the cross sections may not represent the ultrabasic slab accurately in detail they should give a fairly reliable idea of its general distribution for the density limits given.

On the density data, only the third and fourth models are acceptable. Even the density of 3.15 g/cm^3 which corresponds to the thinnest possible slab of ultrabasic rock at Olympus is too low. This suggests that the main positive anomaly is superimposed on a regional negative anomaly. This is also suggested by the fact that Cyprus during the Cainozoic has been an area of considerable isostatic uplift when, with the large mass surplus indicated by the positive anomaly, isostatic downwarp would be expected. This could be explained if tectonic processes had produced crustal thickening in excess of that required to balance the mass surplus of the high density slab. Supplementary evidence is that within 150 and 200 miles of Cyprus the mean anomaly is −18 mgal which could be produced by a crustal thickening of 0.5 mile.

The gravity results indicate that the high density mass under Cyprus has a density of at least 3.3 g/cm^3, is a near-surface, rectangular, horizontal slab, 120 miles east-west, 70 miles north-south and at least 7 miles thick and that the minimum crustal thickening in excess of that required to produce isostatic compensation is 1.5 miles. A thicker high-density slab with a greater crustal thickening would still be consistent with the gravity evidence.

D. Conclusions

Field and petrographic data, already discussed, show the Troodos massif to be the eroded remnant of a basic volcanic pile of tholeiitic affinities that formed in a subaqueous environment in pre-Triassic times. It now remains to correlate the gravity data with the geological evidence to deduce the structural evolution of the area.

The gravity evidence shows that Cyprus is underlain at a shallow depth by an extensive layer of high-density material. The thickness of this layer is at least 7 miles and its density at least 3.3 g/cm^3. Evidence of regional isostatic equilibrium shows that this high-density layer is separated from the mantle proper by a sialic layer of lower density. These results are quite definite. The gravity field also gives an approximate margin for the high-density layer, showing that it underlies the whole of Cyprus with small extensions under the sea. The spaceform of the ultrabasic layer is clearly not batholithic in the sense that it occupies the whole thickness of the crust. On density evidence it would seem that the high-density layer is dominantly of peridotitic composition and petrological and field data leave little doubt that it can be correlated with the Troodos Plutonic Complex.

It is evident from the north-south structures within the massif that east-west tensional stress was dominant throughout its evolution. Although no direct evidence is available, the structure, particularly of the Sheeted Intrusive Complex, is of the type that could be formed on the crest of a mid-ocean ridge where diverging convection cells in the mantle would produce crustal tension. So, it is possible that the Troodos massif represents a volcanic edifice formed on the median ridge of Tethys when that marine area had many other features of present day ocean basins.

Argand (1922) and Blumenthal (1941) indicate that during the Alpine orogeny, the Eurasian hinterland was moving south in relation to the African shield and that during this movement the African shield underthrust Eurasia in places. It seems likely, therefore, that prior to the Alpine movements, the noncontinental area between Africa and Eurasia, especially in the eastern Mediterranean, was wider than at the present time. Indeed, it has been suggested (Bishopp, 1952) that the Troodos massif might represent a volcanic pile which developed in an oceanic region, between the continental masses of Africa and Eurasia where the sialic crust was not present; this undoubtedly would explain the major features of the massif. In agreement with Bishopp's broad concept, it is proposed that the Troodos massif evolved in pre-Triassic times as a volcanic pile in an oceanic environment. The fact that the rocks of the Troodos igneous suite are limited to the Cyprus area could be explained as indicating the size of the original volcanic area. Furthermore, the east-west tensional stress dominant throughout the evolution of the massif would allow partial fusion of the upper mantle in a low-pressure regime and thus provide the basic to ultrabasic tholeiitic material of which the massif is composed. Finally, an oceanic setting would account for the pillowed nature of the extrusives and also for the rarity of sedimentary deposits.

Having postulated that Troodos evolved as a volcanic pile in an oceanic setting, a mechanism must now be sought to explain the presence of sialic crust under Cyprus. During the Alpine orogeny, the two continental masses of Africa and Eurasia converged one upon the other to such an extent that the African foreland underthrust the Eurasian hinterland (Fig. 4.16). It is suggested that during these earth movements the African foreland underthrust the Troodos massif at such a depth that part of the upper mantle was also detached by the thrust. Stages in this movement are diagrammatically represented in Fig. 4.18*b*.

Harrison (1955) gives geophysical evidence why sialic crust must exist under Cyprus. In explaining the arcuate zone of negative gravity anomaly in the eastern Mediterranean, he suggests that the sialic crust fractured in an east-west direction along a plane inclined to the north at 45° and that the southern section of the crust was pushed under the northern section (Harrison, 1955, Fig. 15, p. 305). The mechanism proposed by Harrison is essentially similar to that envisaged here, with the exception that movement of two separate masses is postulated rather than the fracturing of a layer of uniform thickness.

Underthrusting of continental Eurasia by the African shield would result in crustal thickening in the zone of underthrusting and would explain the regional negative gravity anomaly in the eastern Mediterranean and also why eustatic uplift is dominant in the area as a result of isostatic adjustment. The emplacement of a mass of low-density material under Mount Olympus further disturbed the isostatic balance and initiated differential uplift. Factual evidence is provided by de Vaumas (1960) who has shown that the summit of the massif has been elevated by some 10,000 feet since Cretaceous times whereas the rest of the island has risen only some 2000 feet.

In summary, geological and geophysical evidence suggests that the Troodos massif evolved in pre-Triassic times as an oceanic volcanic pile situated between the then more widely spaced continental masses of Africa and Eurasia. During the Alpine orogeny, these continental masses converged, the southern mass underthrusting the Troodos volcanic pile, and parts of the Eurasian hinterland. The underthrusting took place at such a level that not only the volcanic pile, but also part of the upper mantle was uplifted above sea level as an undeformed slice during subsequent isostatic adjustment. Intense erosion has denuded the volcanic pile almost to its roots. It is thought, therefore, that the Troodos Plutonic Complex might represent upper mantle material, partly fused and differentiated *in situ,* to provide the volcanic rocks of the massif.

5. *Alpine Type Ultramafic Associations*

I. INTRODUCTION

P. J. Wyllie

Many rocks of the alpine-type peridotite-serpentinite association, occurring in folded geosynclinal sediments of orogenic belts, have had a complex history. Their early history may be obscured by deformation and metamorphism, which accounts for the uncertainty and controversy about their origin. It has been proposed that they are formed by crystal settling from basaltic magma, either at depth in stratiform complexes or in submarine lava flows; that they have crystallized from ultrabasic magmas; that they are intrusions of solid, primitive mantle material, or of residual mantle material remaining after removal of a basaltic fraction; or that they represent fragments of the oceanic crust incorporated into orogenic belts by mantle convection currents. They have been involved in orogenic deformation to varying degrees with metamorphism causing changes in mineral facies. Most of the peridotites are at least partly altered and many are bordered by a sheath of serpentinite. Later alteration may produce asbestos, talc, or carbonate minerals. The lack of significant thermal metamorphism around most alpine intrusions may be due to late tectonic emplacement of largely crystalline masses. Tectonic migration of serpentinite masses along fault zones can lead eventually to surface extrusion of serpentinite breccias by plastic flow (Dickinson, 1966). Despite their variability, alpine-type ultramafic associations have characteristic features reviewed by Thayer in Chapter 7-IV-A.

The rocks of this association are described in Chapters 5, 6, and 7. The first contribution by Jahns, in Chapter 5-II, is a detailed account of a specific group of serpentinites which introduces many of the problems involved in this association and indicates several of the approaches used to study them. The final contribution by Thayer in Chapter 7-IV is a review of many occurrences of the alpine association, with special reference to structure, chemistry, and origin. Thayer emphasizes that the ultramafic rocks should not be considered apart from the gabbros, basic volcanic rocks, diorites, and granophyres of the plutonic calc-alkali magma series, and he refers to the whole series as the alpine mafic magma stem. Between these two contributions there are articles dealing with specific types of intrusions, as in Chapter 5, or with specific problems related to one or more intrusions. Chapter 6 deals largely with deformational features of ultramafic bodies and the enclosing metamorphic rocks, and Chapter 7 deals mainly with processes or with the conditions of formation of the ultramafic rocks. Sections A, B-1, and E of Thayer's Chapter

7-IV should be considered as an introduction to this set of three chapters.

In Section II of this chapter Jahns describes the serpentinites of Vermont, which occur in regionally metamorphosed rocks of greenschist and epidote-amphibolite facies within the Appalachian ultramafic belt. The structure, petrography, and mineralogy of the small serpentinite bodies are located within the framework of the regional geology, structure, deformation and metamorphism. This permits deduction of the history of the region and in particular the sequence of events related to the origin and emplacement of the serpentinite bodies. The ultramafic rocks are tectonically emplaced masses of crystalline serpentinite, perhaps derived from upward-moving olivine-rich rocks, with their emplacement broadly controlled by the country rock structure and with a marked preference for greenstone layers. Steatitization was later than serpentinization; Jahns has worked out a detailed plan for the migration of elements and lithologic boundaries in the metasomatic process of formation of the talc-bearing rocks.

In Section III Ragan describes the Twin Sisters dunite in the Washington Cascades, which has an outcrop area of 90 square km. This dunite, in contrast to the Vermont rocks, is unaltered except for a marginal zone of serpentinite of variable width, 50 to 700 meters, which formed late in the intrusive history. The dunite is intrusive into thrust plates in low grade metamorphic rocks. Ragan concludes that the macroscopic and microscopic structures of the dunite are consistent with its intrusion and flow as essentially solid material rather than as a crystal mush.

In Section IV O'Hara describes the garnet-peridotites occurring among gneisses and schists of amphibolite or hornblende granulite metamorphic facies. A similar group of rocks is described by Lappin in Chapter 6-III. These are apparently restricted to rocks of Europe metamorphosed during the Caledonian orogeny and, according to O'Hara, their chemical mineralogy distinguishes them from the xenolithic garnet peridotites and eclogites of kimberlite pipes, a conclusion challenged by Davidson in Chapter 10-IV. O'Hara cites evidence for tectonic emplacement of the rocks following a complex magmatic and metamorphic history. He also discusses the spinel-lherzolites of the Pyrenees which are chemically distinct from the other alpine-type peridotites and from lherzolite nodules in basalts (Chapter 10).

Other types of alpine ultramafic rocks were classified in Chapter 1-I-B-4, and of these the high temperature group (4) is described by Green in Chapter 7-III, the metasomatic-metamorphic rocks of group 6 are described by Sørensen in Chapter 7-II, and the ophiolite suite (1) is discussed by Sørensen in Chapter 7-II-C-1, and by Thayer in Chapter 7-IV-B-5. It has already been noted that the Troodos plutonic complex described by Gass in Chapter 4-IV has features of the alpine association. The geochemistry of alpine ultramafic intrusions receives special attention in Chapter 11, and the results of recent geochemical studies have considerable bearing on the origin of these rocks. Only one item from Chapter 11 will be mentioned here. Taylor, in Chapter 11-III-B-5, states that serpentinization of peridotites has apparently occurred without changing the isotopic composition of oxygen. This suggests that much serpentine forms by simple addition of H_2O to the peridotite without appreciable oxygen exchange with adjacent parts of the crust. Furthermore, this H_2O must have an oxygen isotope ratio similar to that of the ultramafic mass itself, which essentially eliminates meteoric water as a possibility, except under exceptional circumstances.

II. SERPENTINITES OF THE ROXBURY DISTRICT, VERMONT

Richard H. Jahns

A. Introduction

The serpentinites of central Vermont lie within the Appalachian ultramafic belt, which comprises hundreds of discrete intrusive bodies in the eastern United States and Canada. These ultramafic bodies are good examples of the "alpine type" (cf. Benson, 1926, p. 6; Wilkinson, 1953; Hess, 1955; Thayer, 1960; Turner and Verhoogen, 1960, pp. 307–311), and characteristically occur in folded and metamorphosed eugeosynclinal sediments of Paleozoic age. They range from small sills and concordant or partly concordant lenses to thickly bulbous and irregularly tabular masses with maximum dimensions measured in miles. All are very small, however, as compared with the dimensions of the entire belt, which is at least 10 miles in average breadth, extends for a distance of 1800 miles from Alabama to Newfoundland, and has a sinuous but prevailingly northeastward trend that reflects the ancient folded structure of the host terrane.

The most abundant and widespread rock types are peridotites, dunites, pyroxenites, and various alteration products of these ultrabasic plutonites. Their primary mineralogy is simple, with magnesian olivine the predominant constituent. Enstatite is locally abundant, and augite is known from a few localities. The only consistently occurring accessories are minerals of the spinel group. Quartz, feldspars, amphiboles, and micas ordinarily are rare or absent.

Most of the ultrabasic rocks have been partly serpentinized, and such alteration has been essentially complete in some of them. Also widespread are the products of steatitization, chiefly talc and carbonate minerals accompanied by various combinations of amphiboles, chlorite, epidotes, garnet, albite, muscovite, apatite, magnetite and ilmenite, rutile, sphene, tourmaline, zircon, pyrite, and pyrrhotite. Owing to numerous differences in kind and degree of alteration, the ultramafic bodies encompass a considerable range of rock types. Some of them have been little altered, some represent serpentinization without steatitization or steatitization without serpentinization, and many show effects of both these processes.

Mining operations within the Appalachian belt have yielded a correspondingly wide range of commercial materials, including olivine, chrysotile asbestos, talc and soapstone, and serpentinites suitable for certain dimension-stone uses. Dominating the last-named category is verd antique, which consists of relatively massive serpentinite that is irregularly traversed by numerous thin veins of finely to coarsely crystalline carbonate minerals. In all known occurrences the carbonate veins are genetically related to nearby concentrations of talc rather than directly to the host serpentinite; thus this rock type is a composite in terms of origin.

The serpentinites of the Roxbury district, in central Vermont, were discovered in 1848 and for more than a century have been worked intermittently for verd antique. They lie on the east side of the Northfield Mountains and low on the west side of the Roxbury valley near the divide between the Dog River and Third Branch of the White River. Quarrying operations and exploratory drilling have provided unusually complete three-dimensional information for the largest of the ultramafic bodies and their internal lithologic units, and the paragenetic relationships among minerals and contrasting rock types can be deciphered from numerous outcrops, quarry exposures, and large blocks on the quarry dumps.

The published record includes no detailed geologic maps and only two systematic descriptions of the Roxbury serpentinites (Jacobs, 1916; Richardson, 1918), but many of the occurrences were carefully studied by Hess (1933) and Bain (1936) in their researches on serpentinization and steatitization. Several other published discussions, based mainly upon investigations elsewhere in Vermont or in eastern Canada, also are pertinent to the Roxbury district (e.g., Jacobs, 1914; Wigglesworth, 1916; Benson, 1918; Gillson, 1927; Phillips and Hess, 1936); special attention should be drawn to a more recent and extremely detailed report by Chidester (1962), which deals with partly steatitized serpentinites in the Waterbury-Waitsfield area 10 to 30 miles north of Roxbury.

B. Regional Geologic Setting

1. General relationships. The Roxbury serpentinites lie within a very thick, steeply dipping, homoclinal sequence of metamorphosed sedimentary and volcanic rocks. This stratified section forms the east limb of the Green Mountain arch, a large anticlinorium that traverses the entire length of the state with typical broadly sinuous Appalachian trend (Fig. 5.1). In the southern half of the state metamorphic rocks of Precambrian age are exposed in the core of this major fold; farther north, at and beyond the latitude of Roxbury, schists and gneisses of Cambrian age are exposed along the anticlinorial axis, and are succeeded eastward by progressively younger Paleozoic formations. Within this part of Vermont the northerly trending regional structure is little complicated by folds, and no faults of substantial displacement appear to be present. The grossly simple pattern of the homoclinal sequence persists eastward to points at least seven miles up-section from the stratigraphic horizon at Roxbury, beyond which it reflects the presence of major folds (White and Jahns, 1950; Chidester, 1962, p. 7).

Table 5.1 shows the succession of rock units that have been recognized in central Vermont. The trace of the thin Shaw Mountain formation (Currier and Jahns, 1941), which lies east of Roxbury, marks a regional boundary between slates, phyllites, and arenaceous limestones of probable Silurian and Devonian ages on the east and schists, phyllites, quartzites, slates, and marbles of Cambrian and Ordovician ages on the west (Fig. 5.1). All known bodies of ultramafic rocks in Vermont lie west of this boundary, and they commonly have been assigned an Ordovician age because of their absence from the younger terrane (Table 5.1).

Other kinds of igneous rocks, in contrast, are more widely distributed. Numerous tabular masses of greenstone, chlorite schist, and amphibolite, representing sills, dikes, flows, agglomerates, and tuffaceous layers of original andesitic and basaltic composition, occur in the Cambrian and Ordovician rocks and locally constitute substantial percentages of the section. The mafic rocks also appear as dikes and sills in the Gile Mountain formation farther east (White and Jahns, 1950, p. 194; Billings and White, 1950), and hence are in part as young as Devonian.

Intrusive bodies of granitic rocks are found throughout most of the section, but they are relatively larger and more abundant within the post-Shaw Mountain formations (Fig. 5.1); nearly all of them are regarded as Devonian in age. The occurrences include the well-known commercial granites of the Barre, Woodbury, and Bethel districts. Those nearest Roxbury are two small elongate stocks and associated dikes four miles to the north-northeast and a much larger composite pluton of granite and slightly older dioritic rocks about five miles to the south (White and Jahns, 1950, p. 193–195). The granites and all older rocks are transected by steeply dipping dikes and sills of unmetamorphosed diabase and lamprophyre, which are late Paleozoic or early Mesozoic in age.

2. Deformation and metamorphism. The entire sedimentary section, along with the

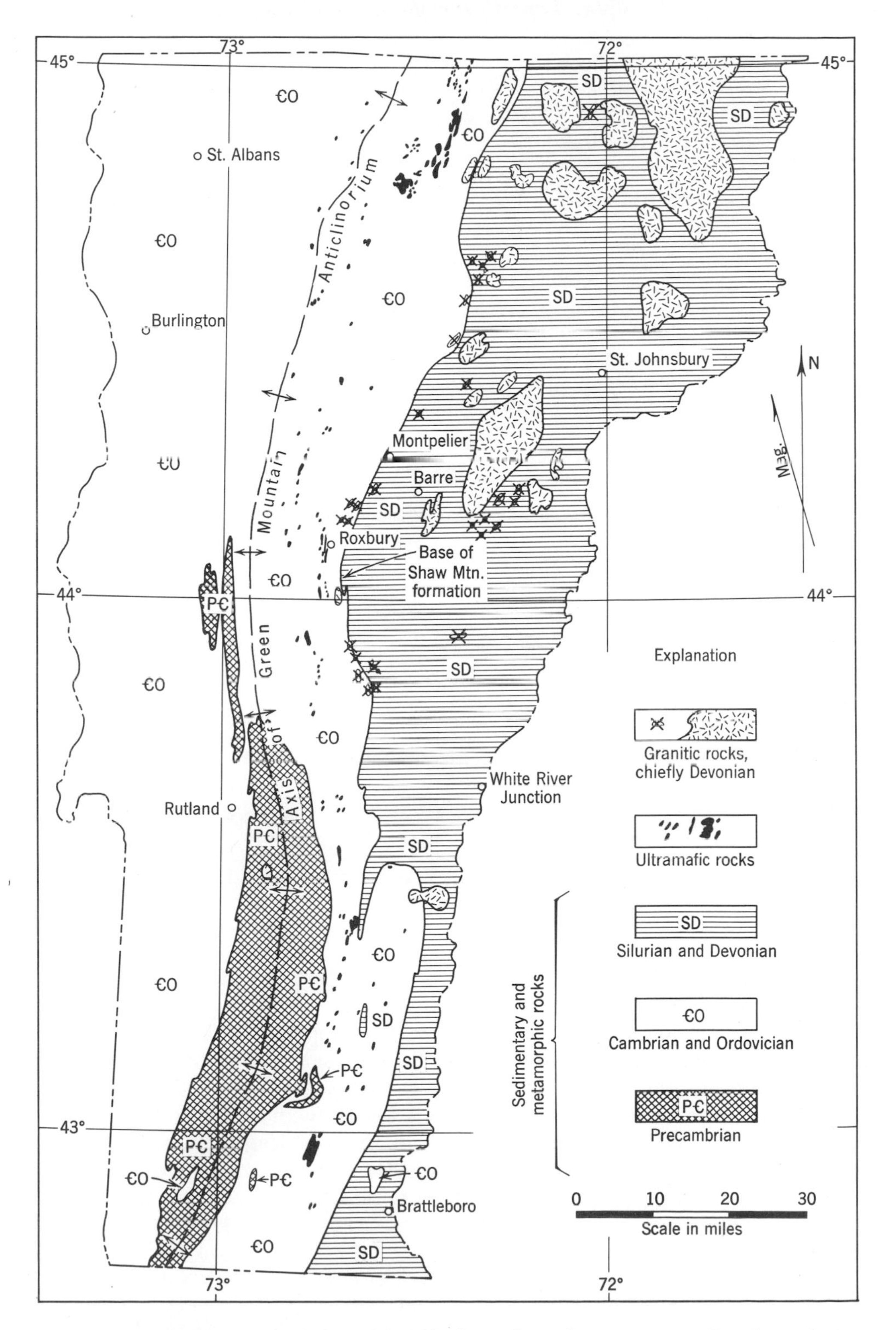

Fig. 5.1 Distribution and geologic setting of ultramafic rocks in Vermont. Based mainly on compilation by A. H. Chidester and W. M. Cady (Chidester, 1962, pl. 1).

TABLE 5.1 Sequence of Rock Units and Major Geologic Events in Central Vermont*

Geologic Age	Rock Unit		Metamorphism and Deformation	Intrusive Ultramafic Rocks
Post-Devonian	Diabase and lamprophyre, in dikes and sills			Age inferred from relationships with greenstones
Devonian	Intrusive granitic and dioritic rocks			
Devonian	Late greenstones and related mafic rocks, in dikes and sills		Rocks antedating major episode of metamorphism; Rocks antedating major deformation—later episode	Age bracket based on structural features
Devonian	Gile Mountain formation		Rocks antedating major deformation—earlier episode	
Silurian	Waits River formation			
Silurian	Northfield slate			
Silurian	Shaw Mountain formation			
Ordovician	Cram Hill formation	Early greenstones and related mafic rocks, in flows, sills, and dikes (include some originally tuffaceous rocks)		General range of observed host rocks
Ordovician	Moretown formation			
Ordovician	Stowe formation			
Cambrian	Ottauquechee formation			
Cambrian	Camels Hump group			

* In large part compiled from Currier and Jahns (1941), White and Jahns (1950), Cady (1956), and Chidester (1962).

associated volcanic rocks and some of the mafic sills and dikes, has been involved in several episodes of deformation. Two of these episodes, representing different stages of major orogenic activity in Devonian time, account for most of the structural features observed in the rocks and are pertinent to the origin of the Roxbury serpentinites. As outlined by White and Jahns (1950), the chief products of the earlier major deformation in central Vermont are open- to sharp-nosed isoclinal folds with an axial-plane schistosity that in most of the rock types is parallel or nearly parallel to bedding. All but a very few of the folds are minor features, with flank-to-flank dimensions of inches to several hundreds of feet, and they have little effect upon the regional outcrop pattern of steeply dipping formations in the homoclinal sequence. They typically plunge at low to moderately high angles, chiefly northward with a sinistral form in plan, and they indicate a consistent upward movement of rocks on the east with respect to those on the west. Both these folds and the accompanying early-stage schistosity are consistent in form and attitude with the Green Mountain anticlinorium, and they appear to be genetically related to this regional arch of Middle or Late Devonian age (Cady, 1945, p. 580).

Features of the later major deformation include slip-cleavage planes, folds, faults, and thin shear zones. Bedding, the earlier schistosity, and even some of the earlier folds are involved in the younger folds, most of which are relatively open and plunge moderately to very steeply northward. Slip cleavage, locally grading into a schistosity (White, 1949, p. 591; White and Jahns, 1950, p. 203, 208), is parallel to the axial planes of these later folds and cuts the earlier schistosity at moderate to large angles, even where folds are not present. In some parts of the region folds of the two generations differ consistently in plunge, and in other parts they differ consistently in pattern; details concerning these and other significant structural relationships have been recorded elsewhere (e.g., White and Jahns, 1950; Cady, 1956; Chidester, 1962). Suffice it to note here that, in most parts of central Vermont, a local assemblage of structural elements generally can be subdivided according to respective identifications of such elements with the earlier or the later episode of major deformation.

All the sedimentary and mafic igneous rocks in this region have been metamorphosed to mineral assemblages characteristic of the greenschist and epidote amphibolite facies. Metamorphism of the lower intensity is much the more widespread, and is represented by various combinations of quartz, chlorite, white micas, and albite in the sedimentary formations and of epidote, chlorite, albite, and carbonate minerals in the greenstones and related igneous rocks. With increasing metamorphic intensity biotite, garnet, and kyanite appear successively in the former rocks, and hornblende appears in the latter.

Most of the granitic rocks in the region lie within a broad area of relatively intense thermal metamorphism, and several major irregularities in the configuration of isograds are systematically related to individual plutons. Thus intrusion and metamorphism appear to have been closely related in time (White and Jahns, 1950, p. 193). That the emplacement of Devonian granitic rocks also marked the closing stages of major deformation in central Vermont is shown by the transection of slip cleavage and associated late folds by these rocks, and by the fact that porphyroblasts in the country rocks are locally, but not generally, deformed and rotated. The regional thermal metamorphism and both episodes of major deformation, which have affected rocks as young as the Gile Mountain formation, therefore can be bracketed within the Devonian (Table 5.1).

C. *The Roxbury Ultramafic Bodies*

1. Geologic setting. The Roxbury district is underlain by greenstones and by quartz-chlorite-sericite schists of the Moretown and Stowe formations (Table 5.1, Fig. 5.2). The schists, which represent original impure sandstones and sandy shales, commonly are distinguished by numerous lenticular masses of granular white quartz several inches in average length. They also contain small quantities of ilmenite and magnetite, pyrite, graphite, apatite, rutile, sphene, tourmaline, and zircon. Albite occurs inconsistently, but is locally abundant. Epidote and carbonate minerals are present in some parts of the section, especially adjacent to layers of greenstone. Nearly pure buff-weathering dolomite with irregular small concentrations of talc is sparsely exposed at several points not far southwest of the village of Roxbury (Fig. 5.2), where one or more beds form a stratigraphic unit 5 feet to nearly 30 feet thick.

The greenstones ordinarily appear as sheet-like masses or aggregates of such masses 10 to 1200 feet or more in thickness, and they constitute 10 to 25 per cent of the bedrock section west of the Roxbury valley (Fig. 5.2). Most of them trend slightly east of north and dip very steeply, in conformity with the enclosing schists. In general they are continuous for considerable strike distances without marked changes in thickness, but local abrupt bulges, bends, and crosscutting relationships bespeak an intrusive origin for many

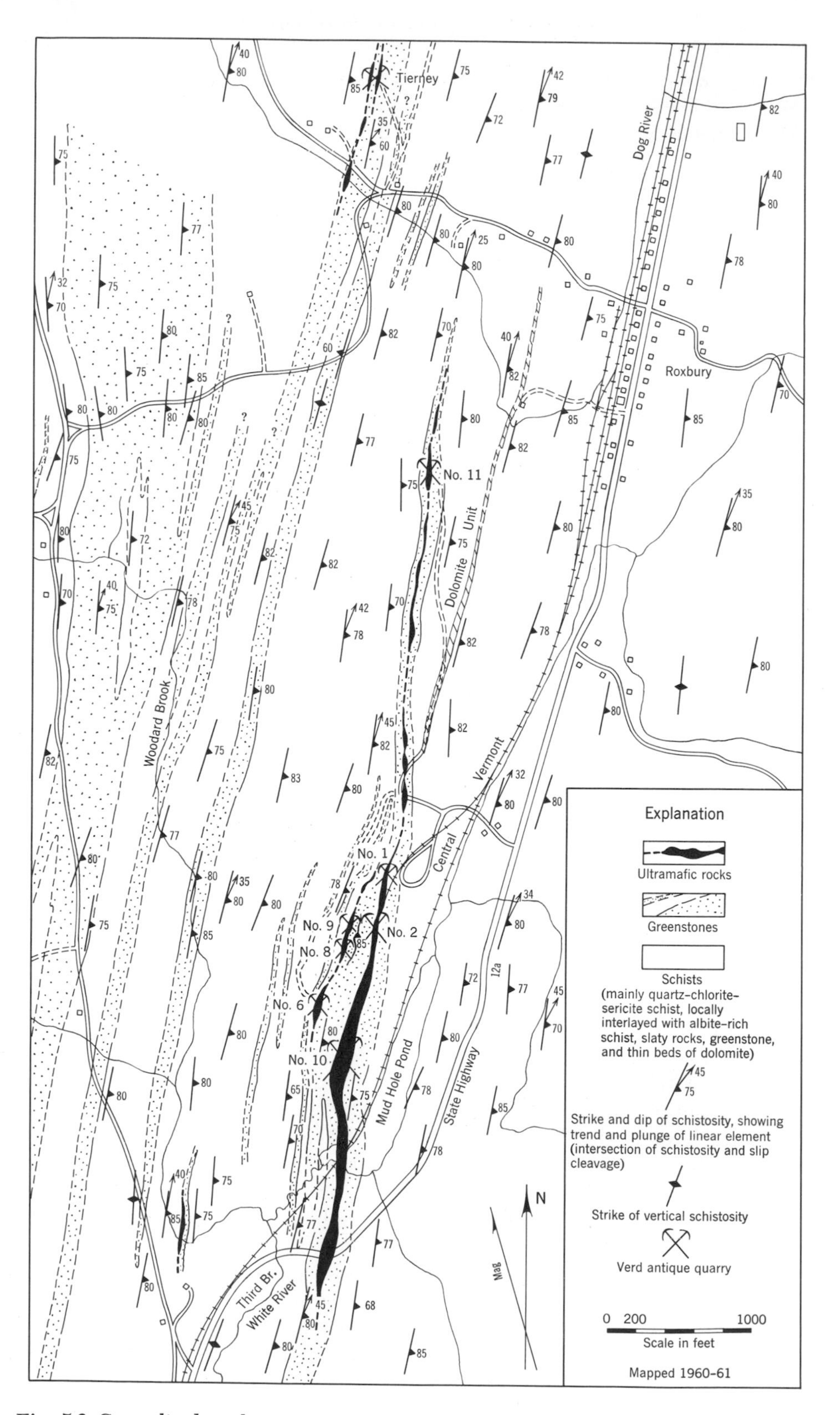

Fig. 5.2 Generalized geologic map of a part of the Roxbury district, Vermont, showing principal bodies of ultramafic rocks.

of them. Others may represent basic flows and tuffs formed penecontemporaneously with the adjacent rocks, as suggested by faintly preserved features akin to agglomerates and pillow lavas, and in several intervals by thin and regular interlayering with finely stratified sedimentary materials.

Many of the greenstones are compositionally layered, many are schistose with or without layering, and others are essentially massive. Numerous crystals of albite in some of the more massive rocks contribute to a markedly porphyritic appearance. Schistosity is commonly present throughout the thinner bodies, but in most of the thicker ones it is prominent only along the margins. Like the associated metasedimentary rocks, all the greenstones in the district represent the greenschist metamorphic facies. Most of them clearly have been affected by both the earlier and the later episodes of major deformation (Table 5.1, Fig. 5.3). Notable exceptions are the greenstones of much younger dikes, a few inches to eight feet thick, that transect folds and schistosity of the earlier deformation in the host rocks but are themselves involved in small folds of the later deformation (Fig. 5.3). In places these dikes, which must be Devonian in age (Table 5.1), also are marked by a schistosity that is parallel to slip cleavage in the adjacent schists.

2. Distribution and occurrence. The ultramafic bodies discussed in this paper are exposed over a rather narrow belt, approximately three miles long, that extends for about equal distances northward and southward from the village of Roxbury. As shown in Fig. 5.2, the largest bodies are highly elongate pinching-and-swelling sheets with bulges 40 to 125 feet in maximum observable thickness. The others appear as individual lenses, some of them thickly pod-like and the remainder much more nearly tabular. The thickest mass in the district, at the Ellis quarries one-half mile north of the Tierney quarry (Fig. 5.2), is an elongate pod nearly 300 feet in outcrop breadth. Like all the other bodies, it is nearly on edge, in essential conformity with the country-rock structure.

Both the sheets and the lenses tend to be strung out along specific horizons in the homoclinal section, and seven such horizons have been recognized within the district. These lie within or along continuous tabular masses of greenstone, and all observed bodies of ultramafic rocks are bordered on at least one side by greenstone rather than schist. Lateral margins of the bodies generally are parallel in detail with the country-rock schistosity, which is deflected in sympathy with many marginal irregularities but is considerably disturbed adjacent to some larger and more abrupt irregularities, including the ends of the more stubby serpentinite lenses. As shown diagrammatically in Fig. 5.3 and 5.4, such local disturbance is expressed in the schistosity attributable to the earlier episode of regional deformation. In contrast, slip cleavage of the later regional deformation is superimposed with fairly consistent pattern upon all the country rocks, regardless of whether or not their earlier schistosity has been disturbed adjacent to the walls of the serpentinite bodies. This relationship suggests that emplacement of the bodies can be bracketed, in terms of age, between the two episodes of Devonian regional deformation (Table 5.1).

The late greenstone dikes, themselves bracketed between these two episodes of deformation, are locally abundant in the area but nowhere have they been observed to cut serpentinite. Such dikes instead appear to be truncated by serpentinite at several localities (e.g., near the edges of the Tierney, No. 2, No. 9, No. 10, and No. 11 quarries), where they contain talc, actinolite, and unusual concentrations of carbonate minerals. Truncation cannot be demonstrated in detail, owing to intense shearing and commonly also to alteration along the serpentinite contacts, but a pre-serpentinite age for these greenstones can be inferred from fairly continuous dikes

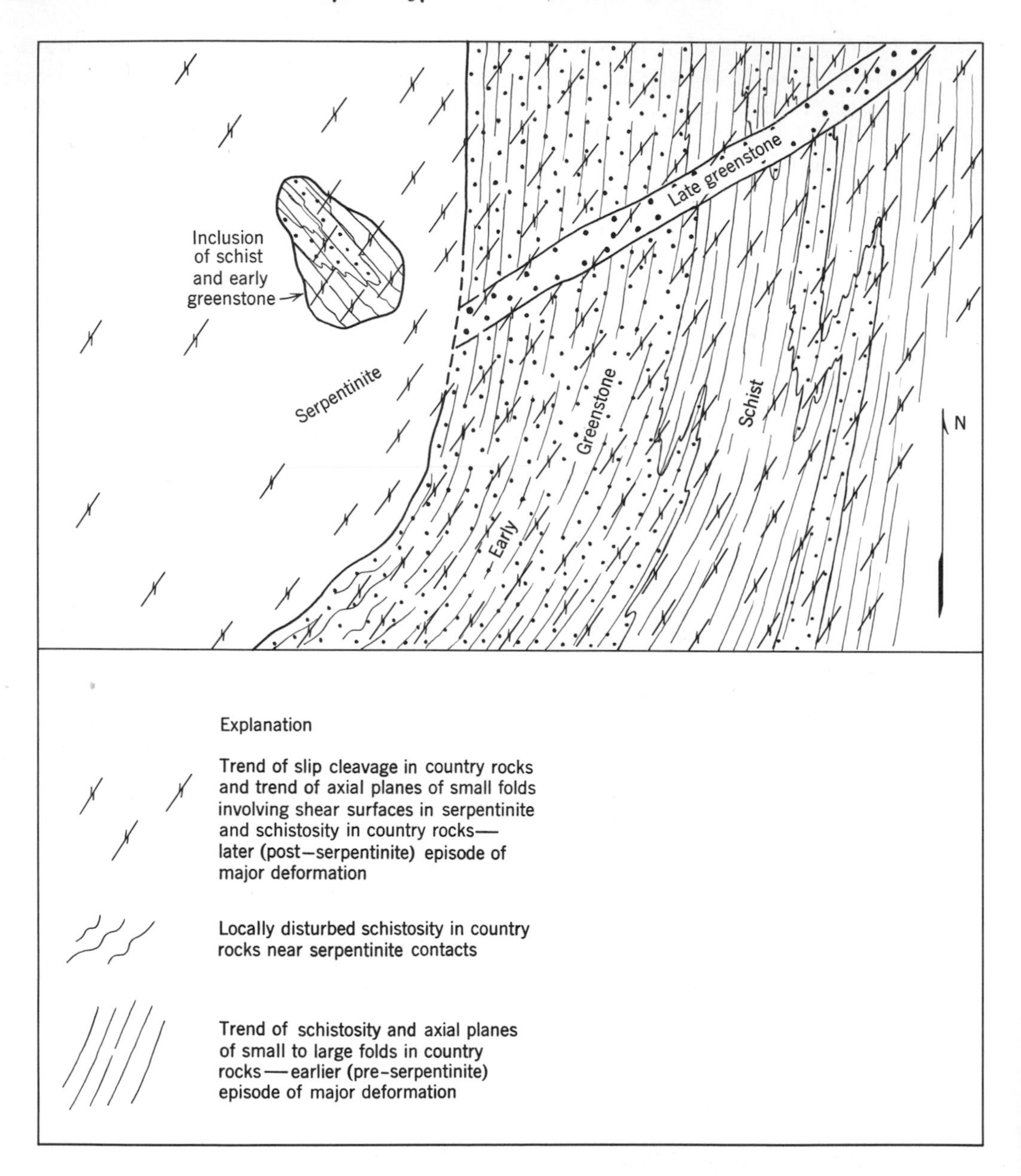

Fig. 5.3 Diagram summarizing spatial relationships and implied relative ages among schist, early and late greenstones, serpentinite, and imposed structural features of two different generations in the Roxbury district.

that extend almost to, but not into, the ultramafic bodies.

3. *Internal structure.* Two distinctly different types of gross internal zoning can be recognized in the ultramafic bodies. One is expressed mainly by the distribution of shear, fracture, and cleavage surfaces and is most readily recognized in bodies that consist almost wholly of serpentinite. The other is compositional, and involves contrasting rock types that were formed mainly at the expense of serpentinite. Zoning of the first type amounts to little more than a progressive inward decrease in number and concentration of structural breaks, as shown diagrammatically in Fig. 5.4. Relationships are highly complex in detail, but the following major elements are characteristic:

(*a.*) *Marginal zone of intensely sheared serpentinite.* Present continuously or discontinuously in nearly all bodies; outcrop breadth ranges from a few inches to as much as 50 feet, with an average of about 8 feet. Abrupt changes in thickness occur in some bodies. Individual shear surfaces, anastomosing in detail, tend to be subparallel with adjacent walls of the host ultramafic body, but not everywhere with schistosity in the nearby country rocks. In general they are closely spaced to form a gross foliation or cleavage, in places the "spaced schistosity" of Chidester (1962, p. 17). Many are wrinkled on a small scale,

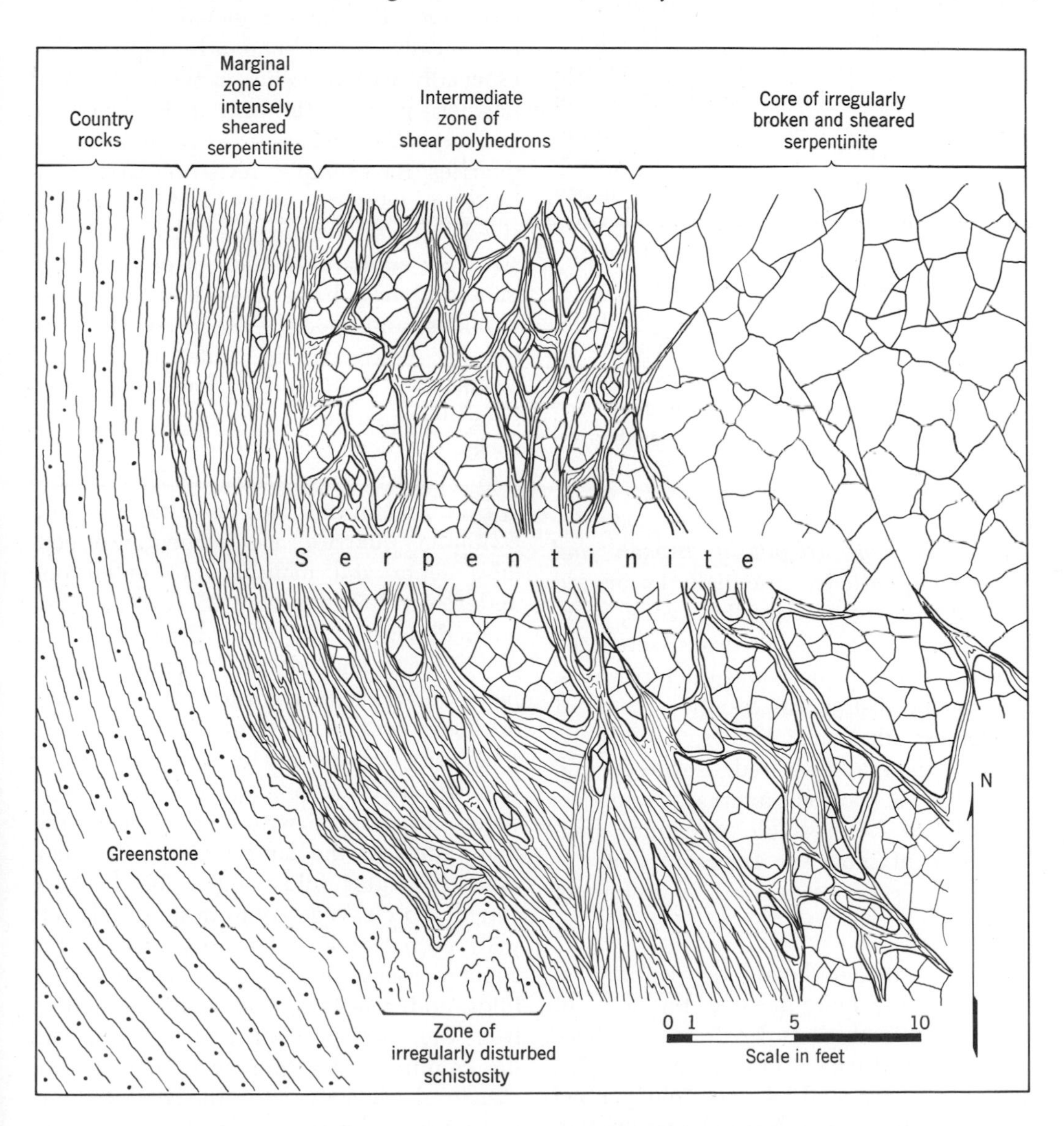

Fig. 5.4 Idealized diagram showing structural variations typical of the serpentinite bodies minimally affected by steatitization, Roxbury district. Planar elements represent schistosity in the greenstone and shear surfaces in the serpentinite, both of which also have been affected by later deformation. Features attributable to steatitization are not shown.

extensively so in some bodies, and are transected by younger and more widely separated shear surfaces.

(*b.*) *Intermediate zone of shear polyhedrons.* Dominant structural unit in most of the serpentinite bodies, and distinguished by spheroidal to thinly pillow-like masses of less broken and sheared serpentinite, termed "shear polyhedrons" by Chidester et al. (1951, p. 7–8), in a matrix of highly sheared serpentinite. The polyhedrons range from inches to tens of feet across, the matrix from a small fraction of an inch to several feet. The size and angularity of polyhedrons increase irregularly but progressively inward from the marginal zone of sheared serpentinite, accompanied by increases in ratio of polyhedron to matrix materials. As judged from external form and internal layering, most polyhedrons cannot be matched with adjacent ones, either absolutely or in terms of orientation. Local enlargement of the matrix is expressed by pods and lenses of sheared serpentinite similar to that of the marginal zone.

(*c.*) *Core of irregularly broken and sheared serpentinite.* Essentially an inward extension of the intermediate zone, comprising cyclopean polyhedrons separated by relatively thin shear and fracture zones, that can be distinguished only in some of the largest ultramafic bodies. Each polyhedron, though fractured, sheared, and somewhat dislocated internally, appears basically to be a single structural unit. Grossly continuous or consistent interior layering can be recognized in a few of these units.

Most of the unsheared serpentinite is megascopically quite massive, but some of that in the northern and extreme southern parts of the district is faintly layered. This layering is expressed by very thin parallel units that differ slightly from one another in color, especially in shades of green and gray on weathered surfaces, and it is locally accentuated by fine trains of magnetite and chromite. It antedates all other structural features observed in the ultramafic bodies, and may reflect a primary feature of earlier rocks from which the serpentinites were derived.

The serpentinite bodies contain no recognizable structural elements akin to those correlated with the earlier regional deformation of the country rocks. In contrast, small folds and slip cleavage characteristic of the later regional deformation are locally but abundantly represented, especially within bodies in the central and northern parts of the district. Exposures in and near the Scampini, Ellis, and No. 11 quarries, for example, reveal much serpentinite in which a spaced schistosity, derived through shearing and locally emphasized by subparallel veinlets of carbonate minerals, has been cast into numerous wrinkles and folds (Fig. 5.5) that are broadly consistent in scale, shape, and orientation with those representing the later deformation in the adjacent country rocks.

In at least two quarries, the Tierney and No. 11, and in outcrops near the Ellis and Scampini quarries, the serpentinite contains septa and inclusions of greenstone and schist 1.5 to nearly 25 feet in maximum dimension. In effect, these are shear polyhedrons and, despite partial or complete alteration to chlorite and talc, a few of them contain recognizable folds with schistosity characteristic of the earlier regional deformation, along with younger shear surfaces and with still younger folds that represent the later regional deformation. The later folds and a locally associated slip cleavage conform in all respects with corresponding later features in the country rocks, but in general the earlier folds and schistosity differ in orientation from the corresponding earlier features in the country rocks. Moreover, these earlier structural elements are truncated by serpentinite at the margins of the inclusions, which evidently had been deformed before entrainment and rotation within the ultramafic bodies during their emplacement.

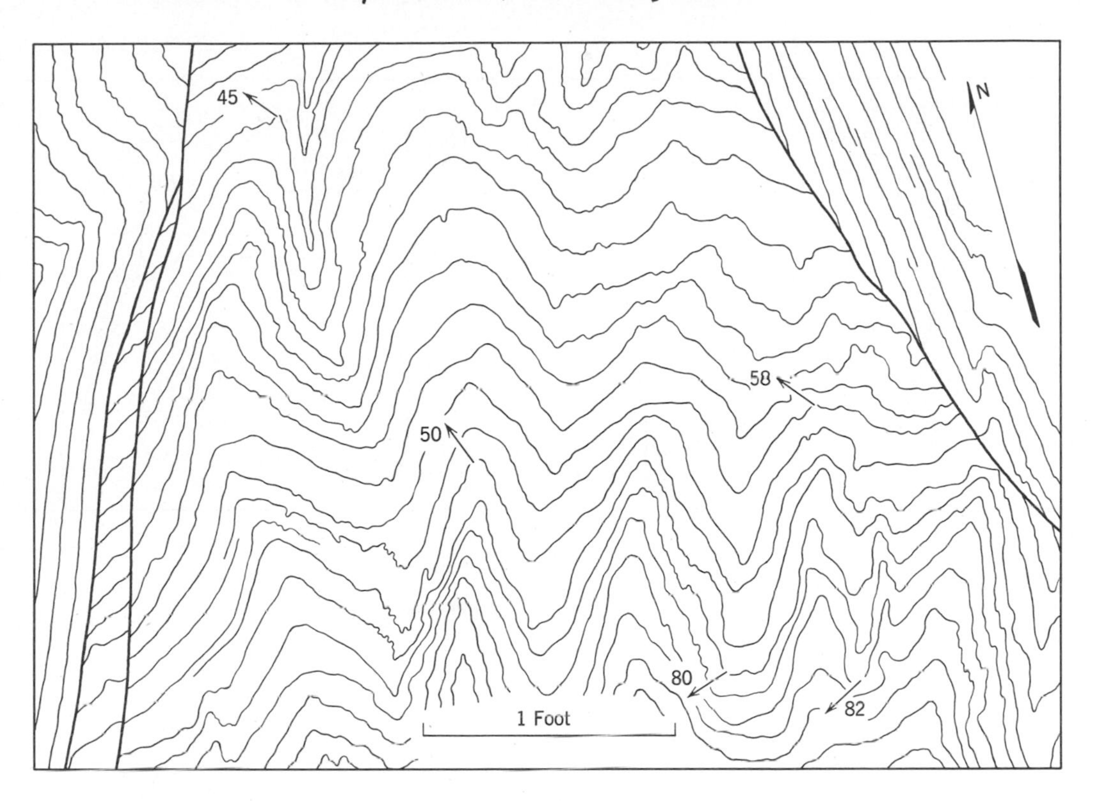

Fig. 5.5 Serpentinite with numerous subparallel shear surfaces wrinkled and folded in a general pattern akin to that of structural features associated with late regional deformation of adjacent country rocks, knob north of Scampini quarry, Roxbury district. Many of the shear surfaces are accentuated by veinlets of unsheared dolomite.

Taken in sum (Fig. 5.3), these and earlier-described structural relationships lead to the conclusion that the ultramafic bodies probably were established in their present positions during Devonian rather than Ordovician time, after intrusion of the youngest greenstone dikes and between the two major episodes of regional deformation.

*4. **Lithologic zoning.*** Although serpentinite is preponderant, other rock types form well defined units within most of the ultramafic bodies in the district. As in numerous localities elsewhere in Vermont (e.g., Jacobs, 1914, 1916; Gillson, 1927; Hess, 1933; Bain, 1936; Phillips and Hess, 1936; Chidester et al., 1951; Chidester, 1962), distribution of the major units is broadly systematic but irregular in detail (Fig. 5.6). The principal features of the rock types can be summarized as follows:

(a.) Rocks of the blackwall zone. Highly foliated to almost massive, mainly dark-colored, chlorite-rich rocks that form thin, sharply defined, and nearly continuous rinds about the ultramafic bodies (Fig. 5.6) and also fringe septa and inclusions of country rocks within the bodies. Such rinds, generally referred to as "blackwall," range in thickness from a knife edge to ten feet, but the average is less than one foot; they are thickest around bodies with the highest percentages of contained talc and carbonate minerals. The chlorite-rich rocks also occur as isolated masses within the bodies, where they appear to represent small xenoliths of former schist and greenstone. The outer margins of the exterior rinds grade rather abruptly into country rocks, and commonly are flanked by local concentrations of porphyroblastic albite, less commonly porphyroblastic muscovite, and rarely by concentrations of graphite.

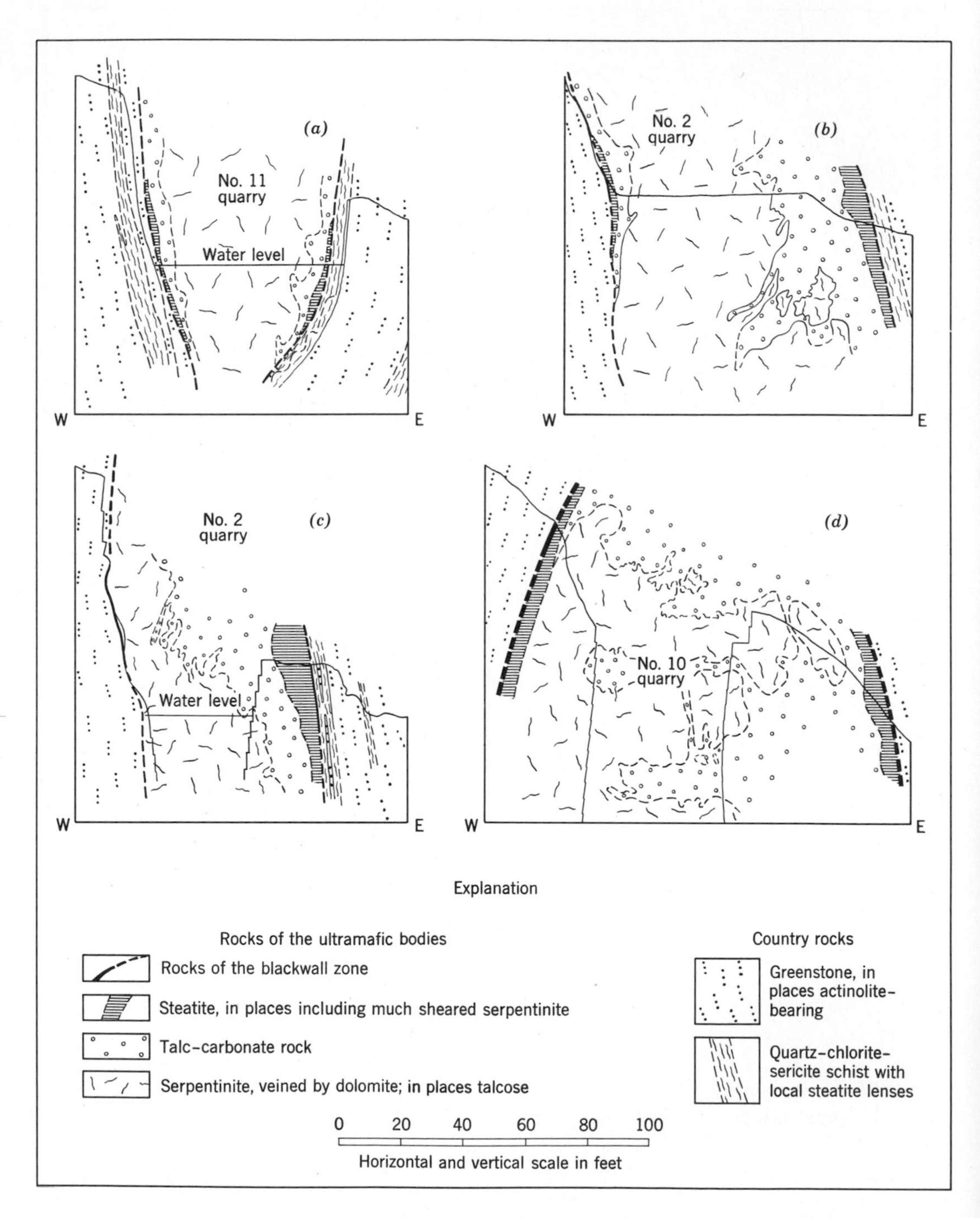

Fig. 5.6 Geologic sketch sections through typical ultramafic bodies, Roxbury district, showing distribution of major rock types. (*a*) southerly part of no. 11 quarry; (*b*) north end of No. 2 quarry; (*c*) south end of No. 2 quarry; and (*d*) north end of No. 10 quarry.

Their inner margins grade sharply into steatite, talc-carbonate rock, or into sheared serpentinite that contains some talc and carbonate minerals. Where they adjoin dolomitic country rocks, as in the vicinity of the No. 1 quarry (Fig. 5.2), the blackwall rocks contain abundant tremolite along with chlorite and some talc. Actinolite commonly occurs with the chlorite, and is most abundant where the country rock is carbonate-rich greenstone.

(*b.*) *Steatite.* Massive to microsheared, compact, pale-blue or green to light gray rock, consisting mainly or almost wholly of fine-grained talc. It occurs typically along the inner margins of the blackwall zone as local layers and irregular lenses rarely more than 5 feet thick (Fig. 5.6), and in places it is separated from the blackwall rocks by thin transitional units rich in actinolite or relict serpentine minerals. Toward the centers of the host ultramafic bodies it grades sharply but irregularly into serpentinite or less sharply into talc-carbonate rock. Thin talc-rich lenses and pods also occur sparsely within the schists adjacent to several of the ultramafic bodies, where they generally are enclosed within miniature blackwall rinds. Such steatite is not directly associated with serpentine minerals.

(*c.*) *Talc-carbonate rock.* Massive to mildly sheared, buff to very pale greenish or bluish gray aggregates of talc and carbonate minerals, generally with carbonate porphyroblasts and commonly veined by younger carbonates. This rock, also known as "grit," extends from the inner margins of steatite masses and blackwall zones into serpentinite, and its sharp to gradational boundaries against the serpentinite are highly irregular over a wide range of scales (Fig. 5.6). Masses of typical "grit" are diversely oriented and locally are as much as 30 feet thick; they range from bulb- or fingerlike projections to rare pods completely enclosed within serpentinite. A few small, thinly tabular masses also have been observed within the blackwall rocks.

(*d.*) *Talc-carbonate veins.* Simple to highly irregular veins and pods, half an inch to nearly 5 feet thick, typically comprising comb-like aggregates of large talc plates and central fillings of coarsely crystalline dolomite. In places the carbonate portions are marginal rather than central, or even extend alone into the wall rock. The veins and pods occur mainly within steatite and talc-carbonate rock, and most of the tabular masses are gently inclined or horizontal. Many are plainly joint controlled, but none are themselves appreciably deformed.

(*e.*) *Serpentinite.* Massive to highly sheared, compact, pale-green to very dark-greenish-gray aggregates of serpentine minerals, with only minor amounts of other constituents. This rock, in most occurrences irregularly veined by carbonate minerals, is the essential type in all the ultramafic bodies and composes the interiors of those in which other rock types also are abundant.

5. Petrographic features. The principal mineralogic and petrographic features of the ultramafic rocks are outlined in Table 5.2, and inferred genetic relationships among the minerals are summarized in Table 5.3. On the basis of optical properties, crystal habit, and X-ray data, the predominant serpentine mineral is antigorite according to the two-fold classification of Nagy and Faust (1956). Lizardite, as distinguished by Whittaker and Zussman (1956), also is present in moderate abundance but is here included with antigorite because the occurrence of these two species in the Roxbury district cannot be defined from X-ray data thus far obtained. The coarsely columnar serpentine commonly referred to as "shear fiber" or "picrolite" by earlier investigators (e.g., Jacobs, 1916, p. 250–254) is antigorite recrystallized from much finer-grained material along local shear surfaces; it is quite

TABLE 5.2 Summary of Mineral Occurrences in the Roxbury Ultramafic Bodies

Rock units	Minerals[1]	General Mode of Occurrence[2]				General Abundance[3]					Crystal Habits and/or Shapes of Grains	Grain Size (long-dimension)		Notes on Compositional Features[4]
		Major aggregates	Disseminations and/or scattered aggregates	Local concentrations	Veinlets	Predominant	Abundant	Moderately abundant	Sparse	Rare		Common range (mm)	Maximum (mm)	
Serpentinite	Antigorite	X			x	X					Flakes, plates, shreds	0.001–0.2	0.5	Av. Mg:Fe ≈ 20:1 Av. Mg + Fe:Al ≈ 60:1
	Antigorite			X				x	X		Columns, blades	5–75	500+	
	Chrysotile		X		X				x	X	Fibers	0.5–1.5	8.5	Av. Mg:Fe + Al ≈ 70:1
	Brucite		X		X				x	X	Fibers, plates	0.01–0.5	1.5	Fe bearing
	Magnetite		X	x				x	X	x	Anhedral grains	0.001–0.5	2.0	In part chromian
	Chromite		X						x	X	Anhedral to subhedral grains	0.5–1.5	2.5	
	Sulfides		X		x					X	Anhedral to subhedral grains	0.01–1.0	7.5	Pyrite and pyrrhotite
	Talc		X		x			x	X	x	Flakes, fibers	0.005–0.1	1.0	
	Carbonates		x		X		x	x	X	x	Anhedral grains	0.1–1.5	5.0	Dolomite, some magnesite
Blackwall rocks	Chlorite	X				X		x			Flakes, plates, shreds, blades	0.05–0.5	1.5	Av. Mg:Fe ≈ 3:1
	Tremolite	X		x		x			x	X	Needles, blades	0.05–1.5	25+	Low Fe content
	Actinolite		x	X				X	x		Needles, blades, columns	0.05–2.0	40+	Av. Mg:Fe ≈ 4:1
	Talc		x	X			x	x	X		Flakes, fibers	0.005–0.1	1.0	
	Magnetite		X					x	X	x	Anhedral grains	0.01–0.1	2.5	
	Ilmenite		X					x	X	x	Blades and ovoid grains	0.05–0.5	2.0	
	Sphene		X					x	X	x	Flat pyramids and ovoid grains	0.05–1.0	2.5	
	Rutile		X						x	X	Needles, blades, ovoid grains	0.001–0.1	0.5	
	Apatite		X						x	X	Prisms, ovoid grains	0.05–0.5	1.2	Fluorapatite
	Zircon		X							X	Ovoid grains	0.001–0.5	1.0	
	Tourmaline		X							X	Prisms, needles	0.05–0.5	1.5	Mainly schorlite
	Pyrite		X							X	Cubes, irregular grains	0.01–0.5	1.5	

TABLE 5.2 (*continued*)

Rock units	Minerals[1]	General Mode of Occurrence[2]: Major aggregates	Disseminations and/or scattered aggregates	Local concentrations	Veinlets	General Abundance[3]: Predominant	Abundant	Moderately abundant	Sparse	Rare	Crystal Habits and/or Shapes of Grains	Grain Size (long-dimension): Common range (mm)	Maximum (mm)	Notes on Compositional Features[4]
Blackwall rocks	Epidote		X	x				x	X	x	Irregular grains	0.05–0.5	1.5	Pistacite and clinozoisite
	Albite			X				x	x	X	Subhedral to anhedral grains	0.1–2.0	5.0	Ab_{97+}
	Carbonates		X	x	x		x	x	x	X	Rhombs and subhedral grains	0.1–1.0	4.0	Calcite, dolomite; mainly ferroan
Steatite	Talc	X				X					Flakes, fibers, shreds, blades	0.01–0.1	1.5	Av. Mg:Fe ≈ 11:1
	Chlorite		X						x	X	Flakes, shreds	0.01–0.3	1.5	
	Tremolite			X				x	x	X	Needles	0.005–0.5	7.0	Low Fe content
	Actinolite			X						X	Needles, irregular blades	0.01–0.5	4.0	Av. Mg:Fe ≈ 4:1
	Magnetite		X						X	x	Irregular grains	0.001–0.05	0.1	
	Ilmenite		X							X	Irregular grains	0.01–0.2	0.5	
	Sphene		X						x	X	Ovoid to irregular grains	0.01–0.5	1.5	
	Apatite		X							X	Ovoid to irregular elongate grains	0.01–0.3	1.0	Fluorapatite
	Zircon		X							X	Ovoid grains	0.001–0.5	0.7	
	Pyrite		X						X	X	Irregular grains	0.005–0.1	0.5	
	Carbonates		X	x	x			x	x	X	Irregular rhombs and anhedral grains	0.05–1.0	3.5	Calcite, dolomite; mainly ferroan
Talc-carbonate rock	Talc	X				X	x				Fibers, flakes, shreds, blades	0.01–0.4	2.5	Mg:Fe ≈ 10:1 to 20:1
	Carbonates	X	x		x	X	x				Anhedral to subhedral grains	0.5–3.0	25+	Magnesite, dolomite, some calcite; nearly all ferroan
	Antigorite		x	X				x	x	X	Flakes, shreds, plates	0.001–0.2	0.5	
	Chrysotile		X		x					X	Fibers	0.1–1.0	2.5	
	Brucite		X		x					X	Fibers, plates	0.001–0.5	1.0	Fe bearing
	Chlorite		X	x					x	X	Flakes, shreds	0.01–0.1	1.0	

TABLE 5.2 (*continued*)

Rock units	Minerals[1]	General Mode of Occurrence[2]				General Abundance[3]					Crystal Habits and/or Shapes of Grains	Grain Size (long-dimension)		Notes on Compositional Features[4]
		Major aggregates	Disseminations and/or scattered aggregates	Local concentrations	Veinlets	Predominant	Abundant	Moderately abundant	Sparse	Rare		Common range (mm)	Maximum (mm)	
Talc-carbonate rock	Magnetite		X					x	X	x	Anhedral to highly irregular grains	0.001–0.1	2.0	In part chromian
	Chromite		X							X	Irregular grains	0.1–0.5	1.5	
	Pyrite		X		x					X	Anhedral to highly irregular grains	0.01–1.0	2.5	
Talc-carbonate veins	Talc	X				X					Plates, blades	5–15	75+	Mg:Fe ≈ 20:1
	Carbonate	X			x	X					Anhedral to subhedral crystals	5–25	40+	Dolomite
	Magnetite		X							X	Anhedral to highly irregular grains	0.01–0.5	1.0	
	Pyrite		X							X	Irregular grains	0.01–1.5	2.5	

[1] Not included in list are extremely rare olivine in serpentinite (relict from primary ultrabasic rocks), locally abundant quartz and sericite in blackwall rocks (relict from country-rock schists), and very rare chrysotile and brucite and locally abundant antigorite in steatite and blackwall rocks (relict from serpentinite).
[2] X—principal mode of occurrence.
x—subordinate mode of occurrence.
[3] X—abundance in most or all of the ultramafic bodies.
x—abundance in some ultramafic bodies or only in parts of some bodies.
[4] Atomic ratios obtained from chemical analyses, most of other data from optical studies.

distinct from the fibrous chrysotile present elsewhere in the serpentinites.

Development of the serpentinites from dunitic or peridotitic rocks is attested by widespread relict chromite and magnetite, and by rare residual olivine observed in specimens from the No. 5, No. 11, Ellis, Scampini, and Tierney quarries. The olivine appears as clusters of tiny irregular remnants within aggregates of antigorite. Concentrations of magnetite form partial or complete "veils" around some of the clusters, and may represent the margins of original olivine grains. No convincing evidence of original pyroxene has been observed thus far in any of the rocks.

The blackwall rocks plainly were formed by replacement of schists and greenstones immediately adjoining the serpentinite bodies. Preserved within them is a nearly complete representation of the country-rock minerals, as well as folds, schistosity,

TABLE 5.3 Summary of Principal Relationships and Inferred Development of Minerals in the Roxbury Ultramafic Bodies

Minerals \ Rock Units	Serpentinite	Blackwall Rocks	Steatite	Talc-Carbonate Rock
Antigorite	Replacement of olivine, etc., in ultrabasic rocks	Relict from serpentinite	Relict from serpentinite	Relict from serpentinite
Antigorite (coarsely columnar)	Mainly recrystallization of antigorite along shear zones			
Chrysotile	Fracture filling, with some replacement of antigorite			
Brucite	Product of serpentinization			
Olivine	Relict from ultrabasic rocks	...	...	...
Chromite		...	...	Relict from ultrabasic rocks
Magnetite	Partly relict, partly a product of steatitization, mainly a product of serpentinization	Partly relict from country rocks, partly a product of steatitization	Mainly relict from serpentinite and rocks of the blackwall zone	Relict from serpentinite
Talc	Chiefly replacement of antigorite; some pseud. after chrysotile	Partly replacement of magnesian carbonate country rocks, partly replacement of chlorite	Replacement of antigorite, chrysotile, chlorite, tremolite, actinolite; commonly pseudomorphic	Replacement of antigorite, chrysotile, magnetite, and some chlorite; commonly pseudomorphic
Carbonate minerals	Fracture filling, with replacement of antigorite, chrysotile, and some talc	Fracture filling and replacement of country-rock minerals, tremolite, actinolite, and some talc	Fracture filling and replacement of antigorite, chrysotile, and minerals of the blackwall zone	Fracture filling and replacement of serpentines, chlorite, and talc; possibly in small part relict from rocks of the blackwall zone
Chlorite	...	Recrystallization of country-rock chlorite and replacement of other country-rock minerals; pseud. after albite, epidote, actinolite, tremolite, and sphene	Mainly relict from rocks of the blackwall zone	Mainly relict from rocks of the blackwall zone representing former septa and inclusions of country rocks

TABLE 5.3 (*continued*)

Minerals \ Rock Units	Serpentinite	Blackwall Rocks	Steatite	Talc-Carbonate Rock
Tremolite	. . .	Mainly replacement of carbonate country rocks, partly a product of steatitization	Relict from rocks of the blackwall zone	. . .
Actinolite	. . .	Mainly replacement of epidote and other country-rock minerals, partly a product of steatitization		. . .
Ilmenite	. . .	Mainly relict from country rocks		. . .
Sphene	. . .	Partly relict from country rocks, partly replacement of ilmenite		. . .
Rutile	. . .	Partly relict from country rocks, mainly replacement of ilmenite	. . .	. . .
Apatite	. . .	Mainly relict from country rocks	Relict from rocks of the blackwall zone	. . .
Zircon	. . .	Relict from country-rock schists		. . .
Tourmaline	. . .		. . .	. . .
Epidote	. . .	Relict from country-rock greenstones	. . .	. . .
Albite	. . .	Relict from country rocks	. . .	. . .
Pyrrhotite	Mainly fracture-controlled; possibly in part relict from ultrabasic rocks	. . .	. . .	. . .
Pyrite		Mainly fracture-controlled; in part derived from country rocks	Partly relict from rocks of the blackwall zone, partly fracture-controlled	Partly relict from serpentinite, partly fracture-controlled

slip cleavage, and other expressions of the two episodes of major deformation that affected the country rocks. That all this deformation antedated the chlorite-producing blackwall alteration is indicated by albite porphyroblasts partly or wholly replaced by chlorite; similar albite porphyroblasts in adjacent country rocks have been superimposed on the pattern of foliation and folds and are themselves undeformed. Much of the blackwall chlorite and associated carbonates is pseudomorphic after epidote, tremolite, actinolite, sphene, and other country-rock minerals, and some of the blackwall tremolite and actinolite shows replacement relationships with respect to relict epidote and carbonate minerals from the country rocks.

The steatite was developed by replacement of serpentinite, blackwall rocks, talc-carbonate rock, and, locally, country-rock schists. Partial and complete pseudomorphs of the talc after chrysotile, antigorite, tremolite, actinolite, and chlorite are abundant and widespread. All these earlier minerals also are veined and corroded by carbonates. Despite its softness, much of the steatite is massive and essentially undeformed. The remainder is microscopically sheared and in places is schistose, but it does not appear to contain structural features akin to those in the serpentinite and country rocks that have been ascribed to the later episode of regional deformation.

The talc-carbonate rock evidently was formed almost exclusively at the expense of serpentinite, as attested by widespread remnants of antigorite and chrysotile and by numerous pseudomorphs of talc and carbonate after these minerals. A local crude schistosity, apparently inherited from parent sheared serpentinite, is transected by porphyroblasts and veinlets of carbonate minerals. The carbonate veinlets, like those in adjacent serpentinite, are little deformed.

D. Genesis of the Ultramafic Bodies

1. Sequential relationships. The structural and petrographic features of the Roxbury ultramafic bodies, taken in the context of their structural and stratigraphic setting, are fully consistent with the following general sequence of events, some of which were in part overlapping:

1. Accumulation, in early and middle Paleozoic times, of a thick section of sedimentary and mafic igneous rocks (Table 5.1).
2. Major deformation of this section in Devonian time, probably accompanied by mild metamorphism of all the rocks (Table 5.1).
3. Emplacement of late mafic igneous rocks, with continued or renewed metamorphism (Table 5.1, Fig. 5.3).
4. Emplacement of serpentinite bodies within Cambrian and Ordovician parts of the section (Figs. 5.1, 5.2).
5. Major deformation, still in Devonian time, of the serpentinites and country rocks, accompanied in the Roxbury district by metamorphism of intensity indicated by the greenschist facies (Table 5.1, Figs. 5.3, 5.4, 5.5).
6. Partial steatitization of the serpentinite bodies, in general corresponding temporally to regional emplacement of Devonian granitic plutons that marked the close of major deformation and the culmination of metamorphism in central Vermont (Table 5.1, Fig. 5.1).
7. Emplacement, in post-Devonian time, of basic igneous rocks that have not been metamorphosed subsequently (Table 5.1).

Without reference yet as to where the various modifications took place, the ultramafic bodies represent a sequence of alteration from olivine-rich rocks to serpentinites to talc-bearing rocks. As noted by previous investigators (e.g., Jacobs, 1916, p. 269; Gillson, 1927, p. 274; Hess, 1933, p. 647; Bain, 1934), steatitization consistently followed serpentinization.

2. Origin and emplacement of the serpentinites. The olivine-rich rocks from which the serpentinites were formed may have crystallized directly from ultrabasic magma derived through partial refusion of subcrustal material, or they may have been crystal accumulates from basic magma that gave rise, over a long period of time, to the abundant rocks that now appear as greenstones and amphibolites in central Vermont. Under any circumstances, the parental ultrabasic rocks must have been formed at very high temperatures (e.g., Bowen and Schairer, 1936; Bowen and Tuttle, 1949), considerably above the maximum level of about 500°C indicated by the mineral assemblages of the Roxbury serpentinites. The country rocks appear never to have contained minerals representing metamorphic intensity beyond that of the greenschist facies, thereby ruling out the possibility of *in situ* crystallization of ultrabasic magma.

With respect to possible fluxing effects of water (e.g., Hess, 1938), the experimental work of Bowen and Tuttle (1949) has shown that hydrous magnesian melts can exist only at temperatures above 1000°C, that magnesian serpentine can be expected to form or to be stable only at temperatures below about 500°C, and hence that there is no likelihood of a "serpentine magma," that is, a system in which olivine and serpentine are in equilibrium with a hydrous melt. The ultramafic bodies accordingly must represent either intrusion of serpentinite in the solid state, *in situ* serpentinization of olivine-rich rocks that had been intruded in the solid state, or some combination of these processes (cf. Benson, 1926; Hess, 1938, 1955; Bain, 1936; Sosman, 1938; Bowen and Tuttle, 1949; De Roever, 1957; Thayer, 1960; Chidester, 1962, pp. 87–89; Raleigh and Paterson, 1965). Emplacement was broadly controlled by country-rock structure, and in some detail by country-rock lithology; a marked preference for greenstone layers is evident even where such layers transect bedding and schistosity in the other country rocks (Fig. 5.2).

Numerous reactions have been suggested to account for serpentinization of ultrabasic rocks (for typical discussions, see Benson, 1918; Hess, 1933; Turner and Verhoogen, 1960, pp. 318–319), but the process basically requires (1) the addition of H_2O to olivine; and (2) either large volume increases, with an extreme range of 20 to nearly 70 per cent, or expulsion from the immediate system of both MgO and SiO_2 in very substantial amounts. Neither of the latter requirements appears to have been met at the Roxbury sites, where the country rocks show no evidence of silica or magnesia metasomatism attributable to serpentinization and where the distribution and attitude of shearing within the ultramafic bodies clearly is related to their emplacement rather than to serpentinization. Even the inclusions of country rocks are akin to the shear polyhedrons of serpentinite, and probably reflect tectonic transport during which they were invaded by tongues of sheared serpentinite.

The ultramafic bodies, therefore, seem best explained as tectonically emplaced masses of crystalline serpentinite, perhaps derived from olivine-rich rocks during upward movement in the crust. Serpentinization probably occurred within the temperature range 350 to 450°C (e.g., Bowen and Tuttle, 1949; Yoder, 1952; Olsen, 1963), and could well have been promoted by repeated dosages of water from the geosynclinal section that was traversed. Alternatively, conversion of the parent rocks might have been essentially completed at greater depth, with subsequent tectonic mobilization of the products. Raleigh and Paterson (1965) have called attention to the high strength of serpentinite at relatively low temperatures (e.g., Paterson, 1964; Handin, 1964), and have suggested that tectonic emplacement would be facilitated by weakening through dehydration of the rock and attendant reduction in effective confining pressure due to the pore pressure of released water. In several experiments they observed weakening in the temperature range 300 to 600°C (see Chapter 6-IV), and most notably above the temperatures at which serpentine minerals break down to form olivine and talc. If such dehydration at depth were a prelude to emplacement of the Roxbury serpentinites, any olivine thus formed must have been since reserpentinized; however, the sparsely disseminated flakes and fibers of talc observed in these rocks (Table 5.2) could be relics of such dehydration.

3. Origin of the steatite and associated rocks. The blackwall and talc-bearing rocks are closely related to one another in space and time, but it commonly has been held (e.g., Gillson, 1927; Hess, 1933) that their development was quite unrelated to the earlier serpentinization. Though denied by Bain (1934), this view has been since reaffirmed for the Waterbury-Waitsfield area by Chidester (1962, p. 91) and can be defended for the Roxbury occurrences via several different lines of evidence. Here the talc-bearing rocks, extending inward from the margins of the ultramafic bodies, were formed at the expense of serpentinite, but nowhere did serpentine minerals replace talc; indeed, the serpentinites are allochthonous rocks that must have been formed prior to their emplacement at present levels, whereas the talc-bearing rocks are plainly autochthonous. The extent of steatitization varies considerably from one ultramafic body to another, and from one part of a given body to another; it is quite independent of the degree of serpentinization, which is complete or nearly so in all the bodies. Finally, contrasting structural features further indicate that the two processes were separated by an appreciable interval of time, corresponding minimally to almost the entire episode of later regional deformation.

Development of the gross zonal structure within the ultramafic bodies (Fig. 5.6) can be viewed most simply in terms of moving boundaries between contrasting lithologic units. Movements were slightly outward in the case of the country-rock-blackwall and blackwall-steatite boundaries and slightly to considerably inward in the case of the boundaries between steatite and talc-carbonate rock, steatite and serpentinite, and between talc-carbonate rock and serpentinite (Fig. 5.7). The corresponding sequences of replacement were country rock → albite porphyroblast rock (locally) → blackwall rocks → steatite at a given point along the original outer margin of an ultramafic body, and serpentinite → steatite or serpentinite → talc-carbonate rock → steatite at a given point inside the margin. As shown in Fig. 5.7, steatite developed in both outward and inward directions at the expense, respectively, of blackwall rocks and of serpentinite or talc-carbonate rock. The steatite and talc-carbonate rock are somewhat independent in their occurrence, but where they are in contact textural relations suggest, though commonly do not prove, that the steatite is the younger. These features fortify Chidester's hypothesis (1962, p. 91) that these two rock types may have been formed by distinctly different phases of a single broad process.

The entire process of steatitization in the Roxbury district can be attributed to a combination of (a) carbon dioxide metasomatism, and (b) metamorphic differentiation across original boundaries between serpentinite and country rocks of markedly different composition (Read, 1934; Phillips and Hess, 1936). All known petrographic relationships and inferred reactions suggest that the exchanges of material occurred at essentially constant temperature corresponding closely to that of the country rocks at or near the peak of their metamorphism, a conclusion similar to that reached by Chidester (1962, p. 94) for steatitization in the Waterbury-Waitsfield area. That the exchanges were accomplished under conditions of nearly constant volume is suggested by numerous examples of undeformed pseudomorphs, undisturbed relict structural and textural features in the blackwall and talc-bearing rocks, and tongues, pockets, and sackform embayments of talc-bearing rocks within host rocks showing no evidence of related disturbance (see also Chidester, 1962, pp. 93–94). No features suggesting either local or extensive volume changes during steatitization have been observed in the ultramafic bodies.

Calculations based on assumed volume-for-volume replacement of serpentinite by talc-carbonate rock indicate that this conversion could have been accomplished simply through introduction of CO_2 and

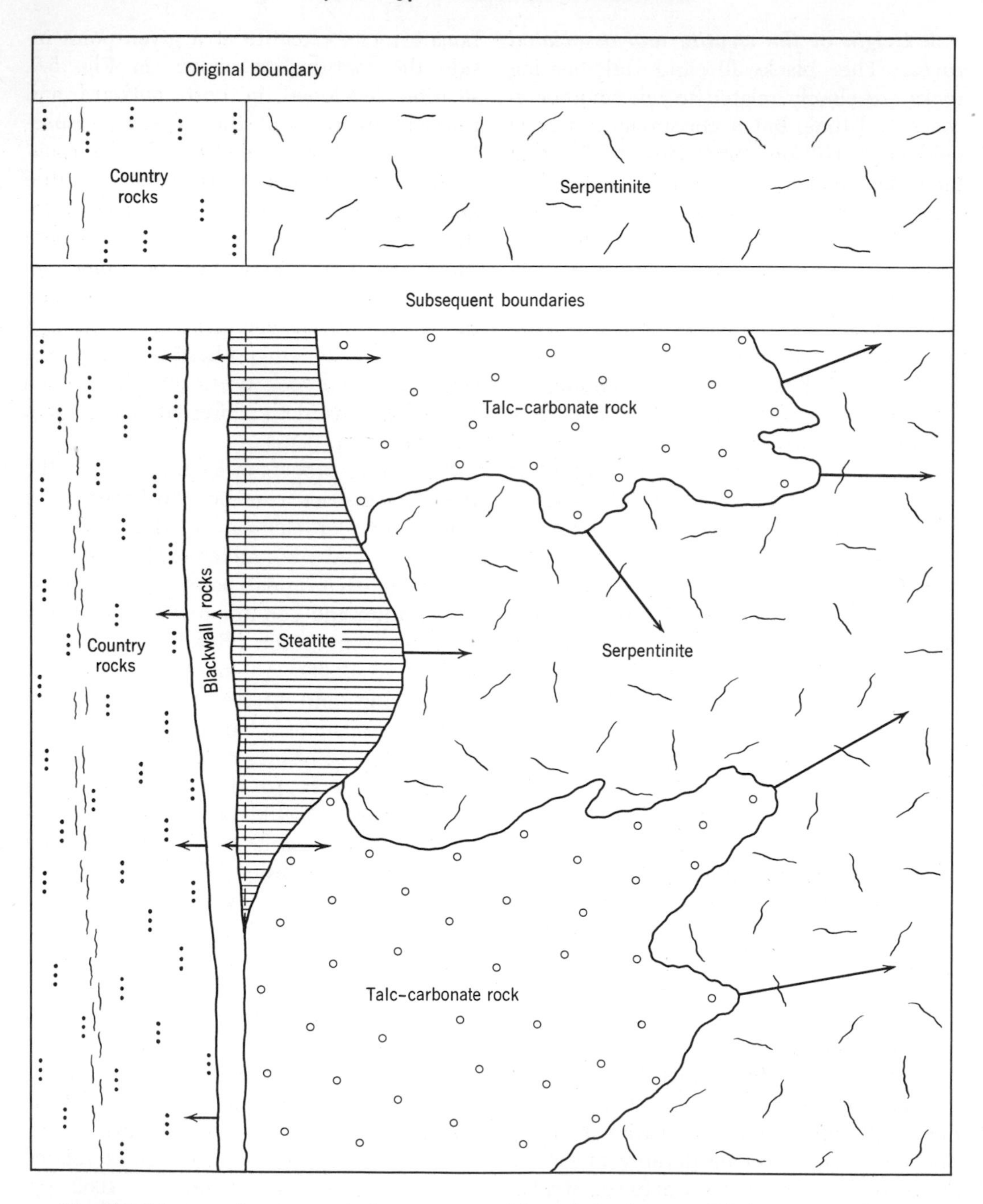

Fig. 5.7 Diagram showing typical movements of boundaries between lithologic zones during steatitization of serpentinite bodies of the Roxbury district. Thickness of blackwall rocks is considerably exaggerated.

loss of H_2O, with formation of talc and carbonate minerals in about the ratio of their actual occurrence. Further calculations of the kind made by Chidester (1962, pp. 94–121) suggest gains and losses of materials during development of the other lithologic units by metamorphic-differentiation reactions involving serpentinite and adjoining country rocks as starting materials. The changes in mineralogy and in-

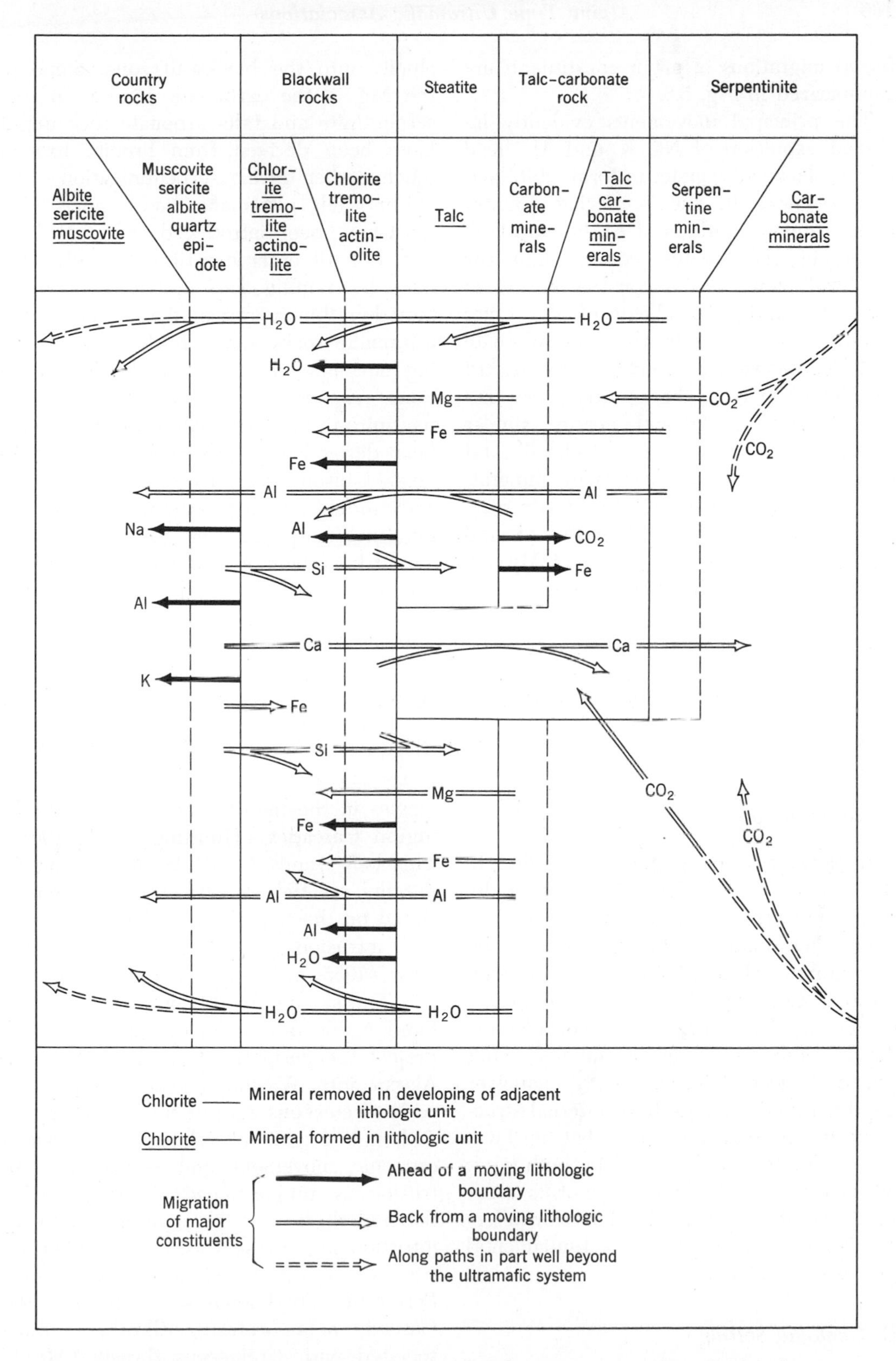

Fig. 5.8 Diagram summarizing formation and removal of major minerals and inferred migration of major constituents during steatitization of serpentinite bodies of the Roxbury district.

ferred migrations of major constituents are summarized in Fig. 5.8.

The principal movements evidently included expulsion of Na, K, and Al ahead of the blackwall contact to form albite and potash micas in the bordering country rocks, similar expulsion of Al, Fe, and H_2O ahead of the steatite contact into the blackwall zone, and inward expulsion of some Fe and CO_2 ahead of the other steatite boundary into the talc-carbonate rock. These were accompanied by inward transfer of Si from the country rocks into the blackwall rocks and steatite, similar transfer of Ca from the blackwall and country rocks to form carbonate minerals in the serpentinite and talc-carbonate rock, and outward transfer of Mg, Fe, Al, and H_2O from the serpentinite and of Mg, Al, and H_2O from the talc-carbonate rock chiefly into the blackwall zone. Some of the Mg in the carbonate minerals of the serpentinite and talc-carbonate rock might have been derived from brucite formed much earlier during serpentinization.

For each ultramafic body much CO_2 must have been introduced and much H_2O lost, but all other constituents could well have been indigenous and have been retained within a system that included the ultramafic rocks and a fairly thin bordering envelope of country rocks. The solutions responsible for conversion of serpentinite to talc-carbonate rock might have been derived from subjacent granitic rocks (e.g., Gillson, 1927; Hess, 1933), but the surrounding country rocks, which were being metamorphosed at the same time, would have been a nearer and more likely source.

III. THE TWIN SISTERS DUNITE, WASHINGTON

Donal M. Ragan

A. Introduction

In seeking a more general solution to the problem of peridotite intrusion, a detailed knowledge of the history of the olivine-rich material during emplacement is required. Hess (1955, p. 402) distinguished two types of tectonic emplacement: (a) by solid flow at considerable depth, and (b) as essentially fault bounded slices of serpentinite at shallower depths. Based on a study of internal structures, it can be demonstrated that the Twin Sisters dunite was emplaced by both types of movement, and a knowledge of its structural evolution during this intrusion offers a fuller understanding of the fundamental processes involved.

B. Geologic Setting

1. Cascade peridotite belt. There are a number of peridotite and serpentinite masses in the middle and northern Washington Cascades (Huntting et al., 1961). This belt trends N 30° W, approximately parallel to the structures of the range. Based on the hypothesis that one serpentinite intrusion may date the entire belt, Hess (1955, p. 396 and Fig. 1) suggests a late Triassic age for this belt. On the other hand, Noble and Taylor (1960, p. 189, 192) project the peridotite belt of southeastern Alaska into Washington and suggest an early Cretaceous age for these same rocks. Although a general relationship between orogenic movement and serpentinite intrusion is unquestioned, in detail both the hypothesis and the suggested dates of intrusion fail in the Cascade belt. Peridotites of a variety of ages are known. Peridotites are known which predate the Cascade metamorphism; still others are associated with Cretaceous thrusts (Misch, personal communication). Finally, post-early Tertiary intrusions are present at widely scattered localities (Ragan, 1963, p. 558). Thus, pre-, syn-, and postorogenic intrusions are present, and a correlation based on broad lithologic similarities alone conceals this more complicated history.

2. *Twin Sisters dunite.* The largest single peridotite mass in the Cascade belt is in the Twin Sisters Range of northwesternmost Washington, 20 miles due east of Bellingham. The Twin Sisters dunite body is an elliptical mass of approximately 90 km^2 total area. The long axis of the mass is parallel to the trend of the Cascade peridotite belt and parallel to the local and regional country rock structures.

Following Misch (1960, 1962), three thrust-bound structural units are recognized in the area. The autochthonous unit is composed of the Jurassic-Cretaceous Nooksack formation. Over this, the Church Mountain thrust brings the Chilliwack group and associated rocks of Devonian to Permian age. The Shuksan or upper thrust brings presumably pre-Jurassic greenschists and phyllites over the Paleozoics. Slivers and Klippen of a pre-Devonian crystalline basement unit are present, often with complex structural relationships, and they are locally associated with the Shuksan thrust zone. The lowest unit is exposed in a window north of Mount Baker, and the middle unit is an elongate, complex half-window.

The Twin Sisters dunite and two smaller dunite masses to the southeast are located along the western edge of the half-window. The Twin Sisters mass is intrusive into the thrust plates and the unconformable Swauk formation of uppermost Cretaceous-Paleocene Age, demonstrating a Tertiary and definitely postorogenic emplacement. The "Sutter Mountain fault," which was projected into the area from the south and thought to have localized the emplacement of the three dunite intrusions (Ragan, 1963, p. 551), has since been shown, both in the vicinity of the Twin Sisters Range, and to the south (Misch, personal communication), to be nonexistent. Rather, the "fault" is actually the steep, westward dipping Shuksan thrust itself. To the north, in the vicinity of the Twin Sisters Range, this thrust plane flattens considerably.

Associated with the peridotite contact are a number of exotic blocks. Lithologically these blocks include highly deformed clinopyroxenites and highly altered and cataclastic quartz dioritic gneisses. These types, separately as well as in association, are virtually identical to rocks of the pre-Devonian metamorphic basement unit found elsewhere. These slices were probably derived directly from the basement during passage by the intrusive mass.

In the surrounding country rocks no deviation from the regional structural trends can be attributed to the presence of the Twin Sisters body. A small Klippe at the northwest corner of the body, still with subhorizontal thrust plane, also attests to the lack of country rock involvement during emplacement. The smooth shape of the mass, and especially the fairly straight sides together with these undisturbed country rock structures, suggests a diapir of considerable vertical extent emplaced by faulting without significant drag effects in the country rock. However, a gravity survey by Thompson (1963, and personal communication) demonstrates that the mass has an average depth of as little as 1200 meters, but no more than 1600 meters. Thompson further suggests that dunite is replaced by serpentinite at depth.

C. *Composition of the Twin Sisters Dunite*

The Twin Sisters mass is composed of typically reddish brown weathering enstatite-bearing dunite. The unaltered rock consists of four minerals: olivine, enstatite, chromite and clinopyroxene. The olivine is slightly more magnesian than Fo_{90}, and has only slight compositional differences throughout the mass. The enstatite has approximately the same Mg/Fe ratio as the olivine. Ubiquitous chromite averages 1 to 2 per cent, but greater concentrations are locally present. The clinopyroxene occurs in trace quantities and is a chromium diopside. All minerals except enstatite have been analyzed chemically by Ross, Foster and Myers (1954, p. 707, 709, 710).

Samples have also been analyzed for a variety of elements, mostly those in trace concentrations (see Ragan, 1963, p. 553). Additionally, Stueber (1965), as part of world-wide study, determined the Na, Mn, Cr, Sc, and Co content of one specimen (Chapter 11-II), and Gaudette (1963) determined by X-ray fluorescent analysis the Ni, Fe, Mn, Cr, and Co content of the olivine, orthopyroxene, and clinopyroxene for 73 dunite specimens taken from a series of traverses across the body. Gaudette's results show that these elements vary only slightly throughout the mass.

D. Structures in the Dunite

The stages in the structural evolution of the dunite itself are critical to an understanding of the physical state of the mass during intrusion. Four types of structures, each gradational with the next, can be distinguished: (1) primary (?) structures, (2) early flow structures, (3) transitional structures, and (4) late cataclastic and related structures.

1. Primary (?) structures. The earliest elements recognizable in the Twin Sisters dunite consist of an apparently directionless fabric of anhedral olivine crystals with irregular and often interlocking boundaries and with a degree of coarseness (single grains up to 5 cm long) which makes interpretation difficult. Enstatite, with clinopyroxene exsolution lamallae, occupies intergranular positions between the olivines, either forming thin zones partly surrounding olivine grains, or as large, isolated, subhedral crystals. Disseminated euhedral to subhedral chromite grains are common, and also occur as concentrations in bands and schlieren.

Such features, especially the layers with euhedral chromite, are suggestive of magmatic relicts. However, this interpretation is based on an incomplete analogy with well-known igneous features, particularly those formed in layered ultramafic masses. Critical igneous features are lacking. Although the history of the earliest events requires much clarification, both the lack of confirmatory evidence and more general considerations (discussed later) suggest that if the dunite material did pass through an igneous stage, the characteristic features of that stage have been effectively obscured by later, solid-state processes. However, it is possible that these observed relict features pre-date intrusion.

2. Early flow structures. Many, but not all, of the thin layers of concentrated pyroxene and chromite in the dunite trend generally parallel to the long axis of the mass and dip steeply. Locally, some of the chromite layers are deformed into folds of similar type, and the axial planes of these folds also dip steeply. A fracture cleavage in the enclosing dunite parallel to these axial planes can often be detected. Locally, small folds are superimposed on the well-defined isoclinal ones. These incipient folds have differently oriented, but still steep axial planes (Fig. 5.9*a*).

A strong preferred crystallographic orientation of the olivine in the dunite is common. It can be detected by the usual universal stage techniques, and by compressional wave measurements (Birch, 1960, p. 1097). Several features of the rock contribute to the great difficulty in interpreting both the detailed orientation and meaning of this measured anisotropy. Principally, the problems relate to the coarseness of the grain and the complex substages of deformation and recrystallization through which the rock has passed. It is possible, however, to state several preliminary results of the fabric studies: (a) distinctly triclinic fabrics seem to be common; (b) certain elements present on the diagrams tend to be oriented parallel to other flow structures in the rock; and (c) in part it is the (100) plane, especially in medium-sized grains (5 to 10 mm), that

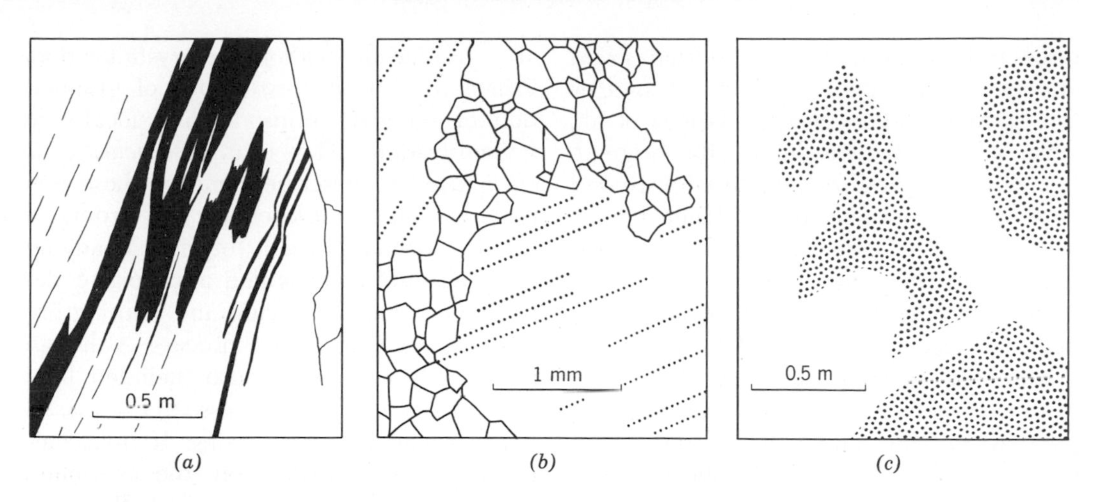

Fig. 5.9 (*a*) Isoclinally folded chromite layers. A fracture cleavage parallel to the axial planes is present in the dunite. Note the small, differently oriented folds in the three thin layers on the right. (*b*) Fine-grained mosaic zones of unstrained olivine surrounding and embaying large strained relicts. The deformation bands in the relicts are shown diagrammatically by the dotted lines. (*c*) Blocks of enstatite-bearing dunite in pyroxene-free dunite. Compare with the breccia-like microstructures of (*b*).

is statistically oriented parallel to the visible structures.

When undisturbed by deformation and recrystallization of later events, boundaries between these coarser olivine grains with a preferred orientation show evidence of recrystallization that includes (a) the presence of straight or curved boundaries, often meeting at sharp angles, and (b) the control, both in location and form, of some of them by impurities (small chromite crystals) located along the boundaries. Both types of feature are indicative of grain boundary migration (Voll, 1961).

It is not yet possible to give a really complete picture of the structural geometry produced during this stage. The steep chromite layers, and especially the similar folds with steep axial planes indicate an upward intrusive flow that is generally related to the gross geometry of the mass. That the dunite also participated in this solid-state flow is shown by both the visible planar structures and by the preferred orientation. The triaxial character of the fabric is probably due to the superposition of several flow directions, each oriented somewhat differently, but all part of the upward movement.

3. ***Transitional structures.*** The transitional stage is defined by the presence, in thin section, of clear-cut evidence of incomplete recrystallization, or by the presence of analogous features on larger scales.

The most common partial recrystallization texture consists of fine-grained mosaic zones surrounding, embaying, and traversing larger nonrecrystallized olivine grains (Fig. 5.9*b* illustrates the general character of these textures; other variations are illustrated in Ragan, 1963, p. 556). These large relicts retain features of internal deformation, particularly the deformation bands of undulatory extinction subparallel to (100) so often found in dunite. The finer grains have little or no evidence of such strain. Proof that this texture is due to the recrystallization of deformed olivine and is not original porphyritic or interprecipitate material is conclusive where a thin unstrained mosaic zone cuts a single strained grain. Further, there is a distinct tendency for some of the mosaic boundaries to be straight and to have triple grain boundary angles of approximately 120°, a characteristic of annealing recrystallization.

Similar textures are observed in experimentally deformed calcite, and the driving force is thought to be the internal strain energy of the deformed crystal and/or the grain boundary energy (Griggs et al., 1960, p. 36). In the dunite, the original, but now recrystallized, material included parts of the strained, but still intact crystals, and also similar material associated with fractured grains.

In part, the fine-grained recrystallized material occurs in well-defined zones. Within the core of the mass there is a distinct tendency for these zones to be parallel to the long axis of the body; near the borders, they are more nearly parallel to the contacts (Gaudette, 1963, p. 32–34).

Certain features of the mass suggest the existence of larger structures analogous to those found on the microscopic scale. At several localities enstatite-bearing dunite is present as blocklike masses surrounded by pyroxene-free dunite. The blocks are generally angular and in part the boundaries of adjacent blocks appear to match (Fig. 5.9*c*). Chromite-rich blocks are also present; Thayer (1961, p. 206) illustrates a small, partly angular mass of banded chromitite embedded in dunite from the Twin Sisters Range. Although more difficult to detect, blocks of dunite-in-dunite also appear to be present. The olivine grains of the blocks have a higher degree of strain than the olivine in the surrounding material.

The presence of these blocks indicates that at an early stage dunite of variable enstatite and chromite content formed separately; this rock was broken into blocks, engulfed and transported by the more dominant olivine-rich material. Most probably the basic mechanism is the same one so clearly operative at the microscopic scale, that is, the break-up of pre-existent material during the later stages of solid flow leaving block-like relicts surrounded by recrystallized material.

4. Cataclastic and related structures. Superimposed on all earlier structures are a series of deformational features which are produced without recrystallization. Principally, the process is one of granulation of mineral grains, leading locally to mylonitization. The term *protoclastic* is often used to describe some of these textures but since these effects are produced totally without benefit of accompanying magma, *cataclastic* is the appropriate descriptive term. Fracturing and jointing are also part of the general process. Although not strictly cataclastic, also included here is the latest stage in the essentially plastic deformation of single grains. If unaccompanied by recrystallization, the continued development of deformation lamellae, and undulatory extinction generally, finally results in actual rupture of the grains.

Almost every thin section of Twin Sisters dunite displays some granulation. These areas generally consist of narrow zones of comminuted olivine. Detailed variations in grain size distribution, zone width, and relationships at the margins of granulated areas clearly represent variations in the differential movement which produced them. Many of these shear zones are prominent enough to be mapped in the field, and the best developed zones are also visible on aerial photographs. Many zones, especially the large ones, are nearly vertical and trend parallel to the long axis of the body.

Though much less extensive, the effects of cataclasis are also present outside the shear zones. In the latest stage of the development of deformation bands in olivine grains, a straight fracture develops between two adjacent bands. These fractures may or may not be continuous across the entire banded grain. In some grains this straight fracture in one part of the grain becomes an irregular fracture in another part, and in a few cases can be related to interference by adjacent grains. More commonly, a different style of undulatory extinction is present, often superimposed on the banded type. This late deformation of grains produces very irregular extinction patterns similar in form to that often seen in cataclastic quartz. Finally, the entire grain is broken into small but still interlocking particles.

Bennett (1940) commented on the presence of two joint sets: one trending parallel to the long axis of the body and with steep dips, the other with moderate dips to the northwest. However, joints with other orientations are also present. Most of the jointed rock is completely fresh. A few joints however, are coated with a thin layer of serpentine, sometimes slickensided. This suggests that they are related to late stage intrusive movement, and a shallow depth is implied. The barren joints, including a well-developed set approximately parallel to the present topographic surface, are later and are probably due to release of stress during uplift and erosion.

E. Serpentinization

Serpentinite occurs around the entire margin of the dunite mass. The width of this marginal zone is variable, ranging from approximately 50 to 700 meters (Gaudette, 1963, p. 77). On the southeast corner of the body landsliding has exposed a complete transition from unaltered dunite to the various types of serpentinite over a distance of about 200 meters.

As the margin is approached from the dunite core, a rapid transition from unaltered dunite to massive serpentinite is observed. In thin section, the serpentinite is seen to form a mesh-structure of antigorite and subordinate chrysotile in the fractures of the olivine grains. The transition from olivine, to olivine with antigorite veinlets, and then entirely to serpentinite with mesh-structure is well displayed.

Beyond the massive zone the rock is slickensided and is succeeded by highly foliated serpentinite at the contact. In moderately slickensided and foliated rock, mesh-structure and shredded antigorite coexist. At the very contact, the rock is a talc-rich, highly crenulated, completely schistose serpentinite containing a few crude, lens-shaped fragments of more massive serpentinite.

Only traces of serpentine are present in the interior portions of the body. Where it is found in the core, it is generally associated with prominent shear zones, or as a thin coating on some joint surfaces. This internal serpentine shows little or no sign of shearing, although some of the joint coatings are slickensided. Only very small amounts of serpentine are present in the massive rock. From these relationships it is concluded that the serpentinization started at the margin and proceeded inward, and the source of the serpentinizing fluid was the country rock.

It is also clear that serpentinization occurred late in the intrusive history of the mass. The degree of development of slickenside and of schistose serpentinites is a measure of the syn- and postserpentinizational movement, but only a small amount is recorded in the interior of the mass. Most of the movement was concentrated within the outermost part of the marginal serpentinite zone, essentially at the contact.

F. Intrusion of the Dunite Mass

From the evidence presented, a reasonably complete outline can be given of the physical state of the dunite and of some of the intrusive processes. In the earliest intrusive stage the dunite material flowed plastically and resulted in the preferred orientation of the olivine, the rotation of the pre-existing compositional layers (or perhaps the segregation of these layers by metamorphic differentiation during flowage), and the folding of some of these layers. Recrystallization of olivine was probably dominant during this stage. Later, but transitional with this early flow stage, the deformed olivine only partially recrystallized. Finally, deformation occurred without recrystallization.

The structures of each of these stages are also related by a common orientation. Planar elements tend to be nearly vertical and to trend parallel to the long axis of the body. It is concluded that the movement which produced them was also vertical and related to the gross shape of the mass. It is also evident that the structural and petrologic sequence of the olivine-rich material is the result of movement from a high to a low PT environment.

During the latest stage of emplacement serpentinization of the dunite occurred, principally at the margins of the mass. Marginal shearing may well have been important during earlier stages, but with the development of the serpentinite sheath it became the dominant mechanism of intrusive movement. This is shown not only by the strongly schistose serpentinites at the contact, but also by the presence of small amounts of unsheared serpentine minerals in fracture zones in the core. The presence of no more than a trace of internal serpentine in the massive dunite indicates that free water was absent during this and earlier stages.

In terms of the transfer of such a large mass of dunitic material from great depth, the intrusion clearly involves forceful injection. The contacts between the solid dunite and the country rocks then, are essentially intrusive faults, and the late stage marginal shearing and the presence of exotic blocks of basement types helps confirm this.

The undeflected structures in the wall rock suggests that the mass upfaulted its roof in attaining its present position, acting like a piston. At some point, perhaps indirectly related to marginal serpentinization, the driving force of intrusion would have exceeded the pressure exerted by the weight of the overlying rocks. At this point it would require less energy to block out the roof by faults and push both dunite and the roof upward. This roof has since been removed by erosion.

Based on direct petrologic evidence, the recrystallization temperature of olivine is between the incongruent melting temperature of enstatite and the upper temperature limit of serpentinization (400 or 500°C, depending on the precise chemical reaction involved). Raleigh (1963, pp. 117–135) experimentally deformed olivine and produced recrystallization (see Chapter 6-IV). At confining pressures of 10 to 22 kb and temperatures of 1300°C olivine recrystallizes. At 450°C, olivine deforms plastically without recrystallization and undulatory extinction is the visible result. The hot but solid Lizard peridotite intrusion of Cornwall (Chapter 7-III) reached its present crustal environment and produced a thermal aureole at temperatures of 700 to 800°C or more (Green, 1964, p. 178). In the Twin Sisters dunite, therefore, it seems quite probable that penetrative flow accompanied by extensive recrystallization occurred at temperatures at least as low as 700°C, and perhaps even somewhat lower. Cataclasis occurred when temperatures were approximately 500°C, but in part overlapped serpentinization.

At the final stage temperatures at the country-rock serpentinite contact were considerably less than 400°C since no thermal aureole is present. However, as Clark and Fyfe (1961) point out, inflow of water may have abnormally cooled the margin. The interior need not have been so cool, although the presence of internal serpentine, both sheared and unsheared, indicates that temperatures here were also less than 400 to 500°C.

G. Conclusions

Bowen and Tuttle (1949) conclusively eliminated the possibility of the existence of a dry, low-temperature peridotite magma. Earlier, Bowen and Schairer (1936) had outlined the idea of the crystal mush, a largely crystalline mass with an associated "complex liquid," presumably of magmatic origin, as lubricant, in order to explain the apparent paradox of low-temperature mobility. Although this concept presents numerous difficulties, it still has its proponents (Thayer, 1964, p. 1516). In contrast to a general consensus (e.g., Turner and Verhoogen, 1960, p. 316), Thayer (1963) also emphasizes the characteristic presence, at least in many bodies, of associated magmatic differentiates, and suggests the existence of an alpine mafic stem from which the peridotites are supposed to be derived.

It is important, therefore, to point out that in some alpine dunites, including the Twin Sisters mass, not only are such igneous differentiates entirely absent, there is nothing demonstrably igneous about the material at all, nor is there any evidence for the existence of a mush. The crystal mush hypothesis is an improvement over former ideas to the degree that it shifts the view away from the magma. However, the terms *mush* and *magma* (a thick, pasty, porridgelike mass; Tyrrell, 1929, p. 46) are virtually identical etymologically. The peridotite mush may have existed where low temperature or hydrous minerals are present, as in the case of the plagioclase and hornblende bearing peridotites (Onuki, 1965). Unfortunately, it has been applied without such justification to nearly pure olivinites as well.

The reluctance of giving up the idea of the crystal mush as the physical state of the dunite during intrusion seems to be based on an intuitive feeling that such solid material should be incapable of such flow, even though the general process has been proved many times in various metamorphic terranes. Griggs and Blacic (1965a and 1965b) found that under certain experimental conditions common silicates, including olivine, are virtually without strength, thus removing even this difficulty.

The demonstration that the Twin Sisters dunite moved as a solid during intrusion is the next logical step away from the magmatic view, and overcomes the principal difficulties of the crystal mush hypothesis. It is then possible to consider that many other dunite masses were intruded as solids; second order factors, such as distance of crustal penetration, thermal history and association with water, could then account for their variable character. This demonstration of solid emplacement also lends considerable weight to deRoever's hypothesis (1957) that perhaps alpine-type peridotites are in general tectonically transported from the mantle.

An important remaining point concerns the ultimate origin of the olivine-rich material. Igneous textures have been postulated for a number of intrusive peridotites. In discussing igneous differentiation processes by which dunitic material could arise, Wager (1958, p. 40, and Wager et al., 1960, p. 76) points out that the making over of a true crystal mush (olivine crystals and interstitial magma) of cumulate origin would really be a form of metamorphism. Strictly then, the dunite need never have been magmatic. Even if an igneous stage is granted, the important mechanical question is when and where did this stage occur? Similar metamorphic textures found in nonintrusive dunite (inclusions found in basalts; Talbot et al., 1963) and the ancient mineral age of the dunite of St. Paul's Rocks (Hart, 1965) show that no necessary relationship between such an igneous stage and intrusion exists.

IV. GARNETIFEROUS ULTRABASIC ROCKS OF OROGENIC REGIONS

M. J. O'Hara

Wherever "garnet" or "garnetiferous" is used in this account, a pyrope-rich pyralspite garnet is implied unless otherwise specified. "Garnet-peridotite" is restricted to rocks containing garnet and magnesian olivine in apparent equilibrium, and excludes the eulysites which are almandine-fayalite bearing metasediments of the granulite facies. "Eclogite" is applied only to garnet-clinopyroxene rocks that are sufficiently rich in Na_2O, Al_2O_3, and FeO to superficially resemble the bulk compositions of common extrusive basalts. "Crustal garnetiferous ultrabasics" indicate those rocks that occur as lenses or parts of lenses among gneisses and schists, distinguishing them from "xenolithic garnetiferous ultrabasics" found as transported blocks in kimberlite and other alkaline basic diatremes (see Chapter 10-IV).

The crustal garnetiferous ultrabasic rocks are divisible into an eclogite (garnet-peridotite) mineral facies group, characterized by the stability of garnet + olivine, the latter often partly serpentinized, and a granulite (spinel-peridotite) mineral facies group, characterized by the stability of two pyroxenes + spinel instead of garnet + olivine. The granulite group includes the assemblage garnet + pyroxene(s) + spinel.

A. *Garnet-Peridotite Facies Group*

These occur as alpine-type ultrabasic masses among gneisses and schists of the amphibolite or hornblende granulite mineral facies, apparently restricted to rocks of Europe metamorphosed during the caledonian orogeny, or rocks of possible caledonian age exposed as 'basement' during the hercynian and alpine orogenies. Contradictory radiometric ages from Norway (McDougall and Green, 1964) have been disputed (O'Hara and Mercy, 1965). Outcrops are known from Sweden (Du Reitz, 1935); Norway (O'Hara and Mercy, 1963; also Chapter 6-III); Czechoslovakia and Germany (Kokta and Nemec, 1935; Hentschel, 1937); Switzerland (Dal Vesco, 1953); Austria, Italy (Hammer, 1921); and France (Brière, 1920; Jérémine, 1938), further references to an extensive literature being traceable through Eskola (1921). Crustal garnet-peridotites are absent from those regions (S. Africa, Siberia and America) in which the world's best known kimberlite provinces are found.

Porphyroclastic textures and other evidence of tectonic emplacement of crustal garnet peridotites in a crystalline state are reported from the German and Norwegian provinces (Chapter 6-III). The mineral facies of the ultrabasic masses contrasts with that of the country rocks. Marginal reaction is slight and typical of low-grade metamorphic conditions (O'Hara and Mercy, 1963). Evidence of intrusive igneous contacts is lacking. Garnet peridotite and garnet-pyroxene rocks generally occur as deformed layers with transitional contacts within much larger masses of garnet-free ultrabasic rocks, but sharply bounded masses of garnet-clinopyroxene rock do occur (Eskola, 1921, description of the Rodhaugen eclogite; Hentschel, 1937) and these may owe their character to the higher resistance of these two minerals to mechanical deformation. Sharply bounded tectonic inclusions of gneisses and quartz-bearing eclogites such as are found also in the country rocks are known from two Norwegian localities (D. A. Carswell, personal communication). Transition into eclogite containing quartz, kyanite or jadeite-rich omphacite has not been observed within an ultrabasic mass.

*1. **Petrography.*** Pink garnet porphyroclasts of 5 to 10 mm accompanied by similar-sized porphyroclasts of bright green jadeite-bearing chrome diopside are accompanied frequently by equally large, more deformed porphyroclasts of pale enstatite and rare ragged porphyroclasts of olivine. These are set in a finer, sometimes very fine grained matrix of olivine, enstatite, tremolite or hornblende, and chlorite, the last three allegedly being new growth minerals during the mechanical deformation (O'Hara and Mercy, 1963). Serpentinization postdates cataclasis. Porphyroclastic textures comparable with those common among crustal garnet-peridotites are rare among xenolithic garnet-peridotites from kimberlite.

Unlike the situation found in xenolithic peridotites from kimberlite, dunite, olivine-rich harzburgite, peridotites with high clinopyroxene/orthopyroxene ratio and rocks rich in garnet predominate in crustal garnet-peridotite masses. Garnet-harzburgite, which is an abundant member of xenolithic suites, is very scarce.

Nickel-rich, calcium-poor magnesian olivine with a higher Fe/Mg ratio than the coexisting orthopyroxene is typical (O'Hara and Mercy, 1963). Co-existing pyroxenes show very limited mutual solid solution implying low temperature equilibriation, lower than that indicated by pyroxene pairs from xenolithic garnet-peridotites, and there is very little Al_2O_3 in the pyroxenes from either environment. The garnets are pyralspites with Cr_2O_3 at 0.3 to 1.9 per cent and $Ca/(Ca + Mg + Fe + Mn)$ remarkably uniform at 0.12 ± 0.02 despite $Mg/(Mg + Fe)$ variation from 0.86 to 0.57. These garnets have lower Cr_2O_3 contents than the otherwise comparable garnets from xenolithic garnet-peridotites ($Cr_2O_3 \sim 1.9$ to 7.2 per cent; sources given by O'Hara and Mercy, 1966). The parageneses of crustal-garnet peridotites have been discussed in detail by O'Hara and Mercy (1963).

Whole rock chemical analyses are or will be available for garnetiferous peridotites, serpentinites, and garnet-pyroxene rocks from Bohemia (Lemberg, 1875; Hentschel, 1937); Switzerland (Dal Vesco, 1953); and Norway (Mercy and O'Hara, 1965b; D. A. Carswell, personal communication). Crustal garnet peridotites are frequently richer in Al_2O_3, FeO, and CaO than xenolithic types and range across the compositional gap in Ca-Mg-Fe projection between xenolithic garnet peridotite and xenolithic eclogite from kimberlite, but are distinguished from crustal eclogite bodies in the country rocks by their higher concentrations of MgO, Cr_2O_3, NiO, and lower concentrations of FeO, Na_2O, K_2O, and P_2O_5 (Mercy and O'Hara, 1965b). The layering in the crustal garnetiferous ultrabasic masses cannot readily be explained in terms of simple igneous crystal sorting, whether of the present mineral assemblage or of some pre-metamorphic assemblage.

Few estimates of the normal geothermal gradient would permit the conditions of equilibration deduced from the mineral assemblage of crustal garnet-peridotites ($\sim 600°C$; ~ 17 kilobars, in the absence of H_2O; see Chapters 1-II and 12-III) to be attained under lithostatic conditions. The low-temperature and low-water content at equilibration rule out a direct igneous origin. Equilibration clearly took place in an environment different from that in which the enclosing gneisses and schists were crystallized where the stability of amphiboles, micas, albite-rich felspars and antiperthites indicates water-rich lower-pressure and high-temperature conditions.

Numerous hypotheses for the origin of garnetiferous peridotites have been suggested. Eskola (1921) regarded the Norwegian examples as igneous, being early crystal accumulates from a huge magma body undergoing fractional crystallization, the residual liquids of which yielded the enclosing amphibolite facies gneisses and anorthosites, whereas Dal Vesco (1953) interpreted the garnet peridotites near Bellinzona, Switzerland, as discrete igneous intrusions retaining primary mineralogy. The specific petrogenetic scheme suggested required an ultrabasic magma which fractionated by precipitating four-phase garnet-lherzolite, yielding residual liquids which consolidated successively to lherzolite, harzburgite and enstatite rock, some of the enstatite liquid becoming contaminated by calc-silicate rocks to yield websterite; this cannot be reconciled with experimental results on ultrabasic synthetic systems. Grubenmann (1908) regarded these same garnet peridotite masses as a stock of differentiated ultrabasic igneous rock that had been metamorphosed subsequently to the present mineral assemblages. Hentschel (1937) proposed a complex sequence of events for a mass in Germany involving the pneumatolytic alteration of a serpentinite followed by pyroxenite facies metamorphism, followed in turn by eclogite facies metamorphism, and Rost (1961) has suggested a metamorphic origin from presumably igneous spinel-bearing peridotites. Davidson (1943) suggested an origin for the Norwegian masses by metamorphism of a layered gabbro-peridotite sequence of igneous origin. Subsequently it has been shown that simple metamorphism of a layered gabbro-peridotite sequence cannot account for the compositional variation in these masses (Mercy and O'Hara, 1965b) and an origin by eclogite facies metamorphism of ultrabasic material followed by tectonic emplacement was preferred over Eskola's hypothesis (O'Hara and Mercy, 1963). Reconsideration of the evidence reviewed above suggests that a better composite hypothesis can be constructed for all these masses.

The European garnet-peridotites may represent layered spinel-bearing ultrabasic masses containing high Al_2O_3 pyroxenes formed by accumulation from basic magmas crystallizing near the base of the crust prior to orogenesis. During rapid down buckling of the orogen these dry, relatively cold rocks were subjected to high pressures and recrystallized to eclogite facies assemblages, with reaction between the layers produced by original igneous processes, before the temperature could rise to the normal values appropriate to the depth of burial, or water gain access from the country rocks. Survival of the eclogite facies assemblage requires the coincidence of a second event, the rapid and extensive isostatic or tectonic uplift of the garnet-peridotites before recrystallization in response to rising temperature or access of water occurs. This preservation of the eclogite facies assemblage may be favored by the additional event inferred to have occurred in Norway, which is tectonic transport of the garnet-peridotite mass into cool, relatively dry metamorphic rocks formed earlier in the orogenic episode. The requisite sequence of events may, therefore, be a high-grade regional metamorphism, followed later by a rapid downbuckling of the cool orogen combined with conditions favoring extensive lateral or vertical tectonic transport of the ultrabasic rocks, and followed rapidly by uplift. The sequence of events postulated is sufficiently complicated to account for the apparent restriction of crustal garnet-peridotites and serpentinites to rocks deformed in a single orogeny within a relatively small area of the earth's surface. Differences of timing of tectonic events within major orogenic episodes elsewhere and at other times might then be expected to produce "alpine-type" peridotite provinces of equally distinctive mineralogy, and there are indications that this prediction is fulfilled. The alpine-type ultrabasic rocks of the hercynian and alpine orogenies in Europe appear to be predominantly spinel-bearing high-Al_2O_3 pyroxene peridotites (e.g. Collée, 1963; Green, 1964a; Lacroix, 1894; Peters, 1963; Peters and Niggli, 1964; O'Hara and Mercy, unpublished) quite distinct from alpine-type peridotites of eastern N. America, New Caledonia and New Zealand which appear to be predominantly chromite-bearing low-Al_2O_3 pyroxene peridotites in which plagioclase may also appear (Ross et al., 1954; Macgregor and Smith, 1963; Challis, 1965a).

Davidson (1943, 1964a) has suggested that the whole suite of eclogite, garnet-peridotite, and granulite facies inclusions occurring as xenoliths in kimberlite is derived from the crust and that the crustal garnet peridotites are a representative source of xenolithic garnet peridotites (Chapter 10-IV). The petrographic, textural, mineralogical, geochemical and distribution differences noted above between the two suites do not support this claim (see O'Hara and Mercy, 1963, for a detailed discussion of this proposition) nor do the inferences about conditions of equilibration reached in Chapter 12-III. Kopesky and Sattran (1962) have described an example of an alkaline basic diatreme cutting and including xenoliths of a crustal garnet peridotite in Czechoslovakia. O'Hara and Mercy (1966) have shown, however, that the garnets from the garnet peridotite in xenoliths and country rock have Cr_2O_3 contents typical of the crustal suite and distinct from those reported from the xenolithic suite typical of most kimberlite diatremes.

B. Spinel-Peridotite Facies Group

Six occurrences are known to date, but the differences between them preclude a common origin. The alpine-type peridotites which penetrate regionally metamorphosed Mesozoic limestones in the Pyrenees (Lacroix, 1894, 1900; Ravier, 1959) are predominantly spinel-lherzolites (including the type lherzolite) that are richer overall in CaO and Al_2O_3 than peridotites forming the bulk of other masses in orogenic zones or occurring as xenolithic suites in kimberlite (O'Hara and Mercy, unpublished). The Pyrenean lherzolites contain layers of ariégite (garnet-2 pyroxenes-spinel rocks; Lacroix, 1900, 1917). The spinels are rich in Al_2O_3 and MgO but the pyrope-rich garnet contains very much less Cr_2O_3 than garnet from crustal garnet-peridotite. The pyroxenes are rich in Al_2O_3 while the clinopyroxenes contain moderate amounts of the acgirine and jadeite molecules (O'Hara and Mercy, unpublished). Inferred conditions of metamorphic crystallization lie within the spinel-peridotite facies close to the garnet-peridotite facies boundary at moderate to high temperatures. Evidence of intense mechanical deformation abounds (Lacroix, 1894) and the mineral assemblages differ markedly from those of the lherzolite nodules in alkali olivine basalts (O'Hara and Mercy, unpublished) although contrary assertions have been made (Lacroix, 1894; Collée, 1963). The lherzolites and ariégites present special problems of interpretation and many conflicting hypotheses of their status and origin have been proposed (e.g., Lacroix, 1894, 1900, 1917; Ravier, 1959, 1964; Zwaart, 1954). O'Hara and Mercy (unpublished) prefer an origin by metamorphism of a layered igneous accumulative harzburgite containing originally a CaO and Al_2O_3-rich orthopyroxene, with reaction between peridotite and more aluminous layers during recrystallization, although most previous authors favor some form of direct igneous origin. Peters (1963) and Peters and Niggli (1964) have reported garnet-bearing rocks apparently similar to ariégite from serpentinized peridotite in the alpine nappes near Davos.

It appears from both the original description (Milliard, 1959) and subsequent studies (J. Kornprobst, personal communication) that the red mineral in a Moroccan peridotite is actually spinel (Ringwood et al., 1964; and Davis, 1964, accepted this as garnet). The mass, nevertheless, contains garnet-pyroxene rocks which appear to be closely comparable with the Pyrenean ariégites (Milliard, 1959).

A large peridotite mass, chiefly spinel-bearing dunite but containing layers of websterite and garnet-clinopyroxene rock outcrops among albite-epidote-amphibolite facies rocks of the Sambagawa metamorphic belt, Japan. The clinopyroxenes vary from jadeite-poor chrome diopside to samples moderately rich in jadeite (Miyashiro and Seki, 1958; Shido, 1958). Yoshino (1961, 1964) suggests a tectonic emplacement for this mass in the core of a major anticline, but does not speculate on its ultimate origin. The conditions of crystallization appear to have lain on the boundary of the spinel and garnet-peridotite facies at rather low temperatures.

Amphibole-bearing garnet-spinel-clinopyroxene rocks occur as a small mass within the serpentine at Knockormal, Ballantrae, Scotland (Bloxam and Allen, 1959). This so-called eclogite is associated closely with serpentinized spinel peridotite and is accompanied by crossite and glaucophane schists and pyroxene granulites which may be tectonic inclusions. The great abundance of Al_2O_3 and paucity of Na_2O in the clinopyroxene (fassaite), and the TiO_2-poor character of the amphibole renders the "eclogite" unique. Bloxam and Allen (1959) infer the presence of very high Al_2O_3 pyroxenes in the adjacent lherzolite and there is textural evidence suggesting exsolution of garnet from the orthopyroxene. This may be a high-temperature, high-pressure, igneous paragenesis formed from a magma containing sufficient water to stabilize an amphibole, but many other hypotheses have been suggested in the literature traceable through the reference given.

Garnet-pyroxene-spinel rocks occur at the margins of spinel and hornblende-bearing lherzolite layers in granulite facies gneisses in northwest Scotland (O'Hara, 1961). High temperatures but moderate pressures of equilibration within the amphibole-spinel-peridotite facies are deduced (O'Hara, 1961, 1965b, and Chapter 12-III). Peach et al. (1907) suggested an accumulative igneous origin from a magma that gave rise to the enclosing acid intermediate gneiss complex. Sutton and Watson (1951) proposed metamorphism of igneous sills in a magmatite complex. Bowes et al. (1961, 1964) regard the ultrabasic and garnetiferous rocks as layered igneous intrusions with primary igneous mineralogy (1961) or metamorphic mineralogy (1964). O'Hara (1961, 1965b) ascribes the garnet-pyroxene rocks to reaction between intrusive alpine-type peridotite and acid country rock during high-grade regional metamorphism.

The two outstanding problems of the garnetiferous ultrabasic rocks of the orogenic regions appear to be the origin of the chemical variations within the masses, and the circumstances leading to emplacement of masses reflecting such different conditions of crystallization in particular orogenic zones.

6. *Deformation of Alpine Ultramafic Rocks*

I. INTRODUCTION

P. J. Wyllie

Many combined methods of analysis are required for understanding of the complex sequences of events involved in the emplacement of alpine ultramafic bodies (Chapter 5-I). This chapter is concerned largely with structural techniques and with deformational features of the rocks. In Chapter 5-II Jahns related the emplacement of the Vermont serpentinite bodies to the episodes of regional deformation. Lapham, in Section II of this chapter, provides a more detailed structural study of serpentinites emplaced in another part of the Appalachian ultramafic belt. Analysis of macrostructures and microstructures in the serpentinite and the regional schists of the Pennsylvania Piedmont permits correlation of the deformational patterns in the serpentinite with the regional orogenic history. The regional structures are superimposed on the serpentinite and stages of serpentinization can be related to the successive deformations.

In Section III Lappin describes structural and petrofabric studies on the dunites and garnet peridotites of Norway, similar to the group described by O'Hara in Chapter 5-IV. These have steep or vertical contacts with the Basal Gneiss complex. The dunite is fresh except for a marginal zone of serpentinite, and it is strongly foliated. Structural analysis of the gneiss reveals four periods of fold movements with two main metamorphic episodes. The dunites appear to have undergone three periods of crystallization. The intrusion and folding of the dunite can be related to shearing in adjacent gneisses. Petrofabric studies show that olivine orientation is always related to a macroscopic foliation. The petrofabric and textural studies suggest that the dunites originated by syntectonic recrystallization, with flow during the final deformation becoming concentrated within certain layers.

In Section IV Raleigh describes the results of experimental deformation of ultramafic rocks and minerals. The experimental work is concerned mainly with the strength of serpentine, and with glide mechanisms in mafic minerals and the origin of intragranular deformational structure. Serpentine under pressure is ductile, like other minerals, until it reaches 600 to 700°C, whereupon its strength decreases markedly and it fails by brittle fracture. The weakening and embrittlement occurs at 300 to 350°C if 2 per cent brucite is present. Weakening and embrittlement of the serpentine results from dehydration. The applications of this result to the tectonic emplacement of serpentinite are discussed. It is proposed also that the tectonic development of the mobile belts may be related to weakening in serpentinite during downwarping and heating.

Finally, in Section V Gold illustrates small-scale deformational features of ultramafic rocks beautifully displayed by asbestos veining in two hand specimens. He summarizes the results of a structural analysis of the specimens and concludes that the asbestos fiber bands formed within the serpentinite by rearrangement of material already available within the rock.

II. THE TECTONIC HISTORY OF MULTIPLY DEFORMED SERPENTINITE IN THE PIEDMONT OF PENNSYLVANIA

Davis M. Lapham

A. Structural Aspects of the Serpentinite Problem

As this volume attests, the origin of serpentinites and ultramafic intrusives is a much discussed problem. Although from a descriptive viewpoint ultramafics have conveniently been subdivided into three general categories—layered intrusives of the Bushveld type, small plutons of the Alpine type, and zoned plutons of the Alaskan type—most authors have pursued a common origin. In one fashion or another this origin usually involves the migration of mantle material through the crust. Whether this ultramafic material is a basaltic differentiate, a product of subcrustal fractional melting, or an entity of its own is still very much a moot question. Comprehensive characterization of deformations that have acted on these ultramafics, especially if assignable to a particular orogeny, yields significant information about mode of emplacement, crystallization sequence, and behavior under tectonic stresses.

Perhaps the most difficult ultramafic to study is the small, unzoned pluton of the Alpine type located in orogenically deformed eugeosynclines. Typically, they are almost completely serpentinized, hence the term "serpentinite," highly sheared especially at their contacts, and surrounded by a relatively low grade of regional and/or contact metamorphism which belies their supposedly high-temperature origin. Thus their tectonic environment raises fascinating questions. In what way are deep-seated structural lineaments responsible for their loci? Is reintrusion, either semicrystalline or solid, responsible for their present crustal position? And from a broader structural view, have the structural features of serpentinite, even though subjected to stresses of varying magnitude, direction, and duration, been preserved with sufficient clarity to help unravel regional tectonisms?

These questions are especially pertinent to the structural concepts of the Pennsylvania Piedmont. Here is a eugeosynclinal sequence that has been battered time and again by orogenic forces of folding, thrust faulting, regional metamorphism, and igneous intrusion (see Chapter 5-II). Original sedimentary characteristics have been so obscured that stratigraphic and structural relationships are still undeciphered. The resultant confusion has given rise throughout the Piedmont to the so-called "Martic Problem" involving questionable thrust faulting of schists of uncertain age against Cambro-Ordovician sediments to the northwest. Absolute age measurement by radioactive dating techniques are complicated by several metamorphic recrystallizations that are not necessarily directly correlative with a particular deformation. The solution of these problems bears directly on the origin of curvature of the Appalachian Mountain System (e.g., Drake and Woodward, 1963), which changes in strike from north-south to nearly east-west at the site of the Pennsylvania serpentinites. Finally, ability to place recognizable patterns of deformation in a particular orogenic framework, if once established, can be extended to apply to other areas within and outside the Piedmont. This report augments the techniques and results initiated by McKinstry (1961), Hopson (1960), Freedman et al. (1964), Lapham and McKague (1964), Lapham and Bassett (1964), and Rickard (1965) for correlating sequential deformational patterns with regional orogenic history.

B. Techniques of Structural Analysis

Structural elements can conveniently be divided into macrostructures and microstructures. Macrostructures are elements measurable in the field, chiefly cleavages, joints, faults, fold axes, axial planes, and large scale compositional banding. Microstructures are elements best observed under microscopic examination and include mineral lineations or foliations and small scale compositional banding. Macrostructures are most useful for revealing regional patterns of deformation and for comparing structurally distinct deformational units and provinces. For example, the more competent a rock unit, the more likely it is to have preserved older deformations, provided the deformational stress per unit time was sufficient to impose a structural grain. Similarly, degree of homogeneity and isotropy will exert a control on the strain pattern with varying fidelity to changes in stress magnitude or direction. Microscopic examination, on the other hand, best reveals three-dimensional orientations of newly crystallized minerals or the recrystallization and/or rotation of preexisting minerals. The extent to which these processes operated under a particular stress field characterizes the intensity, or "style," of that particular deformation.

Briefly, the structural terminology used here (proposed by Freedman et al., 1964, p. 624) is S_0 for denoting bedding, S_1, for the first cleavage, S_2, the next, etc. Analogously, F_1, is the fold associated with the S_1 cleavage, F_2 the second, etc. Corresponding letters and subscripts are used for lineations (L), fold axes (A), and deformations (D). The use of these terms for serpentinite is based on structural analogies. Their physical denotation in serpentinite is almost meaningless, although of important connotative implications. The locations of structure stations are as follows:

Tucquan Creek: 11 miles northwest of Peach Bottom on Susquehanna River
Fishing Creek South: 3 miles northwest of Peach Bottom on Susquehanna River
Bald Friar: 1.4 miles south of Pennsylvania State line on Susquehanna River
Haines Brook: 0.75 miles north of Pennsylvania State line on Susquehanna River
Rhodewalt Quarry: 1.6 miles southwest of Nottingham, Pennsylvania.

Macrostructural analysis consisted of the recorded measurement of attitude and character of S surfaces, axes, and lineations. In the schist adjacent to serpentinite, the significant elements are compositional banding, cleavages, fold axes, and axial planes. Joints and faults appear to be of less utility. Subscripts were assigned in the field where transecting age relationships were clear. The poles to planar elements were plotted on a lower hemisphere Schmidt net stereographic projection. Thus, a northeast striking plane dipping south appears as an emergent pole in the northwest quadrant. Poles to horizontal planes plot centrally and poles to vertical planes peripherally. The poles of linear elements such as axes were plotted directly. Although relatively few poles of any one element in schist define an attitude, in serpentinite a minimum of 100 poles is desirable at any one structure station. Care is required in measuring serpentinite surfaces because of magnetite and typically curved (composite) fracture surfaces. A more complete discussion of accuracy is

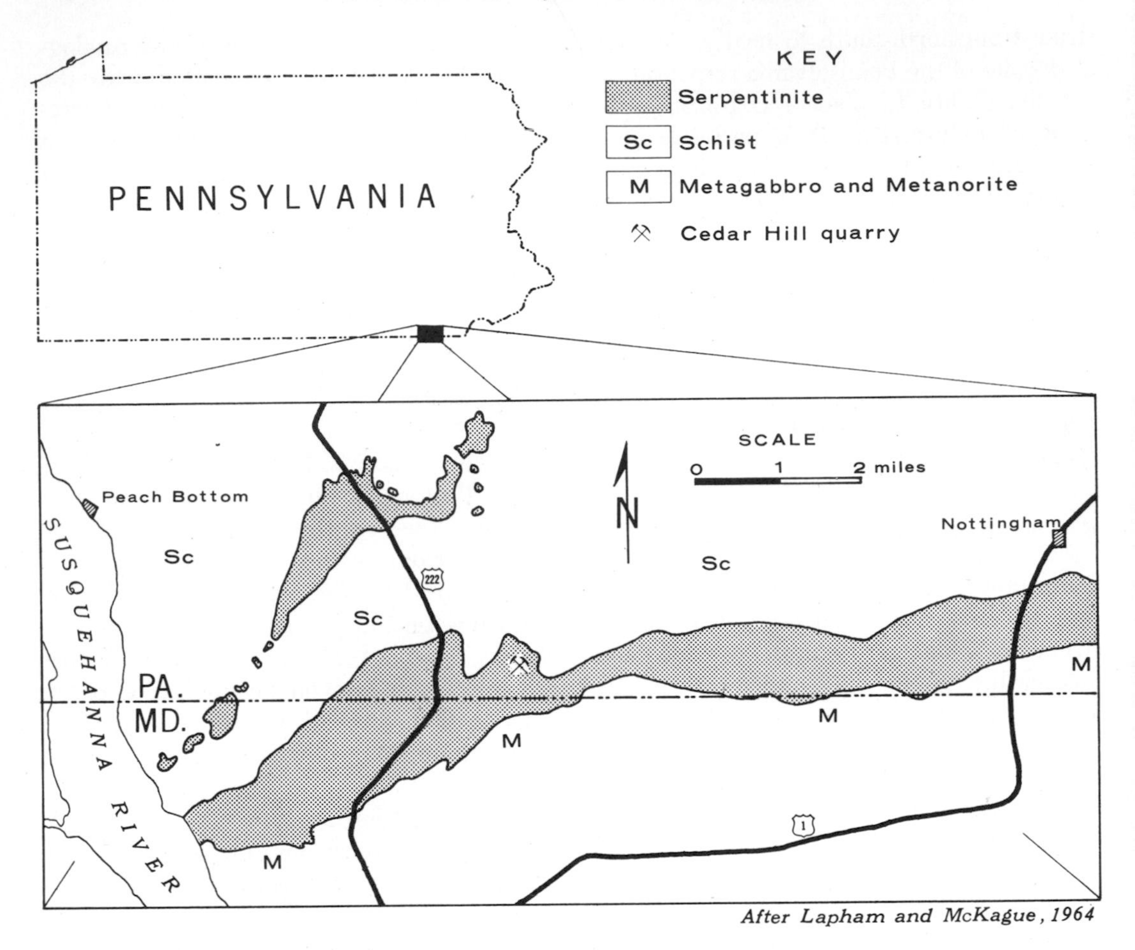

Fig. 6.1 Geologic location map of serpentinite area in Pennsylvania and Maryland.

treated by Freedman et al. (1964), and by Lapham and McKague (1964).

For microstructural analysis, oriented samples were collected from which oriented petrographic sections were prepared. Serpentinite samples were collected from four stations at Cedar Hill quarry (Fig. 6.1). The macrostructures present in each sample were measured to check previous and more extensive observations (709 poles) from the quarry (Lapham and McKague, 1964). Two horizontal sections from each sample provided strike directions for each structural element. Vertical sections cut perpendicular to the strike provided an accurate dip for each of the known macrostructural elements. Correlating a particular strike in one section with its corresponding dip in another section depends on the recognizability and orientational uniformity of that element. At Cedar Hill this was obtainable for early chrysotile, later lizardite and antigorite veins or shear planes, gash-fracture chrysotile, banded chromite, vein magnetite, and occasionally carbonate, deweylite, and brucite veins. The results were plotted on a Schmidt stereographic projection in the same way as for the macrostructural elements.

C. Macrostructures in Schist and Serpentinite

The area under consideration (Fig. 6.1) lies in southern Lancaster and Chester Counties, Pennsylvania, and in northern Cecil County, Maryland, along what is often considered to be northwestern boundary of the Appalachian eugeosyncline. The

Martic line, separating schists from carbonate rocks, is 16 miles north of the serpentinites. The Piedmont in this area is composed of the Glenarm series of quartz-mica-chlorite schists, graywackes, impure quartzites, and thin metabasalts. Compositional distinctions between units are usually sharp and their thickness is commonly less than 100 feet. As a result, the area as a whole is inhomogeneous and behaves anisotropically under stress. The serpentinized ultramafics are intrusive into the Peters Creek formation of the Glenarm series. Two trends, or belts, of serpentinite are present (Fig. 6.1). The more northerly trend is composed of one large and numerous smaller plutons with extensively sheared contacts, which are the result of realignment of these plutons with a major regional trend. Presumably, they are now rootless intrusives. The more southerly trend is the major serpentinite massif. Eastward it diverges from the northern serpentinite and from the regional trend, striking nearly east-west in this area. The structural independence of this larger intrusive is evidenced by its resistance to realignment stresses, which were able to rotate smaller serpentinites and to impose a uniform cleavage upon the country rock.

Freedman et al. (1964) studied fold patterns along the Susquehanna River from carbonates north of the Martic line to schist between the two serpentinite trends. Three distinct, sequential regional patterns emerged, designated D_1, D_2, and D_3, and represented respectively by cleavages S_1, S_2, and S_3. More recent work has extended the patterns both east and west along strike. The first two of these patterns were traced throughout their traverse, but the D_3 pattern first emerged just north of the serpentinites and becomes dominant only in a few of the less competent micaceous schists (Fig. 6.2). These relationships (Freedman et al., 1964) derived from 22 structural stations from north to south are summarized in Fig. 6.2. The S_2 cleavage remains essentially constant throughout the area, whereas the earlier S_1 cleavage has been overturned from steeply south, dipping in the south, to steeply north, dipping toward the north. Near the serpentinites, they were unable to distinguish S_1 from S_2 cleavages because of a similar orientation of the two sets and because of the superimposition of S_3. The S_3 cleavage is clearly distinct. It dips north and is more widely spaced than earlier surfaces. The recumbent D_1 pattern, the earliest recognized (Freedman et al., 1964), represents tectonic transport northward with a root zone of vertical foliation beginning approximately at the site of the

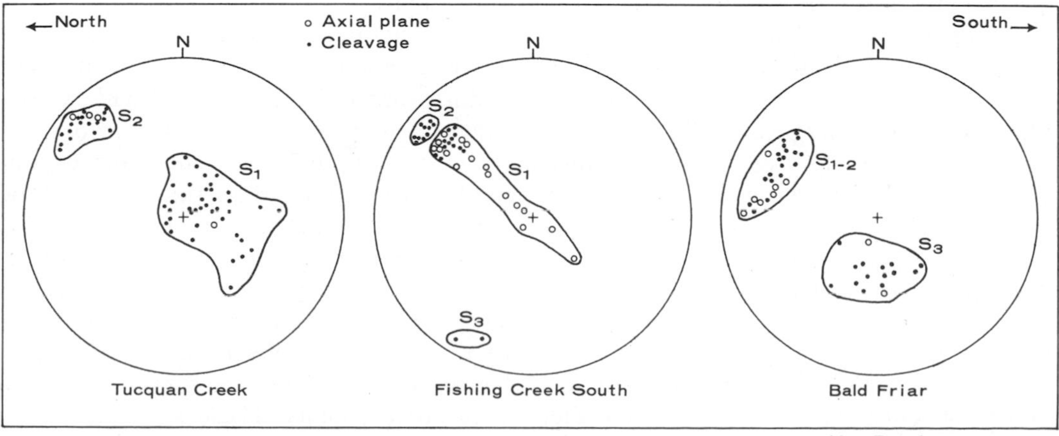

Fig. 6.2 Schmidt projections of migration of axes and poles to planes in schist from north to south along the Susquehanna River illustrating three deformational patterns.

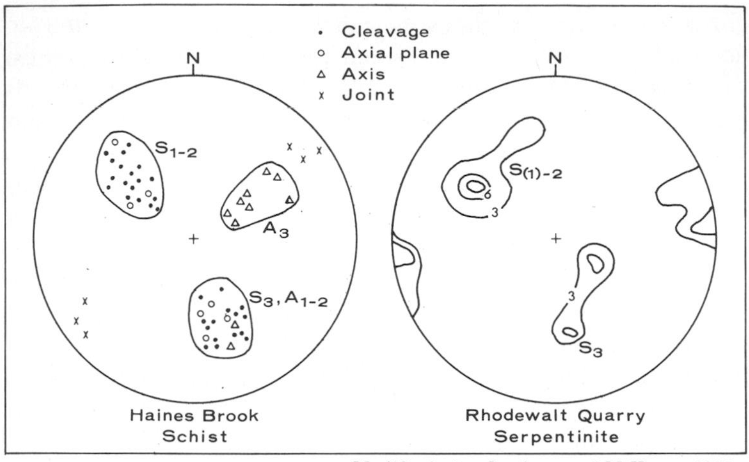

Fig. 6.3 Schmidt projections of axes and poles to planes comparing deformational patterns of typical serpentinite and typical adjacent schist.

serpentinites and continuing to the southeast. This flow pattern and root zone have been tentatively correlated with the analogous nappe structures to the north in Ordovician carbonate formations of the Great Valley structural province (Freedman et al., 1964, pp. 633–634).

Similar structural measurements were made for both serpentinite trends to test the utility of this method of analysis for serpentinite deformation and to determine, if possible, when emplacement of the ultramafic occurred in terms of the regional deformations. The quantity of fractures per unit area is much greater in serpentinite than in schist, there is greater variation in attitude, and the sequence of fracture displacements are usually much less clear than for the surrounding metasediments. In spite of these difficulties, in the more than 3400 serpentinite planes measured (Lapham and McKague, 1964), there is a striking uniformity of pole maxima throughout the southern serpentinite. A typical serpentinite station is compared with that of a typical schist in Fig. 6.3. Although most serpentinite structural stations exhibited a greater variety of maxima than are exhibited by schist, the two major pole concentrations corresponding to S_{1-2} and S_3 of schist are always present. In Fig. 6.3 the nearly horizontal maximum in serpentinite is a release fracture frequently filled with deweylite. The nearly north-south planes are shear surfaces associated with the S_{1-2} pattern. The consistency and congruity of their deformational patterns reveal that both country rock and serpentinite have undergone the same series of deformational stresses. Because of the similarity of S_1 and S_2 orientations in this area of the Piedmont, the two cannot be separated in serpentinite by analogical comparison with the Peters Creek schist. An independent line of evidence is required. Hence, at this point it cannot be demonstrated that the first deformation (D_1) is superimposed upon the serpentinite. Partly for this reason, the combined S_{1-2} of schist is shown as $S_{(1)-2}$ in serpentinite in Fig. 6.3 and in succeeding illustrations.

In addition to regional patterns superimposed upon serpentinite, several other features are notable. Stations with a considerably greater number of planar orientations (see Fig. 6.5*a*) are more representative of serpentinite than the simpler, type pattern at Rhodewalt quarry (Fig. 6.3). Most prominent is a pole maximum representing northwest striking planes that dip steeply southwest. These are perpendicular to the regional strike of both S_1 and S_2; hence, they can be considered as transverse, or *ac*, joints. These joints are much less abundant in schist. As might be expected from superficial observation of serpentinite outcrops, pole scatter is somewhat greater than for maxima in schist. These may represent local stress vector variations during deformation. The relatively homogeneous character of serpentinite would better reveal such small deviations than would the anisotropically layered schist. Near serpentinite contacts and throughout the northern serpentinites, normal regional S_1 and S_2 patterns have been rotated by late shearing movement probably both coincident with and later than D_3. Similarly, axes of folds in schist near these contacts often have been overturned subparallel to the dip of the basal contact of the serpentinite plutons (Lapham and McKague, 1964). As a consequence of this shearing, reserpentinization has gone to completion near the contacts. Elsewhere, the ultramafic rock contains 5 to 25 per cent relict olivine.

D. Microstructures in Schist and Serpentinite

Measurement of microstructures by petrographic examination was initiated to reveal either a distinction between S_1 and S_2 fracture orientations or an earlier orientation, which would indicate that ultramafic emplacement occurred before any of the recognized regional deformations. Radioactive age dating of biotite by K-Ar methods (Lapham and Bassett, 1964) has shown that a small, probably cognate, intrusive at the contact of the major serpentinite pluton is at least 455 m.y. years old. This implies that ultramafic intrusion took place at least 460 to 470 m.y. ago, unless there has been more argon loss than seems probable from examination of the dense, relatively unaltered intrusive. The question that arises, and upon which microstructural examination can shed some light, is whether intrusion is correlative with D_1, or with some earlier, previously unrecognized event.

Detailed studies of mineral reorientation and recrystallization in schist have not been made. However, a few pertinent facts have emerged that bear upon the problem. Predominant growth and orientation of muscovite occurred during D_1, but reorientation into tht *ac* plane of F_2 folds and chloritization occurred during D_2. However, the pervasiveness of this reorientation is not known. Biotite, of somewhat coarser grain size, is present in a few units and may represent an older mica (Lapham and Bassett, 1964) since a slightly older date (about 360 m.y.) than the regional 330 m.y. mica date was obtained. Biotite frequently gives a *younger* age than coexisting muscovite, resulting from preferential argon degassing of biotite. There is also indication of an older date from porphyroblastic muscovite (350 to 365 m.y. dates, Lapham and Bassett, 1964) between the two serpentinites. The age of the porphyroblastic muscovite is compatible with an age of about 460 m.y. (Lapham and Bassett, 1964, p. 665), but the evidence is certainly not conclusive because it has been replaced by a younger muscovite. The regional muscovite from the Glenarm series yielded consistent dates of about 330 m.y., which, in view of the D_2 reorientation and chloritization, has been tentatively correlated with the regional D_2 (Lapham and Bassett, 1964, p. 664). Once again, however, the evidence is inconclusive and must await three-dimensional microstructural petrofabric studies of the Glenarm series.

The dominant microstructural foliation in serpentinite is a foliation of cross-fiber chrysotile ribbons, the first serpentine mineral to replace olivine. This foliation strikes N 55 to 60°E, dipping steeply southeast, and is apparently consistent throughout the strike length of the southern serpentinite. In view of the deformations to which this serpentinite has been subjected, this uniformity is remarkable. However, more significant than its attitude is the relation between primary olivine and the chrysotile which is replacing it. Individual large olivine grains have been considerably "fragmented" by this replacement; yet, regardless of the extent of fragmentation, the separated olivine fragments are still

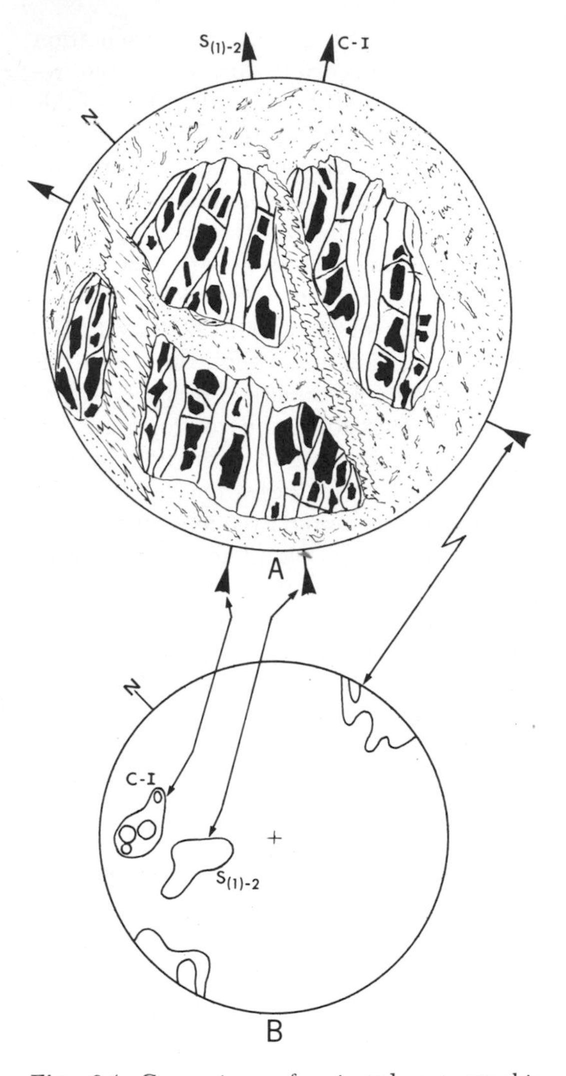

Fig. 6.4 Comparison of oriented petrographic microstructures (A) with corresponding Schmidt projections of macrostructures (B) from Cedar Hill quarry serpentinite. In (A) a fragmented olivine crystal at extinction (solid black) is replaced by chrysotile (foliated ribbons) followed by fracturing and later lizardite serpentinization (matrix). N10°W shear exhibits small optical disorientation of olivine-chrysotile mesh.

optically continuous (Fig. 6.4*a*). These fragments, obviously once a single olivine grain, may be so small that they are barely identifiable, yet optical continuity is maintained. Only about 10 per cent of the relict olivines have been deformationally disoriented previous to chrysotile serpentinization. Thus, the fracture superimposed upon the olivine crystals began near the end of olivine crystallization and controlled the orientation of all the chrysotile (C-I, Fig. 6.4*b* and Fig. 6.5*b*) that immediately followed. A major period of lizardite and/or antigorite serpentinization ("L," Fig. 6.5*c*) was separated from that of early chrysotile ("C-I") by one or more deformations with a different stress orientation (Fig. 6.4*a*, Fig. 6.5*a* and *c*). One of these, striking about N40°E at a small angle to the early chrysotile, only rarely disturbs the olivine chrysotile mesh; the northwest striking fracture, on the other hand, more frequently produced optical discontinuities within the mesh structure (Fig. 6.4*a*).

Schmidt net plotting of these microstructural orientations yields an excellent correlation with the regional pattern (Fig. 6.4*b*). Each large open circle in the northwest quadrant (Fig. 6.4*b*) represents the range of orientation of poles to the plane of chrysotile foliation for a single sample. Fractures striking at a small angle to foliated chrysotile plot exactly at the position of combined regional S_{1-2}. A third microstructural fracture (Fig. 6.4*a*) represents a north-northwest striking shear and appeared as a pole maximum on the Rhodewalt quarry net (Fig. 6.3). A more detailed comparison between macro- and microstructures at Cedar Hill (Fig. 6.5) emphasizes additional relations between mineral orientation and fracture pattern. The two pole concentrations in the northwest quadrant determined from petrographic observation (Fig. 6.4 and Fig. 6.5*b*) exactly match two pole maxima obtained from the field measurement of macrostructures. Previously, (Lapham and McKague, 1964), these two macrostructural maxima were interpreted as the result of S_{1-2} pole scatter. Now, however, it is clear that they represent quite different structural elements which, moreover, clearly indicate a time sequence (see Fig. 6.4). The steeper fracture (chrysotile-I) formed before the shallower fracture ($S_{(1)-2}$). Other, younger macrostructural pole maxima from Cedar Hill similarly correspond to mineralogical foliations, principally lizardite and/or antigorite ("L") and extensional chrysotile ("C-II") in small gash fractures (Fig. 6.5*a* and 6.5*c*).

E. Theoretical Considerations for a Tectonic History

The immediate question which arises is whether the early chrysotile foliation belongs to one of the recognized regional deformations (D_1 or D_2) or whether it represents an earlier, previously unrecognized, deformation (a $D_{1/2}$). This question is of particular significance because the answer could correlate an absolute time, the 460 to 470 m.y. (minimal age) ultramafic intrusion, with a single regional pattern of deformation. This in turn may aid significantly in attaching a particular age, such as the 330 m.y. metamorphism, to a specific younger regional deformational pattern.

In part, this question is already answered. The lineament of the major southern serpentinite is older than the D_2 pattern by which it is transected. A fracture system younger than that of the chrysotile foliation is superimposed upon the serpentinite, and its orientation demonstrates this must be either D_2 alone or D_{1-2} combined. The fact that this younger fracture has not resulted in significant reorientation of the olivine-chrysotile mesh agrees with the character of the D_2 event as one largely of brittle deformation, rather than plastic flow (Freedman et al., 1964). There is also indication that regional muscovites could have been sufficiently affected by D_2 deformation for K-Ar dating to reflect that deformation and hence be correlative with the 330 m.y. age (Acadian orogeny). In any case, the early chrysotile foliation must correlate with a deformation older than D_2, either D_1 or $D_{1/2}$.

In terms of the ultramafic, early chrysotile serpentinization (C-I) can be considered to be a primary foliation since it is so closely allied with the final crystallization of olivine. At the Cedar Hill area, this foliation (Fig. 6.5*a* and 6.5*b*) lies along a partial girdle of pole maxima representing the changing attitude of the northern serpentinite contact (Fig. 6.6) as the strike changes from nearly north-south to nearly east-west. The fracture pattern of which the chrysotile foliation (C-I) is a part follows this curved, steeply dipping contact. Banded chromite to the northwest similarly follows the vagaries of the serpentinite contact. These are primary structural features which belong to the lineament of the ultramafic pluton, all of which are

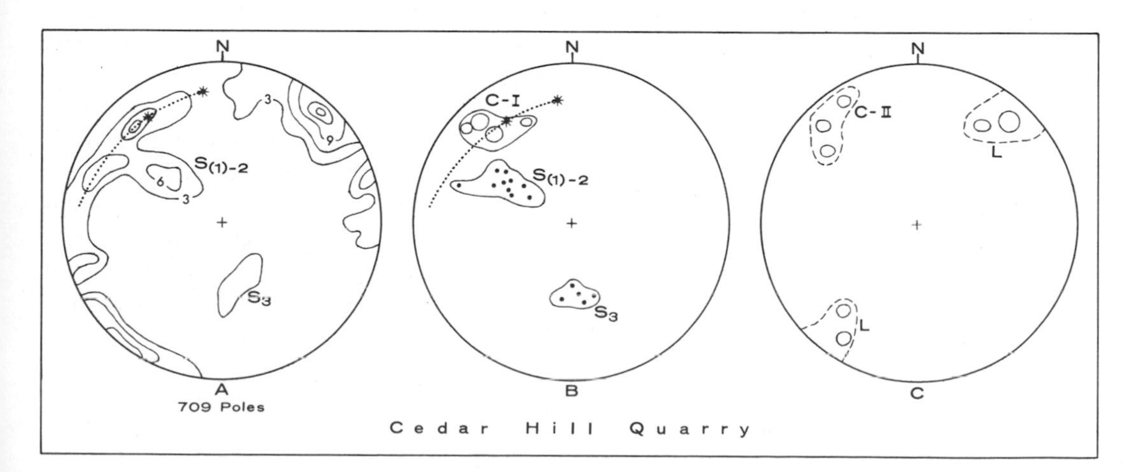

Fig. 6.5 Comparison of Schmidt projections of poles to planes at Cedar Hill quarry for a summary of "S" surface macrostructures (A) and microstructures (B, C) showing early chrysotile orientation (C-I) with extent of scatter (open circles), lizardite and/or antigorite (L), late chrysotile (C-II), and attitudes of basal contact of serpentinite (*).

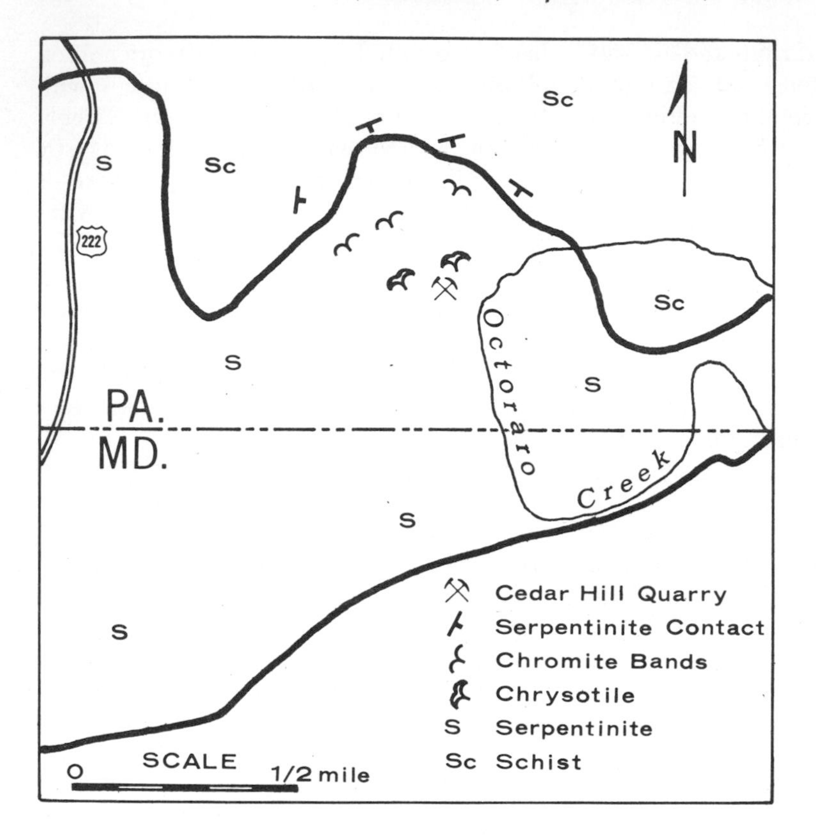

Fig. 6.6 Detailed geologic map of foliations and contact orientations at Cedar Hill quarry.

transected by a D_2 deformational pattern of only slightly different stress orientation.

Up to this point the evidence is fairly clear. An incompletely crystallized ultramafic was emplaced in a crustal environment at least 460 m.y. ago under a regional, crustal deformational stress which had the characteristics of flow deformation and which is visually represented by the strike lineament of the massif itself. This deformation with initial chrysotile serpentinization occurred at some time previous to the establishment of a regional D_2 strain pattern. Succeeding deformation caused renewed serpentinization and brittle yield of the serpentinite without destroying earlier orientations (except along contacts and in less competent, smaller serpentinite plutons). Beyond this point of deduction it is not yet possible to proceed with certainty. However, a few facts bear on the choice of $D_{1/2}$ or D_1 for early chrysotile and hence on the possibility of a 460 to 470 m.y. (early Taconic) D_1 orogeny. One of these is the southward steepening of S_1 planes toward a vertical root zone as the serpentinite area is approached. The steeper and earlier chrysotile foliation exhibits the orientation and relative age that would be expected if regional S_1 were represented in serpentinite by chrysotile and regional S_2 by the fractures that transect the chrysotile. The schist fold axial planes illustrated by Freedman et al. (1964, Plate I) and partially reproduced in Fig. 6.2 suggest two sets of fold axes, one steeper than the other. The steeper schist foliation is very close to the orientation of early chrysotile. Thus, S_1 cleavage may have steepened past S_2, but remained undifferentiable in the highly anisotropic schists. This interpretation would require a shallower dip for S_2 planes than are present to the north (Freedman et al., 1964, Plate 1). On the other hand, if a $D_{1/2}$ existed, the olivine grains and chrysotile should have been so disoriented by the pervasive D_1 stresses that they would no longer be parallel to the basal contact, or "floor," of the ultramafic massif. Such a reorientation apparently has not occurred. Therefore, the suggestion is proffered that ultramafic emplacement may belong to the plastic flow and nappe structure tectonism found to the north in both the Piedmont and Great Valley provinces and that this tectonism, at least in part, belongs to the Taconic orogenic system.

Whatever the final truth of the correlations may be, it is unlikely that this chain of structural and mineralogical deduction will survive, in toto, the acquisition of new data. Rickard (1965) has already proposed a multiple deformation scheme within the framework of the Taconic orogeny. These embrace quite different tectonic styles, some of which previously had been assigned by structural geologists to the younger Acadian orogeny. The same multiplicity may well exist here. The different deformational patterns recognized in this area do not necessarily require different orogenies. What does emerge of importance is that complex methods of analysis combining structural, mineralogical, and geochemical techniques are absolutely necessary to proceed, even slowly, toward ultimate understanding.

III. STRUCTURAL AND PETROFABRIC STUDIES OF THE DUNITES OF ALMKLOVDALEN, NORDFJORD, NORWAY

M. A. Lappin

A. General Setting

The dunites of Sunnmøre and Nordfjord lie in two or more east-west trending zones within the so-called Basal Gneiss complex (Gjelsvik, 1951) whose final metamorphism is dated at about 420 m.y. ago (Neumann, 1961). The Almklovdalen dunites (latitude 62°N, longitude 5°35″E) fall within one of these zones and are noteworthy for their well exposed eclogitic and garnetiferous layers (Eskola, 1921). The mineralogy of similar bodies at Tafjord (about 100 kms. ESE of Almklovdalen) has been discussed in detail by O'Hara and Mercy (1963) (see also Chapter 5-IV.)

The Basal Gneisses of the area are predominantly banded gneisses, augen gneisses, and potash-poor, even-grained grey gneisses of the almandine amphibolite facies. They vary from granitic to granodioritic in composition. Garnet-mica schists, amphibolites, amphibole gneisses, and more rarely quartzites also occur. Inclusions of eclogite and anorthosite are relatively common within the gneisses (Lappin, 1962 and in preparation).

B. Structural Setting

A mesoscopic structural analysis of the gneiss complex using the methods described by Turner and Weiss (1963) shows that these rocks have suffered four periods of fold movements (Table 6.1). Within this sequence of structural events there are two main metamorphic episodes: the formation of the banded complex which probably occurred during or before first folding and a second less drastic metamorphism (K metasomatism ?) occurring during, or late in, second folding.

C. Field and Structural Relationships of the Dunites

The dunites (Fig. 6.7) have steep or vertical dipping contacts against the gneisses and an internal foliation that is in general conformity with these contacts. Some of the larger masses trend obliquely to the regional gneissic foliation that strikes approximately east-west and is steeply dipping or vertical. This regional strike is part of the axial zone of a large synform of

TABLE 6.1 Structures of the Gneiss Complex

	Trend of Minor Structures	Style of Minor Folds	Major Folds
First folds	Variable ?	Rare, rootless, recumbent	None ?
Second folds	Plunging to ENE	Steplike or recumbent, shallow dipping axial planes	Large steplike folds
Third folds	Variable, plunging to N, NE, SSW, and S	Steplike or recumbent, shallow dipping axial planes	Few larger folds, smaller amplitude than above
Fourth folds	Steeply plunging	Brittle zig-zag folds	Shear zones

the second-fold generation. The regional trend of the gneisses either swings around into or is generally conformable with the dunite contacts, although detailed mapping shows that the contacts are disconformable (Lappin, 1962). The three largest masses have been studied in some detail. Two of these masses are externally folded, whereas the third is generally conformable, partly interfingered with the surrounding gneisses,

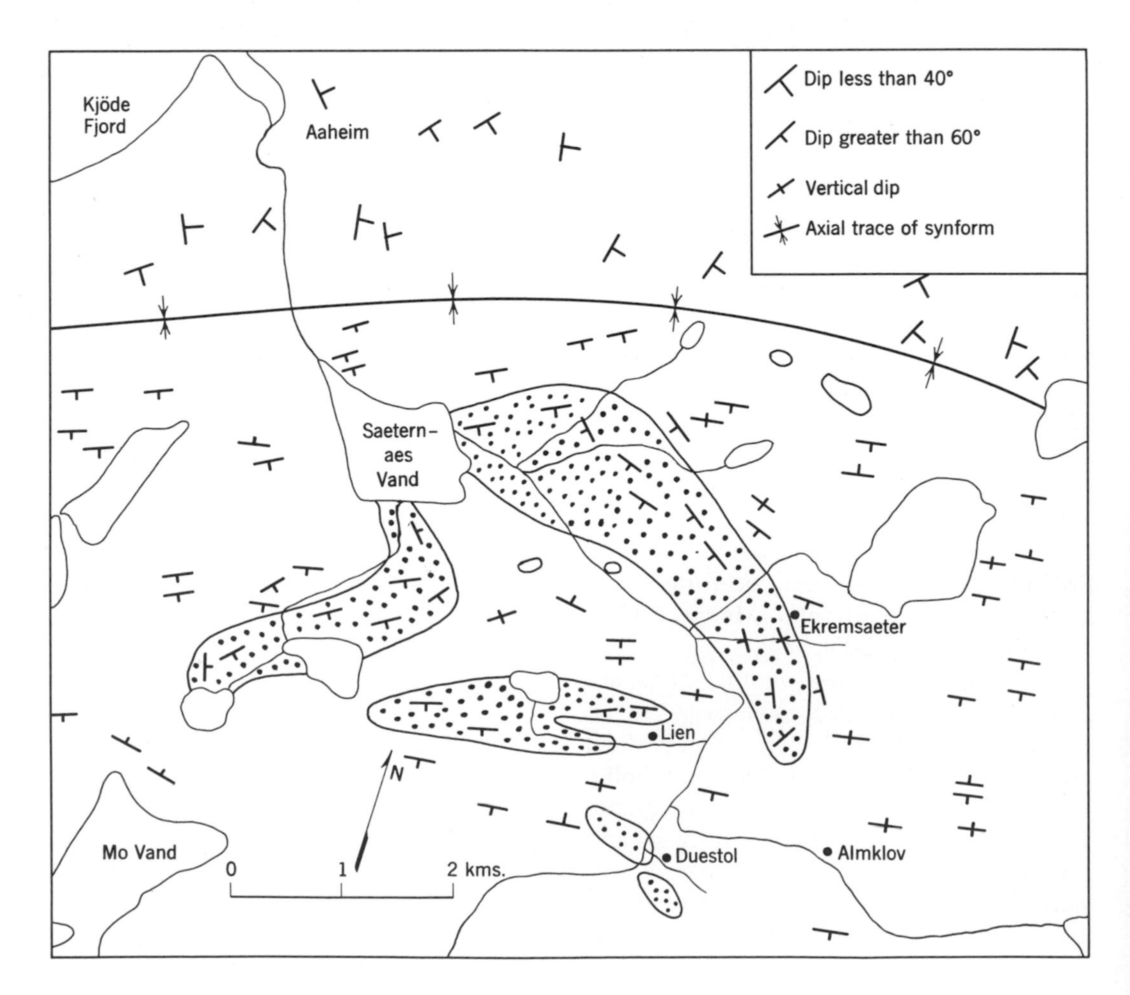

Fig. 6.7 Outcrop pattern of the Almklovdalen dunites.

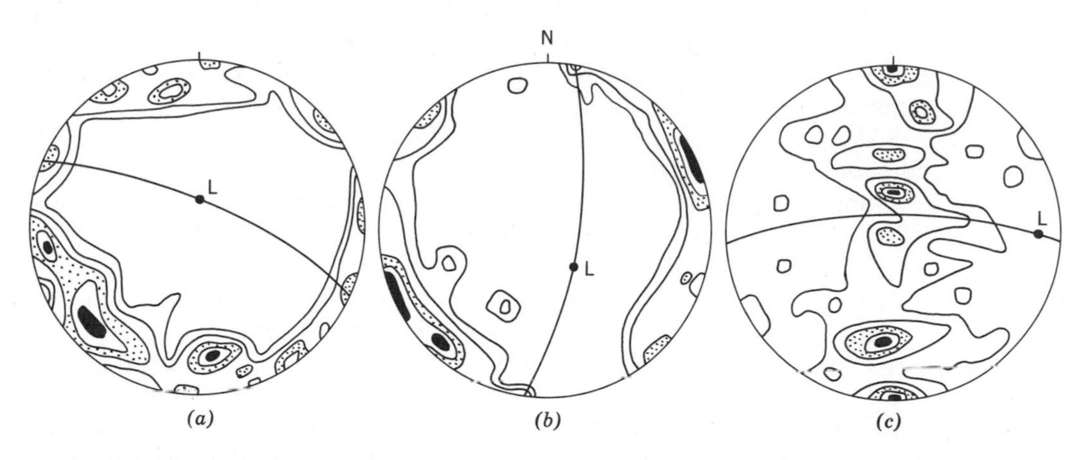

Fig. 6.8 Quartz orientation near the dunite masses (L is linear structure). (*a*) Sheared gneiss; 100 [0001] axes; contours 1, 2, 3, 4, 6 per cent; max. 8 per cent. 0.2 km southeast of Ekremsaeter. (*b*) Sheared gneiss; 100 [0001] axes; contours 1, 2, 4, 6, 8 per cent; max. 12 per cent. Stream 0.8 km south of Saeternaes Vand. (*c*) Gneiss, 200 [0001] axes; contours 1, 2, 3, 4, 5 per cent. 0.8 km west-southwest of Lien.

and contains abundant, steep-plunging small folds.

Eclogites and garnetiferous dunites are interlayered with dunites near the structurally lower margin of each of these three dunite masses. They can be traced only for distances of a few hundred meters along strike.

Serpentinization is limited largely to the contact zones of the dunite and to prominent foliation planes within it. By and large, the dunite is remarkably fresh. The serpentinized contact zone is commonly about 10 meters wide, though it ranges up to 70 meters and locally down to zero. Chemical reactions are limited to a meter-wide zone at the contact. Here the dunites are converted to a radiating tremolite (talc) rock whilst the gneisses are enriched in biotite and sometimes become a matted biotite sheath.

Sheared gneisses are sporadically developed near some dunite contacts and form zones up to 200 meters wide near the externally folded dunites. Similar sheared gneisses occur along strike from the dunites. The close association of the dunites with these sheared gneisses suggests that the introduction of the dunites may be related to the shearing movements.

D. Structural Geology of Sheared Gneisses

Sheared gneisses have a platy appearance and foliation surfaces contain strong, steep or vertical plunging linear structures thought to be due to the intersection of two *S* planes. In thin section quartz forms parallel bands of extremely elongate, sutured grains; these bands are separated by an equigranular mosaic of plagioclase and microcline. Muscovite and biotite form thin laminae parallel to the lighter bands. The mineralogy of the sheared gneisses suggests a tendency towards an equilibrium in the upper greenschist or low almandine amphibolite facies. Petrofabric analyses of these elongate quartzes (Fig. 6.8*a,b*) show a strong maximum plunging gently in the southwest quadrant (quartz and olivine petrofabrics are all shown in geographic orientation). This maximum is part of a girdle of approximately orthorhombic symmetry, essentially co-axial with the steeply plunging linear structure. The orientation of this fabric differs markedly from that of the unsheared gneiss (Fig. 6.8*c*) (collected near the larger, conformable dunite), which has a girdle coaxial with a shallow plunging, second-fold lineation.

The quartz girdles are typical ac girdles

and the steep-plunging lineation is thus a symmetrological *b* lineation. Its orientation is in close agreement with that of β defined in the πS diagram for the area containing the dunites (Lappin, 1962) and with steep-plunging small folds found in the conformable dunite mass (Lappin, 1962). Thus the introduction and/or folding of the dunites can be related to shearing in adjacent gneisses.

The age of this introduction can be dated in terms of the sequence of structural events outlined in Table 6.1. These steeply plunging structures must lie within the general axial plane of appropriate fold movements. Hence this axial plane must be either steeply dipping or vertical and is thus distinct from first, second and third folds, which have shallow dipping axial planes. The shearing is probably late in the structural history, for the time sequence in many metamorphic terrains is from shallow-dipping to steep-dipping axial planes and from plastic to brittle fold styles (c.f. Table 6.1). Textural and mineralogical evidence leads to a broadly similar conclusion (Lappin, 1962).

The fold movements leading to the introduction of the dunites are thus described as fourth fold movements. The traces of axial plane foliations within the dunites and sheared gneisses and the outcrop of dunites in Sunnmøre indicates that the strike of the axial plane of these fourth folds is approximately east-west. It cuts the steep limb of a regional structure in Almklovdalen and a shallow-dipping structure at Tafjord (O'Hara and Mercy, 1963). In Almklovdalen the shape of the folded dunites indicates a sinistral movement within the shear zone allied with a dominantly horizontal direction of transport, if it is accepted that the tectonic *b* axis is, as seems likely, closely related to the symmetrological *b* axis and is hence near vertical.

E. Structural History of the Dunites

The eclogite facies mineralogy of the dunites and their variants contrasts sharply with the facies of the surrounding gneisses. This indicates that the dunites are, in the broadest sense, intrusive.

The dunites show a strong foliation (S) which is defined by a flattening of strain-free olivines within S and by a variable elongation ratio (length/breadth) in this plane. In sections cut perpendicular to S and containing the direction of maximum dip grains without much elongation in S have a tendency towards a six-sided cross section whilst markedly elongate grains tend to have a rectangular outline. The dominance of one or other of these grain types gives rise to characteristic textures which are termed mosaic and elongate textures respectively. Foliation is in many cases emphasized by stringers of chromite (rarely these are oblique to foliation), by platy chlorite and mica group minerals, by a preferred direction of cracking and, in the case of eclogitic and garnetiferous variants, by compositional layering.

Larger rounded olivines (up to 10 cm in diameter) are sparsely but generally distributed through the dunite masses. These olivines are always strained, have plucked boundaries, and show polygonization. They are porphyroclastic relicts within the relatively even-grained dunites and suggest a period of earlier, much coarser grained crystallization (some layers consist almost entirely of such olivines surrounded by finer cataclastic zones). Within these porphyroclasts there is evidence for an even earlier period of crystallization: chromite stringers can be traced through these large crystals and indicate the onetime presence of a chromite-defined foliation (or lineation) around which the large olivines have crystallized. The dunites thus appear to have undergone three periods of crystallization.

In contrast to the generally strain-free fabric of the dunites, the pyroxenes and garnets of eclogitic variants show intense granulation and cataclasis with minor recrystallization to produce a strain-free mosaic aggregate (Lappin, 1962).

F. Petrofabric Studies in the Dunites

Petrofabric studies have been made upon some 17 orientated specimens from the three large dunite masses. It is only possible to offer here certain general conclusions of these studies.

The orientation of olivine is in all cases related to the macroscopic foliation. In the simplest case *X* [010] forms a maximum perpendicular to S and *Y* [001] and Z [100] form maxima and/or girdles in S. More generally, however, *X*, *Y*, and Z lie within three mutually perpendicular planes, one of which is S (these are shown in Fig. 6.9*a*,*b*). Ideally these planes are symmetry planes and the symmetry of the olivine fabric is orthorhombic. In most specimens, the symmetry is less than this. The strongest maxima in the Almklovdalen dunites are formed by *X* and *Y*; in this they differ markedly from those of Dun Mountain (Turner, 1942; Battey, 1960) where Z is stronger than *Y*. This is probably related to the strong development of translation lamellae (approximately perpendicular to Z) at Dun Mountain (Battey, 1960; 25 per cent of grains) which contrasts with the strain-free Almklovdalen textures. Brothers (1960) has shown that, in the case of an olivine nodule, translation lamellae cause a stronger Z orientation.

Two distinct types of olivine orientation are shown by the Almklovdalen dunites (Fig. 6.9 and Table 6.2) and these fabrics can be correlated with the mosaic and elongate textured dunites. The main difference in these fabrics is between the positions of *Y* maxima and the arrangement of partial girdles of *X*. Many dunites however are of an intermediate type and contain elements of both fabrics reflected largely in a complete girdle for *Y* which contains peripheral and central maxima. All fabrics are further complicated by the common feature of substitution, described by

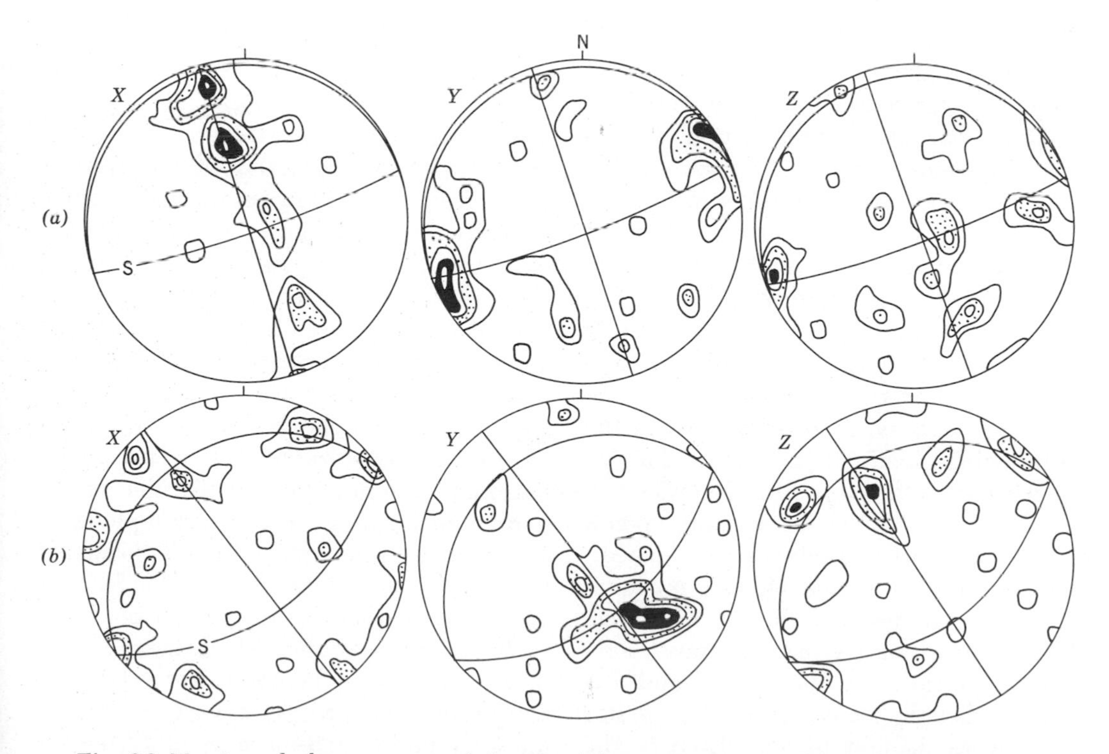

Fig. 6.9 Mosaic and elongate textured dunites. (*a*) Mosaic type; 50 grains; contours 2, 4, 6, 8, 10 per cent. 2 km west of Lien. (*b*) Elongate type; 50 grains; contours 2, 4, 6, 8, 10 per cent. 4 km. west of Lien.

TABLE 6.2 General Characteristics of the Orientation Patterns of Mosaic and Elongate Textured Dunites

	X	Y	Z
Mosaic textures	Maximum perpendicular to *S*, part of a steeply dipping girdle	Shallow plunging maximum, peripheral in *S*	Diffuse girdles and maxima in, and perpendicular to, *S*
Elongate textures	Weaker maximum perpendicular to *S*, part of a peripheral girdle	Steeply plunging maximum, central in *S*	Diffuse girdles and maxima in, and perpendicular to, *S*

Brothers (1959) in porphyritic basalts, where *X* lies in typical positions occupied by *Y* and Z as well as vice versa.

Both *Y* (Ladurner, 1956; Yoshino, 1961) and Z (Battey, 1960) have been correlated with *b* in dunites. In Almklovdalen the central concentration of *Y* in elongate textured dunites coincides with *b* defined within the sheared gneisses (Z shows a rather erratic distribution). Moreover quartz in the sheared gneisses and these olivines share a similar flattening and elongation in S. The elongate textured dunites thus reflect recrystallization during fourth fold movements whilst elements of this fabric in intermediate types probably indicate a partial recrystallization at this time. The mosaic textured dunites either show no response to this stage in the tectonic history or indicate a different recrystallization process during or after introduction. The elongate, mosaic, and intermediate dunite types are apparently completely interlayered one with the other although, as far as can be seen, intermediate and mosaic types are dominant in the conformable dunite mass whilst elongate types occur in the large folded masses.

A detailed study has been made upon a large porphyroclastic olivine and immediately surrounding grains within a predominantly elongate textured dunite. The range of orientations of the parent grain, polygonized portions of this grain, and detached, though nonrecrystallized, grains which were thought to be related to the larger grain are shown in Fig. 6.10*a*. The disposition of axes shows that physical rotation has taken place about the *Y*-axis of the parent grain. This rotation, a direct componental movement, is syntectonic for the girdle occupied by *X*-axes is controlled by the orientation of the large grain and πS the "normal" tectonic position for *X* perpendicular to the foliation (S). Similarly the girdle for Z contains the axes of the large grain and those lying in a more "normal" position within S. *Y* also shows a rotation towards a peripheral position within S suggesting that, in all, two senses of rotation are involved. The orientation patterns of strain-free, presumably recrystallized grains (Fig. 6.10*b*) are similar to those of Fig. 6.10*a*. *X* and Z form girdles containing the orientation of the large grain and more normal tectonic positions (the girdle for Z is rather steeper dipping that that of *X*). *Y* shows a similar peripheral rotation. Recrystallization (indirect componental movement) is thus also syntectonic and can be visualized in terms of a complex rotation picture.

One of the interesting features of this specimen is that the *Y* orientation formed by this recrystallization has a peripheral maximum (mosaic type) whilst that of the normal rock has a central, steep-plunging *Y* maximum (elongate type). Transitional fabrics between these two are in fact recorded as one moves away from the large grain (Lappin, unpublished data). It is uncertain as yet whether this breakdown/recrystallization process always leads to a mosaic type orientation or whether the results recorded are simply a function of the orientation of the parent grain. The presence of transitional fabrics, however, seems to suggest that the mosaic type fabrics become recrystallized to form elongate-type fabrics and thus represent a somewhat earlier stage of recrystallization.

G. The Process of Recrystallization

The flattening and elongation of olivine grains and the cataclastic mode of large olivines (and pyroxenes) shows that the fabric of the Almklovdalen dunites is deformational in origin. Ernst (1935) records a similar opinion.

Olivine is thought to deform in a manner broadly similar to metals. The mosaic textures are similar to triple point equilibrium textures in metals (Flinn, 1965), and although in this sense the elongate textures indicate disequilibrium they resemble textures seen in strained metals and in calcite (Griggs, Turner, and Heard, 1960).

The relationship between metamorphic and metallurgical processes has been ably described by many authors in recent years (Griggs, Paterson et al., 1960; Flinn, 1965). There are three fundamental processes: coldworking in which energy is stored within strained lattices; hotworking where strains are released through recrystallization during stress; and annealing which is the complete or partial recrystallization of a strained cold-worked fabric through later heating. For reasons previously given, recrystallization seems to be a syntectonic process and annealing is thus not important. The first and second processes however seem to offer a direct analogy with the characteristics of various ultrabasic masses.

*1. **Cold worked masses.*** Dun Mountain (Turner, 1942; Battey, 1960). Lherzolite, Pyrenees (Collée, 1963), Twin Sisters,

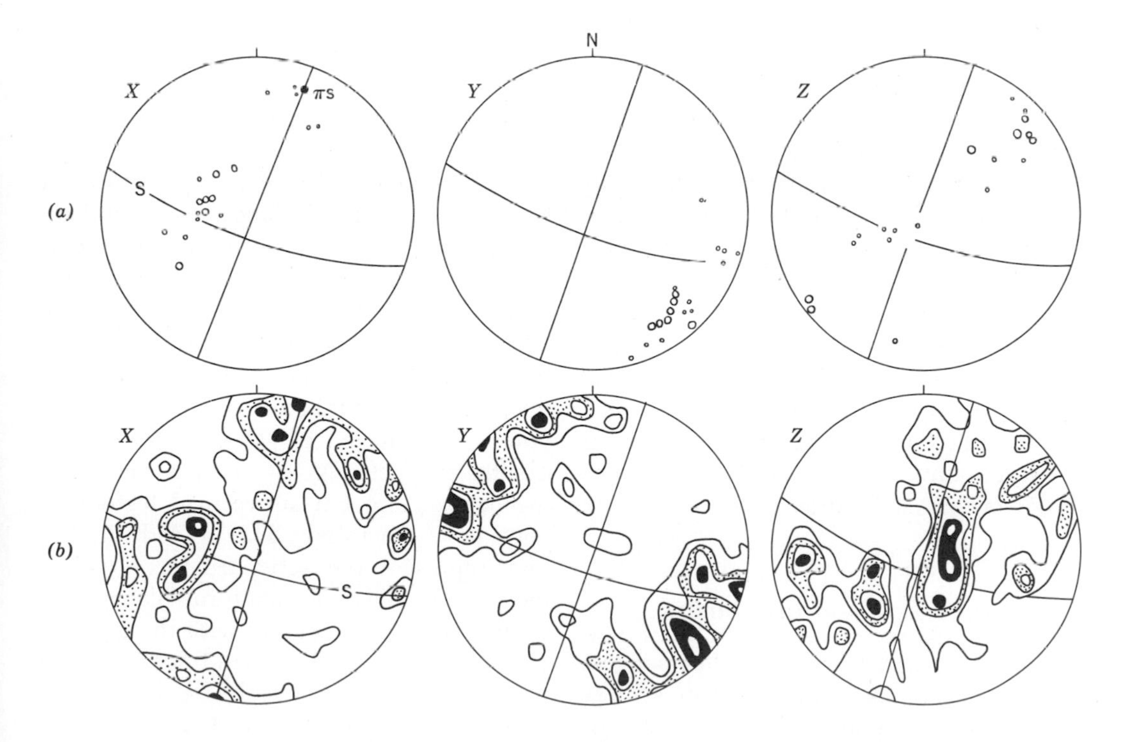

Fig. 6.10 Orientation of a large olivine grain and immediately surrounding grains; quarry 3.9 km west-northwest of Ekremsaeter. (*a*) Orientation of portions of strained large grain (open circles) and of parts of this grain separated from the large grain by physical boundary or by other grains (dots). (*b*) 100 recrystallized grains around large grain; contours 1, 2, 3, 4, 5 per cent. Max. *x* 5 per cent, *y* 7 per cent, *z* 6 per cent.

Washington (Ragan, 1963). In all these masses translation lamellae and/or cataclastic features are common. Z shows the strong concentrations and is either parallel to *b* (Battey, 1960) or at right angles to it (Collée, 1963).

2. *Hot worked masses.* Higashi-akaishi-yama (Yoshino, 1961), Almklovdalen. These masses have equigranular, strain-free textures, *Y* equals *b*; Z generally gives poor maxima.

This subdivision is in accord with the geological positions of these masses. Those of the former group occur in sediments or rocks of low metamorphic grade, those of the latter within metamorphic rocks of the upper greenschist and glaucophane schist facies. Despite the fact that olivine has not yet been recrystallized in the laboratory, its cold/hot working boundary would seem to traverse the green schist and glaucophane schist facies.

Metals deform by gliding. The main glide plane in olivine is thought to be (010) (Turner, 1942), and in all the specimens studied tends to lie within S. The recrystallization of olivine cannot however be simply interpreted in terms of gliding in (010): firstly because the example of calcite in experimental work (Turner and Weiss, 1963, p. 344) cautions against the identification of glide systems from orientation data; secondly because detailed fabrics and substitution show that (010) is not unique within S; and thirdly because the study of the olivine grains surrounding the large olivine demonstrates the complexity of recrystallization.

H. The Introduction of the Dunites

Petrofabric and textural studies suggest that the dunites have a history of syntectonic recrystallization. Continued recrystallization could result in flow and would provide an intrusion mechanism for the dunites. If the age relationships between the elongate and mosaic textured dunites are accepted, then flow during final deformation seems to have concentrated within certain layers (elongate types) though a partial recrystallization is common (intermediate or transitional types). Mosaic types may represent an earlier stage in tectonic history and even perhaps the operation of a different set of tectonic forces.

The conditions for recrystallization may be inferred from the dunites themselves. The masses seem to be "cool," for the absence of contact metamorphism and the limited chemical reactions suggest a low thermal gradient across contacts. Temperatures are probably of the same order as those deduced for the Twin Sisters mass, 500 to 700° (Ragan, 1963). Directed pressures were probably high. The freshness of the dunites and the fact that serpentinization seems to be a late contact phenomenon suggest that P_{H_2O} was probably low. It should be noted that the experimental deformation of calcite is unaffected by water (Griggs, Turner, and Heard, 1960).

The dunites occur in a late, cross-cutting shear zone and their movements and recrystallization are controlled by the shearing forces. One of the puzzling features of the shear zone is its almost horizontal direction of transport despite the fact that the eclogite facies mineralogy of the dunites strongly suggests that they were introduced from below. This difficulty can be avoided if the intrusion mechanism is imagined to contain an element of axial flow. The form of the Almklovdalen dunites in fact suggests that a vortexlike mechanism about a subvertical tectonic *b* may have operated. The folded dunites may represent the active stage of such a movement whilst the conformable mass is essentially static, reacting with the gneisses (interfingered and small-folded), and probably in process of being broken up into much smaller lenses. A vortex movement within such a shear zone would seem to be possible at any competency interface (gneiss/dunite).

IV. EXPERIMENTAL DEFORMATION OF ULTRAMAFIC ROCKS AND MINERALS

C. B. Raleigh

A. Introduction

In contrast with other types of ultramafic intrusions, peridotites of the alpine type are commonly deformed. Folded layering, lineations, preferred crystal orientation symmetrical with the macroscopic structures and undulatory extinction in the constituent minerals have all been repeatedly described in alpine peridotites and are characteristic more of metamorphic tectonites than igneous rocks. Moreover, most alpine ultramafics occur in orogenic belts in tectonic contact with the country rock and in many cases lie along major thrust faults. The geological interpretations which may be constructed to account for these observations depend, in addition to structural studies in the field, on data from experiments on the deformations of ultramafic rocks. The experimental work reported here is concerned with two problems: (a) the strength of serpentinite and its bearing on the mechanism of emplacement of alpine ultramafics and its role in orogenesis; and (b) the glide mechanisms in the constituent minerals of peridotites and the origin of intragranular deformation structures and their relation to the directions of principal stress, to temperature and strain-rate.

B. Experimental Deformation and Strength of Serpentinite

Clark and Fyfe (1961) demonstrated experimentally that ultrabasic liquids can exist only at temperatures in excess of 1300 to 1400°C, at H_2O pressures up to 500 bars. As the country rocks at their contacts with alpine ultramafics rarely are thermally metamorphosed, it was proposed by Bowen and Tuttle that emplacement must be brought about by solid intrusion of a relatively cold mass. Movement in the ultramafic mass at depths and temperatures great enough to permit plastic yielding in olivine was thought to occur by flow; at higher levels, where the peridotite has cooled below 500°C, serpentinization may proceed in the presence of water and further movement was presumed to be facilitated by the weaker plastic shell of serpentine.

1. Experimental Results. In deformation experiments at low temperature, serpentinite is at least as strong as most sedimentary rocks (Handin, 1964) and granites, and only slightly weaker than most other igneous and metamorphic rocks. From room temperature to 300°C, sealed specimens of serpentinite become ductile at confining pressures greater than about 3 kb in short-time tests (Raleigh and Paterson, 1965), yielding at stress differences on the order of 12 kb for antigorite serpentinite and 8 kb for a mesh-textured lizardite-chrysotile specimen. The reduction in strength with temperature of antigorite serpentinite is not greatly different from other rocks at 5 kb confining pressure (Fig. 6.11), up to 600°C. Between 600 and 700°C, however, the ultimate strength falls from over 7 kb to 0.5 kb as shown in Fig. 6.11 (Raleigh and Paterson, 1965). Below 600°C the antigorite serpentinite at 5 kb is ductile; above 600°C, coinciding with the loss in strength, the specimens fail by brittle fracture. The deformational behavior of a lizardite-chrysotile serpentinite containing 2 per cent by weight of brucite is qualitatively similar, but it undergoes a rapid reduction in strength with temperature at around 300 to 350°C. Specimens tested at 25 to 300°C at 3.5 kb confining pressure were ductile; above 350°C, the specimens became weak and embrittled.

The weakening and embrittlement were shown by Raleigh and Paterson (1965) to

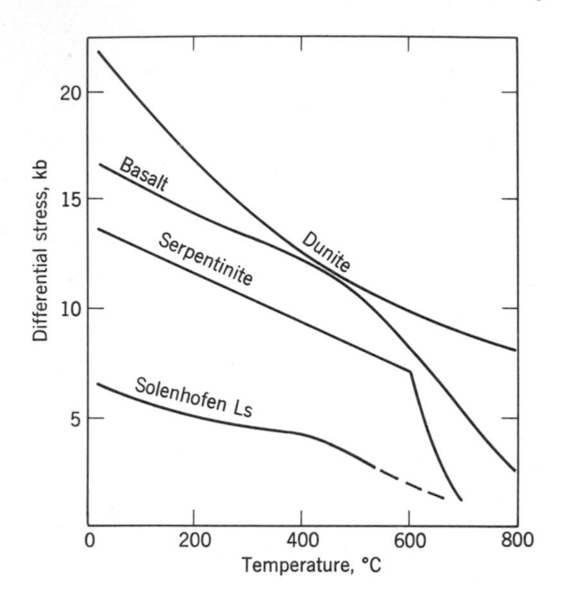

Fig. 6.11 Strengths of rocks at 5 kb confining pressure and 5 per cent strain in compression. (From Griggs et al., 1960; Raleigh and Paterson, 1965.)

result from dehydration of serpentine and serpentine plus brucite. In addition to the loss of cohesion, water released by the reaction fills the pore volume at a pressure less than or equal to the confining pressure, thereby reducing the effective confining pressure. Both effects act in the direction of decreasing the fracture strength and the rock becomes brittle. The reason for the discrepancy in the temperatures at which weakening takes place in different serpentinites is not fully understood but may be attributed partly to the presence of brucite in the specimens that weakened at 300 to 350°C.

2. Tectonic emplacement of serpentinite. The experiments have shown that, although at temperatures below a limit somewhere in the range 300 to 600°C serpentinite is a strong rock with a high coefficient of sliding friction on fracture surfaces, it becomes extremely weak at higher temperatures due to dehydration. Weakening, relative to the country rock, effected in large part by the generation of a pore fluid pressure within the serpentinite, may be expected to occur in nature at the appropriate temperatures and pressures provided the wall rocks are of low permeability. Therefore, at temperatures below 300 to 600°C, tectonic emplacement of serpentinite is improbable because of its high strength; if heated to above that temperature solid emplacement may occur, probably by sliding on discrete fracture surfaces at shear stresses which are small because of the reduction by fluid pressure in the effective normal stress across the fractures. This mechanism of tectonic emplacement accounts for the observations by Lapham and McKague (1964) and others that serpentinites are highly fractured and by Hess (1955), Raleigh (1965a) and others that mesh textures in serpentinite are commonly preserved. Mesh texture was shown by Raleigh and Paterson (1965) to be nearly obliterated by 20 per cent plastic strain, and therefore, plastic flow cannot have been the mechanism of emplacement of serpentinites in which mesh textures are common.

Alternatively, serpentinite and the marginal country rock may be weakened and embrittled by the high fluid pressures generated at the contact of a hot peridotite intruded into wet sediments. For example, Kennedy (1955) pointed out that heating from 200 to 400°C of sediment containing trapped interstitial water at 100 bars will increase the pore pressure to 3400 bars. Considering that fluid pressure gradients in rocks in tectonically active geosynclinal areas are likely to be greater than hydrostatic because of tectonic compression and rapid sedimentary loading (cf. Hubbert and Rubey, 1959, pp. 154–156), it is highly probable that the pore pressure at the margins of a hot, solid or magmatic peridotite intrusion would quickly rise to values approaching or even exceeding the overburden pressure. The marginal envelope of sediment and serpentinizing peridotite into which the water has penetrated under pressure will then be weakened in relation to the cooler surrounding sedimentary rock and, given the appropriate tectonic stress gradient, solid emplacement should be possible.

*3. **Role of Serpentinite in Tectonics.*** In view of the fact that alpine serpentinites are restricted to deformed mountain chains and island arcs and occur along major tectonic breaks (Heard and Rubey, 1966), an hypothesis linking the tectonic development of such regions to weakening in serpentine of the deep oceanic crust or shallow upper mantle has been put forward by Raleigh and Paterson (1965). The evidence that layer 3 of the oceanic crust, which has a seismic velocity of 6 to 7 km/sec, is partly serpentinized peridotite is given by Hess (1962), and consists in large part of (a) the correspondence of seismic velocities obtained experimentally on 70 per cent serpentinized peridotite, and (b) the dredging of serpentinized peridotite from the mid-Atlantic ridge where the sedimentary cover over layer 3 is thin or absent. Hess considers the serpentinization to have taken place where mantle material is convected upward at the median oceanic ridges and crosses the 500°C isotherm. The serpentinized peridotite is then carried away from the ridges by the convection current so that, in time, a layer of serpentinite will cap the oceanic mantle. If a belt of such oceanic crust under lateral compression is heated to the appropriate temperature in the range 300 to 600°C, failure by brittle fracture or cataclastic flow will occur in and be confined to the weakened belt of dehydrating serpentine. Thus, the deformation may be intense and local as is characteristic of mountain building. Donnelly (1964) has proposed that weakening by dehydration may accelerate thickening of the crustal root beneath the Antilles island arc. The required rise in temperature may be brought about by downwarping of the crust, by a local upwarp of the isotherms, or by depression of the crust along the downwelling limb of a convection cell.

The tectonically active island arcs of the present day Pacific continental margins are the most probable sites for the down-welling limbs of convection cells. In Hess's views the continents are carried passively by the convection current, but because they are less dense than the mantle the continents must come to rest at the sites of downwelling and become deformed where the oceanic crust and upper mantle are thrust downwards against their margins. In this case weakening and embrittlement of the serpentinite of the oceanic crust where convection has brought it down into regions of higher temperatures will result in faulting and tectonic emplacement of serpentinite into the overlying deformed sediments of the continental rise. This mechanism of the origin of alpine serpentinites suggested by Dietz (1963) is made more plausible by the experimental evidence for weakening of serpentinite during dehydration.

C. Deformation of Peridotite Minerals

Olivine in alpine peridotites and peridotite nodules from basalts characteristically shows preferred orientation. Although the orientation can in some cases be shown to have resulted from rotation of inequant crystals during gravity settling or intrusive flow (Brothers, 1959; Jackson, 1961a), the olivine fabrics of metamorphic olivine rocks (Ernst, 1935) of many alpine peridotites and possibly some peridotite nodules (Collée, 1963) are more likely to have been brought about by plastic flow or syntectonic recrystallization. There is some controversy over this point (Brothers, 1962; Battey, 1962) but observations by Turner (1942), Battey (1960), and Raleigh (1965a) point strongly towards a tectonic origin for olivine fabrics in at least some peridotites. In addition, olivine and enstatite grains in alpine peridotites and nodules characteristically contain kink bands resulting from translation gliding. Deformation experiments have been carried out on olivine and other minerals of ultramafic assemblages to determine the glide mechanisms and the origin of the internal deformation structures. If the glide mechanisms and the critical shear stresses for slip are known, it should then be possible to predict the preferred orientations which would develop by plastic deformation of dunites. Olivine has also been recrystallized syntectonically in experiments (Raleigh, 1963), but little systematic work has been done.

1. Olivine. Deformation experiments in a range of confining pressures from 15 to 25 kb at temperatures of 400 to 1500°C have been carried out on olivine in the cubic apparatus of D. T. Griggs at the University of California at Los Angeles. The apparatus, consisting of six co-axial, hydraulically driven pistons converging on the faces of a cubic sample holder, has been described in detail by Carter, Christie, and Griggs (1964). The specimens, cores of dunite or olivine single crystals ⅜ inch long by ⅛ inch in diameter, were surrounded by a graphite resistance heating element and pyrophyllite as the confining pressure medium. After deformation at strain-rates of approximately 10^{-4} sec^{-1}, the cores were thin-sectioned for petrographic study. The details of the experimental results are given by Raleigh (1963) and will be treated only briefly here.

At all temperatures and pressures, kink bands and plastic bending of the olivine crystals were produced as a result of dis-

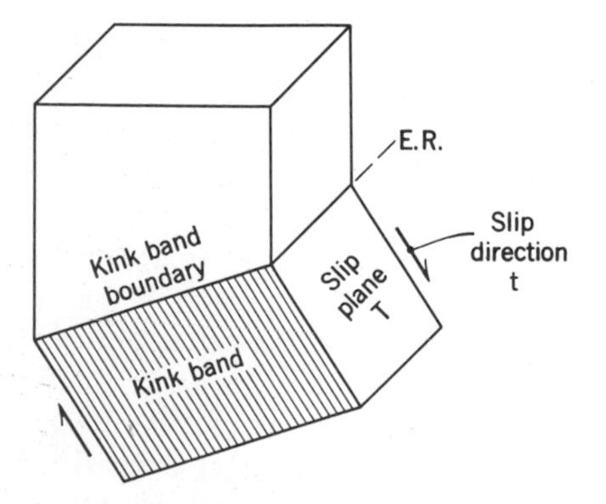

Fig. 6.12 Diagrammatic sketch of kinking resulting from discontinuous slip in a single crystal.

continuous slip along translation glide planes. The kink band boundaries (Fig. 6.12) occurred in three principal irrational crystallographic orientations approximately parallel to the pinacoids (100), (010), and (001). The kink bands formed in olivine of Mount Burnett dunite tend to be of the (010) and (001) orientations below 1000°C and predominantly (100) and (001) above 1000°C.

In addition to the cube experiments, a series of experiments at 5 kb confining pressure and 200 to 1000°C have been carried out in M. S. Paterson's triaxial deformation apparatus at the Australian National University. The confining pressure medium is argon and heating is accomplished by an internal wire-wound resistance furnace to temperatures known to within ±10°C (Raleigh and Paterson, 1965). In these experiments split cylinders of peridotite were polished on a diametral median plane and deformed at a strain-rate of 10^{-4} sec^{-1}. The resulting slip lines on the surface were analysed using the method described by Raleigh (1965b). As slip lines are formed along the intersection of an active slip plane and the polished surface, they must be parallel to the slip plane on any surface through a crystal. The method used involves photographing the slip lines on several crystals on the polished surface and determining the orientations of the different crystals with a universal stage after preparing a thin-section of the surface. The orientations of the axes of each crystal are then rotated to a standard orientation on a projection and the associated slip line becomes rotated to a point lying on the great circle on the projection representing the slip plane. The slip direction in the slip plane is the line normal to the intersection of the slip plane and the boundary of a kink band as shown in Fig. 6.12 (Christie et al., 1964). In Fig. 6.13 is shown an equal area projection of the crystal axes of olivine and slip lines, produced at 700°C and 5 kb, rotated into great circles defining {110} on the projection. The slip system is the

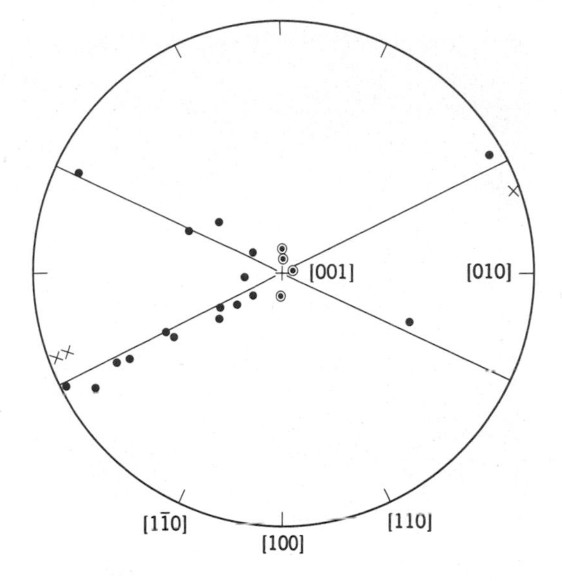

Fig. 6.13 Slip lines from olivines in deformed peridotite rotated on to standard projection of olivine crystal axes. Slip planes are {110}. (⊙) are normals to kink band boundaries. (x) are axes of external rotation.

slip plane, T = {110}, the slip direction, t = [001]. At 1000°C, 5 kb, additional slip lines and kink bands define a second slip system, T = (010), t = [100]. Below 400 to 500°C, slip on T = (100), t = [001] predominates.

Deformation lamellae found in olivine in the experimental specimens are identical in appearance to the lamellae in quartz found by Christie et al. (1964) to be parallel to the active slip plane. In olivine, as in quartz, the lamellae lie at large angles to the kink band boundaries that are symmetrical to the lamellae on either side. One set of lamellae are parallel to the {110} planes found by the slip-line analysis to be the active slip planes in those grains. The other set, parallel to (100) and lying normal to kink bands nearly parallel to (010), were developed only in the cube experiments at lower temperatures and despite the lack of slip line analysis on these specimens, the lamellae are undoubtedly parallel to the slip plane. They are distinct from the lamellar structures parallel to (100) in naturally deformed olivine, which were called "translation lamellae" by Turner (1942) but which in fact are small angle tilt boundaries parallel to kink bands having a large lattice rotation in the same grains (Fig. 6.14) (Raleigh, 1965a). Kink bands and small-angle tilt boundaries on (100) similar to those in naturally deformed olivine occur in specimens deformed experimentally in both sets of apparatus at temperatures of 1000°C and above (Fig. 6.14).

The glide mechanisms determined experimentally are given in Table 6.3 where they are arranged in order of the temperature at which they are observed. For comparison, the slip mechanisms giving rise to kink bands in naturally deformed olivine of the Cypress Island peridotite (Raleigh, 1965a) are also given. The slip direction is taken to be the normal to the kink band boundary at the initiation of slip; the slip plane contains the slip direction and the axis of external rotation of the lattice in the kink band. The axis of external rotation is a line lying in the kink band boundary parallel to the intersection of the slip plane and the boundary. It may be found by construction on the stereographic projection as the intersection of the great circles bisecting $X - X'$, $Y - Y'$ and $Z - Z'$ measured on opposite sides of the kink band boundary. Where the external rotation is small, however, it is difficult to fix the orientation accurately and for this reason the slip planes given for the naturally deformed olivine are questionable in some cases. In particular, the kink bands approximately parallel to (001) have external

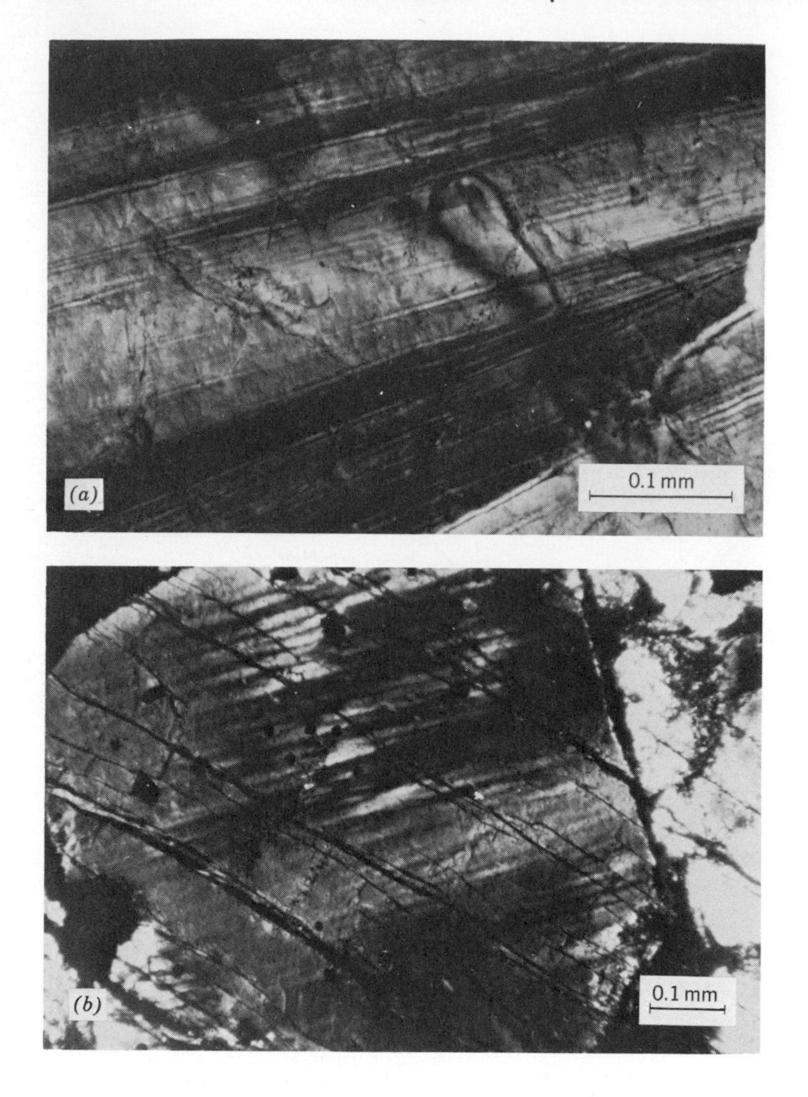

Fig. 6.14 Narrow kink bands parallel to (100) in olivine: (*a*) naturally deformed; (*b*) deformed in experiment at 1200°C., 25 kb.

TABLE 6.3 Glide Mechanisms in Naturally and Experimentally Deformed Olivine

Naturally Deformed		Experimentally Deformed		
T	t	°C	T	t
			(100)	[010]
(010) ?	[100]	< 1000		
			{110}, (100)	[001]
			{110}	[001]
{110} ?	[001]	> 1000		
			(010)	[100]

rotations of only a few degrees and although [001] may be taken to be the slip direction, the error in locating the axis of external rotation does not permit discrimination between (100) and {110} as the slip plane. In the case of the kink bands near (100), axes of external rotation determined in individual kink bands from several grains range in orientation from parallel with [010] to parallel with [001]. It is probable, therefore, that more than one plane in the zone of [100] has operated as the active slip plane. From structural considerations and on the basis of the experimental work, (010), which contains the slip line [100] and the axis of external rotation [001], is most likely to be one of these slip planes. Chudoba and Frechen (1950) determined [001] to be the axis of external rotation in kink bands nearly parallel to (100) and proposed the slip mechanism given here.

In comparing the slip mechanisms of experimentally and naturally deformed olivine (Table 6.3), it appears that glide in the direction [100], which is the predominant mechanism of plastic flow in the natural material, is confined to grains deformed in experiments at temperatures above 1000°C. This means, in effect, that only at temperatures above 1000°C at the strain-rate of the experiments, is the critical resolved shear stress τ_c, for slip on $T =$ (010), $t =$ [100] below that for slip on the conjugate system, $T =$ (100), $t =$ [010], for which no evidence has been reported from naturally deformed olivine. It is not considered, however, that a temperature of 1000°C is necessary for (010), [100] slip at the much smaller strain-rates of geologic deformations. The resistance to plastic flow is thought (McLean, 1962, p. 387) to consist of barriers to motion of defects, certain of which are of sufficiently low energy that thermal agitation can help to overcome them. Long times also increase the probability of favorable atomic motions so that dependence of the critical resolved shear stress on temperature may imply dependence on strain rate. As τ_c for slip on (010), [100] is more temperature dependent than on (100), [010], lower rates of strain may be expected to effect a decrease in the temperature at which slip on the former system is favored.

2. *Enstatite.* Turner, Heard and Griggs (1960) determined the glide mechanism in enstatite deformed at 500 to 800°C and 5 kb from the observations that exsolution lamellae parallel to (100) retained their rational crystallographic orientation in kink bands and that external rotation of the lattice took place around the axis [010]. It was also found that inversion to clinoenstatite occurred in kink bands and Turner et al. (1960), suggested that the transformation was of a displacive type, or martensitic transformation. Raleigh (1965b) confirmed the glide mechanism, $T =$ (100), $t =$ [001], proposed by Turner et al., by analysis of slip lines on polished specimens deformed under similar conditions. Inversion to clinoenstatite was found to occur in kink bands and in fine lamellae parallel to (100) in experiments at 5 kb, 700 to 1000°C. The lamellae are similar in appearance to exsolution lamellae on (100). The optical properties of the clinoenstatite lamellae bear a consistent relation to the optics of the host orthopyroxene, which is, however, at variance with the relations in exsolution lamellae in orthopyroxene. From universal stage measurements, the optic directions in the clinoenstatite and orthopyroxene host are parallel and Z in the lamellae lies at 27° to $Z = c$ in the host. In the exsolution lamellae of diopside segregated on (100) in orthopyroxenes of the Stillwater, Hess (1960) found Z in the lamellae against c in the host to be 40°. Structurally, both types of lamellae are related to the host in the same way. The (100) planes and [001] axes are common to the host and lamellae. The $Z \frown c$ angles in the lamellae of 27 and 40° agree with those given by Winchell (1951, p. 410) for clinoenstatite and diopside respectively.

Sclar, Carrison, and Schwartz (1964) have shown experimentally that at 5 kb above a temperature of 554°C orthoenstatite is the stable form with clinoenstatite being the low-temperature polymorph. The transformation to clinoenstatite in the deformation experiments may have come about during cooling below 554°C after the load was removed in response to residual stresses in the deformed enstatite, but this is unlikely to be the case. Clinoenstatite produced by deformation at 5 kb, 850°C, failed to revert to the orthorhombic polymorph after being heated for six days at 850°C and atmospheric pressure, indicating that the reaction is a sluggish one

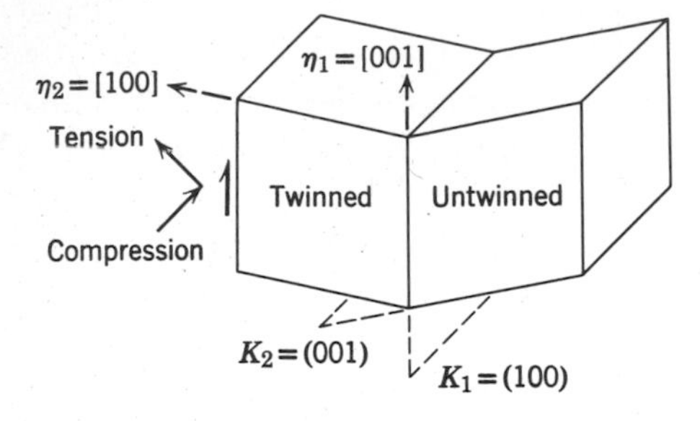

Fig. 6.15 Twin glide elements and preferred compression and tension directions for lamellar (100) twinning in diopside.

at that temperature. However, clinoenstatite was present in a specimen quenched from 750°C, the temperature at which it was deformed, to room temperature in a few seconds due to an inadvertent sudden loss of gas pressure. It is probable, therefore, that the clinoenstatite is formed at temperatures a few hundred degrees above its stability field under the influence of shear stress. If so, it provides the single known example of a true "stress" mineral.

3. ***Diopside.*** In experiments by Griggs, Turner and Heard (1960) diopside deformed at 5 kb, 500°C by twinning on (001) and by slip resulting in kinking with external rotation around the axis, [010]. The slip mechanism responsible for the kinking was shown to be $T = (100)$, $t = [001]$. In addition to twinning on (001), Raleigh (1965b) found that, at 5 kb, 700 to 850°C, diopside developed fine lamellar twinning on (100), accompanied locally by external rotation of the lattice around [010] resulting from variation in the density of the twin lamellae within the crystals. Evidence for minor slip on (100) was found at temperatures of 1000°C. The amount of shear and the twin elements were determined by U-stage measurement in incident light of the angle of rotation of a polished surface by the twins, and the orientations of the twinned crystals were then determined in a thin section of the polished surface. The twin glide plane, K_1, is the composition plane and the glide direction, η_1 is the twin axis. The amount of shear is determined on a stereographic projection by the method of Greninger and Troiano (1949) and the position of the second undistorted plane, K_2, of the strain ellipsoid defined by the twin may then be readily fixed. For the broad twins on (001), the twin elements are: $K_1 = (001)$, $\eta_1 = [100]$, $K_2 = (100)$, $\eta_2 = [001]$; for lamellar twins on (100), $K_1 = (100)$, $\eta_1 = [001]$, $K_2 = (001)$, $\eta_2 = [100]$ (Fig. 6.15).

Lamellar twinning on (100) has been reported in diopside grains in granulites (Naidu, 1955) and calc-silicate skarns (White, 1959). In peridotites, such lamellae might be confused with exsolution lamellae on (100), to which the twins bear a strong resemblance.

The preferred orientation of lamellar (100) twins in naturally deformed rocks may provide a useful indicator of the directions of the principal stresses at the time of deformation. In diopside of the experimentally deformed specimens, twinning is profusely developed in those grains favorably oriented for twin-gliding in the positive direction; that is, towards $+c$, on (100) in the [001] direction. Grains oriented so that the resolved shear stress on the glide plane and direction is small are generally untwinned or contain only a few narrow lamellae. F. J. Turner and his co-workers have used a statistical treatment for analysis of twinning in calcite which may be used to advantage with diopside. For each twinned grain in an aggregate, it is assumed that the maximum and minimum principal stresses were oriented so as to give the greatest resolved shear stress on the twin-glide system. On the stereographic projection, a point representing the maximum principal stress (compression) is therefore placed in (010) at 45° to [001] and 29° to [100] and the least principal stress, (tension) lies at 90° to compression in (010). When this process is repeated for a large number of randomly oriented grains, the compression points should cluster around the direction of maximum principal stress if the twinning was brought about by a single deformation. The diagram in Fig. 6.16 shows compression and tension points for twinned grains in a diopside-scapolite rock deformed 10 per cent under axial compression at 5 kb, 800°C. The direction of compression is well-defined by a maximum of compression points and the tension axes lie in a girdle parallel to the plane containing the least principal stress, $\sigma_3 = \sigma_2$. This method may prove especially useful for pyroxene-bearing mafic and ultramafic rocks where quartz, calcite, and dolomite are not available to provide indications of the directions of principal stress during deformation.

4. Plagioclase. In their recent experiments on deformation of labradorite Borg and Handin (1966) found that mechanical twinning on the albite law occurred at temperatures up to 500°C and 5 kb, but were unable to confirm the mechanical pericline twinning observed by Mügge and Heide (1931) and Starkey and Brown (1964). Neither mechanism is likely to account for the fairly large external rotations observed in naturally deformed plagioclase (Hargraves, 1962) as the twinning shears are small. Preliminary observations on anorthite in a eucrite gabbro deformed at 5 kb and 800°C in this laboratory show that as many as two sets of slip lines occur on polished surfaces of some grains and, therefore, that translation gliding is likely to be responsible for the plastic bending in nature.

D. Conclusions

Experiments on the deformation of ultramafic rocks and minerals have provided some new insights into the mechanisms of plastic flow of peridotite minerals and the role of alpine ultramafic rocks in tectonism. In particular, the weakening and embrittlement of serpentinite at dehydration or under the high pore pressures resulting from intrusion of a hot ultramafic mass into wet sedimentary rocks seems to be the most satisfactory explanation for the field worker's observation that many alpine serpentinites are emplaced tectonically by marginal faulting.

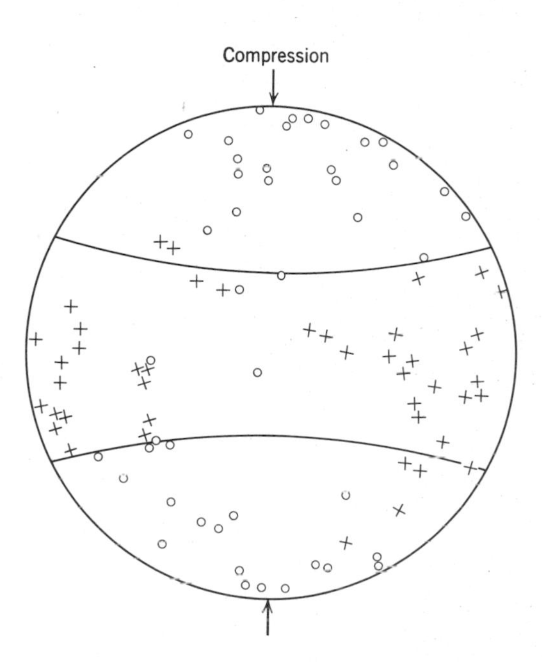

Fig. 6.16 Compression (o) and tension (+) axes for 46 diopside grains twinned in experiment at 800°C., 5 kb. Arrow is parallel to cylinder axis and direction of compression.

It has been shown that the kink bands and lamellae parallel to (100) in naturally deformed olivine result from translation gliding in the direction [100], and that this slip mechanism is favored by high temperature or, possibly, by slow rates of strain. Other minerals of ultramafic rocks commonly contain lamellar twins and kink bands which have also been reproduced experimentally. In the case of diopside, lamellar twinning parallel to (100) is found to be favored in grains in which the resolved shear stress on the twin-glide system is high. This observation may be used to determine the orientation of the principal stresses in natural deformations of diopside-bearing rocks.

V. LOCAL DEFORMATION STRUCTURES IN A SERPENTINITE

David P. Gold

Two hand specimens of ribbon vein asbestos in serpentinite, which shows unusual mesoscopic deformation features, were supplied by members of the Geology Department, Asbestos Corporation Ltd., from their open pit mines in the Thetford Mines area, Quebec. Both specimens contain intersecting seams of magnetite, along whose planes measurable amounts of movement apparently have taken place. Inasmuch as there appears to be a geometric relationship between the magnetite seams and the asbestos bands (mainly cross-fiber), a genetic link between fiber formation and the conditions causing failure is implied. Unfortunately, the specimens were not oriented in the field, and thus correlation with regional tectonic events is not possible.

The geologic setting of the asbestos deposits is a serpentinite host rock, which, according to Riordon (1957), was essentially composed of peridotites, harzburgites and local dunite, intrusive into an anticlinal structure of slate, quartzite, and volcanic rocks. Autometasomatic processes accounted for an "uniform and partial alteration of the peridotite and complete serpentinization of most of the dunite" (Riordon, 1957, p. 83), thus introducing anisotropy (differing competency) in an otherwise rather homogeneous body. The serpentinized dunite bodies flowed while the surrounding peridotite fractured during later adjustment. Next followed intrusion of "numerous small irregular shaped bodies of granite and swarms of even smaller bodies of syenite" (Riordon, 1957, p. 83), serpentinizing the adjacent ultramafic rocks. Major adjustment followed, with development of faults, numerous subsidiary faults and fractures, but these were confined mainly to the peridotite-country-rock contact zones. Intense serpentinization and formation of the asbestos vein occurred during this stage. "In addition, however, the serpentinization, caused by the introduction of the swarms of small acid intrusives, influenced the formation and configuration of the subsidiary faults, and where these intrusives were large they tended to trap the asbestos vein forming solutions" (Riordon, 1957, p. 86).

In the larger specimen, (see Fig. 6.17*a*) the fiber bands are distributed as curved surfaces which tend to be co-planar to the magnetite seams. The geometric correlation of the magnetite seams to conjugate shear directions as developed in test samples under triaxial conditions, and the fiber bands to planes of shear stress concentration, is striking. Note the subsequent breaks in the thicker magnetite seam into en echelon lenses.

Most of the fiber is shorter than is apparent from the figures, as many of the bands are aggregates of discontinuous fine-lenses in en echelon habit. The sense of these lenses is enantiomorphous; a symmetry plane bisects the angle of intersection between the two seams (see Fig. 6.17*a*).

In the smaller specimen (Fig. 6.17*b*) the movement was found to be plane rotational between 37 and 40° about the center of rotation, 4.25 cm vertically below the point marked CR, and on seam 2. Some salient points concerning the distribution of asbestos fiber and its relationship to the magnetite seams are the following:

1. The longest fiber is developed farthest from the seams, with a sympathetic relationship to the distance between bands.
2. A second generation of fiber (commonly oblique fiber) is developed close to the seam.
3. Seam 1 (apparently early) is slightly discordant (about 10°) to the main fiber bands.
4. Seam 2, essentially, is concordant to the fiber bands in the F/W_2-H/W_1, H/W_2-

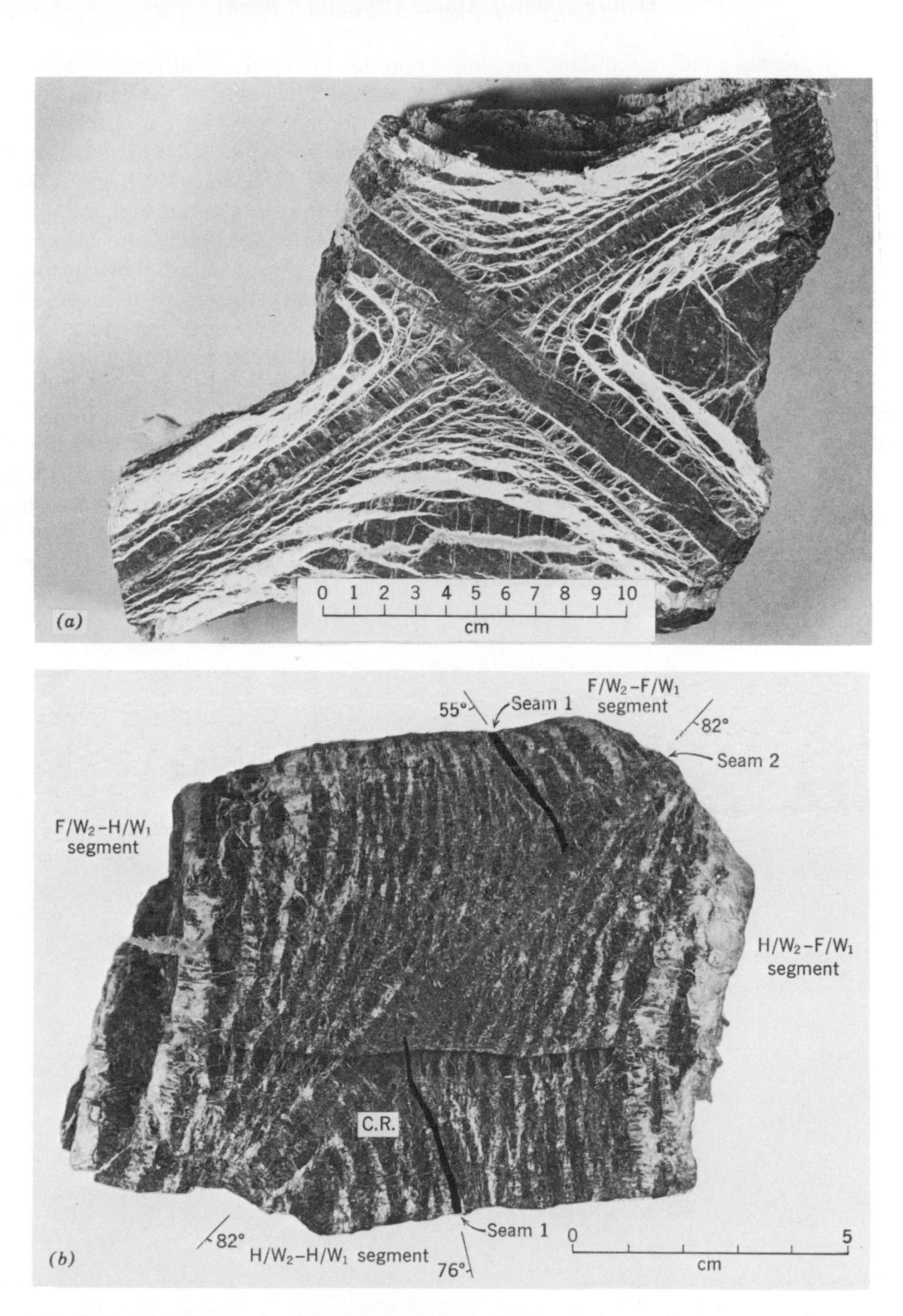

Fig. 6.17 (*a*) Photograph of section through the larger specimen of serpentinite, showing distribution of asbestos fiber bands about conjugate magnetite seams. (Section cut perpendicularly to the line of intersection between the seams.) (*b*) Photograph of the smaller specimen, showing strike separation of seam 1 on seam 2, and plan view of the center of rotation, CR. (H/W_1 = hangingwall seam 1: F/W_2 = footwall seam 2.) The horizontal line across the specimen, about one third of the way from the bottom, is a saw cut.

F/W_1 segments and discordant in the H/W_1-H/W_2, F/W_1-F/W_2 segments.

5. The general attitude of the thicker fiber bands is at 30° to seam 2, becoming concordant nearer the seams.

The obvious sequence is that seam 1 antedated seam 2 (Fig. 6.17*b*), but possibly seam 1 could represent a fracture opened during movement on seam 2 which subsequently filled with magnetite. If we assume the former condition, serpentinization and formation of the main fiber bands preceded development of seam 1. Development of seam 2 with plane rotational movement followed, with subsequent in-filling and/or secretion of magnetite. Before rotation on seam 2 the configuration may have been similar to that depicted in Fig. 6.17*a*.

The development of fiber by introduction of material or alteration agent into fracture openings, as is commonly held (summaries in Lindgren, 1933, p. 395; Riordon, 1962, pp. 312–313; Sinclair, 1959, pp. 54–57; Stockwell, 1957, pp. 175–180), required the development of individual or incipient fractures, which are incompatible with the deduced failure mechanism in the specimens investigated. It is suggested that most of the fiber bands were formed within the serpentinite by rearrangement of material already available (see also Hall, 1930; Riordon, 1962), where shear stress conditions were favorable during the build up and prior to failure. The process envisaged is serpentinization followed by applied stress causing development of fiber, then failure, with later secretion of magnetite on the fracture planes (planes of low chemical potential).

7. *Origin of Alpine Ultramafic Associations*

I. INTRODUCTION

P. J. Wyllie

The origin of alpine ultramafic rocks has been considered in each of the articles in Chapters 5 and 6, but the contributions gathered in Chapter 7 are concerned specifically with the conditions of formation of the ultramafic rocks.

Sørensen, in Section II, discusses a number of associations involving ultramafic rocks in orogenic belts, with special attention paid to those for which a metasomatic or metamorphic origin has been proposed. Some of these belong clearly to the alpine-type associations. Proposals that large alpine-type ultramafic bodies were formed by processes of metasomatism or metamorphic differentiation never gained general acceptance, but there is evidence that some smaller bodies are so derived. Metasomatic transformation of siliceous dolomites, for example, yields the dolomite-serpentinite association, and metamorphic replacement of impure carbonate rocks in zones of high pressure may have produced the dolomite-peridotite association. Sørensen reviews evidence that peridotite and garnet peridotite, when enclosed in amphibolite, are the products of metamorphic differentiation in zones of stress concentration.

The lack of evidence for contact metamorphism is used as an argument for the low temperature emplacement of ultramafic rocks. In Section III Green describes a small group of peridotites with well-defined metamorphic aureoles of dynamothermal character which indicate temperatures of about 1000°C for the ultramafic intrusions. The chemistry of the pyroxenes is consistent with this estimate. Green considers this group of peridotites to be genetically distinct from other alpine-type intrusions. The peridotites have compositional banding which appears to be caused by gravity stratification, and the rocks have higher CaO, Al_2O_3 and Na_2O than other alpine-type intrusions. Green's interpretation is that these rocks crystallized initially under high load pressure, were deformed, moved to higher levels, and recrystallized. An alternative interpretation is given by Thayer in Chapter 7-IV-D-2.

Thayer, in Section IV, discusses the chemical and structural relationships of rocks in the alpine mafic magma stem, which includes the calc-alkaline plutonic magma series. He concludes that the worldwide similarity of features in, and relations between alpine peridotites, podiform chromite deposits and gabbro can be rationalized only by a common origin. Alpine dunite is very difficult to explain as residual mantle material remaining after generation of tholeiite despite conclusions in Chapter 11, Sections II, IV and V. Thayer considers that adequate modern petrological mapping on a scale of 1:50,000 or larger would eliminate the ophiolite hypothesis from serious consideration. The known proportions of ultramafic to feldspathic rocks in alpine intrusive complexes range from 100:0 to 10:90. Chemically, the rocks of the alpine mafic magma stem differ from stratiform gabbroic complexes in that they follow the typical calc-alkaline plutonic trend rather than the Skaergaard rock trend. Peridotite and gabbro are characterized by metamorphic and igneous textures and structural relations, and were probably emplaced as anhydrous crystal mushes. Some problems of alpine intrusive complexes are illustrated by the Baltimore gabbro-State Line complex, and the Lizard peridotite and gabbro in Cornwall. The Baltimore gabbro has been described as a contemporaneously deformed stratiform complex, and the Lizard complex has been described as a high-temperature peridotite intruded into amphibolites. Thayer concludes that both show similar structural relationships between peridotite and gabbro and are normal alpine complexes.

II. METAMORPHIC AND METASOMATIC PROCESSES IN THE FORMATION OF ULTRAMAFIC ROCKS

Henning Sørensen

In textbooks such as Ramberg (1952, p. 263) and Barth (1962, p. 220) and in a number of recent papers ultramafic rocks have been explained as products of metamorphic differentiation or metasomatic replacement. Some of these views, for instance that peridotites and serpentinites should be basic fronts formed during granitization, can no longer be maintained and the metamorphic origin of large bodies of ultramafic rocks has never gained general appreciation. Only in small bodies of ultramafic rocks has a metamorphic-metasomatic origin been fairly widely accepted. In the following sections, various aspects of the relationship between metamorphism and ultramafic rocks will be reviewed and discussed.

A. The Meso- and Catazonal Ultramafites

The masses of ultramafic rocks enclosed in mesozonal and catazonal rock assemblages of orogenic zones have presented severe problems when an emplacement of ultramafic magmas has been considered. The bodies are conformably enclosed by crystalline schists, especially amphibolites and hornblende gneisses (see for instance Forestier, 1962). The ultramafic bodies occur in horizons which are folded in conformity with the other members of the rock series in question. The bodies, which often occur in a boudin-like fashion, attain sizes from the very small to about 1 km in diameter; larger masses are rare. Contact metamorphism of the enclosing rocks is absent; instead there are often zones of reaction between the ultramafic rocks and their country rocks or the contact zones are strongly tectonized. The minerals of the reaction zones are sensitive indicators of the grade of metamorphism (cf. Read, 1934; Phillips & Hess, 1936; Chenevoy, 1950; Sørensen, 1954; and Forestier, 1962).

These field relations indicate that the ultramafic rocks were emplaced prior to the folding and metamorphism responsible for the structures and mineralogy of the country rocks. In accordance with this a dunite at Siorarssuit, West Greenland, was found by isotopic age determinations (Rb/Sr) undertaken by A. M. Stueber (personal communication, 1965) to be about

3400 m.y. old, while the country rocks were metamorphosed 1800–3000 m.y. ago (Bridgwater, 1965).

Even if many authors have considered these ultramafic rocks as intrusive into their present environment, the available evidence strongly favors the view that they were emplaced either in the geosynclinal sediments or in early stages of deformation, as was suggested already in 1859 by J. Dorlhac in a discussion of the peridotites of the French Central Massif (see Forestier, 1962). According to this interpretation the origin of the ultramafic rocks of the meso- and catazone should be sought in their primary associations which will be treated in the subsequent section.

B. Primary Associations of Ultramafic Rocks and Their Products of Metamorphism

Ultramafic rocks may be emplaced into crustal environments in the following ways:

1. As members of intrusive complexes, especially layered basic intrusions where peridotite and bronzitite are associated with gabbro/norite, anorthosite, etc.
2. As ophiolitic complexes in orogenic zones where peridotite/serpentinite is associated with basic lavas, chert and limestone. There is no agreement about their mode of emplacement; magmatic, tectonic and metasomatic processes have been proposed.
3. As sheets or lenses of serpentine/peridotite in sedimentary dolomite in orogenic zones. The ultramafic rocks may have been emplaced as solid or magmatic intrusions or may be metasomatic replacement products.
4. As large masses of peridotite that may have been tectonically emplaced into their environment from deeper zones of the orogens or from the mantle.

By progressive deformation and metamorphism, these pre- or early orogenic rock assemblages are transformed into the meso- and catazonal association of small boudin-like ultramafic masses enclosed in amphibolites and hornblende gneisses. An excellent example of an early stage of this transformation has been described by Weidmann (1964); a possibly very late stage by Berthelsen (1960, p. 211).

Zones of gabbro and norite surrounding masses of dunite and peridotite in the Polar Urals (Morkovkina, 1962) and in West Greenland (Berthelsen, 1962, Sørensen, 1955c) have been interpreted as hybrid rocks formed by disruption and metasomatic transformation of parts of original masses of peridotite.

C. Metamorphic or Metasomatic Ultramafic Rocks

1. The ophiolite association. Vuagnat (1953) has demonstrated in the Alps that serpentinite may be formed by serpentinization of basaltic pillow lavas.

The huge masses of serpentinite/peridotite of New Caledonia were interpreted by Routhier (1954) as effusive formations on top of folded lavas of Eocene age. There is no contact metamorphic alteration of the underlying lavas (Routhier, 1954, p. 52). Other masses of peridotite of New Caledonia are conformably enclosed in supracrustal rocks. In the discussion of Routhier's 1954 paper, Avias pointed out that the discordant sheets of peridotite, rather than being effusive, could have been thrust over the folded lavas.

Avias (1949, 1955) has interpreted the concordant peridotites of New Caledonia as products of metasomatic transformation of basaltic lavas. The metamorphic grade of the lavas corresponds to the greenschist and locally amphibolite facies; the sedimentary rocks may contain glaucophane, lawsonite, epidote, and chlorite. The marginal parts of the ultramafic masses consist of serpentinite. The adjacent rocks are rich in quartz, albite, calcite, epidote, and chlorite. Inclusions of sediments in the serpentinite are enriched in grossularite, zoisite, nephrite, etc. The contacts are generally sharp or locally gradual between

Fig. 7.1 Peridotite (toward the top) with gradual transition to para-amphibolite (toward the bottom). Relics of folds within the peridotite can be seen in continuation of the folds in the para-amphibolite. North coast of Grønøy, northern Norway.

serpentinite and the country rocks. The ultramafic rocks are considered by Avias to have been formed by progressive concentrations of Mg, Fe, Ni, and Cr, possibly as a result of high stress. Si, Al, Ca, and Na were expelled to the adjacent rocks.

Avias has produced much evidence in favor of a metasomatic origin of the peridotite. To me, however, it is difficult to see how such enormous masses of peridotite, which display fine banding with layers of dunite, harzburgite, and chromitite, can be formed in a high crustal level by metasomatic processes. I should therefore prefer to regard the peridotites as fragments of the mantle. The metasomatic contact relations may then be connected with the serpentinization of the peridotite.

2. The association dolomite-serpentinite. In deformed sedimentary dolomite, there are often patches and lenses of serpentinite or talc that may be concentrated in zones of strong deformation or may pass gradually (ophicalcite) into the adjacent dolomite. This association may be considered a product of metasomatic transformation of siliceous dolomite (see Perrin & Roubault, 1955; Zwart, 1953; and Wiik, 1953). As mentioned by Benson (1918) serpentinite formed from carbonate rocks is poorer in Cr and Ni than serpentinite formed at the expense of peridotite. Faust, Murata, and Fahey (1956) have confirmed this. The first group was found to contain less than 0.002 per cent Ni and 0.01 per cent Cr, while the second group contains more than 0.04 per cent Ni and generally more than 0.1 per cent Cr.

3. The association dolomite-peridotite. Already in 1912 Longchambon suggested that the lherzolites of the Pyrenees were metasomatically transformed sedimentary carbonate rocks. This interpretation is hard to defend today (see Ravier, 1954, 1964).

In recent years a number of peridotites from the Caledonides of Northern Norway, in part carbonate-bearing (sagvandites), have been found in intimate association with marble, lime-silicate gneisses and amphibolites metamorphosed under amphibolite facies conditions (Sørensen, 1955b; Reitan & Geul, 1959; Randall, 1960). These peridotites are composed of olivine with about 10 per cent *fa*, enstatite with 10 per cent *fs*, and varying amounts of amphibole, phlogopite, dolomite, green spinel, chromite and secondary serpentine. The peridotite bodies may be a few hundred meters in diameter.

There are gradual transitions from the carbonate rocks into the peridotite which contains bands of the para-schists with preserved orientation; even folds may be traced into the peridotite without the slightest disturbance (see Fig. 7.1). The mechanical properties of peridotite, amphibolite, marble, and lime-silicate schists are so different that disharmonic structures should be expected in the case of folding of bands of peridotite in a series of sedimentary rocks. In the three above-mentioned papers the peridotites are therefore regarded to be formed by metamorphic replacement of impure carbonate rocks. The type of chemical processes involved are best studied at Grønøy (Sørensen, 1955b) where inclusions of lime-silicate rocks in the peridotite and the enclosing rocks are enriched in diopside, epidote-minerals, garnet, and calcite. There are also large crystals of diopside in fractures in the peridotite. These minerals are considered to represent Ca, Al, and CO_2 expelled from the places where the peridotites were formed as a result of a strong concentration of Mg. Crystals of forsterite occur in the marble adjacent to the peridotites. It should be pointed out that forsterite has only been found in marble adjacent to peridotite in this region and that also epidote is confined to the contacts of the peridotite. This indicates that the peridotites were formed under special physical-chemical conditions, according to Reitan & Geul (1959) in zones of high pressure in which the formation of minerals with small mol volumes, such as forsterite and enstatite, is favored (cf. Ramberg, 1952, p. 120). There are no traces of an early formation of serpentine (cf. Section C-2).

At Grønøy the peridotite and sedimentary rocks may be considered a primary association. To the east of Grønøy (Fig. 7.2), the two rock types are separated from each

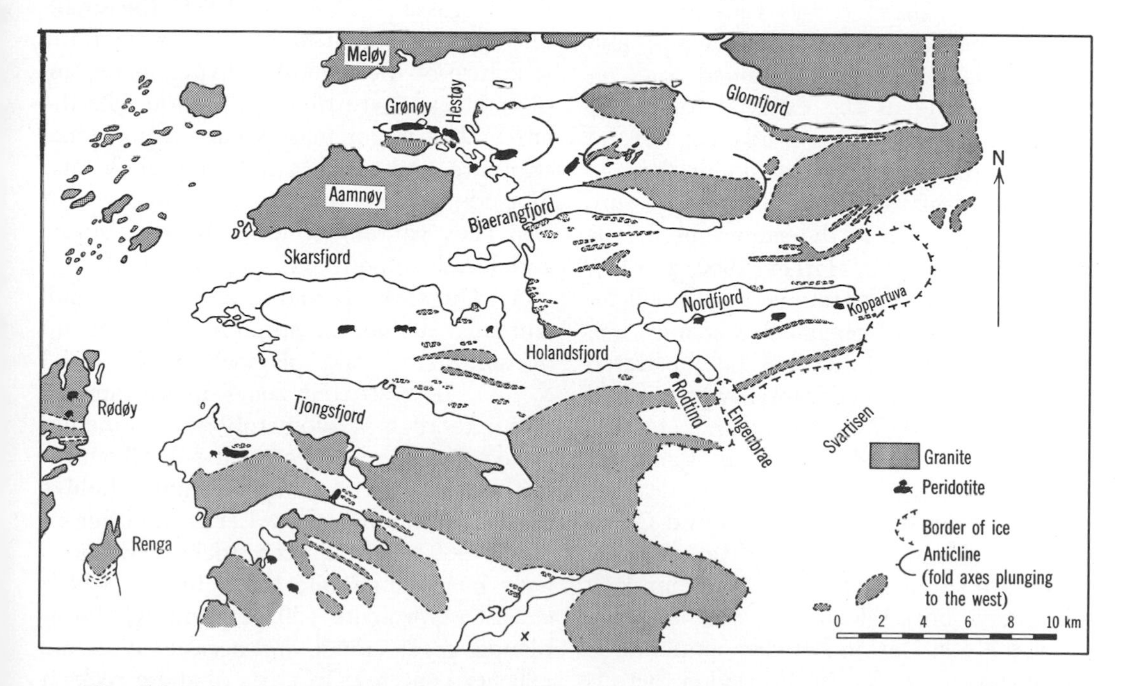

Fig. 7.2 Map of the Holandsfjord-Glomfjord region of northern Norway (after Sørensen, 1955b). The distribution of larger masses of periodotite is indicated.

other by tectonic processes. The bodies of peridotite are broken into boudins, while the marble is plastically deformed (Sørensen, 1955a). It is apparent that the rigid peridotite formed in an early phase of the deformation has had a strong influence on the structural evolution of the enclosing rocks, which have been exposed to considerable stretching.

4. The association amphibolite-ultramafic rocks. Barth (1947), Ramberg (1952, p. 263), Sørensen (1953), Mikkola (1955), Bennington (1956), Chenevoy (1958), von Eller (1961), Oen (1962), and others, have suggested that ultramafic rocks varying from hornblendite through bahiaite, peridotite, and garnet peridotite to dunite are products of metamorphic differentiation, possibly caused by tectonic overpressure in the sense of Birch (1955), Sobolev (1960a), Schüller (1961), and Clark (1961).

Earlier Harker emphasized the importance of tectonic overpressure when discussing the deformation of rocks:

"In so far as they yield, they suffer deformation. In so far as they resist, internal shearing stresses are set up; and these stresses being maintained and renewed so long as the external forces are operative, attain a magnitude far beyond anything that is possible in simple thermal metamorphism. The hydrostatic pressure may be very high at the same time, but is not necessarily so" (Harker, 1960, p. 137). Further: "Shearing stress in a rock will increase the rate of chemical reactions" (p. 146). These principles will be illustrated by means of examples from Tovqussaq and Godthaab Fjord, West Greenland (for the location, see Noe-Nygaard & Ramberg, 1961).

The two localities Tovqussaq and Qugssuk (at the head of Godthaab Fjord), which are situated about 50 km from each other, have been selected for detailed studies of the relationship between amphibolite and ultramafic rocks. In this region there is a great number of bodies of peridotite enclosed in amphibolite and granulite facies gneisses rich in bands of amphibolite (Sørensen, 1953; Berthelsen, 1960 and 1962). These ultramafic bodies attain diameters of up to about 1 km. Besides there are small bodies of ultramafic rocks enclosed in the amphibolites. The amphibolites contain appreciable amounts of diopside and are rich in diopside-garnet-scapolite-skarn. The amphibolites have been interpreted by Sørensen as metamorphosed marly rocks while Berthelsen regards them as metamorphosed ophiolitic assemblages. Berthelsen (1960, p. 210), therefore, when discussing the ultramafic rocks of Tovqussaq, considers them as strongly metamorphosed ophiolitic serpentinites.

I have advanced the view that the ultramafic rocks enclosed in the amphibolites are formed as a result of metamorphic differentiation. This view is based on the following observations:

1. The small bands and lenses of bahiaite, lherzolite and harzburgite enclosed in bands of amphibolite contain relics of diopside skarn from the adjacent amphibolite. At Tovqussaq (Sørensen, 1953) the smallest ultramafic bodies have preserved the structure of the enclosing hypersthene amphibolite and are rich in diopside, like the latter. The larger masses have a polygonal structure and contain less amphibole and diopside and more bronzite (18 per cent *fs*). They contain in addition green spinel and locally olivine (10 per cent *fa*).

At Qugssuk, bahiaite occurs as small lenticular bodies in amphibolite made up of hornblende and plagioclase (Figs. 7.3 & 7.4). In restricted zones in the amphibolite there is a glomeroblastic formation of hypersthene (30 per cent *fs*). Chemical analyses and modes of these amphibolites have been published by Larsen and Sørensen (1960). From such rocks transitions have been found into the bahiaites, which consist of bronzite (20 per cent *fs*), hornblende, green spinel, and occasional olivine (20 per cent *fa*). In parts of these rocks a glomeroblastic origin of the bronzite may still be discerned since the grains of bronz-

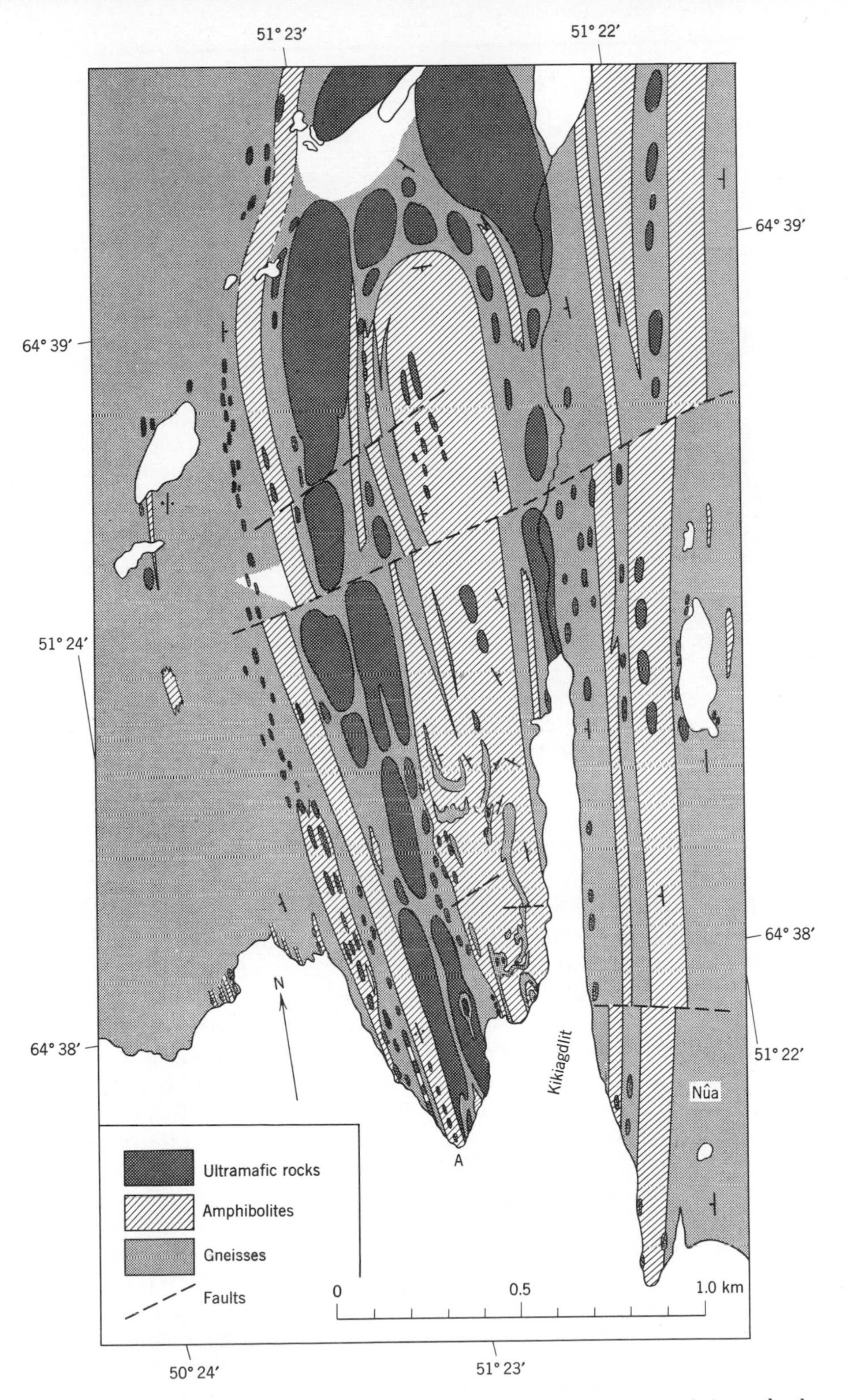

Fig. 7.3 Simplified geological map of a small area on the west coast of Qugssuk, the head of Godthaabs Fjord. A belt of peridotite lenses enclosed in gneisses forms a synclinal structure. Note also the small bodies of ultramafic rocks within the layers of amphibolite. (A geological map of the area of the north of that shown here has been published by R. Lauerma, *Bull. Comm. géol. Finl.*, No. 215, 1964.)

Fig. 7.4 Bands rich in hypersthene (light-colored) in amphibolite (dark) cut by pegmatite veins. The hypersthene appears to be formed later than the amphibolite minerals, and the hypersthene bands are regarded by the writer as embryos of the ultramafic rocks. The point (*A*) to the west of the narrow creek Kikiagdlit in Fig. 7.3.

ite are divided into sectors of slightly different optical orientations separated by small grains of hornblende. In other parts of the bahiaites the structure is polygonal and the homogeneous grains of bronzite are practically free from hornblende inclusions (Sørensen, unpublished observations).

2. Chemical analyses of the amphibolites and ultramafic rocks at Tovqussaq (Sørensen, 1953, pp. 45–47) and at Qugssuk (unpublished) indicate that the ultramafic rocks represent concentrations of Mg, Cr, Ni, and in part Fe, and are impoverished in Si, Al, Ca, Na, and K. The expelled elements appear to be deposited in small pegmatites in the amphibolite adjacent to the bahiaite. The amphibolites at Tovqussaq and Qugssuk contain traces up to about 0.1 per cent Cr and 0.06 per cent Ni. The ultramafic rocks have up to 0.2 per cent Cr and up to 0.15 per cent Ni (Berthelsen, 1960, p. 207; Sørensen, 1953, p. 45 and unpublished determinations). It is worth mentioning that Berthelsen (1960, p. 207) found that the calc-silicate rocks at Tovqussaq contain about 0.02 per cent Ni and 0.08 per cent Cr, which is about the same as is found in the amphibolites.

3. Berthelsen (1960) has undertaken a structural analysis of the Tovqussaq region. It appears from this examination that the ultramafic rocks behaved as plastic masses in the early stages of the deformation. Therefore, the ultramafic masses often occur in the hinge zones of folds (Berthelsen, 1960, p. 65 and 75). This indicates, according to Berthelsen, that the ultramafic bodies originally may have been siliceous dolomite, a mode of formation corresponding to that suggested for some peridotites from Northern Norway (Section C-3). However, Berthelsen (1960, p. 211) prefers to consider the bahiaites as metamorphosed ophiolitic ultramafic rocks. The plastic deformation could then represent a former serpentinite stage.

The folds in ultramafic bodies are explained by Bennington (1956, p. 575) as results of plastic deformation by recrystallization in systems in which the vapors are not entirely expelled. However, many of the ultramafic rocks show no preferred orientation. This is explained by Schüller (1961) as a result of spontaneous growth of minerals in high-pressure zones (cf. Thiessen et al., 1960).

a. Mechanism of metamorphic formation of ultramafic rocks in amphibolite. Sørensen (1953, pp. 35–43) explained the ultramafic rocks at Tovqussaq as products of metamorphic differentiation in zones of high stress in rigid bands of amphibolite enclosed in less rigid gneisses, the strain stored in the deformed rock being relieved by recrystallization under the formation of the ultramafic rocks. The formation of high-temperature mineral assemblages in the zones of high pressure may be explained by the following points:

1. Increasing stress decreases the temperature at which a given mineral will crystallize freely and accelerates the rate of reaction (cf. Buerger and Washken, 1947; and Dachille and Roy, 1960).
2. Hot spots on microslip planes may produce a considerable heat (Bowden and Thomas, 1954).
3. If release of strain is effected through the kinetic component of the energy of deformation, the work is mainly dissipated by heat transfer and deformation by creep (Goranson, 1940). Shearing in connection with bending (folding) of the layers of amphibolite may explain the location of small ultramafic bodies in the hinges of folds.

This kinetic interpretation of the ultrabasification of amphibolites is very similar to that of Backlund (1936) and Ebert (1936) concerning the formation of eclogite. Especially Ebert emphasized the importance of tectonic overpressure (Überdruck) and localized zones of strain (Spannungs-zustände) and pointed out that only a limited region of a given rock (amphibolite) could be expected to be transformed into eclogite by this mechanism.

The chemical processes in operation have been briefly treated above. The concentration of the small ions Mg^{2+}, Fe^{2+}, Fe^{3+}, Cr^{3+}, and Ni^{2+} in zones of high pressure and the expulsion of larger ions such as Ca^{2+}, Na^{+}, and K^{+} recalls the observation by Cottrell (1948, p. 32) who, when speaking about the creep of solids, states that an "atmosphere" of solute atoms may form around a dislocation, large atoms assembling in the expanded region, small ions in the compressed region. A very detailed examination of the migration of matter in and around zones of high pressure has been published by Bennington (1956 and 1959). He considers the ultramafic rocks as residual products of extreme metamorphic differentiation due to high pressure and strong shearing stress. With increasing pressure, minerals with decreasing mole volumes will be formed; therefore forsterite will succeed enstatite with increasing pressure. Chromite may also be regarded as a residual product. The energy of strain is released by the expulsion of H_2O, CO_2, SiO_2, K, Na, Ca, etc. from the system (see also Verhoogen, 1948; and Ramberg, 1952 and 1960). The material expelled may be responsible for the occurrence of lime-silicate rocks (rodingite) in association with ultramafic rocks. Such rocks may, however, also be formed in connection with serpentinization.

b. Metamorphic facies. Experimental work has given strong support to the view expressed by Backlund (1936) and Ebert (1936) that eclogite is a special high-pressure facies. That glaucophane-lawsonite-jadeite rocks are formed in a similar way is now also widely accepted (see for instance Fyfe, Turner, and Verhoogen, 1958). According to Boyd and England (1959), pyrope is at a given pressure stable at lower temperatures than enstatite. It may therefore be suggested that eclogite and peridotite can be formed in zones of tectonic overpressure, which are more or less independent of depth in the crust. The temperature of formation, that is the slope of the geothermal gradient (cf., for instance, den Tex, 1965), may then determine the mineral assemblages stable at the given conditions, so that the peridotite high pressure facies is formed at higher temperatures than the eclogite high pressure facies (cf. Sørensen, 1953, p. 83).

5. Ultramafic veins. Veins of bronzitite, dunite, etc. are confined to the ultramafic bodies and do not intrude into the enclosing rocks. This is explained by Bowen and Tuttle (1949) as a result of hydrothermal reactions along fractures in the ultramafic bodies, since experimental work has shown that water vapor unsaturated in SiO_2 may dissolve SiO_2 from orthopyroxene and thus transform it into olivine, or if saturated with SiO_2 may transform olivine into orthopyroxene. Examples of this have for instance been given by Barth (1950) and Sørensen (1954). As emphasized by Barth, this mode of formation of monomineralic rocks is not logically limited to bodies having a dyke-like relation.

III. HIGH-TEMPERATURE PERIDOTITE INTRUSIONS

D. H. Green

A. Introduction

One of the most commonly used arguments for low temperature of emplacement of ultramafic rocks has been the lack of evidence for contact metamorphism, particularly at temperatures compatible with emplacement of ultramafic liquid. However, recent papers on dunites and peridotites occurring in alpine orogenic zones have, in some cases, produced evidence and arguments for moderate or even high-temperature of emplacement of ultramafic rocks. As a recent example, Ragan (1963, p. 561) has deduced that the Twin Sisters dunite was capable of solid flow and intrusive emplacement at temperatures probably of 600 to 700°C but possibly as low as 500°C (Chapter 5-III). Lipman (1964) deduces similar temperatures for the Trinity ultramafic pluton in the Klamath mountains, California, and in this example there is some evidence of increase in metamorphic grade adjacent to some contacts (Lipman 1964, pp. 216–217). Both the Twin Sisters and Trinity ultramafic bodies exhibit evidence for flow as a solid or near-solid, inhomogeneous crystalline body.

The origin of this inhomogeneity in alpine peridotites is often considered to lie in an earlier period of accumulation and gravity stratification (Thayer 1960, p. 257; Green 1961, pp. 6, 22–23; Challis 1965, p. 360) and the nature of the parent magma cannot be specified with any certainty. Challis (1965a, p. 360) has described some of the New Zealand ultramafic bodies, including the classical Dun Mountain locality, and suggests that these bodies represent accumulates in "deep-level magma chambers of a line of upper Palaeozoic volcanoes." Challis considers that the parent magma was probably tholeiitic and may have approached a picrite in composition. One body, Red Hills, has an unfaulted contact locally at which spilitic volcanics are converted to amphibolites and, right at the contact, to pyroxene hornfels (Challis, 1965b). Challis suggests that temperatures at the contact probably did not exceed 800°C and that the magma temperature was about 1200°C (p. 416). It should be emphasized that this is a temperature suggested for a basaltic or picritic magma and not for an ultramafic magma, the ultramafic composition being regarded as the result of accumulation of early crystallizing chromite, olivine, orthopyroxene, and minor clinopyroxene and very complete removal of interstitial basaltic liquid.

These examples of ultramafic rocks, even though they show evidence of moderate temperatures at the time of their emplacement, do not provide any conclusive evidence for the existence of a high-temperature peridotite magma. Rather their features are consistent with accumulation at crustal levels from more basaltic liquids or (liquid + crystal) magmas. It is not proposed to consider these bodies further in this paper; but there are important problems in the nature of the parent magma, the original presence or absence of a basaltic interprecipitate liquid and the mechanism for removal of such an interprecipitate liquid, and in the expected and observed intensities of contact metamorphism.

Further discussion in this paper is limited to a small group of peridotites that have clearly defined dynamothermal aureoles, external form and internal structures resembling those of salt domes, and are of intermediate size (5 to 15 miles diameter). These peridotites have chemical compositions in which Al_2O_3, CaO, Na_2O in particular are minor but essential components (in contrast to the peridotites and dunites of the examples described above where these components are extremely low or of local, sporadic concentration). Mineralogically, these peridotites are characterized by evidence for initial crystallization at high load pressure and for post-crystallization deformation, movement, and recrystallization. Examples of this type of peridotite intrusion include:

1. Tinaquillo, Venezuela (MacKenzie, 1960; Green 1963).
2. Lizard, Cornwall (Green, 1964a,b,c).
3. Mt. Albert, Quebec (Smith and MacGregor, 1960).

These three peridotite bodies have sufficient features in common and the evidence on their nature and emplacement mechanism is sufficiently unambiguous to merit their recognition as a distinctive type of alpine ultramafic intrusion. There are a number of other peridotite intrusions which are similar in some features to the above type but, possibly because of more complex, post-intrusion histories and in part because of insufficiently detailed descriptions, the diagnostic characteristics cannot be so closely matched. Such peridotites include the intrusions of Beni Bousera, Morocco (Milliard, 1959); Lherz, Pyrenees (Lacroix, 1917, Ravier, 1964); Horoman, Japan (Onuki, 1965); and possibly Dawros, Connemara (Rothstein, 1957, 1961).

B. Metamorphic Aureoles

The metamorphic aureoles of the Tinaquillo, Lizard and Mount Albert peridotites are of dynamothermal character and the rocks that have been recrystallized in the aureoles are foliated amphibolites and granulites. Hornfels textures are not developed and the mineral assemblages are not typical of either hornblende hornfels or pyroxene hornfels facies. The peridotites occur in regionally metamorphosed terrains and their emplacement probably occurred during the regional metamorphism. The grade of regional metamorphism is of lower almandine amphibolite facies [i.e., staurolite-almandine subfacies (Turner and Verhoogen, 1960)] in the Lizard and Tinaquillo examples or greenschist facies as in the Mt. Albert example. In all three examples the metamorphic gradient around the ultramafic body affects rocks of predominantly basaltic chemistry.

1. Mineralogy. In the Lizard area the basic rocks outside the metamorphic aureole are characteristically blue-green hornblende amphibolites with sodic plagioclase, sphene and magnetite. Pale green salite, epidote, grossular, calcite and quartz are present in varying proportions in some bands. The outer margin of the peridotite aureole is marked by the change of the hornblende from the distinctive blue-green type to brown-green hornblende. Chemical analyses of two hornblendes from rocks of closely similar chemistry show that the hornblende color change is matched by a composition change. The contents of the tschermakite, glaucophane, and richterite (soda-tremolite) solid-solution end-members decrease and the contents of the edenite, and cummingtonite solid solutions increase in going from the blue-green to green-brown to brown hornblendes of the aureole (Green 1964b, p. 557).

Accompanying the change in color of the hornblende, the plagioclase becomes more calcic and more abundant, sphene and magnetite are replaced by ilmenite + magnetite and salite appears as a minor constituent in the amphibolites and is not restricted to calcium-rich bands. In the Lizard example, the zone occupied by the green-brown hornblende amphibolites is relatively wide (Green 1964b, p. 560) and, at vertical contacts of the peridotite extends 350 to 500 feet from the peridotite margin and may extend over 1000 feet in some areas.

Higher grade metamorphic assemblages are marked by assemblages of hypersthene + augite + plagioclase ± hornblende + ilmenite + magnetite. The presence or absence of hornblende as a major phase subdivides these near-contact rocks into hornblende granulites and pyroxene granulites. The hornblende is a brown variety, lacking any green coloration in pleochroism, and varying from deep-brown, to very pale brown, almost colorless, probably with increasing Mg/Fe ratio. The plagioclase present in the granulites is andesine-labradorite and the co-existing pyroxenes have compositions matching those of high-grade granulites or intermediate between granulite pyroxenes and magmatic pyroxene pairs. Olivine + orthopyroxene + clinopyroxene + plagioclase assemblages occur and probably represent the highest grade of the aureole indicating that the temperature has locally been adequate to cause the breakdown of hornblende in an undersaturated rock. It may be noted that the bulk compositions of the analyzed rocks from the Lizard aureole are all olivine normative, and in two cases are nepheline normative. In these undersaturated rocks the highest grade assemblages are

olivine + augite + hypersthene + plagioclase + magnetite-ilmenite
augite + hypersthene + plagioclase + magnetite-ilmenite
augite + hypersthene + plagioclase + hornblende + magnetite-ilmenite

It is important in estimating the P-T conditions of this aureole that almandine-pyrope garnet does not occur in any mineral assemblage.

In the Lizard metamorphic aureole there is limited metasomatism over distances of a few inches at the contacts. In the Tinaquillo peridotite, the absence of chemical data on the rocks of the metamorphic aureole makes comparison of metamorphic assemblages more difficult. MacKenzie describes the country rock outside the metamorphic aureole as interlayered hornblende gneiss and plagioclase gneiss. The former rock type consists of roughly 50 per cent oligoclase, 25 per cent quartz and 25 per cent green hornblende while the latter ranges from 90 per cent quartz to 90 per cent albite or oligoclase. The quartz-rich and leucocratic layers are not apparent within the contact aureole and MacKenzie does not describe quartz as a constituent of either the garnet-bearing or hypersthene-bearing granulites. Thus there appear to be chemical differences between the rocks outside the metamorphic aureole and those within it and this makes the evaluation of the metamorphic effects of the peridotite more difficult. There is a possibility of metasomatic interchange with the peridotite but no unequivocal evidence to support this. In the case of the Mt. Albert peridotite, Smith and MacGregor (1960) report essentially constant bulk compositions through the aureole.

MacKenzie distinguishes the outer margin of the metamorphic aureole to the Tinaquillo peridotite by color change of hornblende from green to brown, by the appearance of pyrope-almandine garnet and by composition change of the plagioclase from albite-oligoclase to andesine. Augite may also appear at the outer edge of the aureole, but only becomes abundant in the inner part of the aureole and is there joined by common garnet and by minor hypersthene. MacKenzie attributes a maximum width to the metamorphic aureole of about 5000 feet. Although the change in mineralogy is certainly partly controlled by changes in bulk chemistry, the inner, near-peridotite rocks with typical hornblende granulite mineralogy (18 per cent augite, 2 per cent hypersthene, 20 per cent pyrope-almandine, 20 per cent brown hornblende, 37 per cent andesine, 2 per cent ilmenite-magnetite) are at a higher metamorphic grade than the surrounding hornblende-oligoclase-quartz gneisses. Within the peridotite, tabular bodies of granoblastic, foliated basic gneiss are in some cases concordant and in some cases discordant to the peridotite foliation. MacKenzie (1964) called these bodies "pseudogabbro" and interpreted them as metamorphosed inclusions of country rock (p. 312). This conclusion has been disputed by Thayer and Brown (1961) who preferred a magmatic origin for the "pseudo-gabbro." However, whatever their parentage, the "pseudo-gabbros" are clearly recrystallized metamorphic rocks of basaltic chemistry, and as such invite comparison with the rocks of the inner aureole. Like the rocks of the inner aureole, the mineralogy is that of hornblende granulite with 20 to 30 per cent brown hornblende, about 40 per cent plagioclase (labradorite), 15 per cent augite, 5 to 15 per cent hypersthene and minor ilmenite + magnetite. Small grains of almandine-pyrope garnet occur locally and the rarity of this phase and the increased abundance of hypersthene provide a contrast with the hornblende granulites of the inner part of the metamorphic aureole. While the lack of chemical data again hampers a close comparison, the differences in mineralogy may simply reflect the higher temperatures at similar pressures attained by the bodies included within the peridotite, in contrast to those at external contacts. Thus the left-hand side of equation (1) is favored by higher temperature or lower pressure and this reaction is consistent with the hypersthene + labradorite assemblage within the included basic bodies and the garnet + augite + andesine assemblage outside the peridotite. Free quartz from reaction (1) is unlikely to appear as it would be expected to react with the hornblende present.

$$(1)\quad \underset{\text{hypersthene}}{2(Mg,Fe)SiO_3} + \underset{\text{anorthite in plagioclase}}{CaAl_2Si_2O_8} \rightleftharpoons \underset{\text{garnet}}{Ca(Mg,Fe)_2Al_2Si_3O_{12}} + \underset{\text{quartz}}{SiO_2}$$

A detailed description of the aureole of the Mt. Albert peridotite has not yet been published but Smith and MacGregor (1960) describe the aureole as up to 1000-feet wide and ranging "from greenschist through epidote amphibolite to garnetiferous hornblende-pyroxene granulite" (p. 1978). Plagioclase becomes more calcic towards the contact. The appearance of garnet in the inner aureole invites comparison with the Tinaquillo rather than the Lizard peridotite.

The Horoman and Beni Bousera peridotites, which may be of comparable types to the three just described, have country rocks of pelitic character. The Horoman peridotite (Onuki, 1965, quoting Hunahashi, 1948) has produced cordierite + anthophyllite and cordierite + hypersthene assemblages and conditions of metamorphism appropriate to the pyroxene hornfels facies appear to have been attained. In contrast, the Beni Bousera peridotite (5 km × 15 km) forms the core and culmination of a sequence of metamorphic zones ranging from sericite schists, micaschists (with garnet, staurolite, andalusite), feldspathic gneiss (with biotite, garnet, sillimanite, kyanite) to an inner zone (600-feet wide) mainly of garnet and sillimanite-bearing graphitic gneiss with local occurrence of orthopyroxene-bearing gneiss and also granulites of pyroxene + garnet + plagioclase + hornblende mineralogy.

2. Textures and structures of the metamorphic aureole. In the Lizard area, the amphibolites outside the metamorphic aureole have nematoblastic to lepidoblastic texture, a well-developed subhorizontal foliation with parallel compositional banding, and a strong lineation striking north-northwest due to alignment of hornblende prisms within the foliation plane. Adjacent to the peridotite, a new subvertical foliation, striking north-northwest, developed in the green-brown hornblende amphibolites and in the granulites. This parallels the foliation developed in the marginal zones of the peridotite and locally can be observed under development as an axial plane foliation where the subhorizontal foliation of the country rock is folded into complex rheid or fluid type folds adjacent to the peridotite. The texture of the metamorphic rocks changes from lepidoblastic to granoblastic in the granulites but a foliation in these rocks is clearly defined by compositional banding and lenticular variations in the proportions of minerals present. In contact areas of complex intermingling of peridotite and contact rocks, the basic granulites locally behaved as the more mobile rocks and were capable of intruding and including fragments of the margin of the peridotite (Green, 1964b, pp. 560–562). There is no clear evidence that partial melting of the granulites occurred.

In the Tinaquillo aureole, the garnet + pyroxene + hornblende granulites of the aureole and the pyroxene-granulites of the included "pseudo-gabbro" bodies are both foliated, gneissic rocks. Foliations in the basic rocks and adjacent peridotite are generally closely conformable.

C. The Peridotites

1. Chemistry. Each of the peridotites displays compositional variation in the form of banding and the average composition cannot be well defined. MacKenzie (p. 305) considers that more than 90 per cent of the Tinaquillo peridotite is dunite but the intensely mylonitized yet unserpentinized character of this body makes petrographic distinction between pyroxenes and olivine extremely difficult. Two analyses of typical, very fresh specimens show compositions matching peridotite rather than dunite (Table 7.1). MacKenzie describes small elliptical plugs of enstatite pyroxenite within the peridotite and also thin, sparsely distributed amphibole- and pyroxene-rich layers.

In the Lizard peridotite, textural differences have been used to define a coarse-grained "primary peridotite" within the core of the body and a finely foliated, recrystallized peridotite, closely resembling the Tinaquillo peridotite, nearer the margins of the body. Both types show compositional variation, but this is more clearly observable in the "primary peridotite" as lenticular compositional banding defined by variation in pyroxene content. However, in the Lizard peridotite, the dominant rock type is peridotite with approximately 60 per cent of olivine; pyroxenites, and chromite-bearing, serpentinized dunites comprise less than 10 per cent of the peridotite. An average composition for the Lizard peridotite is given in Table 7.1 (Green, 1964a, pp. 183–184).

No chemical data on the Mt. Albert peridotite has as yet been published, but Smith and MacGregor (1960) describe it as consisting of interbanded dunite and peridotite with minor enstatite pyroxenite. Onuki (1965) has published analyses from the Horoman peridotite which include rocks from dunite to plagioclase-bearing peridotite. The relative proportions of the various rock types are not specified but two analyses (Nos. 4 and 6 of Onuki, 1965) of peridotite and plagioclase peridotite are listed in Table 7.1. Two analyses of "saxonites" from the Beni Bousera peridotite are also given in Table 7.1. These are calculated anhydrous to enable better comparison with the other analyses. Milliard

TABLE 7.1 Chemical Compositions of High-Temperature Peridotites

	Tinaquillo V1460 (Green, 1963)	V336 (Hess, 1964)	Lizard Average (Green, 1964a)	Beni Bousera 6 (Milliard, 1959)	7	Horoman 4 (Onuki, 1965)	6
SiO_2	44.69	43.91	44.77	42.38	43.82	42.55	43.40
TiO_2	0.08	0.06	0.19	...	...	0.04	0.03
Al_2O_3	3.19	2.65	4.16	1.98	5.04	2.10	1.76
Fe_2O_3	0.09	1.44	...	5.21	1.31	1.33	2.01
FeO	7.54	7.23	8.21	6.90	6.20	6.76	6.35
MnO	0.14	0.15	0.11	0.27	0.18	0.11	0.13
MgO	39.80	42.01	39.22	40.13	38.92	44.06	43.15
CaO	2.97	2.02	2.42	2.60	3.88	2.36	2.45
Na_2O	0.18	0.13	0.22	0.39	0.52	0.14	0.19
K_2O	0.02	0.00	0.05	...	...	0.04	0.03
Cr_2O_3	0.45	0.41	0.40	trace	trace	0.24	0.25
NiO	0.26	...	0.24	trace	trace	0.27	0.25
H_2O+	0.38	...	...	...	...	...	...
P_2O_5	0.04	0.00	0.01	0.14	0.13	trace	...
	99.83	100.01	100.00	100.00	100.00	100.00	100.00

(1959) describes the body as garnetiferous saxonite or harzburgite with 50 to 70 per cent olivine, 30 to 50 per cent enstatite and 1 to 2 per cent garnet. The high CaO contents of the analyses indicate that clinopyroxene must also be present.

The comparison of chemical analyses in Table 7.1 illustrates the higher SiO_2/MgO ratio of these peridotites compared with dunites, such as Dun Mountain and Twin Sisters, and implies a pyroxene content of 20 to 40 per cent. Also Table 7.1 illustrates the presence of significant Al_2O_3, CaO, and Na_2O contents, which play an important role in giving rise to mineral phases sensitive to pressure changes. Rocks composed of olivine + chromite or olivine + enstatite + chromite are, in contrast, stable without distinctive mineralogical changes throughout a broad pressure range.

2. ***Mineralogy.*** The chemistry of the high-temperature peridotites is such that, under conditions of increasing pressure at high temperatures, three distinct mineral assemblages may form. In order of increasing pressure these are:

1. Olivine + enstatite + diopside + plagioclase + chromite.
2. Olivine + aluminous enstatite + aluminous diopside ± spinel-chromite solid solution.
3. Olivine + enstatite + diopside + garnet (chromian pyrope).

In the presence of water at moderately high temperatures a fourth assemblage of Olivine + pargasite ± enstatite + spinel may also form. (See Chapters 1-II and 12-II for more details.)

The Tinaquillo and Mount Albert peridotites illustrate the second mineral assemblage. In the Tinaquillo peridotite, plagioclase does not occur in any olivine-bearing rocks although MacKenzie (p. 307) does report plagioclase associated with orthopyroxene in thin bands. There is evidence in the Tinaquillo peridotite for two stages of crystallization—an early, coarse-grained stage characterized by highly aluminous clinopyroxene and orthopyroxene and a later stage of recrystallization during deformation characterized by fine grained olivine, pyroxenes of lower alumina content, porphyroblastic aluminous spinel and minor pargasite (MacKenzie, 1960, pp. 313–314; Green, 1963).

The Lizard peridotite illustrates the derivation of the plagioclase-bearing assemblage by recrystallization of the olivine + aluminous pyroxenes + spinel assemblage under changing P-T conditions. The core of the peridotite preserves the higher pressure assemblage in which enstatite contains up to 6.5 per cent Al_2O_3 and coexisting diopside up to 7.1 per cent Al_2O_3; in both cases the Al_2O_3 is mainly present as Tschermak's silicate $(Ca,Mg)Al_2SiO_6$. The spinel (from 0.5 to 2 per cent of the rock) contains about 50 per cent Al_2O_3 and its textural relations indicate that it was probably the last phase to crystallize. The coarse-grained anhedral, interlocking texture of the core of the Lizard peridotite may be a result of igneous crystallization with a crystallization sequence olivine + enstatite → diopside → spinel. However, the apparent late crystallization of spinel could be a result of decreasing solubility of Al_2O_3 in pyroxenes with decreasing temperature and/or pressure, according to the reaction:

$$(2)\quad \underset{\text{aluminous pyroxene}}{(Ca,Mg)Al_2SiO_6} + \underset{\text{olivine}}{Mg_2SiO_4} \rightleftharpoons \underset{\text{spinel}}{MgAl_2O_4} + \underset{\text{pyroxene}}{(Ca,Mg)MgSi_2O_6}$$

This reaction has been suggested to account for growth of porphyroblastic spinel at the expense of aluminous pyroxenes in both the Lizard and Tinaquillo peridotites (Green, 1963, p. 1401; 1964a, p. 170). The conditions of crystallization of the primary mineral assemblage of the Lizard peridotite and of both the relict primary and recrystallized minerals of the Tinaquillo peridotite were such that olivine and plagioclase were in reaction relationship but plagioclase remained a stable phase in pyroxene-rich bands in the absence of olivine (Green, 1964a, p. 173).

Nearer the margins of the Lizard peridotite, the primary, coarse-grained mineral assemblage is replaced by fine-grained, foliated peridotite with relict augen of large, deformed pyroxene crystals. The recrystallized mineralogy is olivine + pyroxenes + plagioclase + chromite and the reactions giving rise to plagioclase may be written as follows (Green, 1964a, p. 169, 173):

$$(3)\quad \underset{\text{spinell}_{ss}}{(MgAl_2O_4 + FeCr_2O_4)} + \underset{\text{diopside}}{CaMgSi_2O_6} + 2\,\underset{\text{enstatite}}{MgSiO_3} \rightleftharpoons \underset{\text{anorthite}}{CaAl_2Si_2O_8} + 2\,\underset{\text{olivine}}{Mg_2SiO_4} + \underset{\text{chromite}}{FeCr_2O_4}$$

$$(4)\quad \underset{\text{aluminous enstatite}}{Mg_9Al_2Si_9O_{30}} + \underset{\text{aluminous diopside}}{Ca_5Mg_4Al_2Si_9O_{30}} \rightleftharpoons 2\,\underset{\text{anorthite}}{CaAl_2Si_2O_8} + 3\,\underset{\text{diopside}}{CaMgSi_2O_6} + 6\,\underset{\text{enstatite}}{MgSiO_3} + 2\,\underset{\text{olivine}}{Mg_2SiO_4}$$

The recrystallized pyroxenes have lower Al_2O_3 content and also lower contents of CaO in orthopyroxene and MgO + FeO in clinopyroxene; the plagioclase is labradorite in composition and the spinel is deep-brown or reddish-brown chromite. In their chemistry, the recrystallized orthopyroxene and clinopyroxene are similar to pyroxenes from layered igneous intrusives and are considered to indicate a temperature at recrystallization of around 1000°C. The primary mineral assemblage and the coexisting pyroxenes in particular, indicate conditions of initial crystallization of higher temperature and load pressures of at least 8 and probably less than 15 kb. The best evidence for initial crystallization under high load pressure is the incompatibility of olivine + plagioclase. Experimental studies by Green and Ringwood (1967) on olivine normative basalts including extremely magnesian compositions, and by Green (unpublished) on magnesian olivine + labradorite compositions and peridotite compositions closely matching the Lizard peridotite, indicate that magnesian olivine and calcic plagioclase are unstable together at 1100 to 1200°C at pressures above 10 kb. Kushiro and Yoder

(1964a) and T. H. Green (unpublished), in studies of the forsterite + anorthite system, observe reaction to yield aluminous pyroxenes + spinel above 8 kb at 1200°C.

Additional arguments by Green (1964a) used the high Al_2O_3 content of coexisting orthopyroxenes and clinopyroxene as evidence for high pressure of crystallization. This is supported by the experimental work of Boyd and England (1960b, 1963b) demonstrating an increase in the maximum solubility of Al_2O_3 in enstatite with increase in pressure (at pressures below those necessary to stabilize pyrope garnet). However partition of Al_2O_3 between aluminous pyroxenes and spinel is more complex, and it is uncertain at present whether decrease in Al_2O_3 content in pyroxenes and corresponding increase in the $MgAl_2O_4$ content of coexisting spinel, is a consequence of falling temperature at high but constant pressure, or a consequence of decreasing load pressure at essentially constant temperature (cf. Green, 1963, p. 1401).

In contrast to the Lizard peridotite, the Horoman peridotite appears to contain only the low-pressure olivine + pyroxenes + plagioclase + chromite assemblage. Onuki (1965) and Onuki and Tiba (1965), from a detailed comparison of the Al_2O_3 contents of the pyroxenes, conclude that the Horoman peridotite crystallized under similar conditions to the Lizard recrystallized peridotite assemblage, and at a higher pressure than such peridotites as Twin Sisters, Webster-Adie, Dawros, Cuba, but lower pressure than the Lizard primary peridotite.

The Beni Bousera peridotite is distinctive in preserving the highest pressure, garnet peridotite assemblage (see Chapter 5-IV). Milliard (1959, p. 141) notes an increase in foliation within the peridotite adjacent to the margins with the country rock but does not record any changes in primary mineralogy. In comparison with the mineral assemblage in the country rocks, in particular the presence of sillimanite rather than kyanite, the garnet peridotite assemblage is unstable, and if recrystallization during emplacement occurs at the margins as in the Lizard example, the garnet peridotite should be replaced by the olivine + aluminous pyroxenes ± spinel assemblage. The peridotite of Lherz may provide an example of transition between the garnet peridotite and spinel + aluminous pyroxene peridotite assemblages. Thus the type "lherzolite" (olivine + pyroxenes + spinel) is common but eclogite and garnet + spinel + pyroxenes + olivine assemblages also occur. The pressure required for appearance of garnet is sensitively dependent on the Fe/Mg ratio of the rock types and also on the Al_2O_3 content of the rocks in relation to the amount of pyroxene present; thus, apparently contrasting mineral assemblages may in fact be compatible at a given P-T in varying bulk chemistries.

3. ***Texture and structure.*** The Lizard peridotite has a coarse-grained core in which primary banding and incipient foliation due to recrystallization show fold patterns and attitudes not closely related to either the margins of the peridotite or the regional stress field. This is mantled by and passes transitionally into peridotite with a well-developed, fine foliation shown by lenticular variation in relative proportions of olivine, pyroxene, and plagioclase. Relict, coarser grains of enstatite and diopside are commonly preserved and have "tails" of recrystallized, pyroxene-rich peridotite paralleling the foliation. Porphyroblastic spinel is surrounded by lenticular mantles of plagioclase. The texture of the peridotite is a consequence of recrystallization during deformation at high temperature rather than a low-temperature cataclastic mylonization. The attitude of the fine foliation in the Lizard peridotite closely follows the attitude of the peridotite/country-rock contact in areas near to the contact but within the body is subvertical and parallels the *b-c* plane of the regional stress field.

In the Tinaquillo peridotite, the body is entirely composed of finely foliated peridotite with very distinctive porphyroclasts of enstatite and diopside and smaller porphyroblastic spinel. The body as a whole is a moderately dipping tabular mass and the foliation in general is conformable, particularly near the southern contact zone. MacKenzie (p. 306, 313) describes remarkable, lath shaped orthopyroxenes in the Tinaquillo peridotite and regards them as formed by translation gliding of favorably oriented crystals.

Smith and MacGregor (1960) liken the internal structure and steep folds defined by peridotite-dunite banding to the internal structure of salt domes and invoke a similar intrusion mechanism, that is, mobility of a crystalline body involving recrystallization and crystal deformation. Smith and MacGregor record areal differences in chrome-spinel and enstatite compositions, unrelated to the primary banding and irregularly distributed through the body. These are attributed to variations in water content during emplacement.

D. Conditions of Emplacement of High-Temperature Peridotites

A temperature of emplacement of approximately 1000°C has been deduced for all three peridotites, based mainly on the chemical characteristics of the pyroxenes and the metamorphic grade of the contact metamorphic rocks. At this temperature, the peridotites are considered to be completely crystalline and owe their mobility to the ease of recrystallization and plastic deformation of olivine at high temperatures. The large temperature difference between the peridotite and the regional country-rock environment determines that the peridotite is the more mobile rock and capable of intrusion in the solid state.

If the temperature of intrusion and the maximum temperature attainable in contact zones or included country-rock is 1000°C, then it is possible to make fairly closely controlled estimates of the load pressures at emplacement of the bodies. The final level of emplacement of the Lizard peridotite was such that olivine + plagioclase were stable in both the peridotite and basic country-rock. At 1000°C this indicates load pressures less than 8 to 9 kb from experimental work of Green and Ringwood (1967), and Kushiro and Yoder (1964a). The absence of garnet in the contact granulites provides confirmatory evidence of a lower load pressure and its presence in the contact zones of both the Tinaquillo and Mount Albert intrusions is consistent with these bodies preserving the higher pressure peridotite assemblage. Thus, in these rocks the reaction of orthopyroxene + plagioclase to yield garnet + clinopyroxene indicates conditions in the high pressure sub-facies of the granulite facies (De Waard, 1964; Ringwood and Green, 1964; Green and Ringwood, 1967). In the Tinaquillo peridotite, the olivine + aluminous pyroxenes + spinel assemblage in the peridotite coexists with the orthopyroxene + clinopyroxene + plagioclase + hornblende assemblage in included gabbroic bodies. The compatibility of these assemblages at 1000°C means that load pressures lie between 9 and 12 kb approximately. The lower temperature of the country rocks immediately outside the peridotite determines that the basic rocks are there within the ga + cpx + plag granulite field. Similar load pressures may be deduced for the Mount Albert peridotite if a temperature of intrusion of the order of 1000°C can be assumed. If the temperature of crystallization of the primary assemblage of the Lizard peridotite is correctly deduced as above 1000°C and nearer to 1200 to 1300°C, then the stability of the olivine + aluminous pyroxenes + spinel assemblage and of plagioclase + orthopyroxene + clinopyroxene indicate pressures probably between 10 and 18 kb.

In the Horoman peridotite, the stability of cordierite and hypersthene in the contact metamorphic rocks implies low-pressure (pyroxene hornfels) conditions of emplacement, probably at shallower depths than the Lizard peridotite. On the other hand, the presence of ga + cpx and ga + cpx + plag assemblages and the stability of sillimanite rather than kyanite in the contact rocks of the Beni Bousera peridotite imply pressures similar to those of the Tinaquillo and Mount Albert peridotites.

E. Origin of High-Temperature Peridotites

The chemical composition of the high-temperature peridotites is close to a possible mean composition for a peridotite upper mantle and these peridotites have the potential for partially melting to yield 10 to 20 per cent of basaltic magma. Arguments relevant to this hypothesis have been advanced by Green and Ringwood (1963) and Hess (1964). If this hypothesis is valid then the high-temperature peridotites have an important significance in that they represent complete mobilization and intrusion to crustal levels of portions of mantle peridotite. This hypothesis was advocated by Green (1964a) and probably implies the existence of a high-temperature ultramafic liquid or liquid + transported olivine crystals within the mantle. Complete crystallization of such an intrusion occurs in the lower crust or top of the mantle but continued emplacement as a crystalline diapir continues because of temperature and mobility (rheidity) differences between the hot peridotite and cooler country-rocks. This hypothesis would place the high-temperature peridotites as genetically distinct from other alpine ultramafics such as Dun Mountain, Red Hills (New Zealand); Twin Sisters, Klamath Mountains (northwest United States), Musa Valley (Papua), Zambales Range (Philippines), and Camaguey (Cuba).

An alternative hypothesis suggested by recent experimental work on basaltic compositions at high pressure (Green and Ringwood, 1964, and unpublished data; Tilley and Yoder, 1964) is that the initial high-temperature, coarse-grained minerals of the peridotites are accumulates at high load pressure from a picritic or olivine tholeiitic magma. It has been shown (Green and Ringwood, 1964) that the pyroxenes crystallizing at 10 to 20 kb from olivine tholeiite and picritic liquids are rich in Al_2O_3. It is thus conceivable that a picritic or olivine tholeiite magma, held near the base of the crust could precipitate olivine + aluminous pyroxene(s). The residual liquid of alkali basaltic or olivine-poor composition (depending on the depth of differentiation) could then be tapped off and a high temperature, crystalline body of the observed high-temperature peridotite composition be left behind. Slight cooling of such a body would probably cause exsolution of spinel from the pyroxenes and the onset of nonhydrostatic pressure while the crystal accumulate was still hot could cause diapiric, crystalline intrusion to higher crustal levels. This second hypothesis invokes an origin for these peridotites similar to that advocated for the more common alpine ultramafics such as Musa Valley, Dun Mountain, Twin Sisters (see Section A) *except* that the accumulation of crystals from the parental picritic or olivine tholeiitic magma must occur at depths greater than 25 to 30 km whereas the accumulation of such alpine layered complexes as Red Hills and Musa Valley must occur more probably at depths of 5 to 10 km.

It is considered that criteria to distinguish between the hypotheses are at present lacking. Much depends on a knowledge of the type of basaltic liquid produced by partial melting of the mantle at depths of 60 to 150 km. If the liquid formed at minimum temperatures of melting at these depths is picritic with some 30 to 40 per cent normative olivine then the high-temperature peridotites are correspondingly easier to explain as deep-seated crystal accumulates from such a magma. If, on the other hand, the minimum melting liquids are nearer olivine tholeiite with 15 to 20 per cent normative olivine, then it is more difficult or impossible to envisage peridotites with approximately 60 per cent olivine as accumulates at 10 to 20 kb from such relatively olivine-poor liquids.

Although their primary origin is thus an open and debatable question, the high-temperature peridotites provide clear evidence of the following:

1. Mobility of high-temperature but entirely crystalline peridotite within the crust.

2. Movement of such high-temperature peridotites through distances of 5 to 10 km, implying changes of load pressure of at least 2 to 3 kb.

IV. CHEMICAL AND STRUCTURAL RELATIONS OF ULTRAMAFIC AND FELDSPATHIC ROCKS IN ALPINE INTRUSIVE COMPLEXES

T. P. Thayer

A. Introduction

Igneous rocks of the alpine type, as originally defined by Benson (1927) consist of gabbros as well as ultramafic rocks, and include those rocks commonly called "ophiolites." Benson (p. 6) said alpine igneous rocks "are comprised of the majority of "green-rocks" as considered by Suess (in 1909). These are also the "ophiolitic rocks" as defined by Steinmann (in 1905), in which serpentines and gabbros are intimately associated with amphibolites and diabases. . . . They occur in regions that have been intensely disturbed by overthrusting and alpine orogeny." Peridotite and gabbro were accepted matter-of-factly as members of this family of rocks, and still are by adherents to the ophiolite hypothesis. A conceptual divorce of alpine ultramafites from gabbro and more silicic rocks resulted from Hess' (1938) hypothesis of a primary peridotite magma, and has been carried to its logical conclusions in Lizard by Green (1964a, 1964b), in Venezuela by MacKenzie (1960), and in generation of basalts by Ringwood, MacGregor, and Boyd (1964, p. 148). By outlining some genetic relationships of gabbroic, dioritic, and granophyric rocks to alpine ultramafites, I hope to reemphasize a close kinship that was recognized at least 40 years ago. Like Benson, I regard the ultramafic and gabbroic parts of ophiolite complexes as being identical with, and part of, the alpine igneous rock suite.

At least three distinct types of layered plutonic intrusions composed predominantly of gabbroic and peridotitic rocks can now be recognized in orogenic belts: (1) the alpine, (2) the Duke Island (Chapter 4-II), and (3) the Duluth (Taylor, 1964) or Moxie (Visher, 1961). Despite fundamental differences, similarities in the three kinds of intrusions have led to confusion because distinguishing criteria have not been defined. Six of the principal kinds of features that characterize alpine complexes (Thayer, 1960; 1963a; 1963b; 1964) are as follows:

1. Close areal and structural association of ultramafites, gabbroic, dioritic, and granophyric rocks.

2. Predominance of highly magnesian olivine over pyroxene in ultramafic parts of complexes.

3. Podiform chromite deposits.

4. Flow-layering and related structures and textures that are characteristic of high-grade metamorphic rocks.

5. Complicated structural relations between gabbroic and ultramafic rocks, such as intertonguing of major units along flow-layering; intrusive relations between various facies; and dikes of gabbro in peridotite or vice versa, without chilled margins.

6. Distribution of soda-rich dioritic and

granophyric rocks within or near gabbroic rocks, commonly hybrid and accompanied by much albitization and brecciation.

B. Structural Features of Alpine Complexes

The gabbroic and ultramafic rocks in alpine complexes combine many characteristics of plutonic igneous rocks with features, such as extensive flow-layering, foliation and lineation, and tectonite fabrics, that are associated with high-grade metamorphic rocks. Mutually intrusive and gradational relations are believed to have resulted from emplacement of peridotite and gabbro together as crystal mushes containing small but variable proportions of anhydrous magma. Dioritic and granophyric rocks are associated with gabbro mostly as distinct intrusions that have chilled borders, but commonly are accompanied by intense brecciation and albitization that obscure other features. Contact relations with country rocks vary. Against ultramafites, contacts commonly are faulted, but country rocks may be metamorphosed to amphibolite-facies. Gabbros become fine grained near contacts and country rocks are somewhat recrystallized. Around diorite and granophyre country rocks usually are brecciated and albitized, like adjoining gabbro. Gabbro and peridotite together constitute 80 to 90 per cent of most complexes, but vary widely in relative proportions; pyroxenite and dioritic or granophyric rocks probably average about 5 per cent each. Rocks are grouped by chemical affinity, but otherwise major rock units may occur anywhere within a given complex. Ophiolite complexes are shown to be alpine-type and intruded into pillow lavas or other basaltic rocks.

In the nomenclature of alpine rocks, the terms foliation and lineation have the same meanings as in metamorphic rocks, namely: orientation of individual mineral grains or groups of grains in planes or lines, respectively, by flowage of essentially solid rocks. Layers are planar units that differ from adjoining units in mineral composition or textural features and may range in thickness from a few grains or a few millimeters to tens of meters. In stratiform complexes all the layering is assumed to be due to gravitational settling of crystals and related magmatic processes. In alpine complexes, however, we must distinguish between layering whose structural relations show it cannot be related to crystal settling, and other layering that might be so related. In this paper, the general term layering is used in the broad sense and for layers whose origin is unknown; use of the term flow-layering is restricted to layers whose compositional or structural relations are not compatible with original gravity differentiation. The detailed relationships between layering, foliation, and lineation in alpine complexes have been described elsewhere (Thayer, 1963a, 1964).

1. Relations between ultramafic and gabbroic rocks. The internal features of, and structural relations between, alpine ultramafic and gabbroic rocks are directly comparable to those of granulite facies metamorphic terrains. Tectonite fabrics characterize both the ultramafics and gabbros (Bartrum and Turner, 1928; Turner, 1942; Marinos and Maratos, 1957). Deformational structures such as flow-layering, foliation, and lineation (Thayer, 1963a, 1964) predominate, although locally some relict cumulate features (E. D. Jackson, Chapter 2-II) may be preserved. Flowage features may be oriented at any angle to contacts between major rock units. The contacts themselves may be sharp or gradational across a few feet, but more commonly are "interbanded zone(s) of variable width." Where flow layering crosses contacts, "bands of gabbro pinch out along their strike, their place being taken by peridotite. . . . In the Lewis Hills pluton . . . interbanded gabbroic zones grade along strike through feldspathic dunite into dunite" (Smith, 1958, p. 70). Intertonguing at gabbro-peridotite contacts in

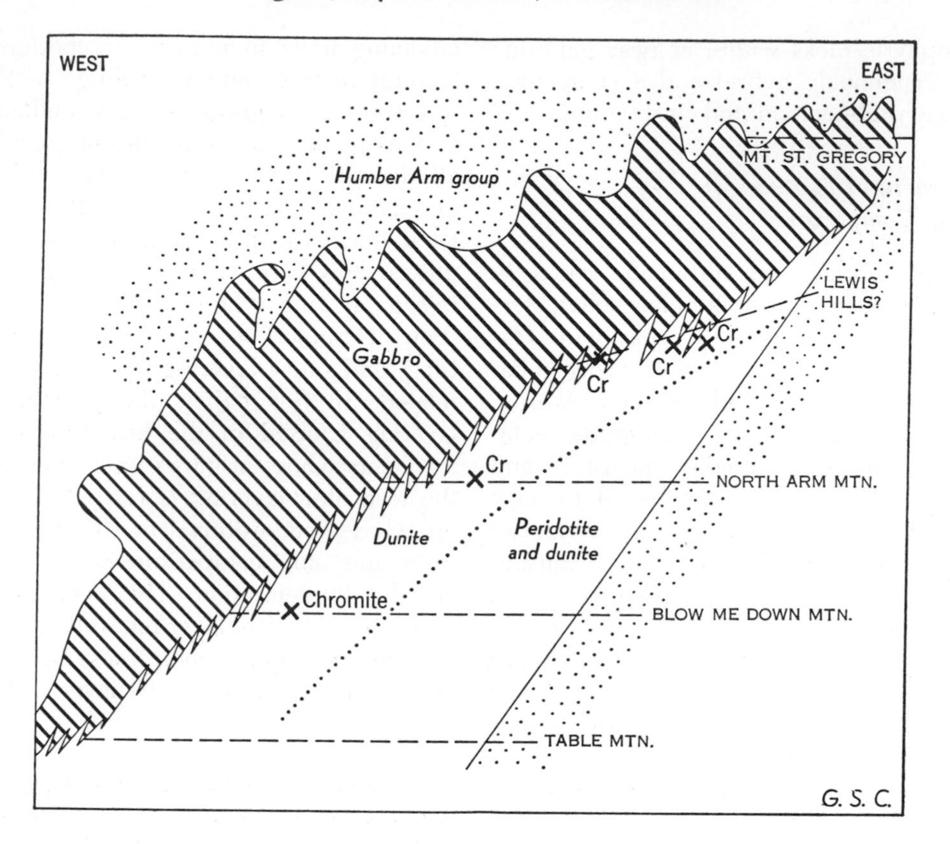

Fig. 7.5 Hypothetical section of parent pluton of Bay of Islands complex, Newfoundland, showing some features of alpine-type mafic complexes. (After C. H. Smith, 1958.)

the Bay of Islands complex is somewhat exaggerated by Smith in Fig. 7.5, but the different sets of layers may overlap by tens or hundreds of feet along their strike.

Flow-layering, as a rule, is most prominently displayed near contacts or in border zones between major rock units, but may occur anywhere within them. For example, in the Zambales complex throughgoing flow-layering (Fig. 7.6) is shown near the Coto mine by distribution of olivine and pyroxene in olivine-rich saxonite, olivine and chromite in dunite, and olivine, pyroxene, and plagioclase in gabbro. Discordant relations between major contacts, flow-layering, lineation, and foliation on large and small scales are well shown in the Canyon Mountain complex, Oregon (Thayer, 1956; 1963a).

Intrusive relationships between peridotite and gabbro may be very complex and even contradictory. Major discordances between internal layering or flow structures in peridotite and adjoining gabbro units are common, and probably indicate successive emplacement of such units. Most intersecting dike sequences follow what is generally considered to be the normal order of crystallization, from olivine-rich (dunite or troctolite) first to gabbroic last, as in the Camagüey district, Cuba (Flint and others, 1948, Fig. 2). Gabbro dikes commonly cut peridotite. In other areas, however, irregular blocks of banded gabbro are enclosed in peridotite and apparently were intruded and recrystallized by it (Figs. 7.7 and 7.8). I have seen two dikes of olivine-rich peridotite a meter or more thick crossing the layering of flow-banded gabbro, one in the Zambales complex and the other in the Vourinon complex. Relations of this sort in

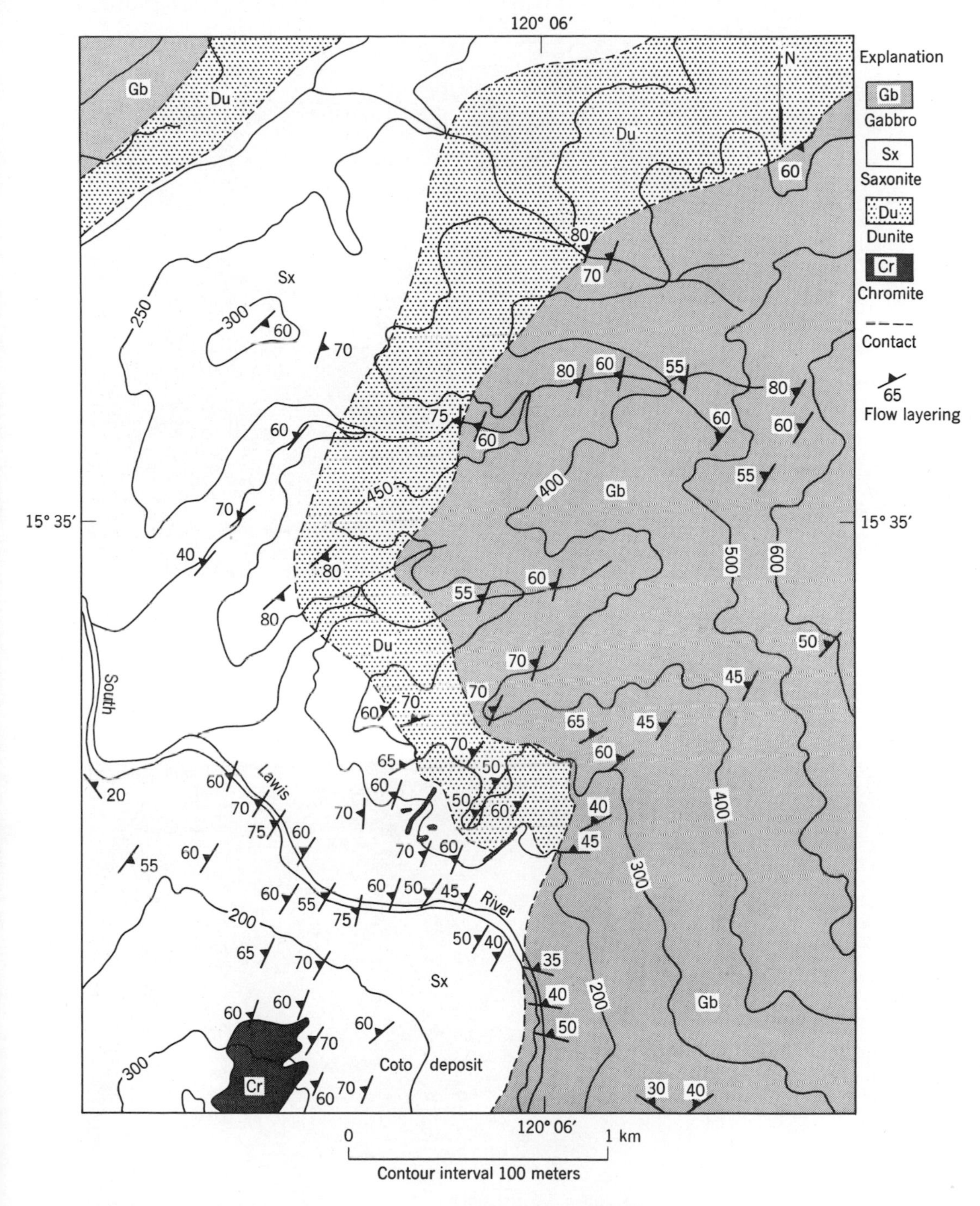

Fig. 7.6 Generalized geologic map of part of the Zambales complex near the Coto mine, Luzon. (Revised after Rossman et al., 1957.)

Fig. 7.7 Flow-banded gabbro (above, light gray) apparently intruded and recrystallized by peridotite (below, dark). Lower contact of large block inclosed in peridotite about half a mile east of the Coto mine, Zambales complex, Luzon (see Fig. 7.6). Man's foot and hand for scale.

Fig. 7.8 Slabs of gabbro in massive peridotite, suggesting broken fold in flow layers above hat. Note thin layer or dike of peridotite in gabbro below hammer. About half a mile southeast of Coto mine, Zambales complex, Luzon (see Fig. 7.6).

the Eastern Townships of Quebec, I believe, probably led Cooke (1937, p. 57) to regard the peridotite and related pyroxenite as intrusive into older gabbro and pyroxenite, whereas podiform chromite deposits, areal distribution of the rocks, and flowage features (Cooke, 1937, p. 64) point strongly to a single alpine mafic-ultramafic assemblage. Hiessleitner and Clar's map and sections of the Chalkidiki complex (Hiessleitner, 1952, pl. 3) in eastern Greece show complicated interlayering of peridotite, gabbro, and pyroxenite with irregular lateral variation over a distance of about 30 miles. At the northwest end of the complex, the Kran Mahale chromite deposits, which occur in fresh dunite, are strongly lineated, and banding in them dips 20 to 30° southeast. About 1 km north of the chromite deposits, the gabbro mapped by Hiessleitner interfingers directly with dunitic peridotite in a distance of 100 feet or less, and prominent flow-layering in the gabbro dips 25 to 30° southeast into, and apparently under, the dunite. Numerous dikes of pegmatitic gabbro cut the peridotite in exposures on the highway grade up to the Vavdos magnesite mine, and petrofabric diagrams by Marinos and Maratos (1957, p. 10) of dunite from this area show unusually good lineation.

2. *Relations of dioritic and granophyric to gabbroic rocks.* Dioritic and granophyric rocks have been recognized as comagmatic with alpine peridotite and gabbro in at least ten areas. Nevertheless, identification of dioritic and granophyric rocks as comagmatic with alpine gabbro and peridotite requires some care, especially where more than one magma series is known to be present (Hopson, 1964, p. 131; Thayer and Brown, 1964). Some gabbro and quartz diorite intergrade, as described by Eric and others in California (1955, p. 33) and by Prostka (oral communication, 1963) in the area south of the Sparta quadrangle, Oregon. In general, however, the two kinds of rocks show very intricate relations. Albite granite forms masses up to half a mile wide and 5 to 6 miles long along the southern edge of the Canyon Mountain complex, and also plugs of quartz diorite a few hundred feet in diameter occur within the gabbro (Thayer, 1956, 1963b). In this area most of the quartz diorite has sharp contacts but is not chilled against gabbro, is hypidiomorphic in texture, consists mainly of strongly zoned feldspar, prismatic hornblende, and interstitial quartz, and in places is markedly lineate. Contact relations commonly are obscured, however, by intense brecciation and pervasive albitization and silicification of gabbro and quartz diorite. Parts of the gabbro have been extensively hornblendized and replaced by hornblende-rich pyroxene-free pegmatites along fractures; other parts have been transformed to albite granite. Similar relations between gabbro, quartz diorite, and albite granite have been mapped by Gilluly (1937) and Prostka (1962) in the Baker and Sparta quadrangles, respectively, in Oregon. Gilluly (1933) concluded that the albite granite formed essentially by metasomatic replacement of gabbro and quartz diorite.

The relations between gabbro, trondhjemite, and granophyres in The Troodos Plutonic complex, Cyprus, are directly comparable to features described in eastern Oregon, although somewhat different terminology has been used in describing them (Chapter 4-IV). "Uralite-gabbro occurs as a continuous zone between the pyroxene-gabbro and the granophyric rocks . . ." (Wilson and Ingham, 1959, p. 92). Near the granophyre the texture of the gabbro becomes variable, epidote is visible to the naked eye, and "diffuse clots of leucocratic rock containing needle-like crystals of hornblende more typical of the trondhjemite, often occur. . . . Rounded xenoliths . . . from two or three inches to over a foot in diameter, and diffuse patches of hornblende-trondhjemite occur in the gabbro. The xenoliths are surrounded by zones of large hornblende crystals." (Wilson and Ingham, 1959, p. 108). Wilson's descriptions and similar features I have seen in stream boulders suggest that the "xenoliths" and patches of hornblende crystals are, more probably, metasomatically recrystallized gabbro. Chemically and texturally the trondhjemites and quartz-granulites of Troodos form a continuous series remarkably similar to the rocks at Canyon Mountain and Sparta, Oregon.

*3. **Contacts with country rocks.*** Contact relations vary near the different components of alpine complexes just as they differ around independent masses of peridotite, gabbro, and diorite. The ultramafic parts of many complexes have serpentinized borders and are faulted against virtually unaltered country rocks. This sort of contact relation is now generally regarded as evidence for either cold diapiric emplacement of the mass, or for serpentinization during emplacement by groundwater moving toward the peridotite (Chapters 5-II and 5-III). Moderate to high-grade metamorphism by peridotite has been described at Mount Albert, Quebec (Smith and MacGregor, 1960), at Tinaquillo, Venezuela (MacKenzie, 1960), and Bay of Islands, Newfoundland (Smith, 1958); it has been postulated at Lizard (Green, 1964b), and it is suggested by amphibolite-facies border zones around peridotite described by Hiessleitner (1952) in the Balkans. See Chapter 7-III.

Thermal metamorphism of country rocks to amphibole- or pyroxene-hornfels facies at contacts with peridotite is usually accompanied by development of strong foliation and/or lineation in both peridotite and country rock and the metamorphism, for the most part, is restricted to zones a few hundred feet wide. Although metamorphism apparently was accompanied by metasomatic changes at Tinaquillo (MacKenzie, 1960, p. 310), Smith and MacGregor found no significant chemical migration at Mount Albert. The highly developed metamorphic aureoles at Mount Albert and Tinaquillo are in previously metamorphosed rocks that could not have contained much water when the peridotite entered them; therefore, other things being equal, I question the presence of such aureoles, per se, as evidence that the peridotites were unusually hot when intruded.

Alpine gabbros show no unusual contact relations with country rocks. They are finer-grained and massive along borders, and the country rocks against them are thermally metamorphosed to pyroxene-hornfels facies. However, because alpine gabbro, like the peridotite, was largely crystalline when emplaced, contact-metamorphic aureoles are comparatively narrow. Where gabbro intrudes basalt, contacts may be very difficult to identify, as Smith (1958, p. 21) has indicated in the Bay of Islands Complex:

"The fine- to medium-grained, massive, basic rocks of the area are the principal problem. They occur in places as an intermediate zone between the coarse-grained plutonic gabbros and the pillowed volcanic rocks. This suggests that they may be either plutonic in origin, representing chilled phases of the gabbro, or volcanic in origin, representing thermally metamorphosed volcanic rocks."

Contacts between alpine diorite and granophyre and country rocks range from sharp and well defined to extremely obscure. Diorite with chilled contacts against locally recrystallized country rocks has been described, but more commonly the contact zone is marked by strong to extreme brecciation of diorite and country rock, and brecciation is accompanied nearly always by albitization, silicification, and extensive recrystallization. For example, dense keratophyres along contacts with the Canyon Mountain Complex have been converted to medium-grained albite granite that is indistinguishable from replaced gabbro of the complex. Much diabase that seems fresh in hand specimen proves to have been thoroughly albitized. Obscure contact relations like those described by Smith in the Bay of Islands (1958, p. 21) are not clarified by superimposing brecciation and albitization! Gradations from granophyre to diabase are well described in Troodos by Wilson and Ingham (1959, p. 108) and in Vourinon by Brunn (1960, p. 124).

4. Proportions and distribution of rocks. Ultramafites and gabbro together constitute 90 per cent or more of mapped intrusive complexes that have been rather certainly identified as being alpine. (See Table 7.2.) The ultramafic rocks for the most part are dunites and olivine-rich peridotites or serpentinized equivalents; pyroxenite (80 per cent or more pyroxene) probably constitutes less than 5 per cent of the total. The common occurrence of highly magnesian peridotite or serpentinite by itself in large and small plutons is the ultimate basis of Hess' (1938) hypothesis of a primary peridotite magma. As indicated in Table 7.2, however, the proportion of peridotite to comagmatic feldspathic rocks in alpine complexes ranges from about 10 to 90 per cent. In a list of 23 intrusive ophiolite complexes in eastern Kazakhstan, Mikhailov (1962, p. 120) lists gabbroic rocks as major components in 18,

TABLE 7.2 Approximate Proportions of Ultramafic, Gabbroic, Dioritic, and Granophyric Rocks in 16 Alpine Mafic Complexes

Complex or Area	Area (square miles)	Ultramafic Rocks (per cent)	Gabbroic Rocks (per cent)	Granophyric and Dioritic Rocks (per cent)	References
Bay of Islands, Newfoundland	260	50	47	3	Smith, 1958
Bowutu Mts., New Guinea	100	50	45	5	Dow and Davies, 1964
Camagüey, Cuba	200	85	15	n.d.[2]	Flint and others, 1948
Canyon Mt., Oregon	60	60	35	4–5	Thayer, 1956, 1963b
Chalkidiki, Greece	30	75	25	n.d.	Hiessleitner, 1952
Guleman, Turkey	6[1]	90	10	x[2]	DeWijkerslooth, 1947; Thayer, 1964
Lizard, England	27	75	20	5?	Flett, 1934, 1946; Flett and Hill, 1912
Baltimore Gabbro-State Line Complex, Md.-Pa.	215	20	75	<2	Hopson, 1964; Pearre and Heyl, 1960
Sierra Nevada, Calif.	25	50	50	x	Durrell, 1940; Eric and others, 1955
Sparta-Baker-Sumpter, Oregon	180	10	60	30	Gilluly, 1933, 1937; Pardee, 1941; Prostka, 1962
Syria-Hatay, Turkey	250	90	10	<1	Dubertret, 1955; Majer, 1960
Thetford, Quebec	55	75	25	x	Cooke, 1937
Troodos, Cyprus	75	30	60	10	Wilson and Ingham, 1959; Bear, 1960
Vourinon, Greece	100	80–90?	10	<5	Zachos, 1954; Brunn, 1960
Zambales, Luzon	530[1]	55	45	x	Rossman and others, 1959
Zhob Valley, W. Pakistan	175	85	5	10	R. van Vloten, oral communication, 1965

[1] Only part of entire complex.

[2] n.d., not described; x, present, amount unknown.

and gabbroic or dioritic rocks as dikes in 12. Just as peridotite occurs alone, alpine-type gabbro has been mapped locally by itself (Eric and others, 1955). In the Sumpter-Baker-Sparta area in eastern Oregon (Gilluly, 1937; Pardee, 1941; Prostka, 1962), one might say that the gabbro contains just enough peridotite to call attention to its alpine affinities, which are confirmed by other characteristics.

The only general principle controlling distribution of rocks in alpine complexes seems to be grouping by chemical affinity: olivine gabbro or mafic gabbro lies between ultramafites and normal pyroxene gabbro, which in turn is altered near or intruded by quartz diorite and granophyre; the last-named rocks rarely cut ultramafites. Within these limits, any rock may occur anywhere in an alpine complex. In Canyon Mountain, except for a mass of gabbro about 3 square miles in area, the rocks form parallel belts with peridotite on the north and quartz diorite on the south (Thayer, 1956). The Zambales complex (Rossman and others, 1959) shows a rude arrangement of gabbro and peridotite in north to northeast belts several miles wide that cut diagonally across its apparent long axis, parallel to the regional trend of flow-layering (D. L. Rossman, oral communication, 1963).

On a smaller scale the distribution of the various rocks is highly irregular. Gabbro and olivine-rich peridotite commonly are interlayered in a manner completely foreign to the orderly successions of rock types in stratiform intrusions (Hiessleitner, 1952, pl. 3; Thayer, 1963a). Dunite, for example, commonly occurs between gabbro and pyroxenic peridotite (Fig. 1; Smith, 1958). Although in some complexes (e.g., Zambales; Camagüey, and Oriente, Cuba; Bay of Islands) the chromite deposits seem to be localized in zones of dunite near major peridotite-gabbro contacts, within these zones they seem to be scattered at random (Fig. 7.5; Thayer, 1964, p. 1501).

A few alpine complexes have been classified (Thayer, 1960, p. 256) as pseudostratiform because the feldspathic rocks appear to be concentrated in their upper parts; Rossello (1964) has advocated application of this feature as a general guide in exploration for podiform chromite deposits. Determination of the structurally higher rocks, however, may be subject to major uncertainties. For instance, over an area of about 50 square miles in the Zhob Valley complex, gabbroic rocks form ridges or mesa-like hills, and contacts with serpentinized peridotite follow around the lower slopes; the gabbro, accordingly, might be regarded as lying on the peridotite. In the local climate, however, gabbro is more resistant to erosion than serpentinized peridotite, and prominent flow-layering in the gabbro consistently dips steeply into and interfingers with the peridotite. Similar erosional and structural relationships are found in parts of the Zambales complex. The Troodos Plutonic complex (Chapter 4-IV) is depicted by Wilson and Ingham (1959, p. 122) and Gass and Masson-Smith (1963) as a sort of pseudostratiform cross between the stratiform and alpine types. Wilson and Ingham's map shows a rudely concentric distribution of the rocks around a core of bastite-serpentine; their sections show peridotite-pyroxenite and the feldspathic rocks as irregular layers that dip radially away from the domical ultramafic core at angles of 20° or less. Steeply dipping flow-layering (mineral banding) in peridotite and gabbro, podiform chromite deposits, and predominance of olivine in the peridotites mark the complex as typically alpine. Because the topographic distribution of the various rocks is at least as consistent on the whole with steeply dipping contacts as with low dips, I question whether the complex really should be classified as pseudostratiform. The Camagüey and Bay of Islands complexes, however, still appear to belong in this category.

5. Alpine-type features in ophiolite complexes. Although I have included the ophiolites, as they were originally defined, in the alpine igneous assemblage, the features reported by advocates of the ophiolite hypothesis require separate consideration. According to Brunn (1960, p. 115):

"In the ophiolite suite are nearly always closely associated coarse-grained rocks (peridotite, gabbros), generally considered as plutonic, and effusive or semi-effusive types (submarine lavas and dolerite or diabase)."

In the Vourinon complex, which he regards as a type example, Brunn sees a regular layered succession, from bottom to top, of dunite, harzburgite, lherzolite, pyroxenite, coarse-grained gabbro, partially banded hypersthene gabbro, quartzose diorite; then "dolerite, sometimes penetrated and remelted by the diorites; submarine lavas, spilites; radiolarites followed by Cretaceous limestones." The igneous succession is explained by differentiation of a massive submarine flow (p. 115):

. . . "Inside a big magmatic pouch, risen to the surface [of the sea floor] and surrounded by a consolidated crust, processes of fractional distillation and fractioned crystallization . . . must start immediately and go on as long as a fluid phase remains."

One would suppose that the products of such a process should be like the rocks of the stratiform complexes in all essential features, for both are presumed to be formed by simple fractional crystallization of basalt. But the features of the Vourinon complex are typically alpine. There is no chilled phase at the base of the complex; instead, serpentinized harzburgite and dunite were faulted against the underlying rocks. The chromite deposits are podiform; most are strongly lineate and intricately folded schlieren (Zachos, 1954), and some contain nodular chromite (Panagos, 1965). The ultramafic rocks are olivine-rich, orthopyroxene-poor, lack the accessory feldspar that characterizes stratiform cumulates, and are strongly foliated gneisses even where completely fresh. Whereas gabbroic rocks constitute half or more of stratiform complexes, Brunn's map indicates that the Vourinon complex is 80 or 90 per cent ultramafic. The normal magmatic succession is interrupted in places by "masses and lenticular layers" of troctolite in the midst of peridotite (Brunn, 1960, p. 125). Brunn indicates the presence of dikes, but conveys no real idea of the complex snarl of pegmatitic pyroxenite and gabbro dikes in peridotite near the gabbro contact in the Aliakmon River, nor does he mention the peridotite dike I saw in the gabbro nearby. Because dikes of gabbro could be formed only by still fluid magma, Brunn (1960, p. 122) postulates that they would have had "to penetrate *per descensum* into the already consolidated parts of the magmatic mass." Brunn (1960, p. 124) also is hard put to account for magmatic breccias of dolerite in gabbro, a description of which he summarizes accordingly:

". . . this arrangement [of blocks in gabbro] recalls at once 'magmatic stoping' which one sees at the top of granitic intrusions. But here, the two rocks have a common origin. The attack of the doleritic cover, originally stable, by the magma, is undoubtedly explained . . . by intervening changes in the latter, become richer in water and mineralizers."

Near the apparent structural top of the complex, quartzose diorite and albitic granophyre appear to intergrade with and replace hornblendized gabbro. Dolerites and flows of dacitic to keratophyric composition (Brunn, 1956, p. 336) above the diorite are described as uralitic and contain epidote, zoisite, and secondary quartz; the feldspar is albitized. The overlying pillow lavas thus appear to be metamorphosed country rocks, not integral parts of the Vourinon complex.

Dubertret (1955) and Majer (1960) disagree completely in their descriptions and interpretations of the ophiolites in northwest Syria and nearby Turkey. Dubertret reported a continuous sequence from dunite to basaltic lavas, but his map is very general, and his descriptions are not detailed enough to be convincing to me. One of his photographs (plate 4, Fig. 2), for instance, shows highly sheared serpentinite but the caption says "The contact, perfectly clearly, shows no trace of dynamic phenomena." Majer summarizes the relations of the various rocks as follows (p. 6):

"Besides peridotites . . . gabbroid rocks . . . amount to less than 10 per cent of the total mass . . . The gabbroid rocks are developed as wider and narrower belts around the peridotites or in . . . smaller or larger protrusions, blocks, dikes, veins or irregular bodies in the peridotites. . . . As protrusions and veins especially represented are coarse-grained varieties of gabbros and gabbro pegmatites, furthermore blocks of leucocratic plagioclasite of frequently mylonitic structure as well as veins of quartz diorite-aplite. . . . Where these rocks are . . . among Mesozoic sediments . . . the contacts are tectonic, the rocks on the borders brecciated, schistose and with slickensides."

Majer describes an amphibolite-facies contact-metamorphic zone in phyllitic rocks under the peridotite (p. 7), and regards the overlying volcanic rocks as much younger.

No explanation for the apparent geographic restriction of ophiolite complexes to the Alpine-Himalayan Mountain belt has been offered. Their internal structural features and textures, the composition of the ultramafic rocks, their juxtaposition of rock types, their lack of high-temperature metamorphic aureoles and chilled margins are the same features diagnostic of alpine complexes. Whatever their origin may be, ophiolite complexes, minus the "integral" lavas and cherts, appear to be identical with alpine complexes.

C. Chemical Affinities in the Alpine Mafic Magma Stem

The chemical relationships between various members of the alpine mafic magma stem are still largely speculative. Although hundreds of analyses of ultramafites (Thayer, in press) and gabbros are available in the literature, identification of many analyzed rocks by genetic type is uncertain, and most of the rocks are altered.

Analyses of known alpine-type intrusive rocks suggest a magnesian differentiation trend that crosses the A-F-M triangle much nearer to the typical calc-alkaline plutonic trend (Hess, 1960) than to the Skaergaard rock trend (see Fig. 7.9). The three upper diagrams in Fig. 7.9 suggest a compositional correlation between alpine gabbro and peridotite with areally associated basaltic lavas in the eastern Mediterranean region; both the extrusive and intrusive rocks appear to be progressively more magnesian from Troodos to Vourinon to Syria-Turkey. Excepting one analysis in Vourinon, all the gabbros are more magnesian than the lavas, and uralitic gabbros are considerably richer in iron than fresh ones. In the alpine composite diagram three dioritic rocks fall near the center of the field; the two lower samples are of soda-rich quartz diorite (0.2 per cent K_2O) and tonalite (0.6 per cent K_2O) from Canyon Mountain and Troodos, respectively, and the upper one is a quartz diorite containing 1.16 per cent K_2O from the Sparta quadrangle (Gilluly, 1933, p. 70). In the granophyric rocks at the left side of the field the ratio of Na_2O:K_2O by weight ranges from 2 or 3:1 in rocks from Sparta, Oregon, to 20 or 30:1 in Cyprus and Canyon Mountain.

The alpine composite diagram indicates a trend in which the MgO:FeO ratio drops from the range 9:1 to 3:1 in peridotite and pyroxenite to about 1:1 or 1:2 in the rocks between gabbro and quartz diorite or tonalite, and finally to about 1:4 in the granophyres. Although the trend itself is not inconceivable as a fractionation path of basalt, differentiation of an alpine complex like Vourinon *in situ* from magma similar to the associated basalts is impossible, because of the great imbalance between the volumes of ultramafic and feldspathic fractions. On the other hand, if the postulated original magma had been peridotitic, lavas of corresponding composition should be present in the chilled roof or crust.

Chemically, the rocks of the alpine mafic suite differ in important respects from the stratiform and other peridotite-gabbro associations. No ferro-gabbros like those in the Skaergaard intrusion (Wager and Deer, 1939) or iron-rich (unmetamorphosed) chromite such as that in the Stillwater, Bushveld, and Great Dyke complexes (Jackson, 1963) have been described in alpine peridotite-gabbro complexes (Thayer, 1964). Neither does the chemistry of alpine complexes appear similar to that of the Duke Island-Union Bay type (Irvine, Taylor, Chapter 4), which differs in predominance of clinopyroxene over orthopyroxene, in proportional abundance of hornblende and magnetite as primary minerals, and in having nepheline, leucite, and even larnite in the norm (Irvine, 1963, p. 45). The hornblende-rich members of the Duke Island and Union Bay plutons imply a significant content of primary water, and this is not consistent with the absence of amphibole in most un-

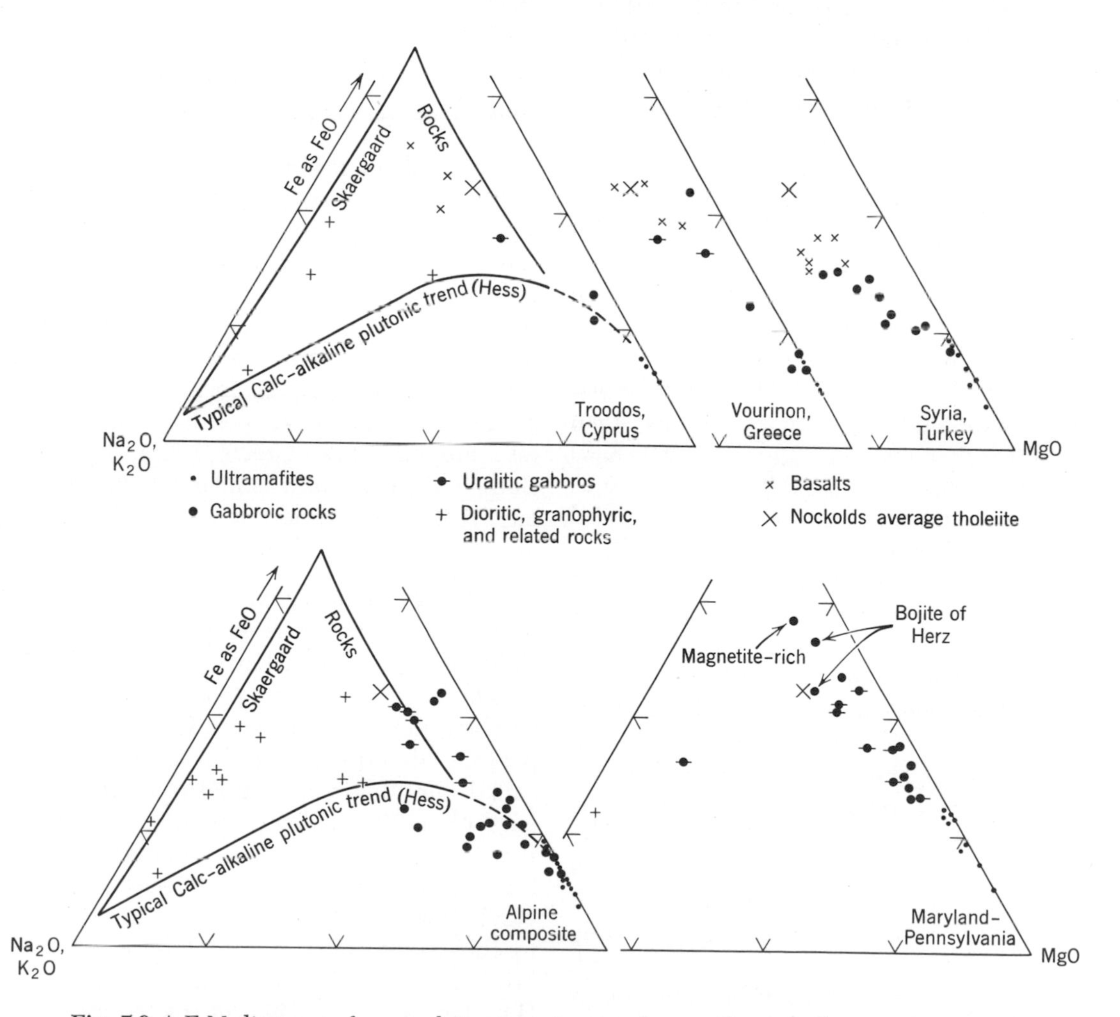

Fig. 7.9 A-F-M diagrams of some alpine intrusive complexes and a compilation indicating the general alpine differentiation trend. Sources of analyses: Troodos, Wilson and Ingham (1959) and Bear (1960); Vourinon, Brunn (1956); Syria-Turkey, Dubertret (1955) and Majer (1960); Maryland-Pennsylvania, Herz (1951), Hopson (1964), and others; alpine composite, numerous sources.

metamorphosed alpine gabbros and pyroxenites. The quartz-rich granophyre and albite granite in alpine complexes like Troodos and Canyon Mountain petrologically are a world apart from the nepheline syenite of the ultramafic-alkalic complexes discussed by Epshteyn and Anikeyeva (1965) in the Soviet Union (see also Chapter 9-II).

The chemical variation diagram (Fig. 7.9) of the Baltimore gabbro-State Line complex in Maryland and Pennsylvania shows a complete chemical gradation from gabbro to peridotite, but also raises some questions. As a group the uralitic gabbros are richer in iron than the others; therefore, possible enrichment in iron or depletion in Mg during uralitization must be investigated. The analysis richest in iron, plotted above Nockolds' average tholeiite, is of a magnetite-rich feldspathic rock (Williams, 1895, p. 672), which is not typical of the complex and illustrates the problem of sampling layered rocks. Two of the analyses notably rich in iron are of controversial rocks that Herz (1951, p. 1000) called bojite because he regarded the hornblende as primary rather than uralitic; one contains 1.13 per cent K_2O. Herz (1950, p. 61) described the bojite as cutting foliation of gabbro in places, and much fresher than most of the gabbro. Iron-rich rocks containing various amounts of primary hornblende, which occur throughout the area south of the Susquehanna River, seem to grade into more typical magnesian facies of the gabbro, according to D. L. Southwick (oral communication, 1965). It seems possible to me, however, that some of these rocks could be mafic dike members of a later granitic series (Hopson, 1964, p. 131), or they might be related to a younger series of peridotite-gabbro plutons, very probably of a different type, that occur farther north in the Appalachian geosyncline and follow a differentiation trend toward ferrogabbro (Visher, 1961, p. 289).

In brief, even though alpine peridotites and gabbros are characterized by metamorphic textures and structures, their chemical affinities to diorite and granophyre are those of known igneous differentiation suites. The composition of the magma from which they differentiated must remain conjectural, but rock analyses suggest close relationships to the plutonic calc-alkaline trend. If one assumes, as I believe most petrologists do, that these rocks are igneous differentiates, the original magma or the fractionation path, or possibly both, was very different from that of the known stratiform intrusive complexes (Wager and Deer, 1939; Hess, 1960; Osborn, 1959, 1962).

D. Structural and Chemical Problems Illustrated by Two Alpine Complexes

The kinds of problems inherent in study of alpine complexes, especially those that have undergone regional metamorphism, can best be illustrated by example. The Baltimore gabbro in Maryland has recently been described as a contemporaneously deformed stratiform complex (Hopson, 1964), and the Lizard complex in England as a high-temperature peridotite intruded into amphibolites (Green, 1964a, 1964b). Both, I believe, show similar structural relations between peridotite and gabbro and are normal alpine complexes.

1. The Baltimore gabbro-State Line complex. Gabbro and related peridotites near Baltimore, Maryland, have been much discussed since Williams' (1886) classic work on their alteration. Recently Hopson (1964, p. 132) described these rocks, which he called the Baltimore Gabbro complex, as part of a 70-mile-long irregular intrusion that includes the Pennsylvania-Maryland State Line chromite district (Pearre and Heyl, 1960, p. 718). I will refer informally to the whole mass as the Baltimore gabbro-State Line complex (see Chapter 6-II). Hopson (p. 149) characterizes the part of the complex near Baltimore as

"a huge folded and faulted sheet, formed initially by magmatic intrusion into flat-lying strata. This is suggested by: (1) its concordant contacts with the country rock; (2) its rhythmic layering parallel to the contacts; (3) its symmetrical distribution around the mantled gneiss domes, except where there was faulting; and (4) the concentration of ultramafic rocks near contacts that would correspond to the base of the sheet. Relict cumulate textures and rhythmic gravity layering support the idea that the ultramafics accumulated as a floor phase of the intrusion. Smaller amounts of rhythmically layered pyroxenite and peridotite that recur at higher levels in the complex can be attributed to recurrent periods of crystal settling, as new drafts of mafic magma came up from depth.

"Regional compression and folding began before the mass had solidified and perhaps even before it had grown to full size."

The gabbros have been metamorphosed subsequently to amphibolites and amphibole schists over large areas. Hopson divides the complex into three belts that he attributes to folding during the rise of a series of gneiss domes. He also suggests (p. 149) that during the intense folding some peripheral masses of peridotite were squeezed laterally out of the original layered sequence. The Relay quartz diorite (in part albite granite) is intimately related to the gabbro, and deformed with it. Metagabbro and associated serpentinite and magnesian schist bodies in southern Montgomery County (Griscom and Peterson, 1961) are regarded by Hopson (p. 153) as probably genetically related to the Baltimore Gabbro complex.

Hopson's four principal arguments for a stratiform origin of the complex will be considered in order. Concordant contacts and rhythmic layering parallel to contacts are indeed typical of stratiform complexes; however, similar relations might be shown by a dry plastic mass that was emplaced along major thrust faults and preexisting folds in stratified rocks. On the other hand, Herz (1951, p. 1002) and other geologists have found major discordances between internal structures in the gabbro and country-rock structure; these Herz ascribes to magmatic flowage during crystallization. Hopson's third point, the symmetry of the gabbro around gneiss domes, depends upon the fourth, the distribution of peridotite at the base of the postulated sheet. At the northern end of the entire complex, in the vicinity of the State Line district, the peridotite unit is olivine-rich and dunitic, is the host of one of the largest known podiform chromite deposits (the Wood mine) in continental North America, and has a maximum width of 1–5 miles. On the southeast this peridotite belt merges with a belt of noritic gabbro 2.5 to 3 miles wide through a narrow discontinuous zone of pyroxenite. The most conspicuous feature of fresh gabbro, where it is not massive, is vertical gneissic structure or layering in which lineation is well developed; small gradational lenses of olivine-rich peridotite several tens of feet wide are well exposed near the center of the gabbro, along the Susquehanna River. Podiform chromite deposits have also been mined in peridotite masses near Baltimore (Pearre and Heyl, 1960, p. 735), which Hopson interprets as originally parts of the main gabbro intrusion. Hopson cites Herz' (1950, pp. 99–121) log of the Baltimore-Patapsco aqueduct tunnel in support of his fourth point. At the western contact, the tunnel revealed about 2000 feet of serpentinite, but at the eastern side of the mass 3500 feet of gabbro and amphibolite lie between the contact and a 5500-foot section that is predominantly olivine-rich peridotite. In comparison, the entire ultramafic zone of the Stillwater complex (Jackson, 1961, p. 4) averages only about 3500 feet in thickness. The distribution of gabbro and peridotite both in the aqueduct tunnel and along the Susquehanna River, therefore, is quite unlike that in the known stratiform complexes.

The Baltimore gabbro-State Line complex and related rocks in Montgomery County have the following alpine characteristics:

1. Olivine-rich peridotite that contained large podiform chromite deposits (now mostly mined out) is an important rock type.

2. Only small amounts of pyroxenite occur between peridotite and gabbro although a few hundred feet of pyroxenite with apparent relict cumulate features occur within the gabbro (Hopson, 1964, p. 144).

3. Ultramafic and gabbroic rocks are intermingled at random, not separated into typical stratiform units.

4. Related dioritic rocks are quartz-rich, highly albitic, and associated with the gabbro.

5. Gabbroic rocks exposed in metaperidotite in the Hunting Hill quarry west of Rockville are not schlieren, as Hopson states (p. 153), but form two or more sets of dikes and irregular masses, all of which are characterized by irregular coarse to very coarse textures and lack chilled margins.

Hopson (p. 189) agrees that "the gabbroic series at Baltimore appears to be a good example of this association [the alpine mafic magma stem], and has many features in common with other examples from Oregon and Cyprus . . ." The origin of compositional layering on a large scale is the fundamental question, and our two interpretations hinge on how it is answered. Hopson attributed most of the layering to gravitational crystal settling, and I believe that most of it was formed by magmatic flowage.

2. The Lizard peridotite and Crousa Downs gabbro. The relations between peridotite and gabbro in Lizard, as described over a period of 80 years by British petrologists (see bibliography in Flett, 1946), seem very similar to those in the Baltimore gabbro-State Line complex. Green's (1964a, 1964b) discussions of the Lizard peridotite (see Chapter 7-III) ignored the Crousa Downs gabbro as part of the petrologic problem and led him to the same conclusion MacKenzie (1960) reached in Tinaquillo, Venezuela, namely, that granulitic rocks of gabbroic composition were formed metamorphically. As at Tinaquillo (Thayer and Brown, 1961), I believe that the "contact granulites" actually are alpine-type norites, and that the Lizard peridotite and Crousa Downs gabbro are comagmatic and contemporaneous.

As mapped and described by Flett (1934, 1946) and Flett and Hill (1912) the Crousa Downs gabbro is about 7 square miles in area and adjoins the Lizard peridotite. Although much of the boundary with the peridotite appears to be faulted, elsewhere it is intrusive:

"In the serpentine there are innumerable gabbro dykes which increase in number rapidly . . . [toward] the actual margin. The exact . . . boundary . . . is difficult to define on account of the great abundance of gabbro *debris* on the serpentine, showing the presence of large numbers of dikes, . . . and the ground is very level. In the gabbro . . . there are many inclusions of serpentine." (Flett and Hill, 1912, p. 82).

Flett and Hill (1912, p. 86) described the fresh gabbro as olivine bearing, as patchily variable in grain size from fine to coarse or pegmatitic, and as ranging in texture from granular to diabasic. Most of the gabbro is a flaser gneiss (p. 87) which grades into saussurite-hornblende schists (p. 91). Flett and Hill (1912, p. 51) regarded hornblende schists, which they called the Traboe schists, as metamorphic derivatives of the gabbro. These schists in places are indistinguishable from the older Landewednack schist, but on the whole are distinctly different; in particular, the Traboe contains relic schillerized pyroxene like that in the gabbro and more calcic feldspar (labradorite to bytownite) than the Landewednack schist. Green (1964b, Fig. 1) mapped the Traboe schist as older country rock metamorphosed by the peridotite.

The relations of gabbro dikes to peridotite and of peridotite or serpentinite to amphibole schists are at the heart of the problem in Lizard. Flett's descriptions of the gabbro dikes are typical of alpine complexes (1946, p. 84) and remind one immediately of those described and figured by Guild (1947, p. 228) in the Moa district, Cuba, and in the Canyon Mountain complex (Thayer, 1963a). The gabbro dikes are for the most part coarse grained or pegmatitic, and are not chilled at the contacts even though they follow joints in the peridotite. Adjacent dikes differ greatly in metamorphism; highly schistose dikes are side by side with undeformed ones, "normal" dikes cut schistose dikes, and vice versa; development of schistosity varies from place to place within single dikes. "Apparently each dyke passed through a stage in which it was especially susceptible to pressure and after that stage it became more resistant" (Flett, 1946, p. 85). The dikes are foliated parallel to their walls but cross the foliation and banding of the Lizard serpentinite. Flett says (1946, p. 83) that "the gabbro dykes never cut the hornblende schists and mica schists."

The structural relations mapped by Green (1964b, Fig. 4) between "two-pyroxene granulite" and peridotite are precisely those of flow-layered norite and peridotite in alpine complexes (Thayer, 1963a, Figs. 1–3). In fact, descriptions of contact relations of the same rocks near Pol Cornick by Fox and Teall (1893, p. 201) led them to conclude that the serpentine is older than the schist:

"Another specimen illustrates the interbanding of the two types of rock . . . Numerous laminae, no thicker than sheets of cardboard, alternate with each other. The bands of schist are composed of hornblende, malacolite [pyroxene] and turbid feldspar. In some bands the hornblende is pale green in colour, in others brown. Detached olivines . . . may be observed along certain planes and by the increase in the number of these olivines . . . are developed bands of peridotite . . . from [which] serpentine has been produced in the usual way. As the olivine increases the feldspar diminishes, but the hornblende of the serpentine is absolutely identical . . . with that of the schist.

". . . Occasionally lenticles of serpentine may be observed in the schist and when this is the case the foliation-planes in the schist wind round the lenticles."

Fox and Teall obviously regarded the rocks as having been sheared together during amphibolite-facies metamorphism, an interpretation that is wholly consistent with the metamorphism of the gabbro described by Flett. Metamorphism of interbanded gabbro and peridotite in Canyon Mountain (Thayer, 1963a, Figs. 1, 2) to amphibolite-facies schists and serpentinites would produce relations just like Fox and Teall saw.

Flett interpreted the mechanism of emplacement and crystallization of the Lizard rocks much as Hopson postulated for the Baltimore gabbro. Hopson (1964, p. 148) said:

"The petrography and structure of the complex reveal a complicated history, which began with magmatic crystallization and development of gravity layering, passed into plastic flowage and cataclasis, and concluded with solid deformation and metamorphism."

Flett concluded (1946, p. 24) that:

"The intrusive rocks of the Lizard were injected during a period of earth pressure, and many of them were foliated before they had cooled down. . . . The serpentine, gabbro, black dykes, and gneisses . . . crystallized under conditions of stress and folding . . . [which] were not continuous but intermittent, and when the pressures were renewed it was always the weakest part of the complex that gave way . . . Local variations in the intensity of metamorphism . . . depend principally on whether the rocks had cooled down or were still hot when the increase in pressure supervened."

All the relations described between the Crousa Downs gabbro, Traboe schist, and Lizard peridotite are consonant with an alpine origin followed by later regional metamorphism, and some of the apparent contradictions would be resolved by this hypothesis. During such regional metamorphism, gabbroic rocks may be completely transformed while massive peridotites are only partly serpentinized (Hopson, 1964). The chemical relationships between peridotite and "granulite" which Green (1964b, p. 549) explains by "two-way migration of selected components" are explained more simply by slight mixing along contacts between alpine peridotite and gabbro and gradation from olivine gabbro to pyroxene gabbro (Section B-4). If the alpine hypothesis is the correct one, gabbroic dikes would not differ significantly in age or composition from gabbro interlayered with peridotite; and, in this regard, chemical analyses of the gabbro and Traboe schist are quite similar. Any other hypothesis requires two chemically similar gabbros of different ages, one older, the other younger than the peridotite.

E. Origin of the Alpine Mafic Magma Stem

The world-wide similarity of the features in and relations between alpine peridotites, podiform chromite deposits, and gabbro can be rationalized only by a common origin. Gravity stratification of peridotite and gabbro in the upper part of the mantle, and their later reemplacement together as crystal mushes containing entrained solid autoliths of chromitite, have been postulated previously (Thayer, 1963a, 1964). As far as I know, the petrologists who regard alpine dunite as "dead-burned" residue from generation of tholeiite magma (see Chapter 11), have made no critical attempt to reconcile the relations of alpine peridotites and dunites to chromite and gabbro with such an origin. Chemically, the alpine gabbros appear to be an integral and important part of the calc-alkaline plutonic magma series; does this mean that alpine peridotites are, too?

The kinship of dioritic and granophyric rocks to the mafic and ultramafic members of the magma series is obscure. The general absence of amphibole in unmetamorphosed alpine peridotites and gabbros, especially in gabbroic pegmatites that obviously are formed late, implies dry magma, but the even later dioritic and granophyric rocks were flooded with Na-rich solutions. In the Canyon Mountain complex and in the Moa district, Cuba, the gabbroic pegmatites contain no magmatic hornblende, and the pegmatitic masses related to albitization in Canyon Mountain contain no pyroxene; we have found no hornblende-pyroxene pegmatites. The relatively small amounts of dioritic rocks and their preferential association with gabbro rather than peridotite indicate that they may be generated from geosynclinal country rocks near gabbro by local heating, and thus lag behind the major intrusion of peridotite-gabbro. Relations like those in the Baker-Sparta area of Oregon, however, imply that the diorites and albite granites associated with alpine complexes probably are only one facet of the general problem of soda-rich igneous rocks and sodic metasomatism in eugeosynclines (Gilluly, 1933, p. 76).

The chemical parameters of the alpine mafic rocks are known only vaguely. Original composition of the average alpine peridotite, before serpentinization, is a moot question (Thayer, in press) which is fundamental to some hypotheses of basalt generation. The trend from peridotite and olivine gabbro through pyroxene gabbro to quartz diorite may or may not represent continuous magma differentiation, but if it does where does uralite gabbro fit in? Might it be possible to distinguish isolated alpine-type gabbro bodies from other kinds, such as the Duluth or Moxie gabbros, by Mg:Fe ratios in olivine and pyroxene, coupled with physical features? How does flow-layering form and how do the chemical relations between minerals in known alpine flow-layered gabbro and peridotite compare with those in gravity-stratified rocks? How much recrystallization may take place after flowage stops and what are its effects?

Resolution of most of the foregoing questions will require much more careful and detailed field mapping and sampling than has been done to date. For example, no large-scale maps of ophiolites have been published, and I am confident that adequate modern petrologic mapping at a scale of 1:50,000 or larger would eliminate the ophiolite hypothesis from further serious consideration. The most meticulous examination of all-peridotite alpine plutons cannot tell more than a small part of the story, any more than studying a zebra in a zoo will portray its behavior in a wild herd. Finally, the fundamental characteristics of the several members of the alpine mafic magma stem must be determined in complexes that have not been subjected to later regional dynamic metamorphism.

8. *Kimberlites*

I. INTRODUCTION

P. J. Wyllie

Kimberlites are rare rocks occurring in small diatremes, dikes, veins, and sills in stable or fractured continental regions. Their distribution appears to be related to deep-seated tectonics with linear trends. The kimberlites were considered in three groups in Chapter 1-I-B-7: clusters of diatremes forming elongate chains, dikes and sheets distributed on a regional scale, and central-complex kimberlites associated with alkalic carbonatite complexes. There are many hypotheses on the origin of kimberlite, none of which is satisfactory for all occurrences. There is increasing evidence that there are genetic links between kimberlites, carbonatites, and alkalic ultrabasic complexes. A symposium on "Carbonatites, kimberlites, and their minerals" was organized by the International Mineralogical Association in New Delhi in 1964 (von Eckermann, 1966). According to Dawson (Chapter 8-V-F-1), hypotheses relating kimberlite to rocks of the nepheline syenite-carbonatite suite (including olivine melilitite) explain most satisfactorily the chemical features of kimberlite and its intimate association in time, space, and tectonic environment with these rocks. Discussion of kimberlites therefore overlaps from this chapter into Chapter 9, which is concerned primarily with alkalic ultrabasic complexes. The main emphasis in Chapter 8 is on kimberlites occurring in diatremes, and Chapter 9 includes accounts of kimberlites with more obvious affinities to carbonatites and alkalic rocks.

Dawson, in Section II, defines kimberlite as a serpentinized, carbonated mica peridotite of porphyritic texture, containing ultrabasic nodules. Diamond was regarded as an essential mineral in some definitions, and by omitting this requirement Dawson includes many mica peridotites as kimberlites. Similar definitions of kimberlite are considered by von Eckermann in Chapter 9-IV and by Watson in Chapters 8-IV and 9-V. Dawson provides a detailed account of the texture and mineralogy of kimberlite (basaltic and micaceous types) followed by a discussion of the rock fragments and inclusions found in kimberlites. The kimberlites have been classified on the basis of their contents of rock fragments into massive kimberlite, intrusive kimberlite breccia, and kimberlite tuffs and tuff-breccias. The different features of these three types probably result from their mode of emplacement, ranging from a magma or crystal mush to a fluidized system. Dawson's review of the world distribution of kimberlites includes accounts of their occurrences in 16 countries or regions, including those described in more detail in subsequent articles in Chapters 8 and 9. Most of these are confined to the interior or margins of stable platforms of continental areas, but the Borneo and Malaita occurrences are in orogenic belts.

In Section III Davidson presents a detailed review of the known kimberlites in the U.S.S.R. Hundreds of kimberlites have been discovered in the Siberian platform since the first one was reported in 1940. Few pipes contain less than 40 per cent xenoliths and they may reach 90 per cent. Inflammable gas has been released from some pipes during drilling, and von Eckermann (Chapter 9-IV) reports the same for a Swedish kimberlite. The geographic association of kimberlites with alkalic ultrabasic complexes is evident in the petrographic province of the Maimecha-Kotui district, where there are also widespread flows of meimechite. Davidson reviews the data on age measurements of Russian kimberlites and concludes that this supports a two-stage emplacement history. Kimberlite magma was emplaced deep in the crust during Sinian times, coeval with the central complexes. In the Mesozoic, the massive kimberlite was invaded by an influx of gases, fluidized, and carried upwards at low temperatures. He concludes that kimberlite breccias originate from separate and independent hearths, each with its own mineralogical and geochemical idiosyncracies.

In Section IV Watson provides a detailed petrographic and chemical account of two kimberlite diatremes from Arizona, which are crowded with inclusions and xenoliths of many sizes and varieties. The xenoliths are enclosed by a serpentine-rich matrix, and exhibit virtually no thermal metamorphism. Watson notes that one pipe contains eclogite inclusions, whereas the other one does not, and he discusses the source of eclogite inclusions and the distinction of eclogites from various sources. Various features of the pipes indicate that the material consisted of a complex fluidization system when emplaced, following the explosion of a gas-charged magma.

Dawson reviews the geochemistry and origin of kimberlites in Section V. The major elements and minor elements are discussed in detail. Basaltic and micaceous kimberlites can be distinguished petrographically, but there is complete chemical gradation between them, and complete chemical gradation to alnoites and to carbonatites. Kimberlites are set apart from other ultrabasic rocks by their chemistry. They have a low Mg/Fe ratio, and unusually high K/Na and Fe^{3+}/Fe^{2+}; the fixed H_2O content averages 7.7 per cent. Kimberlites have relatively high concentrations of two suites of minor elements, those characteristic of ultrabasic rocks, and a suite more characteristic of carbonatites and associated alkalic rocks. The data on carbon and strontium isotopes are also discussed. Dawson presents a detailed list of the features that have to be explained in any hypothesis of origin, discusses the various hypotheses proposed, and reviews the evidence for a kimberlite-carbonatite relationship. Dawson proposes that kimberlite may be the end-product of interaction between a water-rich ankeritic fraction of a carbonatite magma and the granitic crustal rocks.

II. A REVIEW OF THE GEOLOGY OF KIMBERLITE

J. B. Dawson

A. *Introduction*

Kimberlite is one of the rarest of ultrabasic rock types and, even when compared with serpentinites, layered ultrabasic bodies and alpine peridotites, occupies intrusive bodies of extremely small size. Despite its volumetric insignificance, kimberlite is nonetheless a rock type of considerable economic and petrologic interest.

In the first place, kimberlite (and its ultrabasic inclusions) was until very recently the only known primary source of terrestrial diamond, and it has been the problems of the economics and genesis of diamond that have given rise to the major contributions to kimberlite geology. The first of these were the classical treatises of Wagner (1914) and Williams (1932) on the kimberlites of southern Africa. More recently, our knowledge of kimberlites has been tremendously increased by the intensive investigations of Russian geoscientists on the major kimberlite province of Yakutia (e.g., Bobrievich et al., 1957, 1959, 1964; Smirnov, 1959). Initially it was the desire to obtain a source of diamond independent of Western control which caused the Russians to follow up reports of alluvial diamonds in Siberia, leading to the discovery of the province in 1954.

Second, kimberlite contains inclusions of ultrabasic rock-types that many petrologists believe to originate in the upper mantle. Recently these nodules have received much attention from geochemists and experimental petrologists, in connection with investigations on the nature of the upper mantle and the origin of basalts (see Chapters 10 and 11).

B. Definition

Kimberlite may be defined as a serpentinized and carbonated mica-peridotite of porphyritic texture, containing nodules of ultrabasic rock-types characterized by such high-pressure minerals as pyrope and jadeitic diopside; it may, or may not, contain diamond. It occurs in diatremes, dykes, veins, and sills of very limited size.

The name "kimberlite" was first given by Lewis (1887) to the diamondiferous mica peridotite occurring in diatremes and dykes at Kimberley, South Africa, and was later extended to include rocks of similar petrographic character which, although nondiamondiferous, occurred in the vicinity of diamondiferous kimberlite.

Kimberlite, as defined here, differs from

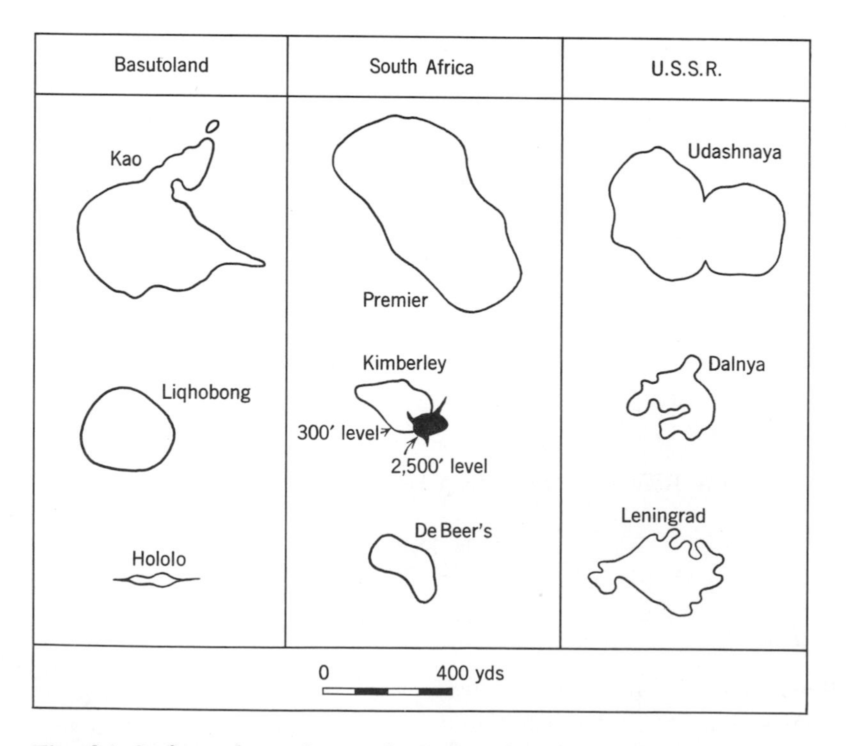

Fig. 8.1 Surface plans of some kimberlite diatremes. (Basutoland, from Dawson, 1962; South Africa, from Williams, 1932; Russia, from Bobrievich et al., 1959.) Intrusions such as Kao, Hololo, and Udashnaya are probably formed by the coalescence of two diatremes.

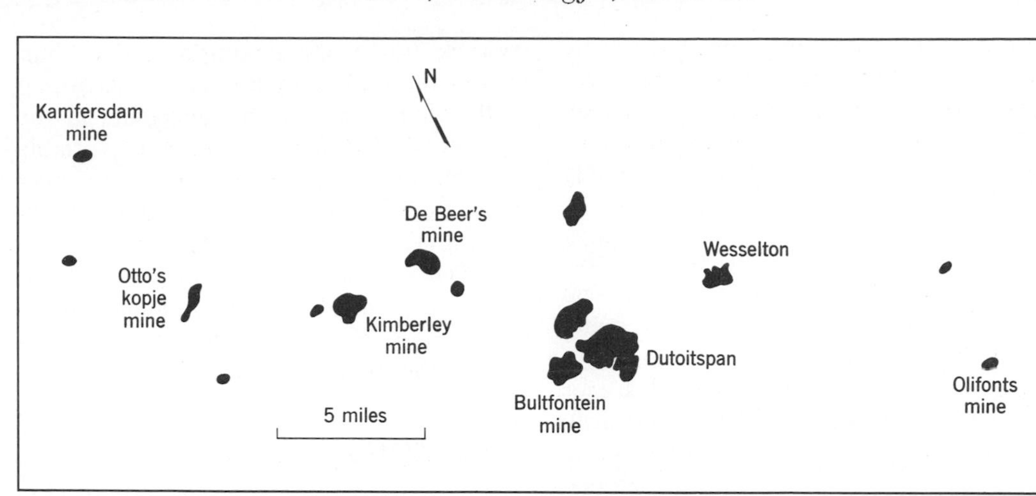

Fig. 8.2 An elongate zone of kimberlite diatremes in the Kimberley area, South Africa (from Williams, 1932, p. 119).

Lewis's original description in that diamond is not an essential mineral, and hence embraces many other occurrences of mica-peridotite (e.g. those of Kentucky, U.S.A.) which do not occur with diamondiferous rocks but which in all other respects resemble the mica-peridotite of the type locality.

C. Field Occurrence

Kimberlite occurs most commonly in small diatremes and dykes, more rarely in sills. The shape of the diatremes is variable in plan, being rounded, oval or very irregular, and they narrow downwards (Fig. 8.1); they are very limited in size, the largest pipe in the world (the Mwadui pipe, Tanganyika) having a surface outcrop of only 0.7 square mile. The diatremes, which tend to occur in clusters (Fig. 8.2), are located on dykes, and chains of diatremes along elongate zones are indicative of unexposed dykes at depth. The diatremes generally coalesce with the dykes, but may also post-date them; the diatreme kimberlites are often cut by later dykes. The dykes themselves are generally quite narrow, rarely more than 10 meters, and may be up to 14 km long; they often occur in swarms that have a preferred strike.

Kimberlitic rocks also occur in dykes or plugs in many carbonatite complexes (e.g., Alnö Island, von Eckermann, Chapter 9-IV). Although these rocks resemble kimberlite so closely as to have been prospected for diamonds in some cases (e.g., at Pilaansberg, South Africa), no diamonds have been found in them and they contain no ultrabasic inclusions. They will be referred to hereafter as "central-complex kimberlites."

D. Classification of Kimberlites

In a kimberlite body three broad types of rock may be encountered. At the surface is "yellow-ground"—decomposed and oxidized kimberlite. It is succeeded in depth by "blue-ground" which is the same rock in a better state of preservation. Hard unweathered kimberlite is known as "hardebank." The distribution of these types is controlled by the depth of surface weathering and percolating groundwater; and in Russia, where the climate is not conducive to chemical decomposition, yellow-ground is absent.

The unweathered kimberlites exhibit a wide textural and mineralogical range, leading Lewis (1887) to divide them into three main types: (a) kimberlite—a massive rock of porphyritic texture; (b) kimberlite breccia; (c) kimberlite tuff.

Wagner (1914) later supplemented this by dividing each type into basaltic or micaceous varieties. The boundaries between the types, however, were vague until Russian geologists (e.g., Rabhkin et al., 1962) proposed definite criteria for each type:

a. Massive kimberlite. This is a massive porphyritic rock and contains few or no inclusions of country-rocks xenoliths, being the result of comparatively gentle intrusion of kimberlite "magma" into dykes or cavities of diatremes which have previously been cleared of country-rock fragments by gas explosions or earlier surges of magma. It is subdivided into a *basaltic* variety, in which olivine or serpentinized olivine is the dominant phenocryst mineral, and a *micaceous* variety in which mica forms >5 per cent of the phenocrysts or comprises a large part of the groundmass. It may be subdivided further on the basis of its mineralogy (e.g., pyroxene-bearing, monticellite bearing). The rock occurs in dykes veins or segments of diatremes, and is hypabyssal or subvolcanic. The presence of flow textures and chilled margins indicates its intrusive nature.

b. Intrusive kimberlite breccias. This type contains 20 to 60 per cent fragments of various rock-types set in a matrix corresponding to massive kimberlite. The rock is classified on this matrix and is then named as (a) autolithic—in which fragments of kimberlite (maybe of several generations) predominate, or (b) heterolithic—in which there are also xenoliths of country rock. The breccias are termed fine, medium or coarse, the dominant fragment size being <1, 1 to 5, or >5 cm, respectively. The breccias occur mainly in diatremes, only rarely in dykes.

c. Kimberlite tuffs and tuff-breccias. This type consists of 60 to 90 per cent fragments of kimberlite and country rocks cemented by hydrothermal-type minerals. The texture is fragmental and flow texture is absent. The *tuffs* consist of kimberlite or kimberlite mineral fragments, with country-rock fragments amounting to <5 per cent of the bulk; they are named according to the dominant type of kimberlite in the fragments. *Tuff-breccia* contains variable amounts of country rock, and if this predominates the breccia is termed xeno-tuff-breccia. The tuffs and tuff-breccias are also classified as fine, medium, or coarse (<1, 1 to 5, >5 cm). They are confined to diatremes or segments of diatremes, and belong to the diatreme facies.

E. Petrography

Kimberlite has a typically porphyritic texture, the commonest *phenocrysts* being olivine (or serpentinized olivine), garnets, pyroxenes, amphiboles, picro-ilmenite and micas. The olivine (Fo_{92-88}) is partly or wholly altered to antigorite (with enclosed magnetite), serpophite or calcite, though in many instances the pseudomorphs retain recognizable olivine shape. The serpentinization is autometasomatic, being independent of the surface-weathering or percolating groundwaters. The antigorite may be rimmed by hydrophlogopite, and in rare cases the olivine has a corona of monticellite (Verhoogen, 1938). The garnets are always rounded and enclosed in a rind of "kelyphite"—a microcrystalline mixture of biotite, spinel, pyroxene, amphibole, and ?plagioclase. They vary widely in composition from pyrope-rich types (Py_{75}) to chrome pyrope and pyrope-almandine; the pyropes are regarded as forming from the kimberlite magma itself, but the others are believed to originate from fragmented inclusions of peridotite, granulite, and eclogite (Nixon et al., 1963). The pyroxenes are enstatite (En_{92-94}) and chrome-diopside, the former sometimes altered to tremolite-actinolite. The mica is phlogopite-biotite with corroded and bleached rims margined by exsolved magnetite; the phenocrysts are often bent or distorted. Potash-free vermiculite also occurs as phenocrysts. The ilmenite is typically rounded and contains high magnesia (5 to 12 per cent) and ferric iron.

The *groundmass* consists of fine-grained serpentine, pyroxene, tremolite-actinolite, hydromicas, calcite, magnetite, chrome-spinel, calcium zeolites, and apatite. A second generation of small groundmass olivines is known in some kimberlites, and phlogopite and apatite also occur in two generations. Perovskite is a constant accessory and may also appear as a reaction rim between picroilmenite and calcite. Diamond, when present, is sparsely distributed in the groundmass. Moissanite, pyrochlore, and potash nepheline are rarer minerals recorded from Russian kimberlites (Bobrievich et al., 1957; Pecherskii, 1965; Lebedev, 1964), and in a recent monograph (Bobrievich et al., 1964) the following unusual secondary minerals are noted: sphene, rutile, anatase, dolomite, aragonite, strontianite, thaumasite, hydrogarnet, haematite, quartz, brucite, pyroaurite, pyrite, marcasite, sphalerite, wurtzite, galena, chalcopyrite, millerite, cinnabar, celestine, barite, gypsum, anhydrite, huntite, magnesite, hydromagnesite, epsomite, halite, and anglesite.

The texture and mineralogy of kimberlite is such as to suggest that the rock is the result of interaction between phenocrysts and fragments of a wide variety of minerals and an interstitial fluid rich in aluminum, iron, calcium, potassium, water, carbon dioxide, and phosphorus. The porphyritic texture and the presence of various minerals in two generations, combined with their peculiar chemistry (see Chapter 8-V), indicate that kimberlites should be classed as a variety of lamprophyre.

Within any one particular kimberlite intrusion (particularly in the diatremes), a considerable variety of petrographic and textural types may occur. Basaltic kimberlite may grade into the micaceous variety within the space of a few feet, while massive micaceous kimberlite in a dyke may grade gradually into basaltic kimberlite breccia when it coalesces with a diatreme. Kimberlite tuff may be intruded by massive kimberlite, or cut by dykes of fine-grained tuff-breccia resembling tuffisite. Some diatremes (e.g., De Beers Mine, South Africa) contain different columns of tuff breccia, each having a distinctive lithology and a characteristic type and content of diamond (Williams, 1932, p. 239). Variations also occur on a regional scale, as for instance in South Africa where the kimberlites of the Orange Free State are mainly micaceous whilst those of Basutoland are dominantly basaltic (Dawson, 1962). In Russia basaltic kimberlite tuff-breccias occupy the Alakit-Daldyn-Vilyui area on the southern side of the Siberian platform, whereas those in the Anabar-Olenek region on the northeastern side are massive micaceous types sometimes containing monticellite and nepheline (Milashev et al., 1963).

F. Inclusions in Kimberlites

Within kimberlite diatremes four types of inclusion may be found:

1. Blocks of rock types derived from formations existing in the area at the time of the kimberlite emplacement, but which have subsequently been removed by erosion. Unlike the other inclusions, these are at a lower level than their true stratigraphic position. They often attain considerable size as shown by the "floating reefs" of the Premier, Kimberley, and Wesselton Mines, South Africa (Wagner, 1914).
2. Angular blocks of the country rocks into which the kimberlites are intruded.
3. Rounded blocks of high-grade metamorphic rocks, such as granulites (some scapolite-bearing), eclogites, gneisses, and schists, derived from Basement complexes at depth.
4. Rounded or discoidal blocks of ultrabasic rocks composed of varying combinations of olivine, rhombic and clino-pyroxene, chrome-pyrope, spinel, picro-ilmenite and phlogopite. These are the garnet peridotites, lherzolites, saxonites and griquaites; they have been derived from considerable depths.

The source of the first three types of inclusion is self-evident, but the origin of the ultrabasic inclusions is a matter for dispute. Some geologists (e.g., O'Hara and Mercy, 1963) believe they are mantle xenoliths incorporated into the kimberlite during its ascent. Davidson (1964) also regards them as xenoliths but considers that they are derived, like the eclogites and granulites, from a deep-seated metamorphic zone in the crust. A third hypothesis is that they represent segregations or "cognate xenoliths" from the kimberlite magma, which crystallized at depth under considerable pressures (Wagner, 1914; Williams, 1932; Dawson, 1962; Bobrievich et al., 1964). On chemical grounds, Nixon et al. (1963) regard some as cognate inclusions and others as mantle xenoliths. The controversy is reviewed in Chapter 10-IV by Davidson.

The proportion and variety of inclusions vary considerably from diatreme to diatreme, and mineral fragments from all these types of inclusion may have been incorporated into the kimberlite, thereby giving it a very complex and hybrid mineralogy. It is also worthy of note that neither the inclusions nor the wall rocks of the intrusions show any signs of thermal metamorphism; the only metamorphic effects are metasomatic.

G. Emplacement of Kimberlite

In Section D dealing with the classification of kimberlites, it was intimated that the main types show differing features resulting from their emplacement. The massive hypabyssal or subvolcanic kimberlites show features such as flow lineation of the phenocrysts and distortion of mica phenocrysts, and it appears that this type was intruded as a magma or crystal mush. Mikeyenko and Nenashev (1961) have suggested that it is emplaced diapirically as a cold intrusion, though this is at variance with recorded examples of chilled margins; for example, the Kisiriri sills, Tanganyika (Williams, 1939). The diatreme-facies tuffs and tuff-breccias present a different aspect. Their fragmental nature had lead many earlier authors to propose explosive boring as a cause of the diatreme formation. However, the shape of the diatremes is largely controlled by the preexisting joint pattern in the country rocks, and there is absence of appreciable uparching of the country rocks. Neither the partial detachment of country-rock appendages from the wall rock, nor the relatively undisturbed state of the "floating reefs" appear to be possible if explosive boring was the method of intrusion, and it is unlikely that each of the deep, narrow pipes would have remained open (especially in soft sedimentary formations) to collect pyroclastic breccias. Moreover, material falling back into a vent has a random distribution, which is at variance with observations that inclusions from particular horizons tend to be concentrated in particular areas within the kimberlite diatremes. All the above features are more consistent with intrusion by fluidization (Dawson, 1962), which also explains the polishing and rounding of the inclusions, and the absence of thermal metamorphic effects.

A composite picture of kimberlite emplacement appears to be as follows:

1. Kimberlite as a fluid or crystal mush is intruded slowly up a system of deep-seated tension fractures and starts to consolidate as dykes. Opinions vary as to whether the kimberlite is charged with high-pressure gas at this time, or whether the halt in the ascent of the magma and the partial consolidation are prerequisites for the gas accumulation.
2. Then, at preferred points, where access to the surface is easiest, the highly gas-charged kimberlite breaks through explosively to the surface, probably from a depth of not more than 2 km (Dawson, 1960; Sobolev, 1960). The preferred points may be at the junction of two or more tensions fractures (e.g., Kimberley Mine; see Fig. 8.1) or where they cross other

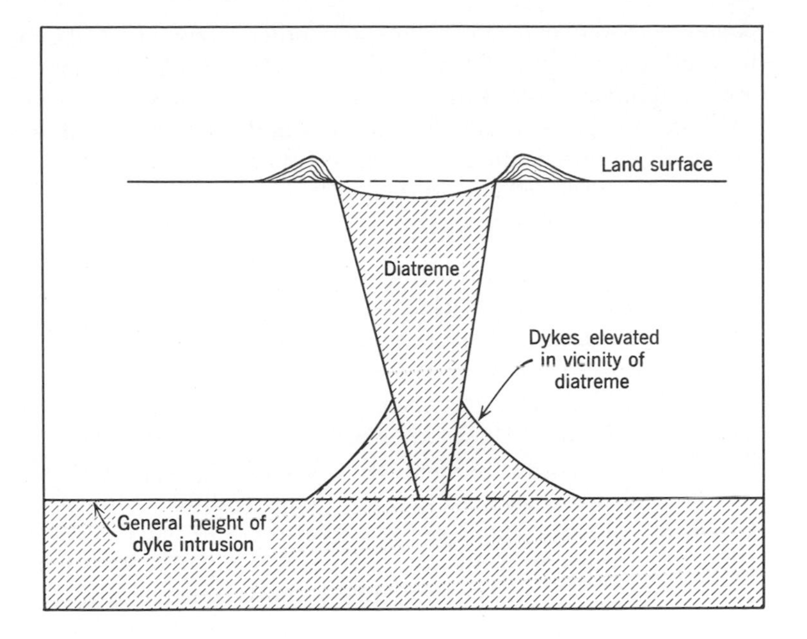

Fig. 8.3 Diagrammatic sketch showing the depth relationships between kimberlite diatremes and dykes (from Dawson, 1960, p. 261).

planes of weakness, such as earlier dykes or the contact between two contrasting rock formations [e.g., in Tanganyika where many of the kimberlites are situated at the contact between granites and roof pendants of metasedimentary rocks (Williams, 1939)].

3. The breakthrough to the surface will be accompanied by a rapid drop in pressure, which is probably the cause of the extensive serpentinization of the olivines in the diatreme. By contrast, in the dykes away from the point of breakthrough (which did not reach the surface and in which the pressure drop is comparatively gradual) the olivines are relatively little altered (Dawson, 1962).

4. The explosion vent is then enlarged and infilled by fluidized fragmented kimberlite, drilling its way upward with a sand-blasting effect and taking advantage of the jointing. Major blocks of country rock subside gently into the uprising gas-tuff streams to form the "floating reefs" (cf. Cloos, 1941).

5. In certain cases later gas surges may emplace later distinctive columns of tuff or tuffisite veins, while cavities in the vent may be infilled with quietly upwelling magma which consolidates as massive kimberlite or kimberlite breccia.

6. The overall result is a diatreme rising above the general level of the dyke system (Fig. 8.3). The surface expression of the diatreme is most likely a small crater with an olivine-rich tuff ring, or an olivine-rich tuff cone.

The apparent random surface distribution of the kimberlite diatremes is due to control by near-surface weaknesses, and the prime factor in the positioning of the dyke swarms and diatreme clusters is the location of the deep-seated tension fractures. After the cease of the intrusive activity, the vent material may settle into the pipe, causing concentric, inward-dipping fracture planes or slumping, depending on the degree of consolidation of the material. Settling may continue for a long time, as shown by distortion of sediments deposited in the crater a considerable time after the close of the activity.

H. World Distribution of Kimberlites

In a review of the occurrences of kimberlite, Dawson (1960) noted the intimate connection between kimberlites and other unusual rock types. Because these rocks are contemporaneous with kimberlites and are intruded in the same general areas and under the same tectonic conditions, they are considered together with kimberlites in the following brief review.

1. North America. Kimberlites are found to the west of the Appalachians in a broad zone running from New York State to Kentucky, and also in Arkansas and in the Navajo-Hopi volcanic province of the Colorado plateau. These kimberlites are described by Watson in Chapters 9-V and 8-IV. Kimberlite also occurs in Ontario (Satterley, 1948), and Quebec (Watson, 1955). In New York State kimberlite dykes grade into alnöite (Martens, 1924), and in Kentucky occur with olivine kersantites and alnöites (Koenig, 1956). The kimberlites of Pike County, Arkansas, are found with nepheline syenite, syenite, tinguaite, ijolite, monchiquite, ouachitite and carbonatite. On the Colorado plateau they are associated with flows of olivine basalt unusually rich in Ba, Ti, Zr, Nb, P_2O_5 and H_2O, and with intrusive monchiquites and minettes (Shoemaker, 1955); at Buell Park, Arizona, kimberlite forms a composite intrusion with minette and trachybasalt (Allen and Balk, 1954).

2. Brazil. Although Brazil was the foremost diamond producer in the world immediately prior to the discovery of the South African fields, few kimberlites are known and most of the diamonds are recovered from alluvial deposits. In the highlands of Minas Geraes, kimberlites occur at Patos and Coromandel (Draper, 1923), whereas in the Abaete alluvial diamond area there is an intrusion of perovskite-bearing porphyritic peridotite (Draper, 1911). In the Bagagem district are pipes of diamondiferous, ultrabasic volcanic breccia named "bebedourite" which Rimann (1931) has compared with kimberlites. Alnöite occurs near the kimberlite at Patos, and the kimberlites of Bagagem and Coromandel are near the carbonatite centers of Catalao, Patrocinio, Salitre, and Araxa. Kimberlite, limburgite and alnöite dykes are recorded from the Sierra dos Lagos, southwest of Rio de Janeiro (Rimann, 1915).

The exact nature of the diamond deposits at Diamantina is in dispute. Draper (1923) and Thompson (1928) believe the diamondiferous conglomerates to be kimberlites, whereas Barbosa (1951) contends they are detrital deposits.

3. Australia. Basic volcanic agglomerate at Ruby Hill, New South Wales, contains pyrope garnet and inclusions of eclogite and granulite. Although it was reported to have yielded diamond and was compared with kimberlite (Pittman, 1901), no further diamonds have been found and its basic, rather than ultrabasic, composition has been reaffirmed by Lovering (1964).

4. Solomon Islands. On the island of Malaita are outcrops of alnöite, alnöite breccia, and magnesian ankaratrite containing ultrabasic inclusions and the kimberlite indicator minerals pyrope, chrome-diopside and picro-ilmenite. These rocks are types intermediate between melilite basalt, alnöite, and kimberlite (Allen and Deans, 1965).

5. Borneo. Intrusive peridotite breccias occur in the alluvial diamond fields of the Pamali River area of southeastern Borneo. One has proved to be diamondiferous (Van Bemmelen, 1949, p. 343).

6. India. One kimberlite pipe is known at Majhgawan, in Panna State (Mathur, 1962).

7. Russia. The Yakutia area of Siberia is now known to be the second most extensive area of kimberlite intrusion, after South Africa. The main areas are around the Anabarsk shield in the headwaters of the Markha, Muna, and Olenek rivers. There is also a small area in the Pre-Sayan, west of Lake Baikal, and another on the northwestern edge of the Aldan massif. These intrusions are more fully described by Davidson (Section III).

On the northwestern side of the Anabarsk shield, in the Meimecha-Kotui area, kimberlites are associated with a wide variety of alkalic and ultrabasic rock types. There are at least 13 ring complexes containing rocks varying from dunite, peridotite, and pyroxenite to ijolite, nepheline syenite, and carbonatite (Sheinmann, 1957; Butakova and Egorov, 1962). Numerous dykes of alnöite and non-diamondiferous kimberlite are present, and also thick flows of meimechite—a rock of similar chemistry to kimberlites and described by Sheinmann (1957) as consisting of olivine, serpentine, and phlogopite phenocrysts set in a black glass containing abundant perovskite and amygdales filled with serpentine and carbonate. On the Olenek River olivine leucitite dykes occur in the kimberlite province (Arseniev and Nechaeva, 1955), and melilite basalts occur with micaceous kimberlites on the Taimyr peninsula (Moor, 1941). The Pre-Sayan kimberlites are associated with carbonatites, nepheline syenites, ijolites, tinguaites, and pyroxenite (Odintsov, 1965). Non-diamondiferous central-complex kimberlite occurs with biotite pyroxenite, ijolite, nepheline syenite, and carbonatite in the Arbarastakh complex in the Aldan shield.

8. Czechoslovakia. Two kimberlites and three breccia pipes are known on the northern side of the Bohemian massif (Kopecky, 1960). They form part of the late Tertiary volcanic suite of the area which, according to Kopecky (unpublished work quoted by Kodym, 1960) embraces olivine basalt, basanite, tephrite, leucitite, nephelinite, hauyne-bearing trachyte, phonolite, polzenite and olivine melilitite.

9. Scandinavia. Central-complex kimberlites occur in the Alnö carbonatite complex (Chapter 9-IV), and rocks similar to kimberlites (damtjernite) occur in the Fen carbonatite complex, Norway (Saether, 1957).

10. Africa. Kimberlite has a more widespread development in Africa than elsewhere in the world, being found from well north of the equator to the Cape Mountains in the south.

11. West Africa. Kimberlite occurs in the vicinity of Kenieba, Mali, and also in Sierra Leone (Grantham and Allen, 1960). Alluvial diamonds are found in Liberia and Ghana, and in the alluvial diamond fields near Seguela, Ivory Coast, diamonds have been traced back to an interesting group of dykes. Of five samples taken from one of these diamondiferous dykes, three have been classified as altered leucite lamproite (fitzroyite) and two as mica-peridotite. Another diamondiferous mica-peridotite dyke has altered the country-rock granite, converting it to a potash fenite of microcline and sodic amphibole. Blocks of fresh fitzroyite have also been found in the area. These rocks are at present under investigation by the Mineral Resources Division of the Overseas Geological Surveys, London.

In Gabon, dykes of carbonated kimberlite outcrop in the vicinity of alluvial diamond deposits in the Bandolo River (Choubert, 1946).

12. Angola and Congo. Kimberlites occur in the valleys of the Chicapa and Luachimo Rivers. They lie within the Lucapa graben which is located on the northeasterly extension of a chain of basic, alkaline, and carbonatite ring complexes (Machado, 1958). In the Congo kimberlites are known at Bakwanga, (Meyer, 1963) and on the Kundelungu plateau (Verhoogen, 1938).

13. Tanzania. Kimberlites are widely distributed on the central plateau of Tanganyika. Until 1940 some 40 occurrences were known (Williams, 1939), but extensive prospecting following the discovery of the Mwadui pipe in 1940 has revealed some 60 more. They are mainly concentrated in the Shinyanga, Singida-Iramba, Nzega and Kimali areas. A recent account of the Mwadui pipe was given by Edwards and Howkins (1966). One of the intrusions contains a rock resembling melilitite. Carbonate-rich kimberlites occur in the Ruhuhu depression in southern Tanganyika (McKinlay, 1955). Olivine-rich tuff-cones, which are tentatively suggested as being the surface expression of kimberlite diatremes, occur at the Igwisi Hills in western Tanganyika (Sampson, 1953, Fozzard, 1956), and at Lashaine in the carbonatite-rich Neogene volcanic province in northern Tanganyika (Dawson, 1964).

14. ***Rhodesia.*** Four kimberlites occur in the Lochard area, 30 miles N.E. of Bulawayo (MacGregor et al., 1937).

15. ***South Africa.*** Kimberlite pipes are more widely developed in South Africa than elsewhere. They have been described by various authors, the most important of whom are Wagner (1914) and Williams (1932). Williams summarized most work prior to 1932 and since then little information has been published on the South African rocks. The kimberlites are spread over a huge, roughly oval area north of the Cape Mountains, covering most of the interior plateau except in the southeast where they are conspicuously absent. The main sites of intrusion are the Pretoria, Kroonstadt, Winburg, Kimberley, Boshof, Barkley West, Koffyfontein, Jagersfontein, Prieska, Victoria West and Sutherland areas, and Bushmanland. In the Sutherland district, the kimberlites are associated with melilitite and at Prieska with aegirine camptonite. At Spiegel River, the kimberlite occurs with melilitite, and in Bushmanland is found with melilitite and nephelinite (Taljaard, 1936). Carbonatite dykes cut the kimberlite of the Premier Mine (Daly, 1925).

16. ***South West Africa.*** Over 40 kimberlite pipes occur in the Gibeon-Keetmanshoop area (Wagner, 1916; Janse, 1964). Melilitite and carbonatite is known in the area, and further north in the Auas Mountains are intrusions and flows of phonolite, trachyte, and nephelinite, some containing inclusions of alkali peridotite (Gevers, 1933). Further north still occurs a large area of ring-complexes including carbonatites (Martin et al., 1960).

17. ***Basutoland.*** Several kimberlite pipes and numerous dykes are present, and one dyke of carbonatite is also known (Dawson, 1962).

I. Age of Kimberlite

From the available evidence, it is apparent that kimberlite magmatism has occurred at several times during the earth's history. The kimberlites of the Colorado plateau and Czechoslovakia are late Tertiary, and the kimberlites (?) at Igwisi and Lashaine in Tanzania are Recent. Many of the kimberlites in South and Central Africa are Mesozoic, and those in Brazil and Arkansas are known to be Cretaceous. Diamonds are found in Precambrian conglomerates in several parts of the world (e.g., Brazil, South Africa, India and West Australia) and also in the basal conglomerates of later formations directly overlying some Precambrian terrains [e.g., the Upper Karroo escarpment grits of the Somabula Forest, Rhodesia (MacGregor, 1921)]. If it can be assumed that kimberlite is the only parent rock for diamond, then the presence of diamond in the conglomerates must be viewed as indirect evidence for kimberlite activity in the Precambrian. This is to some extent confirmed by radiometric datings that give Precambrian ages for kimberlites from Tanzania (2035 m.y.), Mali (1072 m.y.), Ivory Coast (1145 and 1429 m.y.) and U.S.S.R. In addition, Junner (1943) has recorded a diamondiferous phyllite (?metamorphosed kimberlite) from the Precambrian of Ghana.

On the basis that kimberlites of at least four different ages (2100 to 2300, 1150, 700, and 80 to 100 m.y.) are known within a very limited area in West Africa, Bardet and Vachette (1966) have proposed that certain areas of the earth's crust have been subjected to repeated kimberlite intrusion during geological time. A similar persistence is recorded from the Siberian platform (see Davidson, Section III). In addition, the fact that in South Africa, India, and Brazil, Cretaceous kimberlites intrude areas where diamondiferous conglomerates of much earlier age already exist, may be regarded as further evidence for the hypothesis that certain geographical areas are "kimberlite prone."

Recently Mikeyenko and Nenashev (1961) and Davidson (1964) have pointed out a discrepancy between the geologic and radiometric ages of the Russian kimberlite. Whereas the diatremes penetrate late Jurassic rocks, age determinations on phlogopite from the kimberlites have given ages of 630 to 690 m.y; that is, Precambrian. To account for this, Davidson has suggested that the kimberlites were first emplaced in Precambrian times and that in the Mesozoic, when renewed activity occurred, the preexisting kimberlite was invaded by a great influx of low temperature gases by which it was broken up, fluidized, and carried upwards to a higher horizon.

J. Tectonic Environment of Kimberlites

Most kimberlites are confined to the interior and margins of the shield on stable platforms of continental areas. The intrusion of the kimberlites took place during uplift or dilation of the platform areas during epeirogenic movements, along deep-seated fractures either bounding or cutting across the uplifted areas. For example, during the Cretaceous, kimberlites were intruded over much of the South African plateau when it was subjected to widespread vertical uplift, with complimentary downwarping or faulting round the periphery of the continent (Du Toit, 1954). In Czechoslovakia, however, the kimberlites and associated rock types were intruded into major fault zones formed at the margin of the Czech Massif when it was domed and uplifted during the late Tertiary folding in the Alpine and Carpathian orogens (Kodym, 1960). In the U.S.S.R., the Yakutian kimberlites and alkalic rocks are situated in an unfolded area surrounding the Anabarsk shield; Leontiev and Kadensky (1957) have suggested that they were intruded along deep-seated fractures along a major hinge zone between the shield and the relatively downwarped area during the earth movements associated with the folding of the Verkhoyansk belt. Bardet (1963) has suggested that these deep-seated fractures are arranged in geometric patterns which are probably connected with deep tectonics in the upper mantle.

Some kimberlites however (e.g., Kenieba) are situated on local domes whereas others (e.g., northeast Angola) are in grabens associated with unwarped zones that have become sufficiently dilated to be rifted along their crests. The kimberlites of central Tanganyika are situated on the strongly upwarped central plateau.

The kimberlites of Borneo and the kimberlitic rocks of Malaita are anomalous in that they lie within belts of strong orogenic deformation and are associated with Alpine-type peridotites. This anomaly, combined with the evidence of kimberlites within ancient fold areas bordering the platforms [e.g., in the eastern Sayan mountains (Lebedev, 1964)], suggests the possibility of extending the tectonic environment of kimberlites, and appears to necessitate revision of the concepts which consider kimberlite to be an exclusively "platform" formation.

III. THE KIMBERLITES OF THE U.S.S.R.

C. F. Davidson

A. Introduction

Kimberlite was first reported from the U.S.S.R. in 1940, in the form of a dyke rock associated with melilite-basalt on the upper Taimyra river of northwest Siberia. A recommendation that this high-arctic province be prospected for diamonds

(Moor, 1940) led in the early 1950's to the discovery of a few diamond crystals in the alluvium of the Maimecha, Kotui, and Moyero rivers several hundred kilometers to the southeast, where the existence of one of the world's greatest complexes of alkalic-ultrabasic rocks, with associated carbonatites, had already been recognized; but in this region diamond was not found in bedrock until 1961. By that time more important discoveries had been made in the country between the rivers Lena and Yenisei, to which successive geological expeditions had been dispatched from 1948 onwards, encouraged by early records of the occurrence of rare diamonds in heavy-mineral concentrates from Siberian gold placers, and inspired by geological reports of V. S. Trofimov and V. S. Sobolev, which drew analogies between the local geology and that of African diamond fields. Following the discovery of alluvial deposits and the recognition of pyrope and magnesian ilmenite as useful indicator minerals, in August 1954 L. A. Popugaeva located a pipe of kimberlite (Zarnitsa) in the headwaters of the Markha river in Yakutia, just about on the Arctic Circle. The kimberlite proved to be diamond-bearing. At the end of the 1956 field season, 20 pipes had been found.

TABLE 8.1 Analyses of Kimberlite and Meimechite

	I	II	III
SiO_2	27.81	36.76	34.73
TiO_2	1.63	1.24	1.62
Al_2O_3	3.40	2.27	2.88
Cr_2O_3	0.13	0.31	...
Fe_2O_3	5.40	7.35	6.10
FeO	2.82	5.37	3.13
MnO	0.12	0.15	...
NiO	0.14	0.16	...
MgO	25.53	33.24	31.41
CaO	12.21	4.10	5.79
Na_2O	0.33	0.69	0.33
K_2O	0.66	0.40	1.17
P_2O_5	0.50	0.19	1.06
H_2O+	...	7.20	9.20
CO_2	...	0.71	2.58
Loss ign.	19.42	...	...
S	...	0.09	...
Total	100.10	100.25	100.00

I. Kimberlite of Yakutia: average of 339 analyses, from 107 intrusions. Quoted from Bobrievich *et al.*, 1964.

II. Meimechite of Maimecha-Kotui province: average of 10 analyses of lavas and lava-breccias. Calculated from data of Butakova and Egorov, 1962.

III. Average kimberlite, excluding U.S.S.R. occurrences. Quoted from R. A. Daly, 1933.

By 1964 some hundreds of kimberlite intrusions (pipes and dykes) were known throughout the Siberian platform, scattered in small groups over an area of 1½ million square kilometers; and despite the adverse climate the annual production of diamonds from Yakutia, including alluvial stones, had already risen to about an eighth of the world output. Although most of the diamonds are small, at least eight stones in the 32–56 carats range had been found before 1962. In the last decade the Russian scientific publications on these Siberian kimberlites have been so prolific that, excluding popular and technological works, they now exceed 3000 pages—a volume of literature surpassing that available for the rest of the world. A feature of this bibliography is its wealth of chemical analyses of rocks and minerals. Among the more important studies are those of Bobrievich *et al.* (1957, 1959, 1964), Bobrievich and Sobolev (1962), Menyailov (1961, 1962), Milashev *et al.* (1963), Rozkhov *et al.* (1963), Koval'skii (1963), and Milashev (1965). Brief reviews in English have been given by Lebedev (1964), Wilson (1960), and Davidson (1957); in German by Polutoff (1964); and in French by Bardet (1965).

This chapter is confined to an account of the geographical distribution of these rocks, with a few words on their date and mechanism of emplacement and on regional variations in mineralogy. Statistical information is mainly abstracted from Bobrievich (1964). In petrography and mineralogy the rocks do not differ significantly from the world-wide kimberlite type described by Dawson (Section II), whose nomenclature will be followed. The average chemical composition of Siberian kimberlite, and of the related extrusive rock-type meimechite, is listed in Table 8.1. A discussion of the origin of the so-called cognate xenoliths is given elsewhere (Davidson, Chapter 10-IV).

B. The Yakutian Kimberlites

The distribution of kimberlites in Yakutia and adjoining districts is shown in Fig. 8.4. Some features of the various groups of intrusions are outlined below.

Anabar group. At least a dozen pipes, poorly documented, have been found on the eastern slope of the Anabar uplift. The country rock is mostly Sinian (Upper Pro-

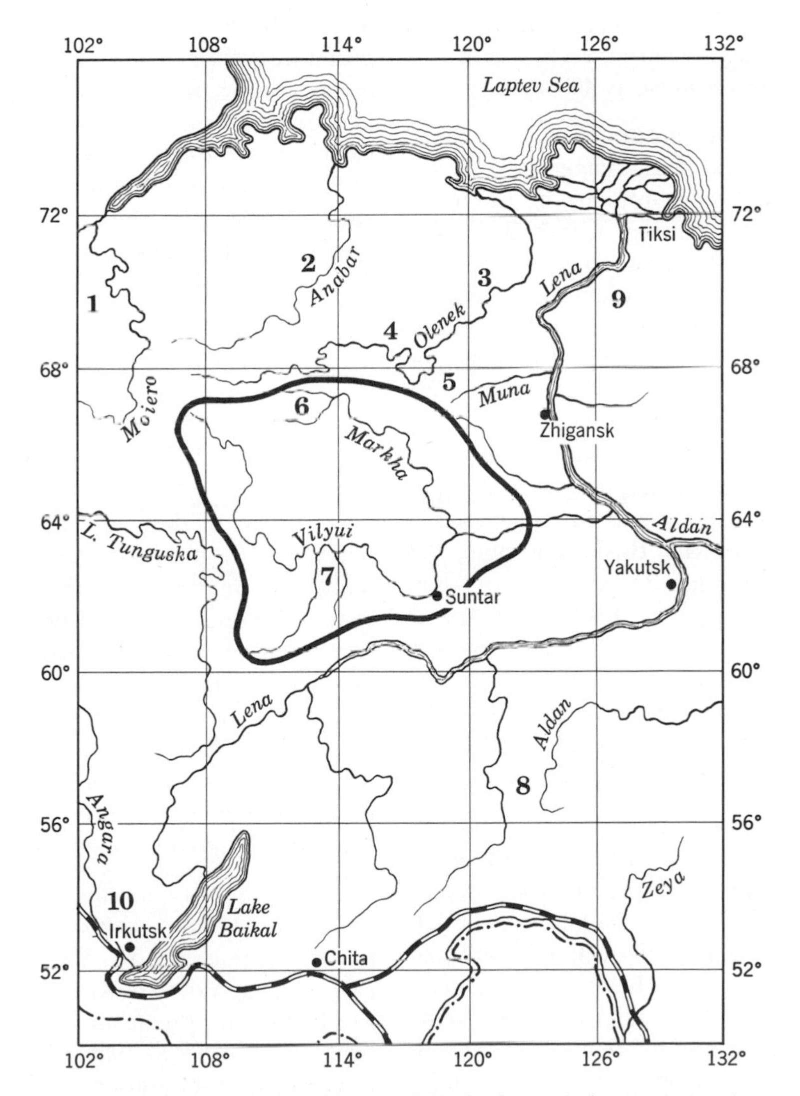

Fig. 8.4 Approximate distribution of kimberlites of the U.S.S.R. The main economic diamond deposits (alluvials and pipes) are within the heavy line. 1. Maimecha-Kotui province; 2. Anabar group; 3. Lower Olenek group; 4. Middle Olenek group; 5. Upper Muna group; 6. Daldyn–Alakit group; 7. Malaya Batuobiya group; 8. Aldan group; 9. Lower Lena alluvials; 10. East Sayan province.

terozoic) dolomite. In one body—a vertical pipe 40 × 80 meters in area that has yielded a few diamonds—the central part of the breccia is occupied by olivine-melilitite. Nodules of micaceous peridotite are among the inclusions.

In this same region, between the rivers Anabar and Olenek, the discovery of a group of alkalic complexes ranging from nepheline-syenites to nepheline-basalts (35 per cent SiO_2) has lately been reported (Erlich, 1964). They intrude Sinian strata and the one age determination yet available, by K:Ar on mica, is 465 m.y.

Lower Olenek group. Ten or more kimberlite pipes and some dykes are known in the lower regions of the river Olenek, mostly cutting Cambrian limestone. Secondary alteration processes are much less marked in them than in any other Russian kimberlites, and the content of fresh olivine ranges from 13 to 28 per cent. Inclusions of crystalline schists are frequent, together with feldspar, hornblende, and garnet (almandine) grains derived from their trituration. Eclogite nodules have been found in the Obnazhennaya pipe. In the Ruslovaya pipe, 0.4 per cent almandine is present but only 0.003 per cent pyrope. Like the pipes of the Aldan group (discussed later) there is a higher than average content of pyrope (0.22 per cent), chrome-spinellids (0.05 per cent) and chrome-diopside (0.036 per cent), but diamond is exceedingly rare.

Middle Olenek group. By contrast, the many (? close on 100) kimberlites on the middle reaches of the Olenek (including the basins of the rivers Omonos, Ukukit, and Merchimden), all cutting Cambrian strata, are much more heavily altered than those of most other regions, fresh olivine being virtually non-existent. Ilmenite always exceeds pyrope, in some bodies forming 2.5 per cent of the rock; and first-generation phlogopite is relatively abundant. Nodules of pyrope (exceptionally up to 5–10 centimeters), xenocrysts of pyroxene, and large zircon crystals are noteworthy. The intrusions form dykes, usually of massive kimberlite and only rarely showing inclusions of the country rock; bodies of lenticular outcrop, from 35–45 meters to 100 × 20 meters, with up to 10 per cent of inclusions usually found in the contact zones; and pipes which are circular to ellipsoidal in plan, from 25 × 8 meters to 200 × 100 meters, some of them vertical but others plunging at 60–80° commonly with from 40 to 90 per cent of their mass formed by xenoliths. They tend to be disposed in groups of from four to seven pipes in an area of 0.5–3.0 kilometers^2. In some instances the surrounding flat-bedded limestones have been forced up periclinally along the contact, with a kimberlite-limestone breccia in the endo-contact zone. Sometimes the dykes are carbonatitized. The content of diamonds is well below a commercial tenor.

Upper Muna group. Nine or more pipes cutting Upper Cambrian and Lower Ordovician dolomites in the upper reaches of the River Muna differ from the kimberlites of adjacent regions in having a very low content of ilmenite (the highest value noted is 0.07 per cent) and a rather high tenor of unaltered olivine (0.4–7.9 per cent). Pyrope is low (average 0.09 per cent) but many of the bodies are high in perovskite (up to 0.11 per cent). Kimberlite dykes have not been recorded. The horizontal sediments may show an upward flexure (4–6°) around the pipes, and they are cut by fissures bearing calcite, sepiolite, aragonite, magnetite, pyrite and celestine.

Daldyn–Alakit group. More than 50 pipes ranging up to 400–700 meters in diameter are now known in and around the Markha basin, the scene of the initial kimberlite discovery in 1954. The country rock is Ordovician limestone or dolomite. Most of the pipes are tuff-breccias essentially devoid of unaltered olivine, but some contain many blocks of massive kimberlite. About one in ten of the intrusions is of compound type, exhibiting either two adjacent channelways or repeated introductions of material through the same chimney. The most noteworthy of these twin diatremes is Udachnaya (Fig. 8.5), an important source of diamonds. Here the west pipe is formed of tuff and breccia in which unaltered olivine is non-existent, and the east pipe a breccia of massive kimberlite blocks which contain up to 14 per cent fresh olivine. The tenor of ilmenite and

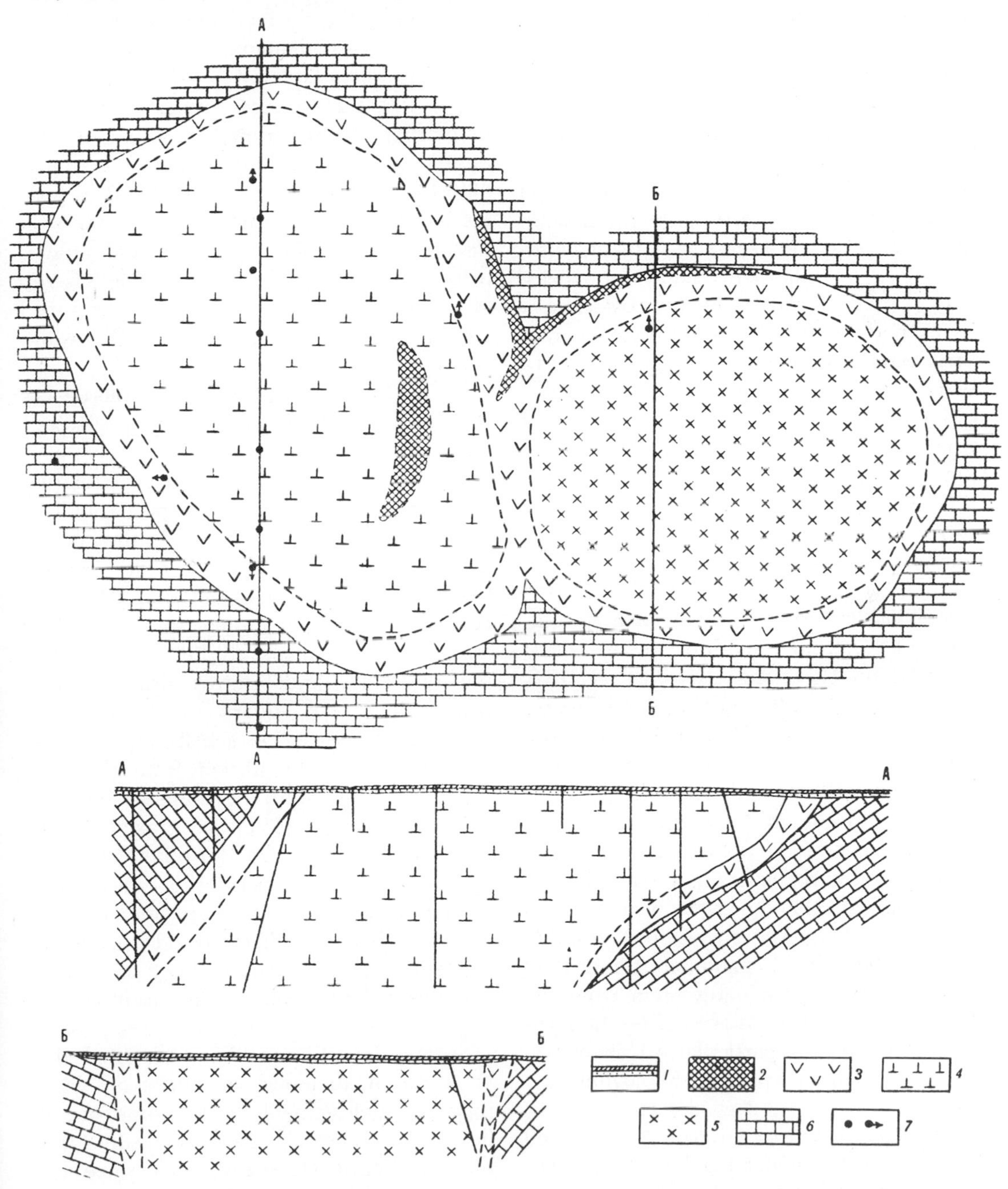

Fig. 8.5 Plan and section of the Udachnaya pipes. *1.* eluvial kimberlite; *2.* intensively altered clayey kimberlite; *3.* yellow carbonated kimberlite; *4.* blue-gray kimberlite breccia; *5.* massive kimberlite; *6.* limestone country-rock; *7.* drill holes. Maximum diameter about 850 meters (Bobrievich, 1959).

pyrope is much the same in each diatreme, the two minerals varying sympathetically with ilmenite consistently predominating. In this region kimberlite dykes are rare, but the Polunochnaya pipe has in plan an outline like a knobkerry with a 9–10 meter dyke extending southwestwards for 220 meters from a circular chimney.

Among the 23 pipes for which petrographical details are available, 17 contain xenoliths of crystalline schists and granulites of Basement origin. The Zarnitsa pipe and a few others carry garnet-pyroxene-granulites, kyanite-eclogites, plagioclase-eclogites, grossular-pyroxene-kyanite rocks, and related enclaves. In the Udachnaya twins nodules of garnet-peridotite, lherzolite, harzburgite, enstatitite, and hornblendite are also present. The greatest range of crystalline xenoliths is reported from the pipes richest in diamond. Few pipes contain less than 40 per cent xenoliths and the proportion may reach 90 per cent, enclaves of the local country-rocks (limestones and traps) being most common. Diamond drilling at the Udachnaya pipe was interrupted by a flaming outburst of gas from a depth of 360 meters, of composition H_2 50–90, CH_4 30.4, N_2 12.8, $C_2H_6^+$ 3.7, O_2 1.9, undetermined hydrocarbons 0.3, He 0.032, Ar 0.016 per cent. (Inflammable gas has also been encountered in South African kimberlites: whether it is of crustal origin, or derived from the mantle like the comparable gas in dunites and carbonatites, is debatable; but it is significant that the argon: nitrogen ratio is extremely low.) Strong sodium chloride brines (150 g/liter) encountered in drilling the same pipe presumably stem from the Cambrian country rocks. The Daldyn-Alakit kimberlites, particularly Udachnaya, support a diamond plant at Shologontzy.

Malaya Batuobiya group. At least 60 pipes lie in the upper reaches of the river Vilyui, many being in the drainage basin of its tributary, the Malaya Batuobiya. The country rock is Ordovician limestone, locally capped by Carboniferous and Permo-Triassic red beds and tuffs and by Lower Lias sandstones and conglomerates. Large sill intrusions of the Siberian traps are ubiquitous. The best-known pipe is Mir, the most publicized diamantiferous diatreme in the Soviet Union, on which is based the new diamond town of Mirnyi. This has been explored by diamond drilling to 1200 meters. No significant chemical or petrographical variation is found to this depth, save for a high tenor of sodium chloride (up to 3.80 per cent Cl, 3.28 per cent Na_2O) at approximately 700–800 meters. Here halite, epsomite, and anhydrite occur in the kimberlite. They have clearly been introduced from lenses of Upper Cambrian evaporites in the wall rocks.

Throughout the 1200 meters explored in the Mir pipe olivine rarely exceeds 0.01 per cent. Ilmenite and pyrope vary sympathetically but are somewhat irregularly distributed—in 61 samples respectively averaging 0.75 and 0.51 per cent. In the immediately adjacent pipe Sputnik, however, the tenor is only 0.06 per cent and 0.03 per cent. Traces of almandine are present in almost all specimens studied from these two diatremes, and Sputnik also carries a fair amount of quartz and feldspar. Nodules of crystalline schists and granulites are practically absent from the Mir pipe, but a xenolith of diamond-bearing eclogite believed to be of crustal origin has been reported. On the other hand inclusions of garnet-peridotite, enstatitite, dunite, and serpentinite are much more common than elsewhere. In 11 specimens of garnet-peridotite the content of pyrope averages 5.8 per cent, ranging up to 16 per cent.

Several investigators have reported the presence of diamond in limestone wall-rock and inclusions of the Mir pipe; and it has been argued by Botkunov (1964), a mine geologist at Mirnyi, that since the country rock within a few meters of the pipe margin, and the abundant limestone xenoliths, sometimes carry as much diamond as clean kimberlite though traversed by not more than 10 per cent of kimberlite veinlets, it is unlikely that the diamonds can have originated at great depth. This extraordinary claim is said to be founded on sampling statistics from mining work, but no supporting data have been published. At Mir, as at Premier and Kimberley in South Africa, the tenor of diamonds in the kimberlite decreases with depth.

Aldan group. In the extreme south of the Siberian platform, bordering the Aldan shield, a small group of kimberlite dykes and pipes cuts Lower Cambrian strata. These intrusions are somewhat unusual in carrying very numerous xenoliths of metamorphic rocks derived from the Archaean Basement, which locally lies at a depth of no more than 160 meters, and heavy minerals derived from the Basement (particularly hornblende, almandine, rutile, sillimanite and tourmaline) are commoner than elsewhere. The pipes (and adjacent alluvials) are not diamond bearing, but they are characterized by a particularly high content of pyrope (average 0.72 per cent), chrome-spinellids and chrome-diopside. On the other hand there is an almost complete absence of ilmenite. Olivine is wholly serpentinized. In the same region (the basin of the river Chompolo, a tributary of the Aldan) stocks and laccoliths of syenite and associated quartz porphyry invade Jurassic sediments and are apparently coeval with the Mesozoic deformation of the Aldan shield.

Kimberlite dyke rocks, and two pipes, are also found associated with at least two of a half dozen, zonal–concentric, alkalic complexes, of late Sinian date, occurring at widely separated localities in the far east of the Aldan shield. Neither diamond nor pyrope has been reported from the kimberlites, which are not brecciated; but the associated carbonatite contains moissanite. Potassium:argon age determinations on these massive kimberlites (648, 699 m.y.) agree well with uranium:lead ages on the central complexes (Arbarastakh, Ingilitsky).

Lower Lena region. Along the lower reaches of the river Lena, on its west bank, widespread alluvial diamonds have recently been found, particularly in Lower and Upper Jurassic basal conglomerates. The accompanying pyrope grains still bear kelyphitic shells and have obviously not travelled far, but the parent kimberlites have not yet been discovered. Alluvial diamonds found in a Lower Jurassic conglomerate of the Priverkhoyansk foot-hills may be from the same source.

The Maimecha–Kotui province. The great alkalic-ultrabasic petrographic province of the Maimecha-Kotui district, bordering the Caledonian metamorphic rocks of the Taimyr peninsula, lies in the extreme north of the Krasnoyarsk administrative region, to the west of northern Yakutia. Here the Guli (Gulinsky) intrusion, with seven or eight phases ranging from dunite to nepheline-syenite, covers an area of 2000–3000 square kilometers: it has two cores or plugs and many dykes of carbonatite. A dozen much smaller masses, a few kilometers or less in diameter, are of comparable mineralogy, sometimes with platinoids occurring in the dunites. Among them the Kugda complex of alkalic and nepheline syenites carries very minor phases of melilite-monticellite-olivine rocks chemically akin to kimberlite. The country rock is everywhere Sinian and Cambrian dolomite, and (according to K:Ar dates on phlogopite) the intrusions are probably of Lower Permian age. Accompanying these complexes there is a widely developed effusive phase of alkalic–ultrabasic rocks, locally presenting a thickness exceeding 1500 meters of lava-form and tuffaceous meimechite, a rock type comparable to kimberlite in its richness in magnesian olivine, phlogopite, and perovskite but differing from it in the absence of pyrope. (For a chemical comparison, see Table 8.1.) This effusive phase is interbedded with shales bearing an Upper Permian to Lower Triassic flora. Some dykes of alnöite carry inclusions of hypersthene-granulite and anorthosite-gneiss derived from depth, but these xenoliths are extremely rare (Butakova and Egorov, 1962; Sheinmann *et al.*, 1961).

The discovery in 1959 of three small alluvial diamonds accompanied by detrital pyrope and chrome-diopside led to the recognition two years later of the first kimberlite-breccia pipe (Krasnoyarsk) in this region. Two more pipes and 10 kimberlite dykes were found in 1962. The Krasnoyarsk "pipe" is a composite diatreme, about 350 by 350 meters, and contains more than 50 per cent xenoliths, dominantly dolomite. The xenoliths range from grit-size to tens of meters in diameter. They include not only traps but also monchiquites, nepheline-syenites, and tinguaites, from which it is deduced that the kimberlite is younger than the youngest rocks of the central complexes; but locally the kimberlites include patches of eruptive breccia with a carbonatitized alkalic syenite cement. Rare inclusions (1–2 centimeters) of metamorphic gneisses have undoubtedly been brought up from the Basement, which lies at a depth of about 3000 meters. Xenolith-free kimberlite consists of about 50 per cent of phenocrysts of olivine and phlogopite with rarer (<1 per cent) pyrope and chrome-diopside, set in a wholly carbonatized groundmass. The dykes, 1–7 meters thick, are formed mainly of massive micaceous kimberlite in which both xenoliths and grains of pyrope and chrome-diopside are rare. Apparently diamond has not yet been recognized *in situ* (Makhlayev and Surina, 1963). This province, described by Surina (1966) illustrates more clearly than any other the intimate connection between kimberlites and alkalic–ultrabasic central complexes with carbonatites.

C. Other Russian Kimberlites

East Sayan. Rather widespread alluvial diamonds were found in the late 1950's in the southwest part of the Siberian platform, in the basins of the rivers Biryusa, Uda (Chuna), Iya, and Oka. The country rocks are principally Lower Palaeozoic strata overlain by Jurassic sediments and traps. Two small dykes of micaceous kimberlite, only 20 centimeters wide, were discovered in the middle reaches of the river Oka in 1959, the heavy concentrates from which yielded diamond, chromite, pyrope, and pyrochlore; and a pyrope-free pipe (Yuzhnaya) has been located cutting Upper Proterozoic schists on the river Belaya Zima. Detrital pyrope is present in continental sandstones of Upper Devonian age but has not been found in older rocks. Although this kimberlite province is as yet little known, it appears to be more ancient than the Yakutian pipes. It may be contemporary with the Caledonian central complexes of nepheline-syenite, carbonatite, and alkalic ultrabasics of the East Sayan mountain-land to the south, and with the Devonian alkalic basalts of Minusinsk (Pecherskii, 1965), in which at least one basaltic breccia pipe carries xenoliths of peridotite, pyroxenite, and sparse grains of pyrope (Kryukov, 1964).

Ukraine. Minute alluvial diamonds have recently been found in an ilmenite-zircon sand of Tertiary age derived mainly from the Ukraine-Voronezh shield (Kashkarov and Polkanov, 1964), and several earlier discoveries in this region are on record. No local kimberlites are known; but two groups of nephelinic intrusions occur in the southeast Ukraine, respectively dated at 1300 to 1600 and 380 m.y., and camptonite-monchiquite dykes in the former suite carry inclusions of crystalline schists and, rarely, plagioclase-eclogite.

Urals. More than 200 diamonds had been found at scattered localities on the western slopes of the middle Urals before 1914, and alluvial deposits were worked on a very small scale from 1941 to 1944. The sources of the stones is not known, but because pyrope is found in Devonian sandstones they may stem from some undiscovered phase of the Caledonian alkalic complexes in this region.

Tadzhikistan. A group of 20 pipes and numerous dykes of camptonite, monchiquite, and "picritic porphyrite" has lately been found at south Gissar in central Tadzhikistan, cutting Hercynian granite. The pipes, from 10 by 5 meters to 250 by 60 meters in plan, are filled by a breccia of analcime-basaltoids (monchiquites), and more rarely picritic porphyrites resembling some massive kimberlites of Siberia. Xenoliths are very abundant and comprise fragments of the surrounding granitoids, of ultrabasics such as pyroxenites (±olivine) and phlogopitized peridotites, and of garnetiferous (almandine-pyrope) granulites from the Basement. Xenocrysts of olivine, chrome-diopside and garnet (unspecified) are found, but diamond is not known (Mushkin *et al.*, 1964).

D. The Age of the Yakutian Kimberlites

The prevailing country rocks cut by the Siberian kimberlites range from Sinian to Ordovician in age. In the Obnazhennaya pipe (Lower Olenek group), a xenolith bearing the rostrum of an Upper Jurassic or Lower Cretaceous belemnite has been found, and two other pipes here cut and metasomatize Permian sandstones. In the Middle Olenek group the Aerogeologicheskaya pipe intersects fossiliferous sediments of the Upper Lias. In the Daldyn-Alakit region, however, several observers have reported that pyrope and related minerals occur in conglomerates of supposed Permian age, and it has been claimed that Permian terrigenous deposits, dated by pollen analysis, overlie kimberlite at the Sytykan pipe. Although the validity of the latter conclusions has been assailed by Mikheyenko and Nenashev (1962), the field evidence suggests that there were periods of kimberlite volcanism both in Palaeozoic and Mesozoic times.

Radiometric dates on minerals from these kimberlites, published by Mikheyenko and Nenashev (1962), by Gerling and Matveeva (1964), and by Sarsadskikh and others (1966) are listed in Table 8.2. The ages show a very wide spread, reminiscent of that of the Siberian traps which, until recently thought to be Permo-Triassic, are now accepted as ranging from early Caledonian to Mesozoic (Davidson, 1964). The phlogopite of the Obnazhennaya pipe (1, 2) has an average age of 195 m.y. (Upper Triassic), although on palaeontological grounds it seems the pipe cannot be older than Upper Jurassic. Uncertainties which attach to pyroxene ages because of argon occluded at the time of crystallization suggest that the very high result obtained on chrome-diopside from this pipe (7) is unreal; but the high ages obtained on eclogite and peridotite nodules from Obnazhennaya (5, 6) can be accepted as confirmation of the xenolithic nature of these rocks. Other pipes in the Lower Olenek group give ages on phlogopite (3, 4) very much older than the Obnazhennaya kimberlite and older than their wall rocks. Similarly in the Middle Olenek region three analyzed phlogopites (8 to 10) pre-date the Cambrian country rocks. The mid-Permian ages of 246 m.y. determined on phlogopite from a pipe in the Anabar region, and 248 m.y. for one in the Prilensky (?Lower Olenek) district, relate to diatremes which carry intrusions of trap conventionally interpreted as mid-Upper Trias. The Mir pipe (403 m.y.) which cuts Ordovician limestone was initially thought to be late Mesozoic; but more recent studies on the stratigraphical distribution of heavy minerals have suggested a date older than mid-Carboniferous, with which the argon age agrees. The argon ages of the kimberlites in the Daldyn-Alakit region (350 m.y.) are in keeping with claims made on geological grounds that they are pre-Permian and post-Ordovician; but an ill-defined young date on olivine (17) is anomalous.

Although these data are somewhat difficult to interpret, two important conclusions can be drawn. First, the kimberlite diatremes in a single province may be of more than one age—a circumstance paralleled in South Africa (Davidson, 1966)

TABLE 8.2 Potassium: Argon Age Determinations on Kimberlite Diatremes

No.	Mineral	Pipe	Region	Age (m.y.)
1	Phlogopite	Obnazhennaya	Lower Olenek	185 ± 10
2	Phlogopite	Obnazhennaya	Lower Olenek	205 ± 10
3	Phlogopite	Chomur	Lower Olenek	652
4	Phlogopite	Nadezhnaya	Lower Olenek	865
5	Olivine from peridotite inclusion	Obnazhennaya	Lower Olenek	543 ± 70
6	Eclogite	Obnazhennaya	Lower Olenek	635
7	Chrome-diopside	Obnazhennaya	Lower Olenek	1410, 1490
8	Phlogopite-rich matrix	Flogopitaya	Middle Olenek	635
9	Phlogopite (0.1–1.0 mm)	Flogopitaya	Middle Olenek	678
10	Phlogopite (1.0–10.0 mm)	Flogopitaya	Middle Olenek	694
11	Phlogopite	Maiskaya	Anabar	246 ± 10
12	Phlogopite	Novinka	Muna	360 ± 10
13	Phlogopite	Komsomol'skaya	Muna	375 ± 15
14	Phlogopite	Mir	Batuobiya	403 ± 15
15	Phlogopite	Moskvichka	Alakit	350 ± 15
16	Phlogopite	Udachnaya	Daldyn	350 ± 15
17	Olivine (xenocryst)	Udachnaya	Daldyn	180 ± 70
18	Phlogopite	Molodo	? Lower Olenek	248 ± 10

References: 4, Milashev *et al.* (1963); 3, 8, 9, 10, Mikheyenko and Nenashev (1962); 5, 6, 7, Gerling and Matveeva (1964); others, Sarsadskikh *et al.* (1966).

and in West Africa (Bardet and Vachette, 1966). Second, in many instances potassium: argon dates obtained on phlogopite are older than the geological age of the kimberlite irruption. It is tempting to conclude that these phlogopite ages are unreal, attributable to sorption of argon; but since there is much evidence that potassium: argon dates on phlogopite are satisfactory for a wide range of igneous, metasomatic, and metamorphic rocks (Davidson, 1965, 1966), this assumption cannot be maintained. The only apparent alternative explanation is that the kimberlite diatremes were emplaced in the crust in two or more stages, initially as a massive magmatic rock which was later (sometimes very much later) brecciated and fluidized, and conveyed upwards to a higher level in a triturated, solid form by a flow of gases at a relatively low temperature. The initial period of emplacement may have been contemporary with carbonatite activity, as in the Meimecha-Kotui district. (In African and Australian diatremes of kimberlite, similar anomalously old ages are obtained on phlogopite. An extreme case, described by Edwards and Howkins (1966), is that of the richly diamantiferous Mwadui pipe in Tanzania where around 1000 feet of Cretaceous sediments occupy the crater of a kimberlite diatreme dated on phlogopite at 2035 m.y.). Perhaps the conditions in depth for successive periods of fluidization, involving a large release of gases from the mantle, were created as a consequence of the emission of the floods of plateau basalt that antedate the diatremes.

The low temperature of intrusion of this fluidized slurry is indicated not only by the retention of argon in the phlogopite but also by the absence of metamorphic effects other than occasional mild metasomatism in limestone xenoliths and wall rocks, and by the completely random magnetic orientation of the kimberlite breccias. The kimberlite breccia found in the pipes is always grossly admixed with country rocks and rocks from depth, and it appears that the garnet has been introduced from the breakdown of deep crustal garnet-peridotites, granulites, and eclogites (see Davidson, Chapter 10-IV). Meimechite lavas and tuffs from which high-pressure minerals are absent probably represent primary unadulterated kimberlite material, which reached the surface as a magma either of direct mantle origin or formed by refusion in depth of pre-existing primary kimberlite.

E. Conclusion

The kimberlites of Yakutia, like those of southern Africa, display interesting regional variations. Dykes are relatively more common in the outlying fields (Anabar, Olenek, Aldan) than in the central ones where pipes predominate, the latter lying at a somewhat higher stratigraphical level, and inclusions of the underlying Basement gneisses tend to be somewhat more abundant in bodies at the lower horizons. Conversely, diamonds are most abundant at the higher levels. Although two pipes side by side (e.g., Udachnaya, east and west) may differ greatly in their degree of serpentinization, the overall proportion of unaltered olivine tends to be consistently low in some regions (<0.01 per cent) and high in others (5–20 per cent). Pyrope and picroilmenite tend to vary sympathetically in a single diatreme, but the relative proportion differs greatly according to district, sometimes ilmenite predominating (Middle Olenek, Daldyn–Alakit, and Malaya Batuobiya), sometimes pyrope (Aldan, where pyrope is highest and ilmenite almost entirely absent). Assessed over 37 diamantiferous breccias, one finds a complete lack of any parallelism between the tenor of these minerals and that of diamond. The predominant morphological features of the diamonds also change from one field to another: for example, in the Malaya Batuobiya group 72 per cent are octahedra and 8 per cent rhombic dodecahedra (with 19 per cent transitional forms), and in Daldyn–Alakit 23 per cent octahedra and 62 per cent dodecahedra (15 per cent transitional forms). From these observations it seems apparent that the various groups of kimberlite breccias originate from separate and independent hearths, each with its own mineralogical and geochemical idiosyncrasies.

IV. KIMBERLITE PIPES OF NORTHEASTERN ARIZONA

K. D. Watson

A. Introduction

Diatremes, dikes, and flows of minette, monchiquite, trachybasalt, and limburgite are abundant in northeastern Arizona and adjacent parts of New Mexico and Utah (Fig. 8.6). Most of them lie within the Navajo and Hopi Indian reservations. They have been described by Gregory (1917), Williams (1936), Hack (1942), Balk and Sun (1954), and by Shoemaker, Roach, and Byers (1962). Those within the Hopi Buttes area (Fig. 8.6) are composed of monchiquite and limburgite and those occurring elsewhere are mainly minette and trachybasalt. Lying within this part of the Colorado Plateau are a few diatremes or pipes consisting of abundant xenoliths in a matrix rich in olivine and/or serpentine and wholly devoid of feldspar. Some of these rocks have been called kimberlite tuff (Balk, 1954; Balk and Sun, 1954) or kimberlite (Shoemaker, 1956; Shoemaker, Roach, and Byers, 1962). Although they differ from typical kimberlite in their lack of phlogopite and in some less important respects, the name is somewhat appropriate and is retained in this paper.

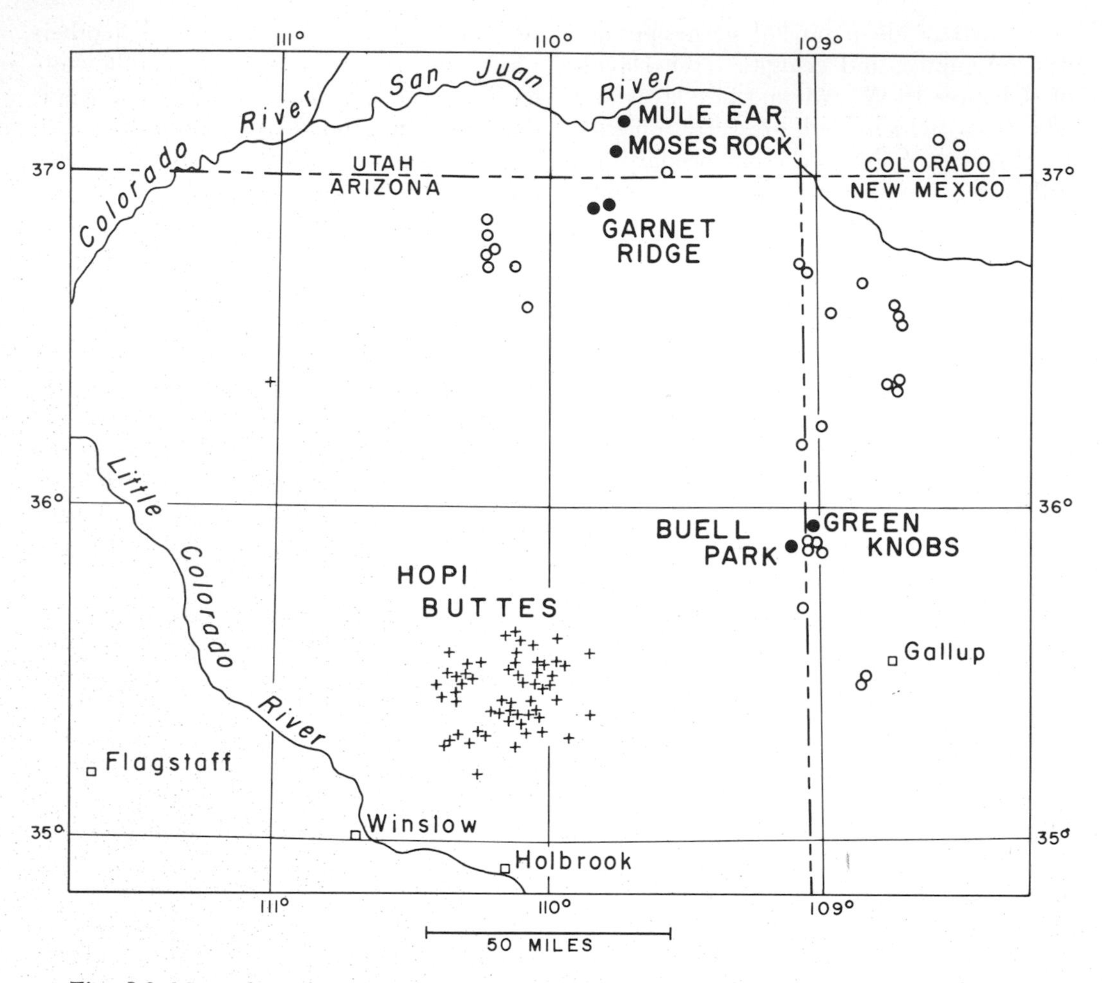

Fig. 8.6 Map of northeastern Arizona and adjacent parts of Utah, Colorado, and New Mexico showing distribution of kimberlite-serpentinite (black circles), minette-trachybasalt (open circles), and monchiquite-limburgite (crosses). Mainly after Shoemaker (1956) and Shoemaker, Roach, and Byers (1962).

B. Garnet Ridge

Rubble pipes, consisting of a heterogeneous assemblage of sedimentary and crystalline xenoliths in a serpentine-rich matrix, occur in a narrow zone extending along the Comb monocline in northeastern Arizona and southeastern Utah. These include four pipes at Garnet Ridge and the intrusive bodies at Moses Rock and Mule Ear (Fig. 8.6). A few serpentinite dikes and sills containing abundant inclusions also occur at Garnet Ridge and a similar sill has recently been found by J. Ziony (oral communication) about five miles south of Mexican Hat. The serpentine-rich nature of the pipes at Garnet Ridge was first recognized by Malde (1954, p. 618). Subsequently, a detailed description of the pipes, accompanied by maps, has been published by Malde and Thaden (1963, pp. 54–61).

Garnet Ridge, which owes its name to the presence of pyrope and almandine there, is a low oval butte about eight miles long. It consists of Jurassic sedimentary rocks which are pierced in four places by serpentinite pipes choked with xenoliths. One pipe is at the crest of the ridge and is about 1000 feet across; the other three are two miles northeast and lie within an area measuring 1500 by 4000 feet.

The pipes are irregular in plan view but have steeply dipping walls. The pipe shown in Fig. 8.7 is bounded in part by nearly vertical walls that are parallel to northwestward-trending joints.

The wallrocks of the pipes are generally unaltered and undeformed, except for widely spaced fractures. However, the rocks of the Carmel formation along the north edge of one pipe (Fig. 8.7) are folded and cut by reverse faults along which serpentinite has been injected and the Entrada sandstone at the southeast corner of this pipe is closely fractured and bleached in a zone 20 feet wide (Malde and Thaden, 1963, p. 56).

The surfaces of xenoliths in contact with serpentinite are smoothed or polished and, in some cases, striated. The inclusions of fossiliferous Paleozoic limestone show no evidence of metamorphism. However, a few inclusions of black shale and red sandstone have been slightly bleached.

The serpentinite matrix of the pipes is a medium grayish green, fine grained, massive, somewhat friable rock. Microscopic and X-ray diffraction studies show that it consists mainly of serpentine, montmorillonite, calcite, and chlorite. Minor constituents include biotite, chromian diopside, pyropic garnet, magnetite, ilmenite, chromite, quartz, K-feldspar, plagioclase (mainly An_{20-25}), white mica, and amphiboles. Probably the micas, quartz, feldspars, and amphiboles represent disintegration products of xenoliths. Malde and Thaden report that in addition, melilite, zeolites, and gypsum have been identified (1963, p. 57) and that pseudomorphs after olivine have been recognized (1963, p. 58).

The xenoliths within the pipes include abundant blocks of Jurassic sedimentary rocks, many of which are extremely large (Fig. 8.7). Almost all of these blocks are from the Morrison formation and the San Rafael group. These blocks of sedimentary rocks, which are now in juxtaposition, were originally far apart stratigraphically and all have subsided to their present positions. The pipe shown in Fig. 8.7 includes a few blocks of dark gray shale containing "species of pelagic Foraminifera such as are found in the Mancos shale, stratigraphically about 1200 feet higher" (Malde and Thaden, 1963, p. 57).

The serpentinite between the large breccia blocks (Fig. 8.7) contains abundant sand-sized to boulder-sized xenoliths derived from the Paleozoic sedimentary rocks and the Precambrian igneous and metamorphic basement below. Most of the inclusions are of pebble size and are subangular; the larger inclusions, however, are well rounded and reach diameters of 10 feet. The fragments derived from the igneous and metamorphic basement have ascended at least 4000 feet (Malde and Thaden, 1963, p. 56). They are predominantly granite gneisses, granites, and amphibolites. They include also granulites of gabbroic composition (probably the source of some of the garnet found in the colluvium and alluvium at Garnet Ridge), peridotites, serpentine-actinolite-carbonate rocks, pyroxenites, eclogites, and a great variety of other kinds of igneous and metamorphic rocks.

The eclogite inclusions are sparse and their presence was not recorded until fairly recently (Watson, 1960, pp. 2082–2083). Similar eclogite has been found by the writer among the xenoliths at Moses Rock and Mule Ear in Utah. The eclogites are medium- to fine-grained rocks in all of which bright green pyroxene and pink to red garnet are readily visible megascopically. In some inclusions, white lawsonite or an extremely fine-grained aggregate consisting mainly of zoisite derived therefrom, white mica, or an occasional crystal of rutile may also be seen megascopically. The eclogite inclusions range in density from 3.3 to 3.6. Commonly they consist of about two thirds pyroxene and one third garnet, although some are richer in garnet, and others are much richer in pyroxene

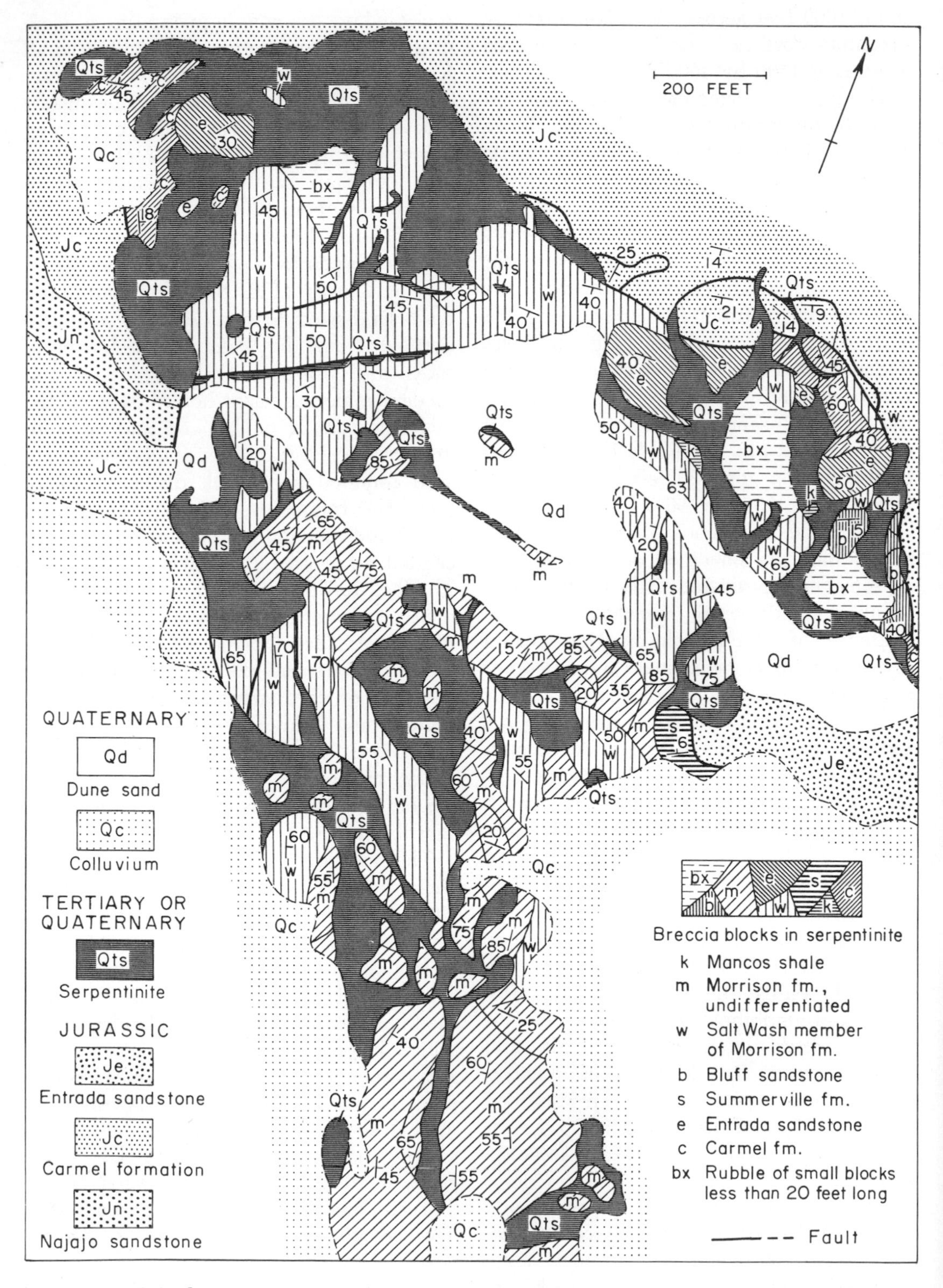

Fig. 8.7 Geologic map of serpentinite pipe, Garnet Ridge, Arizona. After Malde and Claus (in Witkind and Thaden, 1963). Malde and Claus map the northernmost part of the serpentinite as extrusive.

and appropriately could be named pyroxenite (Table 8.3). Most eclogite inclusions are essentially massive, but some show a distinct alignment of the pyroxene prisms.

Chemical analyses of samples of pyroxene from three eclogite inclusions show that it is essentially diopsidic jadeite ranging approximately from 60 to 75 per cent $NaAlSi_2O_6$. Chemical analyses of samples of garnet from three inclusions reveal that it is essentially pyropic almandine ranging approximately from 10 to 25 per cent $Mg_3Al_2Si_3O_{12}$ and from 65 to 70 per cent $Fe_3Al_2Si_3O_{12}$. O'Hara and Mercy have also determined that the pyroxene is exceptionally rich in jadeite and that the garnet is rich in almandine (M. J. O'Hara, written communication, 1965). A chemical analysis of one sample of the white mica, whose textural relations clearly indicate that it is primary, shows that it is a phengite, unusually rich in sodium and calcium.

Coleman, Lee, Beatty, and Brannock (1965, p. 485) have divided eclogites into the following groups, based on mode of occurrence: Group A, inclusions in kimberlites, basalts, or layers in ultramafic rocks; Group B, bands or lenses in migmatite gneissic terrains; Group C, bands or lenses within alpine-type metamorphic rocks, including glaucophane schists.

The pyroxene in Garnet Ridge eclogite differs markedly from those of other eclogites for it is much richer in jadeite than those of Group C and very much richer than those of Groups A and B (Coleman, et al., 1965, p. 496). The pyrope content of the garnet is within the range characteristic of Group C and less than the ranges of Groups A and B (Coleman et al., 1965, p. 499). Regardless of the disparity in composition between the minerals of Garnet Ridge and Group B eclogites, the association of eclogite nodules along with abundant xenoliths of granite gneiss and granite at Garnet Ridge may suggest that they are derived from eclogite lenses occurring in a migmatitic granite gneiss basement. However, the fact that similar granite gneiss and granite inclusions occur in abundance without eclogite in minette diatremes nearby does not favor this suggestion. An alternative suggestion is that the eclogite has been derived from a part of the deeper crust or even the upper mantle where penetrated locally by ultramafic material.

TABLE 8.3 Mineralogical Composition of Eclogite from Garnet Ridge, Arizona (percentage by volume)

	1	2	3	4	5	6	7	8
Clinopyroxene	48.2	88.3	92.9	46	51	54	59	62
Garnet	43.2	9.8	5.0	36	29	35	33	33
Rutile	3.9	1.5	0.7	4	3	4	3	5
Lawsonite and altered lawsonite	4.1	0.1	0.5	14	17	2	5	tr
Mica	...	...	...	...	...	4	...	...
Apatite	0.5	...	...	...	...	...	...	...
Pyrite, hematite, and goethite	0.1	0.3	0.9	...	...	1	tr	

Moses Rock and Mule Ear in Utah are similar in most respects to the xenolith-choked serpentinite intrusives at Garnet Ridge. Moses Rock, which is being studied intensively at present by T. McGetchin of California Institute of Technology, is sickle-shaped, dike-like in part, and extends for about five miles in a north-south direction. It is emplaced in sedimentary rocks of Permian age. Mule Ear, which is being investigated by H. J. Moore of the United States Geological Survey, measures approximately 2000 feet by 5000 feet in plan. It is emplaced in rocks of the Cutler formation (Permian) and Moenkopi and Chinle formations (Triassic) and contains large inclusions of Mancos shale (late Cretaceous).

C. Buell Park

At Buell Park, Arizona (Fig. 8.6), Permian sedimentary rocks of the Cutler formation and DeChelly sandstone, which

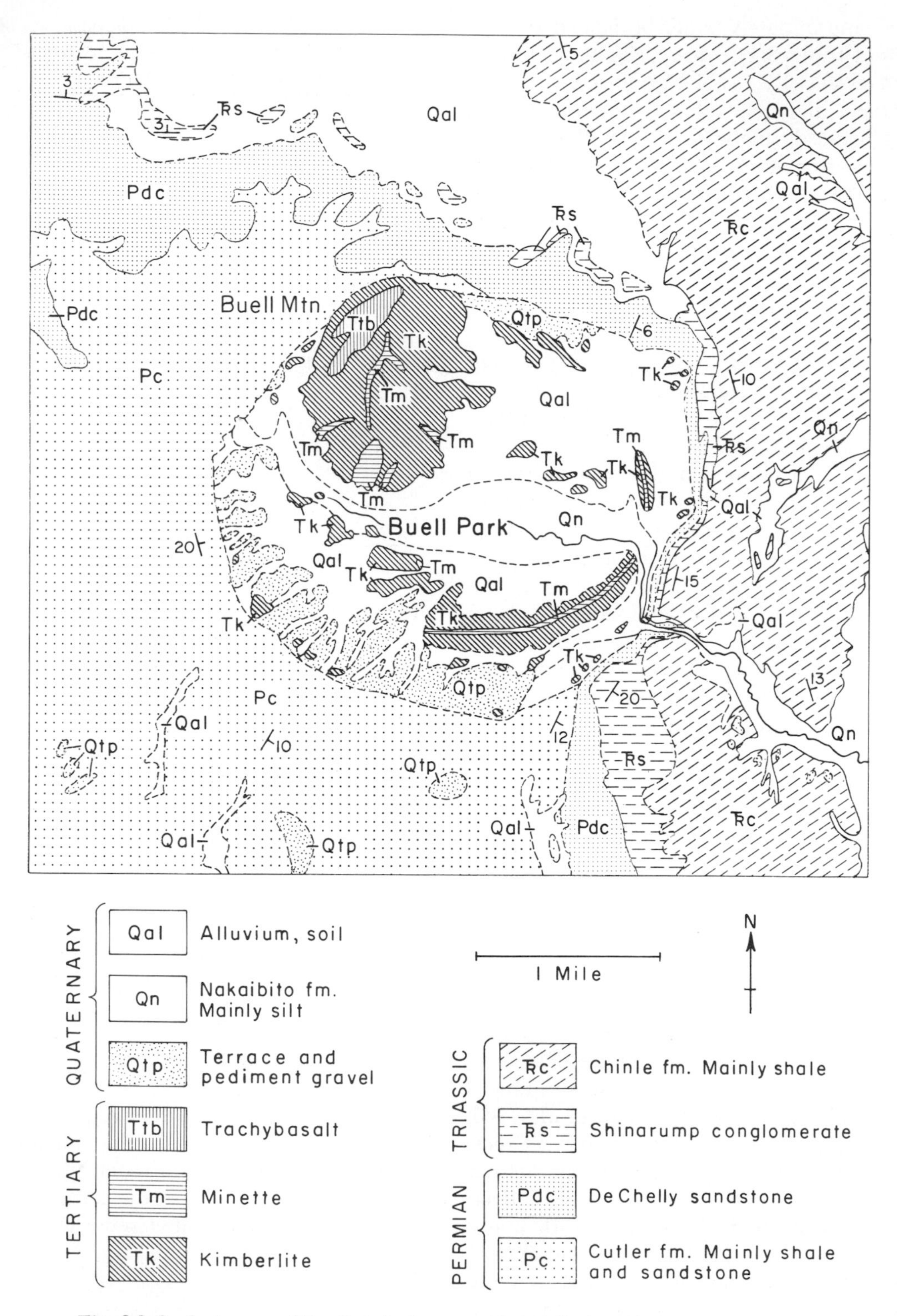

Fig. 8.8 Geologic map of Buell Park, Arizona. After Balk (in Allen and Balk, 1954).

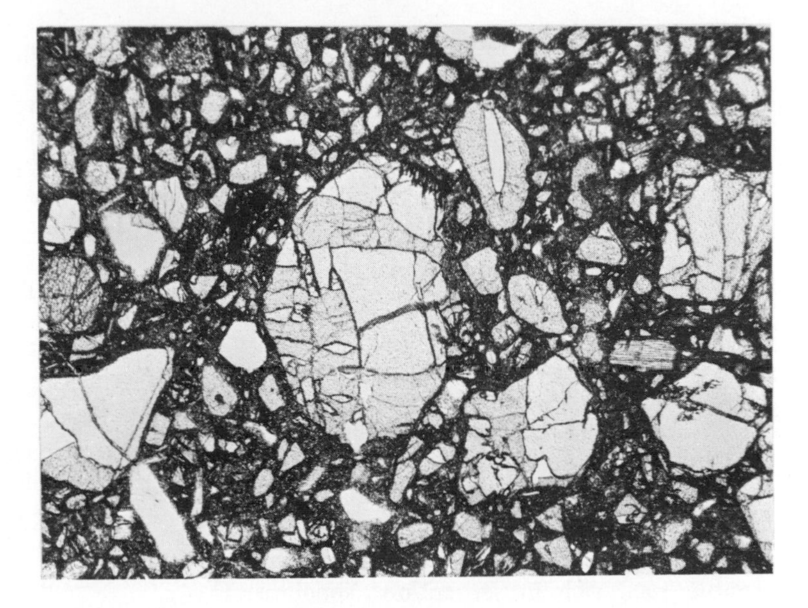

Fig. 8.9 Photomicrograph of kimberlite tuff, Buell Park, Arizona. Crystals of partly serpentinized olivine and of enstatite and occasional fragments of quartzite in fine-grained matrix rich in serpentine. ×22.

are exposed in the Defiance uplift, are intruded by kimberlite. The geology of Buell Park, modified slightly from Balk's map (1954), is shown in Fig. 8.8. Balk mapped the kimberlite as two units—kimberlite tuff and lapilli tuff. These two rock types probably grade into each other and they differ mainly by the presence of a greater proportion of xenoliths in the latter (Balk and Sun, 1954, p. 100, 103).

The kimberlite tuff is a purplish-brown or olive-green rock consisting of a fine-grained matrix containing innumerable fragments that are mainly light gray fine-grained quartzite. The matrix is made up of olivine (Fo_{91-93}), enstatite, chromian diopside, pyrope, magnetite, titanclinohumite, ilmenite, apatite, and abundant serpentine (Balk and Sun, 1954, pp. 100–101) (Fig. 8.9). The olivine, which occurs as anhedral or subhedral grains, is either fresh or altered to serpentine or iron oxide. Buell Park or its vicinity is probably the source of the garnet in which Rosenfeld and Chase (1961, pp. 528–530) noted pronounced piezobirefringent haloes surrounding inclusions of other minerals.

A chemical analysis of kimberlite tuff from Buell Park (Balk and Sun, 1954, p. 102) is listed in Table 8.4 and average compositions of kimberlites, compiled by Nockolds (1954, p. 1023), are included for comparison. Balk and Sun (1954, p. 101) attribute the high silica content to the presence of small xenoliths of fine-grained

TABLE 8.4 Chemical Analyses of Kimberlite

	1	2	3	4
SiO_2	47.50	35.00	35.02	36.33
TiO_2	0.08	0.10	1.22	1.89
Al_2O_3	1.38	1.70	3.90	5.09
Fe_2O_3	4.34	5.35	5.15	7.43
FeO	2.37	2.92	4.14	3.40
MnO	0.12	0.15	0.06	0.10
MgO	31.26	38.53	31.29	26.63
CaO	0.65	0.80	6.80	6.78
Na_2O	0.11	0.14	0.34	0.37
K_2O	0.37	0.46	1.05	2.43
H_2O+	10.88	13.41	7.43	7.25
H_2O-	1.15	1.42	...	...
P_2O_5	0.02	0.02	0.87	0.66
CO_2	0.00	0.00	2.73	1.64
Total	100.23	100.00	100.00	100.00

1. Kimberlite tuff, Buell Park, Arizona (Balk and Sun, 1954, p. 102).
2. Kimberlite tuff, Buell Park, Arizona. Analysis 1 recast with silica reduced to 35 per cent.
3. Average of 10 "basaltic" kimberlites (Nockolds, 1954, p. 1023).
4. Average of four "micaceous" kimberlites (Nockolds, 1954, p. 1023).

quartzite in the analyzed sample. Accordingly, the analysis has been recast with a silica content of 35 per cent and the result given in Table 8.4. It is seen that even after this adjustment the kimberlite of Buell Park has a considerably lower content of K_2O, TiO_2, P_2O_5, CaO, and CO_2 than the average kimberlites of Nockolds or those in eastern North America, Africa, Siberia, and Sweden, listed elsewhere in this volume (Tables 8.1, 8.5, 9.4, and 9.7).

The variety of kimberlite mapped as lapilli tuff by Balk (1954) underlies much of Buell Park and all of the small plug known as the Green Knobs lying about four miles to the northeast in New Mexico. It is light- to medium-green, fine-grained, friable rock rich in serpentine. Xenoliths are much more abundant than in kimberlite tuff and fresh olivine, chromian diopside, and garnet are less common.

The xenoliths found in the kimberlite consist not only of quartzites, which greatly predominate, but also of a wide variety of sedimentary, igneous, and other metamorphic rocks. They include granites, granite gneisses, diorites, amphibolites, metarhyolites, gabbros, and peridotites. Unlike Garnet Ridge, Moses Rock, and Mule Ear, Buell Park has yielded no eclogite nodules.

In a few places at Buell Park the contact between the kimberlite and the surrounding sandstone is exposed. Here the contact is vertical and the sandstone is devoid of contact effects. Irregular dikes of kimberlite extend from the main body for short distances into the adjacent sandstone.

Layering in the kimberlite dips gently southeastward near the northwest edge of the mass; farther to the east it is almost horizontal. This suggested to Balk and Sun (1954, p. 108) that the structure might resemble a stack of upright saucers, since such a saucerlike arrangement is well exhibited at the Green Knobs nearby. They attribute this structure to gradual compaction of the pyroclastic material upon expulsion of volatiles.

D. Mode of Emplacement

Explosion of gas-charged magma probably marks the initial stage in the formation of the kimberlite pipes. At Buell Park, the explosion may have reached the surface for olivine, pyrope, and chromian diopside are scattered over a wide area (Balk and Sun, 1954, p. 109). Shoemaker, Roach, and Byers, who have studied intensively the limburgite- and monchiquite-bearing diatremes in the Hopi Buttes (Fig. 8.6), point out that "some of the kimberlite vents in the northern part of the Navajo Reservation, in particular, show most clearly the initial stages of opening of the diatremes" (1962, p. 341). They summarize the inferred events as follows (p. 327):

"The initial opening of the diatremes is attributed to the rapid unmixing of gas from magma ascending through the crust along many separate fissures. Fractures were propagated to the surface hydraulically, and decompression waves were then propagated into the ascending magma and fissure walls as the gas was drained away. Enlargement of the channels of gas flow is attributed chiefly to spalling. The funnel-shaped orifices of the diatremes, which formed the craters at the surface, were in many cases later enlarged by slumping and collapse of the crater walls during subsidence of the materials filling the vent. The most important causes of the subsidence are probably stoping and assimilation of the porous vent debris by the underlying magma and displacement of the magma."

Shoemaker, Roach, and Byers (1962, p. 344) infer that the rock fragments spalled from the walls of the boiling magma column would become entrained in the moving gas and liquid to produce a complex fluidized system. As they point out (p. 344), "Intricate mixing, rounding, and polishing of debris derived from depth, particularly in some of the kimberlite-filled diatremes in the northern part of the Navajo Reservation . . . suggest fluidization."

E. Age

Although the age of some of the igneous rocks shown in Fig. 8.6 is well known, that of the serpentinite or kimberlite has not been established within narrow limits.

The monchiquite and limburgite in the vicinity of Hopi Buttes are known to be Pliocene for, in some places, limburgite tuffs and flows are intercalated with lacustrine and fluvial sedimentary rocks comprising part of the Bidahochi formation. The age of these sedimentary rocks, determined from their mammalian fauna, is Hemphillian (middle Pliocene) (Shoemaker, Roach, and Byers, 1962, p. 332).

Some geologists have assumed that minette and trachybasalt of the adjacent regions are also Pliocene. This is not an unreasonable assumption since transitional rock types, such as monchiquite containing abundant biotite and minette containing analcime in the groundmass, are present. Some bodies of minette definitely intrude the Mancos shale, which is late Cretaceous in age. Elsewhere in the area, other bodies penetrate the Chuska sandstone, which is regarded as Pliocene (?) (Allen and Balk, 1954, p. 100). The absolute age of a minette in Monument Valley, based upon the K-Ar ratio in its biotite, is 27 million years (late Oligocene or early Miocene) (J. Ziony, oral communication).

Blocks of Mancos shale have been recognized in kimberlite at Garnet Ridge (Fig. 8.7) (Malde and Thaden, 1963, p. 57) and at Mule Ear (J. Ziony, oral communication). Thus the maximum age of intrusion is late Cretaceous. Balk and Sun (1954, p. 108) and Shoemaker, Roach, and Byers (1962, p. 329) have assumed that the kimberlite and alkalic rocks are of about the same age. At Buell Park, however, (Fig. 8.8) kimberlite is somewhat older than minette for it is cut by a ring dike and several other dikes composed of minette. Moreover, at Outlet Neck, which lies about two miles east of Buell Park, the minette contains a xenolith of kimberlite 60 feet in diameter (Balk and Sun, 1954, p. 114).

V. GEOCHEMISTRY AND ORIGIN OF KIMBERLITE

by J. B. Dawson

A. Introduction

Kimberlite is an ultrabasic rock because it contains a high proportion of cafemic oxides relative to its silica content. Within these broad terms, however, kimberlites show a wide range of chemical composition, and there is a considerable range in the weight percentage of the individual oxides (see Fig. 8.10). This wide variation should be stressed, although values for the average basaltic and micaceous kimberlites have been calculated, and are compared with analysis of major rock types in Table 8.5.

B. Major Elements

1. Silica. Kimberlites are silica-undersaturated, the silica content of most being <40 per cent, with the concentration peak being about 30 per cent (see Fig. 8.10). It is generally considerably less than the value for other ultrabasic rocks. In some cases the depression of the silica content is a consequence of a high amount of combined water, but when it is less than 30 per cent it usually coincides with an increase in the calcite content of the rock.

2. Titania. Titania is present in unusually high amounts, the values being more

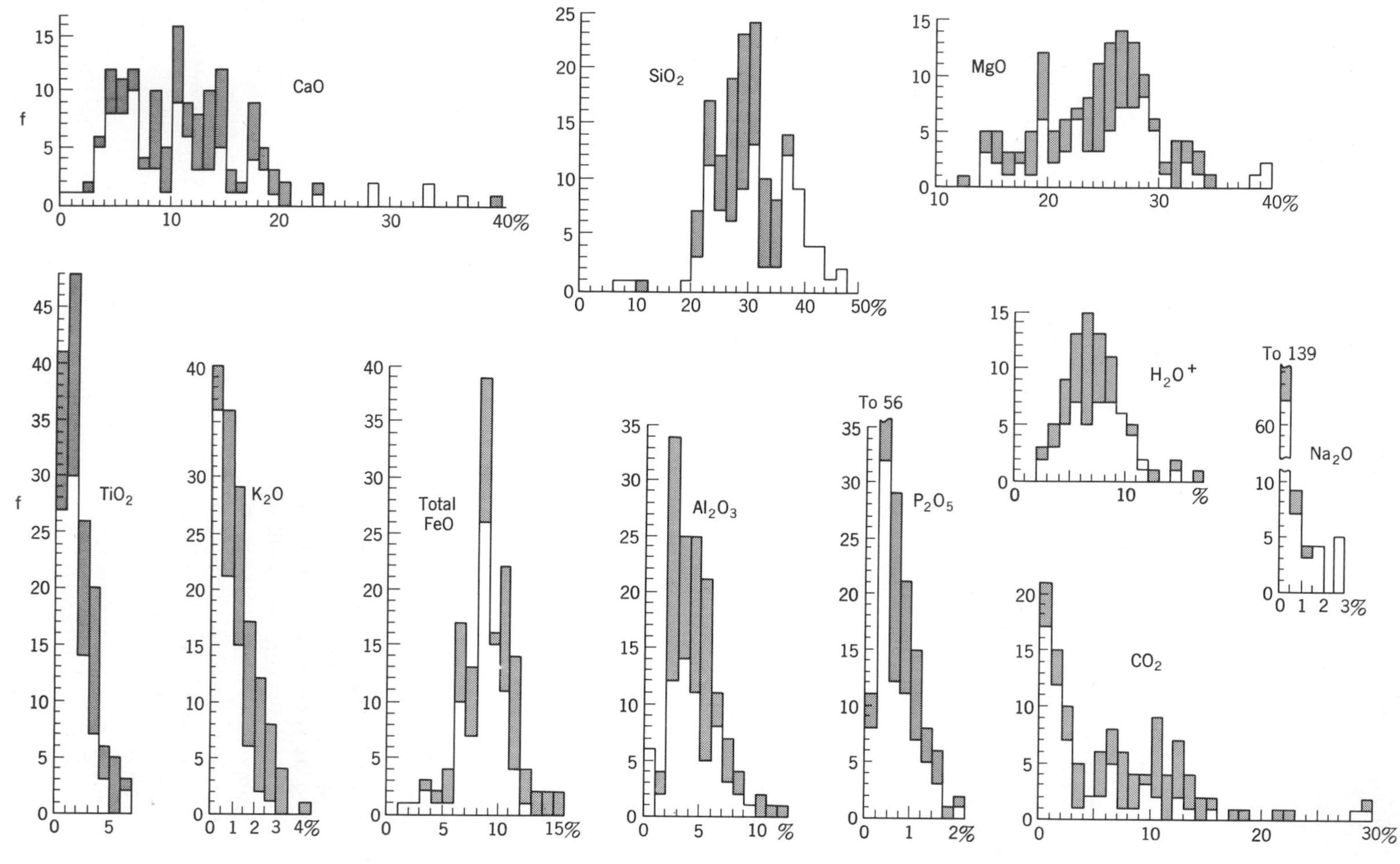

Fig. 8.10 Histogram showing frequency distribution of various oxides in basaltic kimberlites (in white) and micaceous kimberlites (in black). Compiled from data in Wagner, 1914; Daly, 1924; Martens, 1924; Williams, 1932; Holmes, 1936; Verhoogen, 1938; Van Bemmelen, 1949; Allen and Balk, 1954; McKinlay, 1954; Koenig, 1956; Dawson, 1962; Mathur, 1962; and Bobrievich et al., 1964 (which incorporates the analyses appearing in earlier Russian works).

in keeping with alkalic rocks and carbonatites; it is contained in ilmenite and perovskite.

3. Alumina. Alumina is very variable, but in most kimberlites is present in much greater amounts than those in ultrabasic rocks.

4. Iron. Iron occurs in amounts that are of the same order as those found in ultrabasic and basic rocks. However, the oxidation state of kimberlite is quite different, the Fe^{3+}/Fe^{2+} ratio being as high as 7.5, whereas in peridotites and dunites Fe^{3+}/Fe^{2+} is always <1. The Fe^{3+}/Fe^{2+} ratio of kimberlites varies directly with the water content, and must be assumed to result, at least in part, from the serpentinization. It is also of interest that the picroilmenite itself has a high content of ferric iron.

5. Magnesia. Magnesia is present in amounts varying from 8 to 35 per cent, the concentration peak lying in the range 25 to 30 per cent, which is considerably lower than for ultrabasic rocks. Combined with the relatively high iron content, this gives Mg/Fe values of 2.2 and 1.8 for basaltic and micaceous kimberlite compared with 3.4 for ultrabasic rocks. The magnesia and lime content of kimberlites is generally antipathetic.

6. Lime. Lime ranges in content from almost zero to nearly 40 per cent in some highly carbonatized varieties; in most analyses the value is considerably higher than in ultrabasic rocks. The lime content generally rises with an increase in CO_2 content, but it is always present in excess of the amount required to form calcite. While some is held in perovskite, apatite and clinopyroxene, it is of interest that the saturated equivalent of melilite (anorthite) usually appears in the kimberlite norm, and that the hydrated equivalent of melilite (calcium zeolites) occur in the groundmass of kimberlite. The presence of perovskite is also worthy of note, its presence being due to a combination of two factors: (a) the high lime content, preventing formation of rutile or anatase, and (b) a low silica content, favouring perovskite rather than sphene, its silica-saturated equivalent. Petrographically the association between high amounts of mica and calcite is very

TABLE 8.5 Major Element Content of Kimberlites and Other Igneous Rocks

	Ultrabasic	Basic	Intermediate	Felsic	Syenite	Basaltic Kimberlite	Micaceous Kimberlite
SiO_2	40.6	51.3	55.6	69.2	62.2	35.2	31.1
TiO_2	0.05	1.5	1.3	0.4	0.58	2.32	2.03
Al_2O_3	0.85	16.5	16.7	14.5	16.6	4.4	4.9
FeO	12.6	10.9	7.5	3.5	4.7	9.8	10.5
MnO	0.19	0.26	0.15	0.7	0.12	0.11	0.10
MgO	42.9	7.4	3.6	0.93	0.96	27.9	23.9
CaO	1.0	9.4	6.5	2.3	2.5	7.6	10.6
K_2O	0.04	0.99	2.8	4.0	5.4	0.98	2.1
Na_2O	0.77	2.6	4.1	3.7	5.4	0.32	0.31
H_2O+						7.4	5.9
CO_2	0.04	0.04	0.07	0.10		3.3	7.1
P_2O_5	0.04	0.32	0.36	1.6	1.8	0.72	0.66
Mg/Fe	3.4	0.5	0.4	0.3	0.15	2.2	1.8
K/Na	0.05	0.45	0.76	1.2	1.1	3.4	7.5

Figures for ultrabasic–felsic rocks calculated from data by Vinogradov (1962).
Figures for syenite calculated from data by Turekian and Wedepohl (1961).
Kimberlites from Dawson (1960).

marked, though this is not necessarily reflected chemically by covariance of K_2O and CaO.

7. Alkalies. In both basaltic and micaceous kimberlite the average soda content is just over 0.3 per cent (Table 8.5), which coincides with the histogram peaks. In kimberlite from Dutoitspan, South Africa, soda is present up to 2.7 per cent, coinciding with silica values of up to 47 per cent (Williams, 1932), and up to 1.4 per cent soda is found in some Russian kimberlites. These high soda values are atypical of kimberlite. In contrast to soda, *potash* is present in much greater amounts than is usual for ultrabasic rocks (Table 8.5), and results in a K/Na ratio of 3.4 for basaltic kimberlite which is much higher than that for ultrabasic rocks (0.05) or even felsic rocks (1.2). The K/Na ratio of 7.4 for micaceous kimberlite is of the order usually found only in leucite-bearing rocks.

8. Volatiles. The fixed *water* content of kimberlite is unusually high, the average being 7.7 per cent, and the *carbon dioxide* content is also considerably in excess of that found in ultrabasic rocks. The *phosphorus* content is much higher than that of ultrabasic rocks, being more like that of granitic or syenitic rocks. *Sulfur* is common in relatively small amounts, though 2.18 per cent SO_3 is reported from a Russian kimberlite (Milashev et al., 1963).

9. Differences between basaltic and micaceous kimberlites. Although the two kimberlite types can be distinguished petrographically, it is impossible to draw firm chemical boundaries as there is complete chemical gradation between them. However, comparison of the averages (Table 8.5) indicates *general* differences. Basaltic kimberlites tend to contain higher SiO_2, MgO and H_2O, whereas micaceous kimberlites contain more Al_2O_3, CaO, K_2O, and CO_2 due to their higher amounts of mica and calcite.

10. Normative minerals of kimberlite. The undersaturated nature of kimberlite is expressed in the norm by a high percentage of olivine while, in more extreme cases, leucite, kaliophilite, nepheline, and calcium orthosilicate may appear. Acmite appears in the norm of one of the soda-rich kimberlites from Dutoitspan, South Africa.

Summary

Kimberlite is an undersaturated ultrabasic rock. For a rock of such basicity, it contains unusually high amounts of K_2O, Al_2O_3, TiO_2, CaO, CO_2, P_2O_5, H_2O, and SO_3. Compared with other ultrabasic rocks it has a low Mg/Fe ratio, but unusually high K/Na and Fe^{3+}/Fe^{2+} ratios. These features serve to set kimberlites apart from other ultrabasic rocks.

C. Minor Elements

The minor elements of kimberlites are compared with those of other major rock types in Table 8.6. As in the case of the major elements, they can be divided into two contrasting suites:

1. A suite, comprising Co, Ni, Cr, and Ge, in which the elements occur in amounts characteristic of ultrabasic rocks. The high Cr, Ni, and Co are a result of their substitution for Mg and Fe^{2+}, and the low amount of Ge is in keeping with the low silica content of kimberlite. The Ni/Co ratio is that of ultrabasic rocks.
2. A suite of elements that occur in greater amounts than is usual for ultrabasic rocks. These elements are Li, B, Sc, V, Cu, Ga, Rb, Sr, Y, Zr, Cs, Nb, Ba, La, Ta, and Pb. The large amounts of Sc, V, and Cu reflect the high iron content, and the large amounts of Rb, Pb, Ba, and Cs are due to the large amounts of potassium. Similarly the large amounts of alumina are reflected by the elevated amount of Ga; that of Ca by high Sr, La, and Y content; and the large amounts of Nb and Ta are attributable to the high Ti content. In addition the Al/Ga, K/Rb, Ca/Sr and Nb/Ta ratios in kimberlites are quite different from other ultrabasic rocks. The concentrations of La,

TABLE 8.6 Trace Element Content of Kimberlites and Other Rocks

	Ultrabasic Rocks (1)	Basic Rocks (1)	Intermediate Rocks (1)	Felsic Rocks (1)	Syenite (2)	Carbonatite (3)	Yakutia Kimberlites (4)	Yakutia Kimberlites (5)	Basutoland Kimberlites (6)	South West Africa Kimberlites (7)
Li	0.5	15	20	40	28			34	16	20
B	1	5	15	15	9			149		
Sc	5	24	2.5	3	3	10		10	25	15
V	40	200	100	40	30		170	120	120	160
Cr	2000	200	50	25	2		1500		1440	1000
Co	200	45	10	5	1	17	40		77	50
Ni	2000	160	35	8	4	8	450		1140	1200
Cu	20	100	35	20	5	2.5	60		100	
Ga	2	18	20	20	30	1			9	10
Ge	1	1.5	1.5	1.4	1			0.5		
Rb	2	45	100	200	100			11	21	250
Sr	1*	465*	440*	100*	200	2450	200	1140	445	600
Y	0*	21*	35*	40*	20	96			46	40
Zr	30	100	260	200	500	83	200	97	445	190
Cs	0.1	1		5	0.6			12		
Nb	1	20	20	20	35	1690	70	160	240	200
Ba	1	300	650	830	1600	2240			740	1000
La	0*	15*	45*	55*	70	284			370	
Ta	0.018	0.48	0.7	3.5	2.1			8.6		
Pb	0.1	8	15	20	12				9	30
Al/Ga	2250	4866	4425	3850	2700				3100+	
K/Rb	150	182	230	167	435				120+	
Ni/Co	10	3.6	5.5	1.6	4		11		15	
Cr/Ni	1	1.2	1.4	3.1	0.5		3.1		1.2	
Ca/Sr	700	153	58	53	90	99			72+	
Nb/Ta	55	41	26	6	17			28		

(1) From Vinogradov (1962), except with asterisks which are from Turekian and Wedepohl (1961).
(2) From Turekian and Wedepohl (1961).
(3) From Gold (1963).
(4) Average of 459, from Litinski (1961).
(5) Averages of between 19 and 57 specimens from the Mir, Zarnitza and Udashnaya kimberlite pipes, from Burkov and Podporina (1965).
(6) Average of 14, from Dawson (1962).
(7) Average of four, except Y which is average of two, from Janse (1964).
+ Average of only three (from Dawson, 1960).

Zr, and Nb are most similar to those found in carbonatites and their associated alkalic rocks. The high B content of the Russian kimberlites is worthy of note; generally boron is only found in such quantities in granitic pegmatites, but Sahama (1945) found 31 ppm in serpentinites in southern Finland.

With regard to variance and covariance of the elements, in the Basutoland kimberlite Zr, Nb and La vary sympathetically, as do Rb, Sr, and Ba (Dawson, 1962). In the same rocks Co and Ni are covariant, but this is not the case in the Russian kimberlite (Milashev et al., 1963).

Micaceous kimberlites contain more Ba, Rb, Sr and La than basaltic varieties due to their high K and Ca content (Dawson, 1960), and Burkov and Podporina (1965) note that the magmatic cement of kimberlite breccias contain higher amounts of Li, Cs, Sr, B, Nb, Zr and Nb, but lower Ni, Co, Sc, and V, than bulk specimens of kimberlite; presumably this is due to the latter group substituting for iron and magnesia in the olivine and serpentine phenocrysts.

D. Isotope Chemistry

Carbon isotope determinations of seven specimens of Russian kimberlite give C^{12}/C^{13} ratios ranging from 89.49 to 89.69, average 89.60. Six diamonds from the Yakutia kimberlite have an average value of 89.63 (Vinogradov et al., 1965) which suggests that the carbon in the kimberlite and diamonds have a common origin.

The Sr^{87}/Sr^{86} ratio of kimberlite ranges between 0.705 and 0.729, with an average of 0.712 (14 specimens) (Powell, 1967). For comparison, Powell's average for carbonatite is 0.7032 (range 0.7016 to 0.7051), while oceanic and continental basalts give 0.707 and 0.708 respectively (Faure and Hurley, 1963); granites give values between 0.740 and 1.003, according to their age (Gast, 1961). Thus, like the basalts, kimberlite lies intermediate between carbonatite and granite.

E. Comparison with Other Rock Types

The rock type which is chemically most similar to kimberlite is alnöite, the principal differences being in their Ca/Mg ratios and their water content; in fact Williams (1934) has declared his belief that kimberlite is hydrated alnöite. This intimate relationship is borne out by the field evidence that kimberlite may grade into alnöite along the length of a dyke (as in New York State). With increasing CaO, kimberlite grades chemically into alnöite and, with increasing CO_2, into carbonatite (Fig. 8.11).

Rocks of similar chemistry to kimberlite are rare. Other suites that are also characterized by high K_2O, TiO_2, P_2O_5, Sr, Ba, Rb and Zr, combined with high basicity, are the leucite-bearing rocks of southwestern Uganda (Holmes, 1950, 1956, Higazy, 1954); the leucite lamproites of West Kimberley, Australia (Wade and Prider, 1940); the rocks of the Leucite Hills, Wyoming (Cross, 1897) and the Navajo province of Arizona (Williams, 1936). The Tertiary volcanic rocks in the region of the Rhine graben, Germany, also

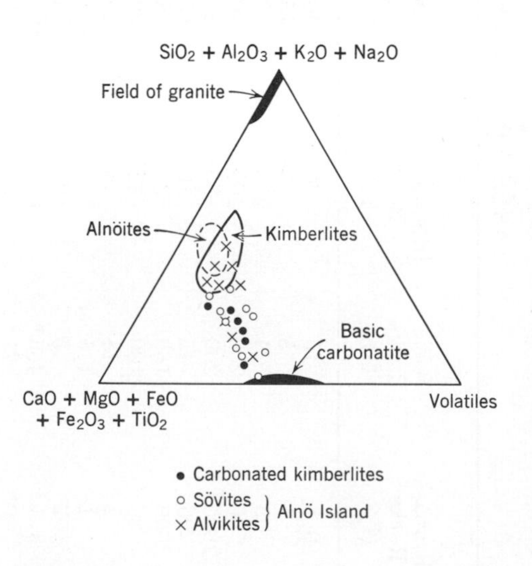

Fig. 8.11 Triangular diagram showing the chemical relationships between kimberlite, alnöite, and carbonatite (from Dawson, 1960).

possess similar chemical characteristics (Van Wambeke et al., 1964).

F. Origin of Kimberlite

Any acceptable theory for the origin of kimberlites must explain the following features:

1. The unusual chemistry of kimberlite, and the wide range in composition.
2. The intimate spatial, chemical, tectonic, and time relationships between kimberlites and rocks of the olivine melilitite-carbonatite association.
3. The very small amounts of kimberlite.
4. The presence of high-pressure minerals such as diamond and pyrope.

The presence of the high-pressure minerals and the broadly ultrabasic composition has led numerous authors to propose that kimberlite originates in the peridotitic rocks of the mantle (Wagner, 1914; Williams, 1932; Verhoogen, 1938, Sobolev, 1960; Boyd and England, 1964). This receives support from laboratory experiments in which diamond has been synthesized under conditions which normally exist only in the mantle (Bovenkerk et al., 1959), whilst the results of Boyd and England (1964) on the system pyrope-enstatite "are consistent with the hypothesis that kimberlites have been erupted into the crust from a depth of 125 to 250 kms." It should perhaps be pointed out that in the experiments mentioned above, the syntheses were carried out on relatively simple chemical systems, and the addition of other elements may cause crystallization of these minerals at much less extreme conditions. For example, during the experiments on the synthesis of diamond from pure graphite, no diamond was formed even at 120 kb pressure; however the addition of small amounts of various metals (Ta, Cr, Fe, Cu, Ni, Ru, Pa, Pt, In) had a catalytic effect, enabling diamond to be formed at 55 to 100 kb and 1200 to 2400°C (Bovenkerk et al., 1959). Furthermore, it should be remembered that the "pyrope" found in kimberlites is not pure pyrope but contains some 25 to 30 per cent of the almandine, grossularite, and uvarovite molecules. This is particularly relevant since Coes (1955) has shown that, with the addition of only a small amount of iron (equivalent to 5 per cent almandine), pyrope-rich garnet may be synthesized at 900°C and 25 kb; this corresponds to a depth of approximately 80 km which is considerably less than that proposed by Boyd and England (1964). These two examples serve to illustrate that caution must be applied when extrapolating from experimental data to natural multicomponent systems, particularly when the system may be rich in volatiles, as in the case of kimberlite.

Evidence that appears to conflict with a mantle origin for kimberlite is that the kimberlite mineral assemblage phlogopite-pyrope-picroilmenite-diamond has never been found in the dunites, peridotites, and ultramafic xenoliths in basalts which, despite their world-wide distribution, have an extremely consistent mineralogy and are thereby regarded as being representative of the mantle (Ross et al., 1954). Another feature is that distinctive suites of diamonds (recognizable on their morphology, color and tenor) occur within individual kimberlite diatremes. In some cases entirely different suites are obtained from diatremes as little as one mile apart indicating that each kimberlite body was a discrete entity before the crystallization of its diamonds. A mantle origin for the diamonds therefore seems improbable since the rather remote possibility of the kimberlite of each diatreme being completely isolated from its neighbors following formation in the mantle and during an ascent through 30 to 40 km of crust is precluded by the evidence that the diatreme clusters have a common origin in the dykes beneath them. Nor do the workers who desire kimberlite from the mantle attempt to explain the departure of the kimberlite chemistry from that of other mantle-type ultrabasic rocks (in particular their potash enrichment), though some Russian geologists suggest that the peculiarities of kimberlite lie in its high volatile content which is "probably connected with progressive 'degassification' of the mantle" (Lebedev, 1964). Recently, Janse (1964) has suggested that the potassic nature of kimberlites is due to original mantle peridotite being modified by the process of zone refining, similar to that proposed by Harris (1957) for the origin of potassic basalts; it is suggested that the process would take place gradually only in exceptional circumstances of prolonged tectonic stability. This prerequisite appears to be contrary to the evidence that considerable vertical uplift or doming is a characteristic feature of kimberlite magmatism and, as pointed out by Turner and Verhoogen (1960), the products of zone refining might be expected to be abundant and widespread, which is at variance with the insignificant amounts of kimberlite.

There is an intimate spatial relationship between kimberlite and olivine melilitite. The authors referred to hereafter discuss a rock consisting of melilite, olivine, and augite ± nepheline or analcime. Some have called it "melilite basalt," others have used "olivine melilitite." The latter term is adopted here. This association, first noted in South Africa (Wagner, 1914), was examined at length by Taljaard (1936) who concluded that kimberlite is merely carbonated and hydrothermally altered olivine melilitite. At the same time Holmes (1936) suggested that kimberlite results from volatile "emanations" mixed with inclusions of mantle peridotite and olivine melilitite magma, a proposal recently adopted by O'Hara and Mercy (1963). Eckermann (1961) has also proposed an olivine melilitite parent through which carbon dioxide streams to remove lime, thereby giving rise to a residuum of kimberlite; however, extraction of lime might be expected to result in a rock richer in silica than the parental rock. These hypotheses do not explain the potassic nature of kimberlite but Nixon et al., (1963) explain this as being due to crystallization, from parental olivine melilitite magma, of cognate xenoliths with a relatively high soda content (held in soda-bearing pyroxene) thereby enriching the residue (kimberlite) in potash. A similar process (crystallization of sodic eclogite) had been proposed by Holmes and Harwood (1932) to account for the potash-rich lavas of southwestern Uganda.

The "olivine melilitite" theories, although attempting to explain the relationship between kimberlite and olivine melilitite, do not clarify the association of the kimberlite with the much more widespread rock types of the nepheline syenite-carbonatite suite (which incidentally include olivine melilitite). In recent years a growing number of workers (Eckermann, 1948, 1961; Holmes, 1950, 1956; Saether, 1957; Dawson, 1960, 1964, 1967b; Garson, 1962; Davidson, 1964) have recognized the intimate relationship between carbonatites and their associated alkalic rocks, and kimberlites and similar potassic ultrabasic rocks. Besides the intimate time and spatial relationship, the kimberlite/carbonatite association is reinforced by the following features:

1. There is a complete chemical gradation between kimberlite and carbonatite (Fig. 8.11).
2. Both rock types contain high amounts of Ba, Ti, P, Sr, La, Y, and Nb.
3. The rare minerals moissanite and pyrochlore have been reported from both rocks in Russia.
4. Garnet peridotite nodules, identical to those in kimberlite, have been found in carbonatite tuffs in Tanganyika (Dawson, 1964).
5. The phenomenon of potash fenitization, a common feature at carbonatite contacts, has now been recorded alongside a dyke of diamondiferous mica peridotite in the Ivory Coast.

The exact relationship between kimberlite and carbonatite is a matter of some uncertainty. Both Saether (1957) and Garson (1962) believe that carbonatite is a differentiate from a kimberlite parent. This is difficult to reconcile with our present knowledge that carbonatite is volumetrically a more abundant rock-type, unless one invokes large quantities of kimberlite at depth, for which we have as yet no evidence. The writer has made the somewhat radical suggestion (Dawson, 1960; 1967b) that kimberlite may be the end product of interaction between the water-rich ankeritic fraction of a carbonatite magma and granitic crustal rocks, as shown in Table 8.7.

This process goes a long way to explaining the chemical peculiarities of kimberlite and their intimate association with rock types in whose formation carbonatite may have played a major role. Differential interaction with the "granite," and chemical differences both in the carbonatite and the "granite" could account for the wide compositional range of kimberlites, and the gradations into alnöites and carbonatite. The small quantities of kimberlite are consistent with such an "end-stage" process. In addition, the strontium isotope data are consistent with the "carbonatite + granite" hypothesis, but caution must be adopted since the ratios may be due in part to minute xenoliths (Powell, 1967). It is not clear whether, in this process, the kimberlite was actually formed by disruption and hydration of the subvolcanic skarn during eruption, or whether (as in the case of other carbonatite skarns and fenitization aureoles) the skarn was partially mobilized and then admixed with the residual fluids.

The "carbonatite + granite" hypothesis, which is virtually a "turning inside out" of the limestone assimilation hypothesis, is not without precedent, as Holmes (1956) has proposed a similar carbonatite skarn process to explain the origin of the biotite-peridotites found with the potassic basalts of Uganda.

Like the other explanations of kimberlite genesis, the "carbonatite + granite" hypothesis, is not without difficulties. In the first place the existence of carbonatite magma is by no means accepted by all geologists, and some prefer to regard it as a differentiate of the basic alkalic rocks

TABLE 8.7 Possible Process for Development of Kimberlites

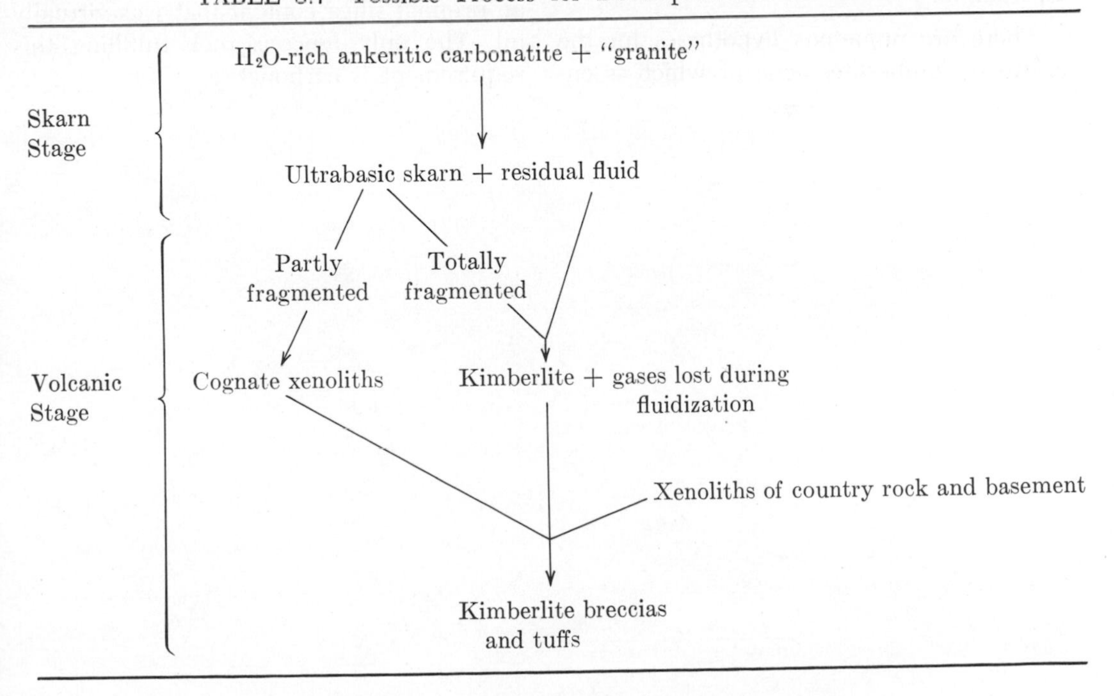

(e.g., ijolite) with which it is commonly associated. Secondly, what would be the ultimate source of the carbonatite? In this connection it is pertinent that in South Africa, Brazil, and the U.S.S.R. the kimberlite eruptions closely follow widespread extrusions of flood basalt. In the case of the rather similar circumstances in the Neogene volcanic province of northern Tanganyika, where widespread carbonatite volcanism follows extensive basaltic activity, it has been suggested that the carbonatite originates by preferential streaming of volatiles into the area of pressure-relief caused by the basalt extrusion, combined with structural gas-trap (Dawson, 1967a). A third problem is whether the pressures necessary for the formation of diamond could be achieved within or at the base of the crust. It has been suggested that this may be attained by a combination of (a) lowering of the diamond stability field due to crystallization in a volatile-rich, multicomponent system; and (b) gas overpressures creating, for short periods of time, pressure conditions more typical of the mantle (Dawson, 1960).

G. Summary

There are numerous hypotheses for the origin of kimberlite, none of which is entirely satisfactory. Hypotheses relating kimberlite to rocks of the nepheline syenite-carbonatite suite (including olivine melilitite) explain most satisfactory the chemical features of kimberlite and its intimate association in time, space, and tectonic environment with these other rock types. Whether the carbonatites, the nepheline syenites or the kimberlites are the parental material, or whether they are all the result of partial fusion of the peridotite rocks of the mantle (cf. O'Hara, 1965a) is a matter requiring further investigation. The possibility must not be excluded that rocks of kimberlitic aspect may evolve in more than one way.

In conclusion it is important to reassert the potassic nature of kimberlite, and in this context it is perhaps relevant that Turner and Verhoogen (1960), after a comprehensive review, conclude that assimilation of granitic material into a parental magma is the most likely explanation for the genesis of potassic basic igneous rocks. Should this be the case for kimberlite, it is interesting to speculate that, in order to end up with a rock type so silica-deficient, the magma into which the granite was assimilated must have had an original silica content that was virtually nil. The only igneous rock fulfilling this requirement is carbonatite.

9. *Alkalic Ultrabasic Rocks, Kimberlites, and Carbonatites*

I. INTRODUCTION

P. J. Wyllie

The affinities between kimberlites, alkalic ultrabasic rocks, and carbonatites were mentioned in Chapter 8. Some of the direct and indirect links are as follows: the alkalic ultrabasic rocks of ring complexes occur in the same tectonic environment as kimberlites; the ring complexes often include carbonatite intrusions; carbonatites are sometimes associated with "central-complex kimberlites"; many kimberlites contain much carbonate that may be primary. This chapter includes accounts of alkalic complexes that contain ultrabasic rocks, and of kimberlites obviously related genetically to carbonatites or in which carbonates play an important role.

In Section II Upton reviews the alkaline pyroxenites and related ultrabasic rocks that usually occur in alkalic intrusive ring complexes. These are almost exclusively associated with continental cratogenic areas, and often directly associated with alkaline volcanic fields. Upton reviews the petrology of several ring complexes, and notes the recurrence of a concentric zoned pattern in cylindrical or funnel-shaped intrusions. This is structurally similar to the zoned complexes occurring in orogenic zones (Chapter 4). Many alkalic complexes have well developed gravity stratification, but Upton points out that early magmatic features in these rocks, such as layering, may be progressively obscured as a result of extensive fenitization and recrystallization produced when the late stage liquids become enriched in alkalis and volatiles. He concludes that the late stages produce a carbonatitic residuum. Pyroxenites and related peridotites form nodules and ejectamenta in the alkaline volcanic fields. Upton provides a summary of the petrogenesis of the alkaline pyroxenites and associated rocks and concludes that the ultramafic and ultrabasic rocks are usually formed by fractional crystallization of alkalic, undersaturated magmas such as olivine melilitite.

In Section III Gold reviews the petrology of the alkalic rocks of the Monteregian petrographic province which includes stocks, necks, plugs, dikes, and sills. The igneous activity appears to be controlled by a deep-seated fault system linked to a first-order structure in southeastern Canada. The rocks change from west to east, suggesting migration of magma upwards from west to east with outlets forming essentially vertical magma chambers at regular intervals. Gold plots the many named alkalic rocks of the province within the basalt tetrahedron of Yoder, Tilley, and Schairer, in an effort to simplify the confused nomenclature of the rocks. He summarizes the mineralogy and petrology of 12 of the plutonic complexes in the province. The association peridotite-pyroxenite-gabbro-diorite-syenite is consistently developed, with only a small proportion of the rocks being ultrabasic or ultramafic. Where structural traps were available volatiles were collected, and this process led to the development of the undersaturated peralkaline nepheline-rich trend at Oka, with the formation of a variety of ultrabasic rocks including carbonatite. Gold concludes that fractionation of the standard primary alkali basalt magma produced the rocks of the association.

In Section IV von Eckermann describes the relationships between the alnöites, kimberlites, and carbonatites of Sweden, where their consanguinity is well displayed. The kimberlite and carbonatite diatremes are separately located, but probably related genetically. He proposes that the separation of immiscible carbonate globules decreases the lime content of a parent melilite basalt or alnoite, yielding a kimberlite magma and a carbonatite fraction. Comparison of the kimberlites from Sweden, South Africa, and the U.S.S.R. confirms that they have similar primary mineral assemblages, and very similar chemical correspondence. In chemical variation diagrams the Swedish group diverges from the Russian and South African groups only at the stage where nepheline appears in the Swedish rocks. A sample of a tuffitic Alnö kimberlite contains small crystals that may possibly be diamond.

In Section V Watson reviews the geology, mineralogy, and petrology of the suite of rocks occurring in eastern North America which includes peridotite, mica peridotite, and kimberlite. They contain abundant serpentine and carbonate, and some resemble impure carbonatites. Most occur in nonorogenic environments, and others are apparently postorogenic. Those in the Montreal area are probably related to the Monteregian intrusions (Gold, 9–III). These rocks occur mainly as dikes and sills ranging from several inches to a few feet in thickness, and from several tens of feet to a few hundreds of feet in length. They are narrow yet remarkably persistent with tenuous offshoots suggesting fluidity. Emplacement temperatures deduced from contact effects on coal seams, oil-bearing sandstones, and salt are 600°C or less. Their chemistry closely matches the kimberlites of Sweden, Africa, and Siberia and contrasts markedly with alpine-type and other ultramafic rocks. Watson gives a detailed account of one dyke from Bachelor Lake, Quebec, and presents evidence that the calcite is a late crystallizing primary phase. He concludes that these kimberlites were emplaced at relatively low temperatures as an accumulation of crystals transported by a highly fluid liquid rich in CO_2 and H_2O.

In Section VI Franz and Wyllie describe some experimental results from the system CaO-MgO-SiO_2-CO_2-H_2O that support Watson's conclusions and suggest that the "highly fluid liquid" could be a carbonatite magma. They report that a "synthetic carbonatite magma," composed of $CaO + CO_2 + H_2O$ with small amounts of dissolved MgO and SiO_2, can precipitate calcite, monticellite, forsterite, brucite, and portlandite at temperatures of the order of 600°C. The fact that the low-temperature carbonatitic liquid can coexist in stable equilibrium with the "high-temperature" magnesian silicate minerals forsterite and monticellite provides support for the existence of genetic links between kimberlites and carbonatites. Certainly, the calcite abundant in many kimberlites can no longer be classified with confidence as an alteration product.

II. ALKALINE PYROXENITES

B. G. J. Upton

A. Introduction

The rocks forming the subject for discussion in this chapter are those ultrabasic and ultramafic rocks that, almost exclusively, are found in association with the alkaline volcanic fields of continental cratogenic areas. Attention will be more specifically directed towards those composed principally of pyroxenes, although it is not easy to consider their petrology in isolation without some digression on the related rocks and wider issues of alkaline rock genesis.

The subordinate minerals commonly encountered in the typical pyroxenitic rocks include olivine, magnetite, apatite, biotite, and hornblende; with increasing contents of these minerals there is gradation into peridotite, magnetite pyroxenite, and biotite and hornblende pyroxenites. Similarly with increasing tenor of nepheline, the alkaline pyroxenites grade into melteigites and ijolites. Feldspars are uncommon accessories and orthopyroxenes are typically absent. The lack of these, combined with the presence of such distinctive minor constituents as perovskites, garnets (andradites and schorlomites), calcite and analcite—together with their restrictive field-associations—obviates, in the great majority of cases, any possible confusion with the pyroxenites produced as differentiates of normal basalts.

B. Pyroxenites of Alkaline Intrusive Complexes

Perhaps most familiar to petrologists are the alkali pyroxenites occurring within intrusive "ring-complexes" such as those at Magnet Cove, Arkansas (Erikson and Blade, 1963) and Spitskop, Transvaal (Strauss and Truter, 1950) in which their field-associates commonly include, not only members of the melteigite-ijolite "series," but also carbonatites and nepheline syenites.

From the literature of the last two decades it has become increasingly clear that the greatest variety and frequency of occurrences of such rocks is to be found in the fractured and rifted pre-Cambrian terraines of the U.S.S.R. and Africa. Of the many Soviet localities from which alkalic ultrabasic rocks have been described, the Afrikanda complex in the Kola Peninsula is one of the best documented (Kupletsky, 1936, 1937, Afanassiev, 1939; Tomkeieff, 1961). Here, an intrusion with an outcrop area of 11.5 km^2, cuts ancient gneisses and appears to have the form of an asymmetric funnel. The gneisses in the immediate vicinity have been converted to fenite. An incomplete ring of pyroxenites and melteigites is seen in the outer parts of the intrusion, passing inwards towards "ore-pyroxenites" containing many schlieren and veins composed of titanomagnetite and the cerium-rich perovskite, knopite. In the central zone, globular xenolithic masses of banded olivinite and melilite-olivinite are contained in a matrix of coarse-grained pyroxenite. These dunitic rocks contain relatively small quantities of titanomagnetite, clinopyroxene, and knopite. The whole assemblage is cut by alkalic pegmatites composed of nepheline, clinopyroxene, schorlomite, knopite, and titanomagnetite, which Kupletsky (1937) regarded as the final products of an almost fully crystallized magma. The nearby, almost perfectly concentric complex at Khabozero [alternatively transliterated Kovdozero (Tomkeieff, 1961)], is similar, but has an unbrecciated core of "ore-olivinite" consisting mainly of magnesian olivine (Fo_{90}). The olivinite (dunite) displays primary lamination and compositional banding.

Analogous ultrabasic rocks have been described by Derby (1891) and Melcher

(1954) from a locality in São Paulo, Brazil, which has given the name "jacupirangite" to those varieties consisting almost exclusively of titanaugite and magnetite. Here, too, fenitized basement gneisses are cut by leucocratic alkalic rocks surrounding an ultrabasic suite. The latter comprises a partially serpentinized dunite (with Fo_{90}) grading out with increasing percentage of pyroxene and then of nepheline, into pyroxenite and then to ijolite. The typical jacupirangites occur near a central intrusion of carbonatite. Melcher considered the ultrabasic rocks to be the result of gravitative settling within a magmatic conduit, the carbonatites the final differentiate, and the leucocratic alkaline rocks partially mobilized fenites.

In the exposed core of Napak volcano in Uganda (King, 1965), a younger carbonatite similarly penetrates the silicate rocks. In this instance pyroxenite occurs as xenolithic masses within a matrix of melteigite-urtite rocks in a manner reminiscent of the way the Afrikanda olivinites occur within a pyroxenite-melteigite assemblage.

The association of dunitic rocks with pyroxenites is also well known in Africa as at Shawa in Southern Rhodesia (with Fo_{87}; Johnson, 1961), Bukusu in Uganda (Davies, 1956; King, 1965) and at Phalaborwa in the Transvaal (Russell, Hiemstra and Groenveld, 1954). At the latter locality the olivine-magnetite rock ("phoscorite") is remarkable for its high content of apatite.

The Ice River complex, British Columbia (Allan, 1914, and Campbell, 1961) is a stratified intrusion with ultrabasic rocks of jacupirangite type at the base passing upwards through ijolites and urtites into nepheline and sodalite syenites. This assemblage Allan, like Melcher, ascribed to the action of gravitative differentiation within a cooling magma. Aluminum, alkalis, and volatiles were concentrated in the later liquids, and Fe, Mg, Ca, Ti, and P were being removed in the higher temperature crystallization stages. Carbonate masses in the complex are, for the most part, derived from the country-rock sedimentary limestones although some pyrochlore-bearing masses may conceivably be of igneous origin.

Chemical analyses of pyroxenites are compared in Table 9.1.

C. Alkali Pyroxenites as Bombs or Nodules in Volcanic Fields

Fragments of ultrabasic rocks, similar to those encountered in the intrusive alkaline complexes, contribute to the tuffs and agglomerates of certain volcanic provinces. These provinces are found in the same tectonic environments as the intrusive complexes and there is little doubt that they are surface manifestations of the same igneous processes. The volcanism is characteristically violent, and pyroclastic products generally predominate over lava flows. The volcanic rocks are invariably strongly alkaline and undersaturated. Pyroxenites, together with ijolitic rocks, have been described from the tuffs of Oldoinyo Lengai, Tanzania (Dawson, 1962a, 1962b) and from Elgon in Uganda (Davies, 1952). In these volcanoes the predominant effusives are nephelinites, melanephelinites, and ankaratrites. Deeper erosion at Napak, an essentially similar volcano (King, 1949, 1965), has revealed a pyroxenite-ijolite-carbonatite complex occupying the eruptive throat. King (1965) regards magmas of melteigite/nephelinite composition as being immediately parental to the ijolite-series of eastern Uganda, with the qualification that still more primitive magmas were more magnesian and produced accumulative olivine-rich rocks.

Biotite pyroxenites and peridotites occur among the ejectamenta of the Western-Rift volcanics in the neighborhood of Ruwenzori (Holmes and Harwood, 1932). Here the volcanic rocks are distinctly more potassic than those of eastern Uganda or the Eastern Rift and include K-rich olivine melilitites (katungites) as well as mafurites and ugandites in which olivine and

TABLE 9.1 Compositions of Some Alkaline Pyroxenites

	1	2	3	4	5	6	7	8	9
SiO_2	38.39	35.42	37.47	40.25	41.20	41.39	44.49	43.35	44.39
TiO_2	4.54	4.05	1.07	4.76	3.63	2.55	2.26	4.38	3.91
Al_2O_3	7.05	9.21	2.86	2.74	3.14	4.91	8.72	9.67	6.37
Fe_2O_3	9.07	8.94	11.77	10.83	9.56	10.37	4.54	5.26	5.11
FeO	6.17	7.17	7.83	7.38	7.70	9.77	4.55	2.65	4.86
MnO	0.32	0.29	0.16	0.16	0.20	0.21	0.10	0.09	0.10
MgO	11.58	7.77	10.12	12.04	12.20	10.06	12.38	15.74	14.20
CaO	19.01	20.83	21.68	20.21	20.22	18.02	17.81	12.20	17.02
Na_2O	0.74	1.47	0.47	0.42	1.03	1.52	0.80	0.44	0.50
K_2O	0.75	0.62	0.93	...	0.18	1.40	2.42	4.74	2.35
H_2O^+	0.33	1.05	0.73	0.46		...	0.68	0.59	0.35
H_2O^-	0.14	0.11	0.27	0.46		...	0.03	0.07	0.05
P_2O_5	0.82	2.23	4.33	0.45		0.02	0.77	trace	0.26
CO_2	0.32	0.11	0.36	0.07				0.04	0.04
BaO	trace	0.00	0.06	0.03				0.30	0.16
SrO	...	...	0.14	trace				...	0.03
SO_3	...	0.12	...	...				...	...
S	0.42	0.38	0.04	0.02				trace	0.02
F		0.17	0.36	...				0.11	0.04
Cl		0.02	...	trace				trace	0.04
V_2O_3			0.12	0.04				0.04	0.05
Cr_2O_3								0.05	0.03
NiO								0.04	0.01
CuO								0.03	
Li_2O								trace	trace
Loss on ignition					0.46				
	99.65	99.96	100.77	100.32	99.52	100.22	99.55	99.79	99.89
		0.26	0.15					0.04	0.03
		99.70	100.62					99.75	99.86

1. Jacupirangite. Jacupiranga, São Paulo, Brazil, Washington, 1901.
2. Jacupirangite. Magnet Cove, Arkansas, U.S.A. Erickson and Blade, 1963.
3. Apatite pyroxenite. Libby, Montana. U.S.A. Larsen and Pardee, 1929.
4. Pyroxenite (fine-grained). Iron Hill, Gunnison Co., Colorado, U.S.A. Larsen, 1942.
5. Pyroxenite (fine-grained). Afrikanda, Kola Peninsula, U.S.S.R. Kupletsky, 1937.
6. Pyroxenite. Napak, Uganda. King, 1965.
7. Pyroxenite block in agglomerate. Villa Senni, Alban volcano, Italy. Washington, 1927.
8. Biotite pyroxenite. Ejected block. Lutale Ridge. Bufumbira, Uganda. Holmes and Harwood, 1937.
9. Biotite pyroxenite. Ejected block, Katwe Crater. Holmes and Harwood, 1937.

diopsidic pyroxene appear as phenocrysts. The potassic volcanic rocks of the Roman province also produce similar specimens, as, for example, those of the Alban volcano agglomerates at Villa Senni, described in detail by Washington (1927). The leucite-nephelinites, etc., of the Laacher See district in Germany are accompanied by tuffs containing pyroxenites, carbonatites, and syenites (Frechen, 1962). Further examples include the Schwabian (Germany) and Sutherland (South Africa) olivine-melilitite provinces in which pieces of peridotite, biotite pyroxenite and biotite-hornblendite have been blown to the surface. Many other instances are listed by

Holmes and Harwood in their memoir on the Bufumbira volcanic rocks (1937).

D. Mineralogy

The olivines recorded from alkaline dunites, peridotites and pyroxenites are magnesian varieties with compositions in the range Fo_{90-80}. In the magmas the oxidation state probably increases rapidly since H_2O and CO_2 concentrations rise with advancing crystallization and the absence of iron-rich olivines is quite characteristic. Olivine is accompanied by knopite in the Afrikanda and Khabozero dunites. Magnetite and apatite may also occur in the dunites and Davidson (1964a) remarks that the olivinite cores of the six concentrically zoned alkali complexes of the Aldan Shield, Siberia, are notably platinum-rich. Green spinels have been described by Johnson (1961) in association with the magnetites of the Shawa dunites.

The pyroxenes are invariably Ca and Mg-rich clinopyroxenes and, with increasing differentiation three general trends can, be distinguished. Perhaps the commonest described from pyroxenite-melteigite-ijolite series, is one of increasing Fe^{3+} and Na^{+} content, from diopside towards aegirine-diopside. A second trend is from diopside towards titanaugite and a third involves enrichment in ferric iron without any concomitant introduction of sodium, that is, a series extending from diopside to ferrian diopsides with up to 10 per cent Fe_2O_3.

The magnetites, which are almost always present in the pyroxenites, are not only typically titaniferous, but have relatively high contents of magnesium. Harrington (1907) reports 9.47 per cent MgO in magnetites from Magnet Cove and magnesioferrite-rich ores are also recorded from Afrikanda (Kupletsky, 1936) and Jacupiranga (Melcher, 1954). Micas, often poikilitic or interstitial, range from pale phlogopites to strongly pleochroic iron-rich biotites. Muscovite is not uncommon in the pyroxenites as a late-stage alteration product.

Other constituents commonly encountered in the pyroxenites include brown hornblende, perovskite, sphene, calcite, cancrinite, nepheline, leucite, zeolites (analcite, natrolite, thomsonite, phillipsite), feldspar, pyrite, pyrrhotite, andradite-schorlomite, cebollite, and vesuvianite. Melilite or melilite-pseudomorphs may occur as reaction products of the pyroxenes wherever the latter have been allowed to attain equilibrium with their residual liquids at relatively low pressures. The Isle Cadieux alnöites (Bowen, 1922) represent an extreme case where reaction between an early formed olivine-clinopyroxene mush and residual liquid resulted in a melilite-rich product. Krank (1929) likewise believed that the melilite-bearing turjaites of Kola were derived from original olivine-pyroxene rocks by reaction with low-temperature residual liquids and expressed a similar opinion for the generation of the uncompahgrites of Iron Hill, Colorado.

E. Petrogenesis

Holmes and Harwood summarized in their 1937 memoir much of the information concerning alkali pyroxenites that was available at the time and proposed possible petrogenetic schemes. Holmes (1937) suggested that the ultrabasic rocks of the olivine-biotite-pyroxene ("O.B.P.") series represented primary peridotite modified by emanations from a source unknown. In 1950, however, Holmes discarded this hypothesis and proposed that the rocks were formed by the reaction of magmatic carbonatite and granite. Tilley and Harwood (1931) had clearly demonstrated that small bodies of alkalic pyroxenite could be produced by the reaction of basalt and limestone. Larsen (1942) believed the Iron Hill pyroxenites were formed by assimilation of marble (since shown to be intrusive carbonatite) by basalt followed by plagioclase fractionation. Von Eckermann (1948) maintained that many of the jacupirangitic rocks of Alnö came into being through the desilicification of fenite by sövite, the melanocratic rocks being merely the "femic remains of a fenite." So too at Spitskop, Strauss and Truter (1950) concluded that the biotite pyroxenites and jacupirangites were generated through fenitization processes. In discussion of the genesis of the ultrabasic inclusions in the Western Rift volcanics, Higazy (1954), following Holmes, suggested that they arose through hybridization between magnesian carbonatite and granitic crust and that, while the former contributed Mg, Cr, and Ni, the latter provided the Si, Al, K (+Ga, Rb, Ba, and Zr). According to the proportions of carbonatite and granite involved, peridotite, pyroxenite or glimmerite resulted. The hypothesis is implausible; carbonatites are not known for their richness in Cr or Ni and, whereas passage of alkalis into country-rock granite is thoroughly substantiated, the same cannot be said for magnesium. The high Mg, Cr, and Ni can readily be explained in terms of accumulation of the olivines and pyroxenes that occur copiously as phenocrysts in many of the associated lavas. The relative richness of the rocks in K, Ba, and Zr as well as their other geochemical peculiarities is also susceptible to simple explanation in terms of crystal fractionation within mantle derived magmas unmodified by sialic contamination (O'Hara, 1965a, p. 32).

A priori, it is likely that accumulitic suites of olivinites (dunites) and pyroxenites would develop whenever magmas, in which olivine and clinopyroxene were among the first crystalline phases to precipitate, were cooled slowly providing that there was a significant density differential between the crystals and the magma. The magmas involved would include the alkalic, undersaturated and Mg-Ca-rich types such as olivine melilitites, katungites, mafurites, ugandites, melanephelinites, ankaratrites, monchiquites, alnöites, olivine leucitites and others, crystallizing under such conditions that diopsidic augite, rather than monticellite, merwinite or akermanite or other calcium-rich phases, was precipitating during the early stages of crystallization. Recent experiments by Kushiro and Yoder (1964b) confirm the instability of both monticellite and akermanite at high pressures, already suspected on petrological grounds. The extreme rarity of merwinite in natural rocks suggests that the stability field for this mineral is rarely encountered during the crystallization of magmas (although it has been tentatively identified in the Homa Bay ijolitic suite, Kenya, by Pulfrey, 1949). Evidence from phenocrysts, moreover, confirms that magnesian olivine and diopsidic pyroxene are, for a wide spectrum of alkaline magmas, the stable phases in equilibrium with liquid under the conditions existing prior to eruption. Judging from the rarity of alkaline ultrabasic lavas or tuffs free from phenocrysts, it is probably normal for such magmas to be at or below their liquidus temperatures during their ascent to the surface and, although the more highly magnesian examples of alnöites, melilitites, monchiquites, and their relatives probably represent the least fractionated of the ultrabasic alkaline magmas reaching high crustal levels, they themselves have almost certainly undergone considerable differentiation during the ascent. The more sodic may go on to produce ankaratritic and nephelinitic residuals with increasing Fe/Mg ratios and rising aluminum, alkalis and volatiles; the more potassic may produce liquids leading through to leucitites.

Low magmatic viscosities would certainly facilitate crystal settling during crystallization. Furthermore, there is a general consensus of opinion among petrologists that volatiles, most particularly water and carbon dioxide, are highly soluble in the undersaturated magmas under discussion and that it is the explosive exsolution of these gases with lowering confining pressures that imparts the fragmental nature to volcanoes like those of the Eifel district or the Western Rift. The low silica content and the high Mg, Fe, and Ca contents, together with perhaps over 10 per cent dissolved volatiles, give reason to suppose that these magmas have viscosities comparable with, if not less than, those of basaltic magmas. Holmes and Harwood (1937) dismissed the possibility of biotite pyroxenites forming through gravitative accumulation on the grounds that magmas of similar composition were known to exist but this rejection does not now seem to be warranted.

The evidence for fractionation by gravitative settling of olivine and pyroxene depends largely on descriptions of complexes where basal pyroxenites are overlain by successively more leucocratic rocks (e.g., Ice River) and those, like Afrikanda, where there are occurrences of laminated and mineralogically banded dunites with textures comparable to those of the more familiar olivine accumulates of basaltic magmas. However, such high-level intrusions of undersaturated magmas in which gravitative differentiation has occurred to give a layered succession appear to be rare. Conceivably such bodies may exist at deep crustal levels and accordingly it is just possible that the assorted alkaline blocks in the tuffs of Schwabia or Oldoinyo Lengai have been plucked from deep-seated layered intrusions during the rapid ascent of relatively undifferentiated olivine melilitites or nephelinites. The suggestion by Wade and Prider (1940) that the extraordinarily potassic West Kimberley volcanics evolved from potassic mica-peridotite magma (= alnöite ?) by olivine subtraction carries the implication that accumulative dunites or peridotites are present at depth. These authors also describe lavas (cedricites) with diopside, leucite, and (pseudomorphed) olivine phenocrysts that contain cognate xenoliths rich in diopside, possibly indicative of the presence of accumulitic pyroxenites. Erikson and Blade (1963) believed that the Magnet Cove jacupirangite suite originated as an accumulitic gas-charged residue in the lower part of a magma reservoir which, when tapped by fractures, streamed as a crystal mush to occupy the fissures. Von Eckermann (1948), although regarding much of the Alnö melanocratic suite as a direct result of exchange reactions between carbonatite and country-rock, felt compelled to postulate an accumulative origin for the olivine-bearing jacupirangites with measurable Cr_2O_3 that occur as inclusions within the largest carbonatite dykes.

Separation of the early formed crystals need not, however, necessarily involve crystal settling. As soon as surface rupture has been accomplished much of the crystallization can be expected to proceed adiabatically during the separation of the gas phase. In those cases where the magma in the conduit contains a high proportion of crystalline material, the interstitial liquid, impelled by rapidly escaping gas, may be discharged as lapilli, tuffs or, more rarely, lavas. Crystal tuffs would be abundant but much of the crystalline material may be left as mush that eventually consolidates within the conduit. The process is, in fact, one of fractional crystallization where the separation of crystals from liquid is brought about mechanically during violent ebullition of the dissolved gases. Depending on the stage of crystallization reached at the time the gas phase appears and the efficiency of the separation, different members of, for example, the dunite-pyroxenite-melteigite suite may be formed.

On the evidence provided by intrusive complexes like Jacupiranga, and phenocrysts in volcanic rocks, it seems reasonable to infer that, under plutonic conditions, many of the Ca.Mg-rich undersaturated magmas precipitate olivine ($\pm$spinel) on or close to their liquidus, jointed after a temperature lapse by diopside. With falling temperatures, generalizations as to order of crystallization become increasingly worthless and each rock suite requires individual consideration.

Nevertheless it seems that in many instances, particularly where the olivine-melanephelinite-nephelinite series is involved, that nepheline appears later than the pyroxene and that nepheline and pyroxene coexist with liquid over a considerable temperature interval, during which the melteigite-ijolite-urtite series can develop. Thus in a wholly idealized situation a (relatively sodic) ultrabasic magma, cooled from above its liquidus, could produce a layered succession ranging from basal dunites through pyroxenites to an urtitic or even more extremely differentiated top. In the case of apatite-rich pyroxenites and peridotites, as at Phalaborwa and Libby, Montana (Larsen and Pardee, 1929) and Elgon (Davies, 1952), the apatite probably commenced crystallization at relatively elevated temperatures. Magnetite also seems commonly to be among the first three or four minerals to crystallize. As the crystallization of an alkaline ultrabasic magma proceeds, the residual liquids become increasingly enriched in alkalis and volatiles. Providing these are retained, a carbonatitic residuum may be expected. Davies (1952), Saggerson and Williams (1964) and King (1965) are among those who have discussed the generation of carbonatites in this manner.

Crystallization of these volatile-rich magmas may possibly be extended over a temperature range of several hundred degrees centigrade and, where the volatiles are held to the closing stages of crystallization, not only may very extensive fenitization occur but recrystallization of the early formed magmatic rocks may be thorough. In particular the early olivine-pyroxene assemblages of a fractionated suite would be especially susceptible to alteration mineralogically and texturally if they are brought into contact with the low temperature and probably highly fluid carbonatitic residuals. The complex reaction sequences brought about by the action of late liquids on crystals appropriate to higher temperature equilibria at Isle Cadieux and Turja have been previously referred to. Larsen and Goransen (1932) have also described such sequences in detail for the Iron Hill pyroxenite-uncompahgrite complex.

It is almost certainly at this deuteric stage that the textural and mineralogical heterogeneity typical of pyroxenite-melteigite occurrences, comes into being. Such rocks commonly show great variability of grain size and are criss-crossed by a ramifying profusion of alteration veinlets and pegmatoid schlieren. Serpentinization of the olivines and the production of vermiculite or glimmerite rocks from the dunites is probably contemporaneous with the recrystallization of the pyroxenitic rocks. These processes are analogous to the late stage alterations characteristic of kimberlite pipes but are generally less extreme. Consequently, any layering features comparable to those of, say, tholeiitic gabbros differentiated by fractional crystallization, that these rocks may have possessed at high temperatures, are likely to be progressively obscured during the course of crystallization.

So far, stress has been laid on the probable dominant role of fractional crystallization in the petrogenesis of alkaline pyroxenites. The possibility however, that thermodiffusive processes are also important in their genesis should not be overlooked. In volcanic throats in which a blockage has occurred, strong compositional gradients may be set up across the magma column below in response to the thermal gradients. Outward migration of the volatiles plus alkali meta-silicates may lead to the production of peripheral zones rich in the low-melting constituents as well as generating fenites, (and possibly rheomorphic fenite magmas), by reaction with the wall rocks. Consequently, with further cooling, crystallization may commence from the center outwards, tending to produce a concentrically zoned intrusion, as in many of the Soviet instances, in which the more refractory materials would be confined to the core. Gravitative differentiation could take place at the same time as the diffusive process was proceeding in the magma.

A further point that should be emphasized is that although alkali pyroxenites may represent segregations of early crystallized minerals whose bulk compositions do not match any natural magma others may result from the nonfractional crystallization of magmas of the appropriate composition and under the appropriate physical conditions. Thus pyroxenitic minor intrusions ("augitites") have been described from the monchiquite dyke suite at Turja by Krank (1929), who notes, significantly, that they possess completely glassy black margins. Many fine-grained hypabyssal or effusive rocks described as monchiquites (whose bulk compositions can scarcely be far removed from that of the immediately parental magma, minus volatiles) have high contents of modal clinopyroxene and a mineralogy very similar to that of the typical "plutonic" alkali pyroxenites described earlier in this chapter. In fact the dividing line between monchiquites and moderately fine-grained alkali pyroxenites is not easily drawn. Not only may monchiquitic magmas crystallize nonfractionally to yield pyroxenitic rocks but they are also capable of producing accumulitic ultrabasic rocks. The hornblende-bearing biotite-pyroxenites (+hornblendites and glimmerites) found as nodules in monchiquite dykes in New South Wales (Wilshire and Binns, 1961) were probably formed in this manner.

Other natural magmas rich in normative diopside could, under certain circumstances crystallize nonfractionally to form pyroxenitic rocks. Thus Yoder and Tilley (1962) demonstrated experimentally that at high pressures an olivine nephelinite could be recrystallized as a mica and spinel-bearing pyroxenite. This interesting experiment may serve as a reminder of the extensive heteromorphism that can be exhibited by the ultrabasic alkaline rocks.

F. Summary

It is difficult to make valid and acceptable generalizations for a condensed review in so complex a field of petrology and much of the foregoing discussion on petrogenesis is necessarily speculative. Nevertheless three main conclusions may be drawn:

1. Because a wide compositional range of undersaturated alkaline magmas, whether sodic or potassic, can be judged to remain in equilibrium with diopsidic pyroxenes over an extended temperature interval at moderate to high pressures, many pyroxenites may be the result of fractional crystallization.
2. Since however, some alkaline undersaturated magmas at some stage in their evolution may have compositions approaching that of diopside, even nonfractional crystallization under the appropriate PT conditions will yield a pyroxenitic rock.
3. Allowance must always be made for the possibility that some pyroxenites in alkalic environments may result from reaction between silicate rock and carbonatite magma and also that small quantities may be produced by the assimilation of limestone by silicate magmas.

III. ALKALINE ULTRABASIC ROCKS IN THE MONTREAL AREA, QUEBEC

David P. Gold

A. General Geology

1. Introduction. Extending eastward from Montreal along a slightly curved belt is a group of seven hills spaced at intervals of 10 to 20 miles (see Nos. 2 to 8, Fig. 9.1). Igneous rocks of closely related types form the cores of these hills, and geologists early recognized that these rocks belong to a distinct petrographic province. For the hills, Adams (1903) proposed the name "Monteregian Hills" after the type hill,

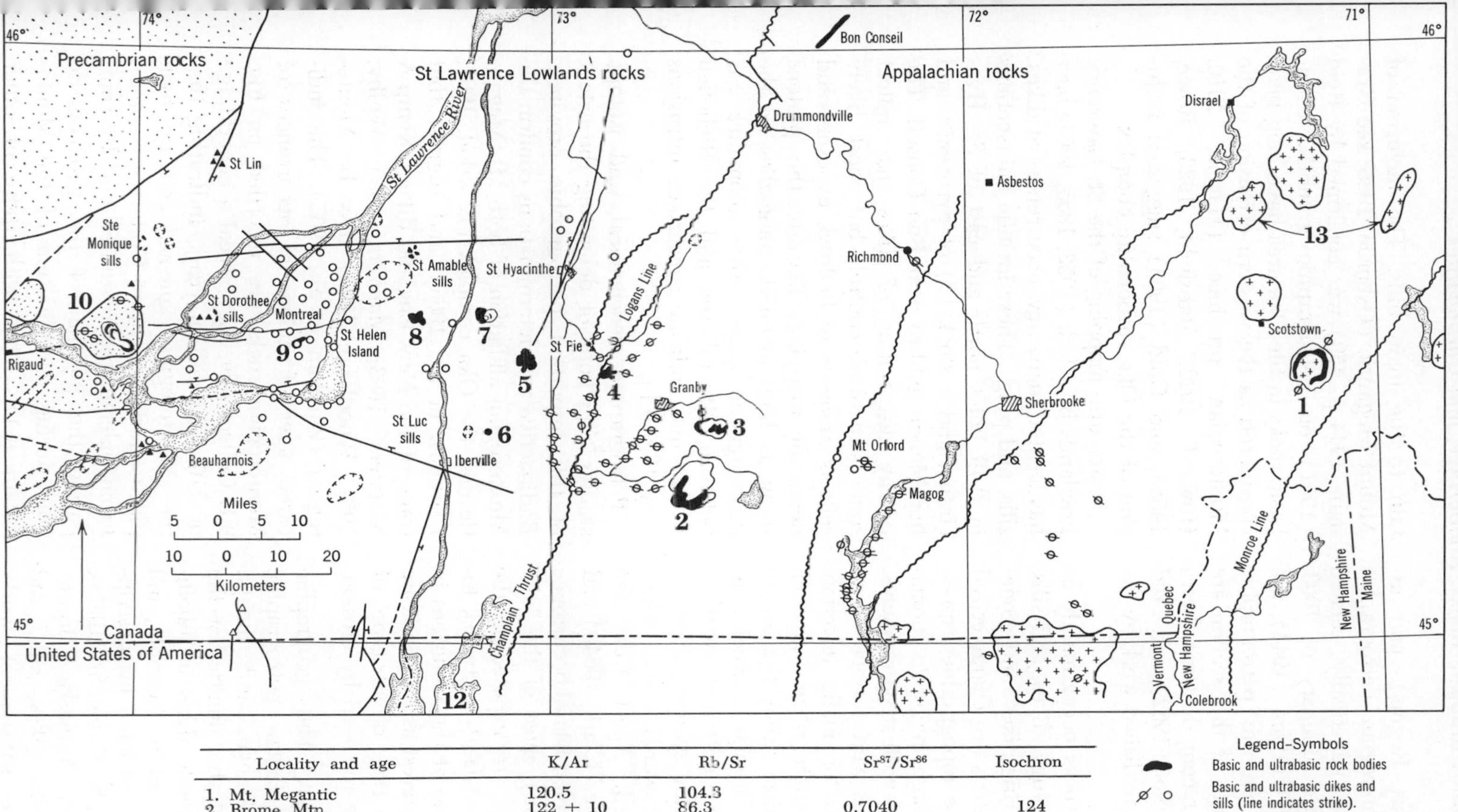

Locality and age	K/Ar	Rb/Sr	Sr^{87}/Sr^{86}	Isochron
1. Mt. Megantic	120.5	104.3		
2. Brome Mtn	122 ± 10	86.3	0.7040	124
3. Shefford Mtn				124
4. Mt. Yamaska			0.7049	
5. Rougemont Mtn			0.7047	
6. Mt. Johnson	110 ± 10	111 ± 6	0.7036	
7. Mt. St. Hilaire		99.5 ± 4	0.7036	
8. Mt. St. Bruno			0.7040	
9. Mt. Royal	100 ± 25		0.7043	
10. Oka complex	95 ± 5	114 ± 7	0.7032	
12. Lake Champlain dikes	136 (General 120–150 m.y.)			
13. Granite plutons	360–400 m.y.			

Isotope data from Lowdon, 1960, 1961; Hurley et al., 1959; Fairbairn et al., 1963; Zartman et al., 1965. Note: average ages are given: all × 10^6 years.

Fig. 9.1 Map showing the distribution of the main Monteregian plutons and some basic and ultrabasic dikes, sills, and breccia pipes (from D. P. Gold, 1965).

Mount Royal (Mons Regius), and assigned to the "Monteregian Petrographic Province" the local, genetically related rock occurrences. His summary of 1903, and the synthesis of Graham (1944), are the standard works on this petrographic province. The contents of this section are drawn mainly from recent doctoral theses by Beall (1962), Pouliot (1962), and Gold (1963), and from unpublished work by the writer.

The Monteregian rocks occur mainly as small stocks, necks, plugs, dikes, and sills, less commonly as ring-dikes and cone-sheets. The main plutons are characterized by a marked positive topographic expression (except Oka), high magnetic anomalies, and gravity highs with steep gradients. Generally, the plutons were formed by an initial ultramafic and/or mafic injection, followed by a later more silicic intrusion. Peridotites, pyroxenites and titanaugite gabbros, are linked through normal gabbros and essexite, monzonite and syenodiorite to strongly alkaline syenites. There is a general tendency towards a more silicic composition eastward. Apart from the breccia pipe at St. Pie (Clark, 1964b) and the well-known St. Helen Island occurrence (Osborne et al., 1936), most of the "diatreme" type breccias are exposed in the Oka area and on the islands eastward, towards Montreal. Some of the inclusions in the breccias are of interest as they indicate the presence, at the time of intrusion, of formations long since removed by erosion.

*2. **Extent and age.*** The geographic limits of the Monteregian petrographic province are not known, and though Adams (1903) noted the affinities of the camptonite and bostonite dikes in adjoining Maine, New Hampshire, Vermont, and New York State, he restricted his description to Mounts Royal, St. Bruno, St. Hilaire, Johnson, Rougemont, Yamaska, Brome, Shefford, and satellite dikes, sills, and plugs. Most of the subsequent works (Dresser, 1903, 1906, 1910; Young, 1906; O'Neill, 1914; Burri & Niggli, 1945; Kapp, 1961; Larochelle, 1962; Pouliot, 1962) pertain to the main hills. The inclusion of Mount Megantic (Osborne, 1935; see Graham, 1944 p. 459) was confirmed by Reid (1961) on petrographic grounds. Ultrabasic rocks in the Oka area have long been considered as the western extension of the Monteregian province (Harvie, 1910; Howard, 1922; Stansfield, 1923; Rowe, 1958), and Gold (1963) suggested inclusion of the Oka carbonatite complex.

Systematic mapping of the St. Lawrence Lowlands by Clark (1952, 1955, 1964a,b,c) has located many new occurrences of dikes, sills, and plugs. These include intersections in drill holes north and east of St. Hyacinthe, and a stock (?) of pyroxenite and hornblende gabbro near Bon Conseil. The patchy distribution of dikes may reflect some structural control, but most likely reflects amounts of bedrock exposure and detail of mapping. Because the plutons show as high magnetic anomalies on the aeromagnetic maps, other anomalies (as between Mt. Johnson and the Richelieu River) may indicate subsurface intrusions (see Fig. 9.1).

Petrographic, geochemical, and isotope studies offer hope of delimiting the extent of this important petrographic province. Radioactive age determinations confirm the Monteregian affiliation of both Mt. Megantic and the Oka complex (Lowdon, 1961; Fairbairn et al., 1963), and suggest that some of the New England dikes (Kemp & Marsters, 1893; Marsters, 1895; Welby, 1961; Woodland, 1962) may be Monteregian (Zartman et al., 1965). The indicated ages of individual occurrences of Monteregian rocks are recorded on Fig. 9.1. Collectively, they reveal a general age of 110 ± 20 million years, indicating that the Monteregian igneous activity took place during Lower Cretaceous times. From paleomagnetic studies, and by comparing the position of the geomagnetic pole during consolidation of the Monteregian mafic rocks with those of other North American rocks, Larochelle (1962) concludes they were intruded during the Jurassic or later.

Westward, the alignment of the Monteregian Hills with the Ottawa Valley and the Ottawa-Bonnechere graben is striking. The presence of kersantite dikes near Buckingham, the Meach Lake carbonatite near Ottawa (Hogarth, 1964), and the carbonatite complexes in Lake Nipissing (Rowe, 1958), suggest an early igneous phase along the same lineament.

*3. **Structure.*** Arcuate dikes, partial ring-dikes, cone-sheets and plugs, emplaced along the axis of a northwest-trending arch (Gold, 1964) are recognized at Oka. Mounts Royal, St. Bruno, St. Hilaire, Johnson, Yamaska, and Rougemont are the remnants of vertical and subvertical necks or small stocks, with high gravity anomalies disposed symmetrically with respect to their basic rocks. Subvertical lineations and/or flow banding are seen in all the above hills except St. Bruno and Rougemont, which appear to be massive. Flow structures, concentric compositional zoning (basic centers to silicic margins), and cell structures (in certain syenite masses), suggest a complicated emplacement mechanism within an essentially cylindrical conduit. Subvertical lineations in the syenite, and the gravity pattern indicate that Brome and Shefford are broad funnel-shaped masses (Pouliot, 1962), and not laccoliths or denuded portions of the same laccolith as suggested earlier (Dresser, 1903). In Mount Megantic, a central granite plug (youngest) is partially surrounded by gabbro, which in turn is partially enclosed by nordmarkite, suggesting emplacement as ring-dikes (Reid, 1961).

*4. **Structural control.*** That the Monteregian igneous activity transgressed a variety of tectonic provinces (craton, shelf, mio- and eu-geosynclines), suggests control by a deep-seated fault system, linked to some first order structure. The easterly trending line along which the hills lie, the faults of the St. Lawrence Lowlands (see Fig. 9.1) and the Ottawa graben, meet the axis of the Appalachian uplift at the apex of a flexure in which the Appalachian trend changes from north to northeast (see Graham, 1944, p. 457), a condition conducive to the formation of rift valleys and grabens (Carey, 1952; Wilson, 1954). Pouliot (1962, p. 14) states:

"This linear distribution is further emphasized on gravity maps as a broad positive anomaly which parallels the hills and cuts across the regional low that exists elsewhere on the north and northwest flank of the Sutton Mountains. This anomaly suggests a common source for all the intrusives, located at some 10–15,000 feet at depth."

B. Petrology

*1. **Rock types and nomenclature.*** The mafic rocks, which comprise more than 60 per cent of the outcrop area of the Monteregian Hills, are generally referred to as essexite because nepheline appears in most of the norms. However, most are subsiliceous gabbros, titanaugite gabbros, and olivine-titanaugite gabbros. True essexites are exposed only on Mounts Johnson, St. Hilaire and Yamaska, and represent only about 5 per cent of the mafic rocks exposed in the nine main plutons (Pouliot, 1962).

Monteregian rocks vary widely, not only chemically and mineralogically, but also in nomenclature. Most were described during the early development of the quantitative mineralogical classification of rocks, which led to an unnecessary proliferation of names (mainly local) such as montrealite, an olivine-rich titanaugite gabbro; yamaskite, a melanocratic rock of pyroxene, hornblende and minor plagioclase; rougemontite, a plagioclase-rich variety of yamaskite; rouvillite, a nepheline-rich rock of plagioclase, alkali feldspar, minor amounts of augite, hornblende, biotite, and accessory apatite, sphene, and opaque oxides; beloeilite, a sodalite syenite; monnoirite, a rock transitional between essexite and pulaskite; okaite, a melilite rock with minor amounts of magnetite, nepheline, calcite, and accessory biotite, apatite and perovskite. They are illustrated diagram-

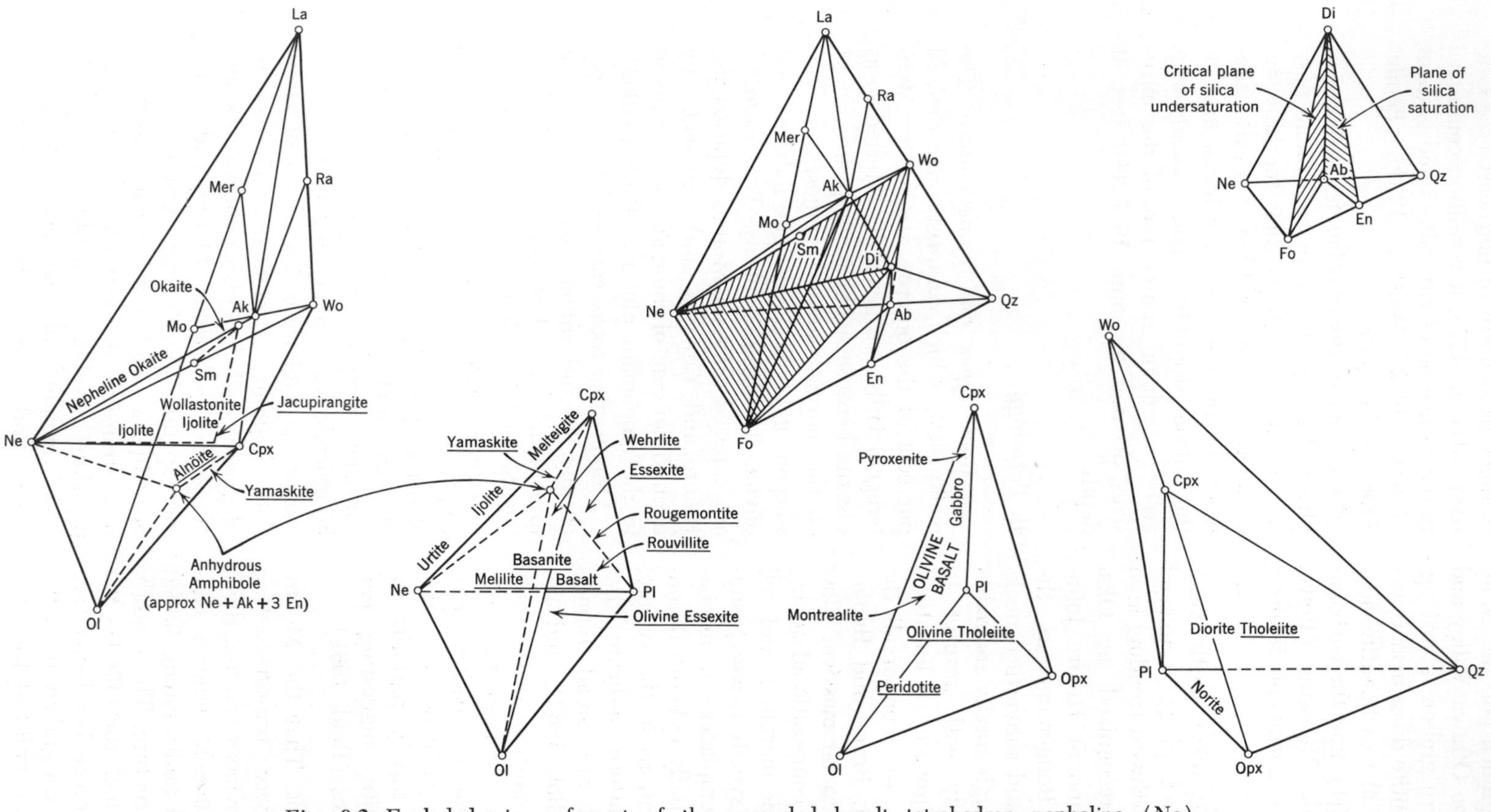

Fig. 9.2 Exploded view of part of the expanded basalt tetrahedron nepheline (Ne)–forsterite (Fo)–larnite (La)–silica (Qz), showing planes of silica saturation enstatite (En)–diopside (Di)–albite (Ab), and albite–diopside–wollastonite (Wo), and the planes (ruled lines) Di–Wo–Ne and Di–Fo–Ne, which separate albite from akermanite (Ak) (Schairer and Yoder, 1964). The generalized simple basalt system is illustrated in the upper right inset (Yoder and Tilley, 1962) with the main basalt types recorded in the exploded views. Also entered are the names of Monteregian rocks whose major modal phases are contained in the tetrahedron. Names underlined are within the tetrahedron: names on faces are written parallel to base. The anhydrous hastingsite composition (Amphibole) is contained in the nepheline–olivine (Ol)–clinopyroxene (Cpx)-plagioclase (Pl) tetrahedron, and is shown schematically within it and also projected onto the Ne–Ol–Cpx face. Mo, monticellite; Ra, rankinite; Sm, soda melilite; Opx, orthopyroxene.

matically in Fig. 9.2, an exploded view of the expanded basalt tetrahedron (Schairer and Yoder, 1964).

2. *Petrochemical character.* The available chemical analyses of Monteregian rocks (Faessler, 1962; Gold, 1963; Woodland, 1962; Lacroix, 1923) have been summarized in the form of petrographic diagrams. The alkali-lime indices (see Peacock, 1931) for St. Hilaire, Mt. Royal, and Oka rocks correspond to the 48.5, 48, and 42 per cent SiO_2 compositions, well below the 51 per cent that separates alkalic from alkali-calcic rocks.

Monteregian rocks classified according to the Rittmann (1962) suite index σ, are overwhelmingly Atlantic (alkalic) in character, and correspond closely in σ distribution to the volcanic rocks of the eastern Rift Valley in East Africa (El-Hinnawi, 1964). Rocks of Mediterranean character (potassic-alkalic) occur mainly in the western portion of Monteregian province (Oka, Como, Ste. Monique) as late phase lamprophyres. Those of Pacific character (calc-alkali, and calcic) center around Rougemont, with minor amounts from Mts. Royal and St. Bruno. Alumina is present in excess of alkalis except in an aplite inclusion in alnoite from Ile Cadieux.

3. *Summary of individual occurrences, from east to west.*

a. Mount Megantic. About 25 per cent of the hill is underlain by gabbroic rocks, which separate the central granite core from a peripheral syenite ring. The gabbro consists of plagioclase and varying amounts of hornblende, augite, biotite and magnetite. Amphibole commonly occurs as large poikilitic phenocrysts enclosing feldspar (Reid, 1961).

b. Brome Mountain. Mafic rocks, consisting of plagioclase, pyroxene, olivine, amphibole, with minor to accessory amounts of opaque oxides, apatite and biotite, underlie about 36 per cent of the mountain. Red-brown hornblende occurs as rims about titanaugite (z ^ c 43 to 52°, 2V 45 to 55°) crystals and aggregates, and as irregular poikilitic crystals enclosing plagioclase. Rims of brown biotite commonly surround magnetite. The plagioclase varies in composition from An_{70-85} in the olivine gabbro, to An_{50-70} in the titanaugite gabbro.

c. Shefford Mountain. The mafic rocks, which underlie about 37 per cent of the pluton, consist mainly of monzonites, diorites, and minor hornblende gabbros. Intensely pleochroic hornblende (z ^ c 11 to 20°) is the principal mafic mineral, and occurs as poikilitic aggregates with plagioclase that includes pale augite crystals. Brown biotite as rims around magnetite, accessory apatite, sphene, and zircon, complete the assemblage. The composition of the plagioclase varies from An_{14} in monzonite to An_{60} in the gabbro.

d. Mount Yamaska. The mafic rocks, which underlie about 90 per cent of the pluton, and akeritic rocks bordering on the north and western sides, form a continuous series. A compositional variation from pyroxenites (augite > hornblende, plagioclase An_{50-85}), through gabbros, essexite, and diorite (hornblende > augite, plagioclase An_{50-25}) to akerite, is well demonstrated, as is the apparent binary association between titanaugite (z ^ c 34 to 54°) and kaersutite (z ^ c 2 to 19°). Biotite is most abundant in the nepheline-bearing rocks, occurs as rims around magnetite, and as the alteration products from other ferromagnesian minerals.

e. Rougemont. Rougemont is composed of melanocratic peridotites and pyroxenites containing but little plagioclase (up to An_{93}), local plagioclase-rich segregations (rougemontites), and a border facies of olivine gabbro. From the few analyses available, it is seen that these rocks belong to the calc-alkali or calcic suites.

f. Mount Johnson. Though only 50 per cent consists of mafic rocks, the pluton is made up of a suite that varies from an olivine essexite core, through essexite, a transition rock (monnoirite), to peripheral pulaskite in a series of vertical coaxial cylinders. The essexites grade from a fine-grained rock consisting of plagioclase (An_{55-30}), nepheline, augite, hornblende and olivine, with accessory magnetite, biotite, apatite and sphene, to a coarse-grained porphyritic rock with rare olivine and more hornblende. Phenocrysts of plagioclase in the transition rock vary within the range An_{22-28}. Because of an excess of alkali over silica, Osborne (1935) postulated the presence of an undersaturated feldspar anemousite, but Pouliot (1962), because of the absence of any antiperthite, concluded that potash remains in solid solution as a consequence of rapid cooling, which is borne out by the higher structural state of the feldspar.

g. Mount St. Hilaire. Mafic rocks underlie the western part and represent approximately 65 per cent of the exposed portion of the pluton. The rocks grade outward from magnetite-rich pyroxenites and peridotite, through titanaugite gabbro, gabbro, and essexite to peripheral nepheline-rich essexite (rouvillite). They form a chemically and spatially related suite, cut by later syenitic injections. It is of interest to note that the pegmatitic bodies and segregations of sodalite syenite (tawite) within the syenitic mass, qualify chemically (41.84 per cent SiO_2) as ultrabasic rocks (for analysis see O'Neill, 1914). The feldspars vary in composition from An_{85-70} in peridotite to An_{45-10} in rouvillite. Potash feldspar in the rouvillite is monoclinic, and forms rims and overgrowths around earlier formed plagioclase. Nepheline occurs as irregular blebs, commonly interstitial to feldspar or intergrown with albite in graphitic textured grains.

This pluton is taken as the representative "Monteregian Hill," not only because a broad spectrum of Monteregian rocks are exposed and analyses available, but also because the ratio of mafic to silicic rocks conforms closely to that established for the Monteregian Province (Pouliot, 1962). The average composition of the pluton (column 10, Table 9.2) is derived by averaging an analysis of each major rock type (olivine pyroxenite, pyroxenite, porphyritic titanaugite gabbro, gabbro, essexite, rouvillite, sodalite syenite, nepheline syenite, and tinguaite). This may be compared (column 11) with the average of 10 alkali basalts from the East Pacific Rise (Engel et al., 1965).

h. Mount St. Bruno. This apparently single intrusion is composed mainly of peridotite, olivine pyroxenite, and olivine gabbro, with minor umptekites, and more feldspathic and dioritic rocks near the eastern border. Olivine ($Fo_{75}Fa_{25}$, optically negative) may constitute up to 45 per cent of the rock, and may contain sagenitic magnetite or spinel. Titanaugite ($z \wedge c$ 42 to 52°, $2V_z$ 45 to 50°) is typically Monteregian, and in places is surrounded by red-brown hornblende. The feldspar ranges in composition from An_{77-30} and commonly occurs in clusters interstitial to the pyroxenes.

i. Mount Royal. More data are available on this, the type hill, than any other. It consists mainly of mafic rocks intruded on its western side by small bodies of nepheline syenite. Pyroxenite, olivine pyroxenite (wehrlite), titanaugite gabbro, olivine gabbro, gabbro, diorite, and essexite are exposed or were intersected in a railway tunnel through the hill. The intrusive sequence envisaged by Bancroft and Howard (1923) is the following:

1. Essexite, forming the larger part of the pluton.
2. Dikes of bostonite and tinguaite, followed by camptonite and monchiquite.
3. Nepheline syenite as dikes and plug-like masses.
4. Dikes of camptonites, maenites and other varieties.
5. Numerous dikes of camptonites, with brecciation of the intruded rocks.
6. Younger nepheline syenites and pegmatitic varieties.
7. Camptonite dikes of at least two different ages.

TABLE 9.2 Analyses of Some Alkaline Rocks from the Oka Complex and Composite Averages from the St. Hilaire Pluton and East Pacific Rise

	1	2	3	4*	5	6	7	8†	9	10	11
SiO_2	30.58	30.01	34.90	31.91	33.52	43.16	38.87	35.41	27.81	44.88	47.54
TiO_2	1.64	2.78	1.16	2.11	3.95	0.46	0.59	2.57	1.33	3.82	2.90
Al_2O_3	9.52	11.27	15.99	14.69	11.30	14.97	13.59	11.25	7.59	16.47	18.21
Fe_2O_3	9.17	8.55	7.28	6.12	9.18	2.88	5.57	6.27	8.67	4.72	4.21
FeO	4.50	4.36	3.82	3.38	3.52	3.03	1.98	5.07	6.57	6.33	5.86
MnO	0.83	0.62	0.72	0.63	0.25	0.77	0.68	0.24	0.08	0.31	0.17
MgO	6.40	6.09	5.02	5.98	8.38	4.07	3.10	13.29	11.21	4.43	4.94
CaO	27.28	24.76	19.35	19.62	22.61	12.81	21.26	18.42	28.06	8.19	8.73
SrO	...	...	...	...	0.24	...	...	0.12	...	...	...
BaO	...	0.99	...	...	0.67	...	...	0.22	...	...	...
Na_2O	4.29	3.30	7.27	7.55	1.90	8.57	6.50	2.53	1.47	5.91	4.03
K_2O	0.71	0.81	2.08	0.98	0.54	4.98	2.41	2.20	1.26	2.67	1.68
P_2O_5	1.84	1.95	0.68	2.15	2.33	1.41	2.98	1.05	1.66	1.13	0.93
CO_2	2.13	1.93	1.29	1.87	0.90	1.81	1.56	0.24	2.51	0.36	...
H_2O^+	0.78	2.15	0.60	1.19	1.08	} 1.31	0.51	1.21	1.24	0.65	0.80
H_2O^-	0.02	0.29	0.02	0.05	0.06		0.20	0.00	0.11	...	...
	99.69	99.86	100.18	99.62	100.43	100.23	99.80	100.09	99.57	100.00	100.00
S.G.	3.14	2.98	2.98	2.99	3.21	3.03	3.04	3.17	3.10		
Modal constituents in volume per cent. (Point counted in thin section):											
No. of points	4243	3087	5458	3227	3255	2695	4061	3425			
Melilite	87.3	59.7	40.9	26.9	...	...	...	‡	...		
Nepheline	...	18.8	41.3	...	14.4	57.6	57.5	‡	c		
Pyroxene	...	...	...	8.8	69.5	37.7	11.5	32.9	a		
Olivine	...	...	...	...	...	...	...	6.3	c		
Biotite	2.5	3.0	2.3	8.5	4.8	0.2	...	22.7	b		
Opaque min.	3.9	4.7	3.0	2.7	2.0	...	0.1	3.7	...		
Apatite	1.6	3.2	1.8	4.1	5.4	3.4	2.6	‡	...		
Calcite	2.3	5.4	3.1	4.8	2.7	0.1	3.3	‡	c		
Perovskite	2.1	3.4	0.9	2.0	1.2	...	...	...	...		
Hauynite	0.3		6.7	42.0		...	...	...	...		
Melanite				0.2		1.0	10.2	‡	...		
Wollastonite							14.8	...	...		
Matrix								34.4	a		

* Also contains 1.39% S, calculated from SO_2.
† Total adjusted for 0.17% Cl.
‡ Constitute matrix, with glass(?) and zeolite minerals.
a = essential; b = subordinate; c = minor.

1. Okaite, Dufresne Hill. Sample Oka A-463. Analyst, H. Ulk, 1964.
2. Okaite, nepheline-rich. Sample DDH E8-36. Analyst, H. Ulk, 1961.
3. Nepheline okaite. Sample Oka A-72. Analyst, H. Ulk, 1964.
4. Titanaugite-hauynite okaite. Sample Oka A-172. Analyst, H. Ulk, 1964.
5. Jacupirangite, nepheline-rich. Sample DDH S9-370. Analyst, H. Ulk, 1961.
6. Coarse-grained ijolite. Sample Oka A-394. Analyst, H. Ulk, 1961.
7. Wollastonite-melanite ijolite. Sample DDH G15-330. Analyst, H. Ulk, 1963.
8. Alnoite, Bond zone. Sample Oka A-368. Analyst, H. Ulk, 1962.
9. Camptonite (alnoite), Hurereau Hill. Howard, 1922.
10. Average of 9 chemical analyses representing the major rock types of the St. Hilaire pluton, summed to 100.00.
11. Average of 10 alkali basalts from the East Pacific Rise. Engel et al., 1965.

j. Oka carbonatite and alkaline complex. At Oka carbonate rocks of at least seven different types and three main groups of alkaline ultrabasic rocks are associated in a double-ring structure intrusive into Precambrian gneisses and anorthosites. The first group, the okaite-jacupirangite rocks, are characterized by the presence of melilite and/or titanaugite, and grade from melilite-magnetite rocks, through nepheline-bearing varieties, melilite-nepheline-titanaugite rocks, to titanaugite-nepheline rocks, and titanaugite-rich rocks. Minor amounts of biotite, calcite, apatite, hauynite and perovskite may be present. Locally biotite, calcite and apatite are abundant. For variations in composition see Table 9.2, columns 1 to 5. The second group, the ijolitic rocks, include melteigite, ijolite, urtite and juvite, and are characterized by the presence, in varying proportion, of nepheline and sodian augite. Varietal types include melanite- and melanite-wollastonite urtites and ijolites (see Table 9.2, columns 6 and 7). The third group encompasses lamprophyric rocks (mainly alnoite) intruded as dikes, plugs and breccia pipes, and represents the final phase of intrusive activity. The analyses of two alnoites are given in Table 9.2, columns 8 and 9.

k. Alnoite plugs and breccia pipes. These represent a gas-rich pipe drilling phase during the closing stage of the Monteregian igneous activity (Gold, 1963). Phenocrysts of phlogopite, olivine ($Fo_{90}Fa_{10}$), titanaugite, and hornblende, in a matrix of fine-grained phlogopite, titanaugite, olivine, amphibole, nepheline, calcite, melilite, opaque oxides, apatite and perovskite, comprise the alnoite rocks. The alnoite breccia pipes and dikes at Oka contain lapilli of alnoite, which range from 0.1 to 30 mm in diameter, commonly enclosing phenocrysts, together with fragments of country-rock gneiss, Palaeozoic cover rocks, and various rocks associated with the Oka complex, in a carbonate-rich matrix. The "diatreme" breccias consist of country and cover rock fragments in a carbonated matrix of comminuted country rocks and rare phlogopite crystals. The alnoite plugs, alnoite breccia pipes, and "diatreme" breccia pipes apparently grade one into the other in the same conduit. Their emplacement is best explained by a gas-streaming or fluidization process (Gold, 1963).

Alnoite plugs, breccia pipes, and dikes are particularly abundant in the Oka area, where Gold (1964) has suggested that emplacement has been controlled by conjugate fractures about the axis of the Beauharnois arch. The St. Helen Island breccia pipe has long been of interest as some large blocks (up to 200 feet across) of Devonian rocks (Heldeberg and Oriskany limestone) indicate the presence at one time of post-Ordovician sediments in the Montreal area. During recent excavations on St. Helen Island for the World's Fair, alnoitic igneous rocks were exposed containing rounded inclusions of Precambrian gneiss. Breccia pipes, exposed in Precambrian gneiss near the north and northeastern margins of the Oka complex, contain Palaeozoic rock fragments from as high up in the succession as Utica. Lower Devonian limestone, at least 2000 feet below its normal stratigraphic position, was intersected in drill holes in the nepheline syenite breccia on Mt. St. Hilaire (Gold, 1963). Estimates of the amount of erosion since the time of intrusion are 4800 feet above the summit of Mt. Royal (Clark, 1955) for the Montreal area, and 8000 to 10,000 feet in the Oka area (Gold, 1963).

l. New England dikes. Unmetamorphosed dikes, many with distinct alkaline affinities, are exposed in the northern New England States and southern Quebec. The following types have been recognized: olivine diabase, camptonite, augite camptonite, fourchite and monchiquite, as well as silicic varieties.

C. Mineralogy

1. Olivine. Olivines ($Fo_{76}Fa_{24}$ to $Fo_{62}Fa_{38}$) in the Monteregian "gabbros" are associated with pyroxene, and appear to have precipitated in cotectic fashion from a single liquid (Beall, 1962). The common olivine mineral in the carbonatite at Oka is monticellite, though locally rare forsterite is present. Chrysolite ($Fo_{85}Fa_{15}$) is common as phenocrysts in alnoite; in places it is rimmed by later monticellite. Alteration is rare, except in the Bon Conseil plug and in the hydrothermal zones of the Oka complex.

2. Melilite. Melilite in the okaite rocks at Oka is unzoned and conforms to the general formula $NaM_{35}Ge_{11}Ak_{54}$, where NaM represents sodamelilite, Ge gehlenite, and Ak akermanite. Nowhere else is melilite found except in melilite carbonatite, alnoite, and in the skarn rocks on Mounts Royal and St. Hilaire.

3. Pyroxene. The typical Monteregian pyroxenes are purple-brown "titanaugite" with $2V_z$ 45 to 55°, and extinction $z \wedge c$ 34 to 54°. The pleochroic formula is commonly: N_x, light yellow brown; N_y and N_z, light purplish brown. Many contain zones of sagenitic rutile. Their TiO_2 content (about 1.5 per cent) is low when compared with the 4 per cent for titanaugites from other peralkaline rocks (LeBas, 1962), and is probably due to the coprecipitation of either sphene, titaniferous hornblende, or perovskite acting as a sink for titanium. Beall (1962) analyzed 14 pyroxenes from 8 plutons and found greater concentrations of Ti, Fe^{3+}, Na, and Al than in those from layered ultramafic complexes. The high Fe_2O_3 content (about 2 per cent, and up to 5 per cent in rocks from Oka), suggest high oxygen fugacities, probably through outgassing of a magma under near surface conditions (Beall, 1962). The accompaniment of Na with Fe^{3+} in coupled substitutions, and the soda-rich environment, accounts for the high soda content. Alumina substitution in the Z position decreases with differentiation, marked by the sequence diopside-augite-aegerineaugite. In places (Yamaska, St. Pie), the augites are zoned with light green diopsidic cores ($z \wedge c$ 34°, $2V_z$ 30 to 35°), in which the rims are richer in Fe^{2+}, Fe^{3+}, Ca, Ti and poorer in Mg, Al, Na, K than the core (Beall, 1962, p. 197). Sodian augite is found in ijolitic rocks, and "soda-pyroxene carbonatite" at Oka. A 24.7 Al substitution in Z in Oka jacupirangite is close to the theoretical limit.

4. Amphibole. Except at Oka, where the dominant amphibole is richterite, the common Monteregian amphibole is a red-brown to rusty-brown, titanium-rich oxyhornblende, with a small extinction angle ($z \wedge c$ 2 to 20°). The pleochroic formula is: N_x light yellow brown, N_y dark brown, N_z red-brown. Three analyses of amphiboles from Mts. Royal and Johnson represent oxyhornblende, intermediate in composition between the end members hastingsite, ferrohastingsite and ferrihastingsite, with Ti^{3+} substituting for Al^{3+} and Fe^{3+} (Beall, 1962). Lamprobolite is present as phenocrysts in the alnoite.

5. Plagioclase feldspar. These are common in all plutons except Oka. Compositions range from An_{93} to An_0; zoning is widespread, with up to a 15 per cent spread in composition. They are commonly twinned according to the albite and carlsbad laws. In a study of the composition and structural state of plagioclase (see Fig. 9.3) from the 8 central plutons, Pouliot (1962) found that: (a) there were no high forms, (b) that the plagioclase from the smaller plutons were more disordered than those from the larger, and (c) the structural states were consistent with those from hypabyssal rocks, and higher than those of the layered ultramafic intrusive bodies.

D. Petrological Considerations

1. Field aspects. The continuous chemical and mineralogical variations, and in places the spatial arrangement of rock types, suggest that the Monteregian rocks are products of magmatic differentiation. The lack of marked chemical variation among the mafic rocks of certain plutons,

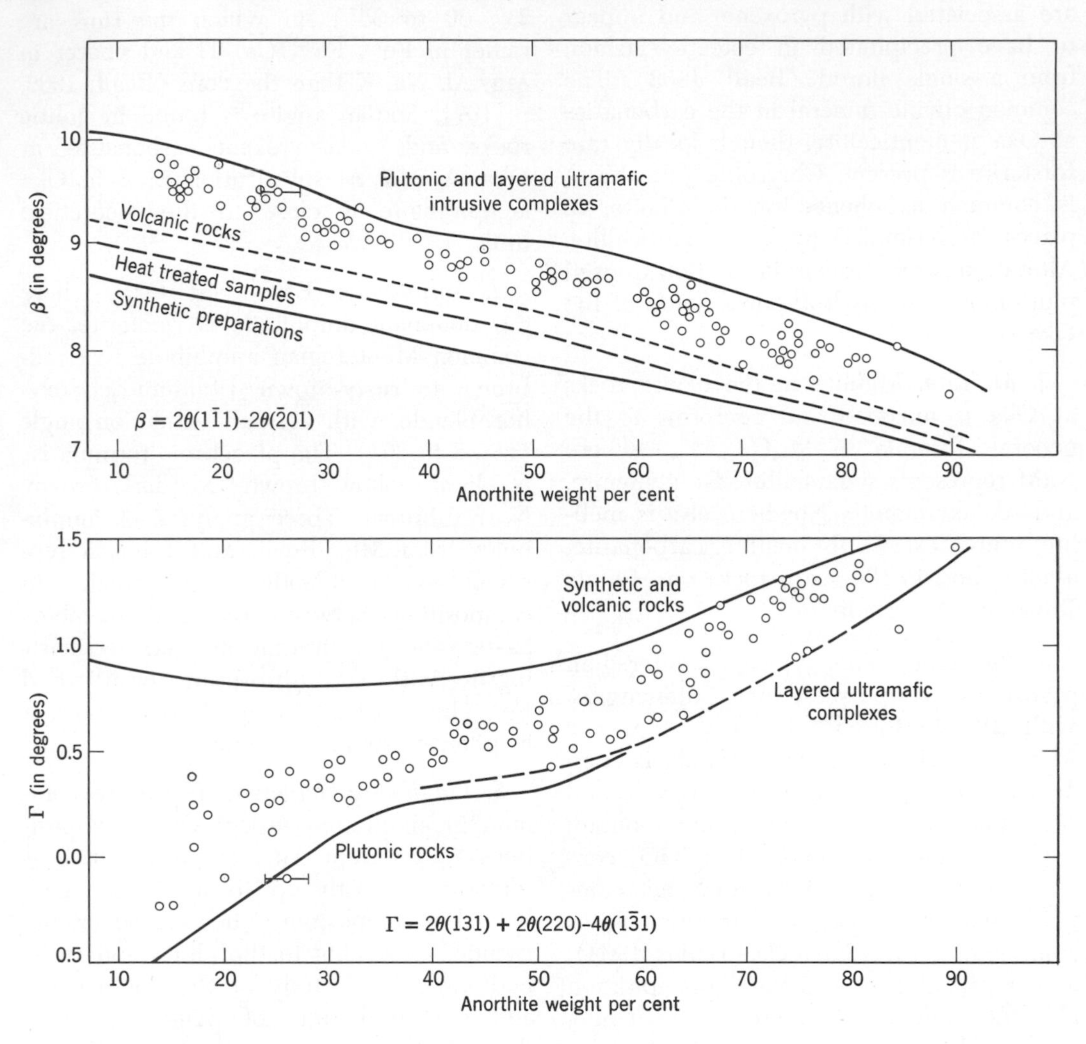

Fig. 9.3 Diagrams showing the structural state of plagioclase from some Monteregian plutons. The general Monteregian trend is compiled from data on rocks from Mounts Royal, Bruno, St. Hilaire, Rougemont, Johnson, Yamaska, Shefford, and Brome, given by Pouliot (1962), and compared with those of layered ultramafic plutons, plutonic rocks, volcanic rocks, heat treated samples, and synthetic preparations, given by Smith and Gay (1958). Values of 2θ are for CuKα radiation.

for example, overall peridotitic composition of Mounts St. Bruno and Rougemont, gabbro of Brome and Megantic, diorite of Shefford, alnoite in the late pipes —suggest modification through differentiation or selective melting of the source material at depth, whereas the consistent association of peridotite-pyroxenite-gabbro-diorite-syenite in Mounts Royal, St. Hilaire, Johnson, Yamaska, and pyroxenite to nephelinite at Oka, suggests parallel differentiation trends from local magma chambers. The horizontal variation into essentially vertical cylindrical pipes at Mounts Johnson and St. Hilaire may reflect continuous crystallization in a local chamber, with progressive emplacement and consolidation of the more acid rocks peripherally and the more basic rocks in a mobile core of diminishing diameter. Phenocrysts in trachytic textured rocks, the zoning of plagioclase and pyroxene crystals, attest to movement of a partially crystalline melt and to disequilibrium conditions between crystals and melt.

2. Differentiation trends. Three independent differentiation trends appear to have developed. One a nepheline-free, saturated trend as in Brome, Shefford, and Megantic; the second an intermediate, subsiliceous trend in which there is normative, but not necessarily modal nepheline as in the central plutons; the third is an undersaturated, peralkaline, nepheline-rich trend as exemplified by the rocks at Oka. Pouliot (1962) recognized a saturated (nepheline-free) trend and an undersaturated (nepheline-bearing) trend in his study of the feldspars (see Fig. 9.4). The above trends are consistent with the basalt types proposed by Yoder and Tilley (1962) (see Fig. 9.2). The general chemical trend is for an increase in alumina and alkali, and a decrease in ferromagnesian and lime components with increasing SiO_2 content; that is, a normal Niggli diagram (see Gold, 1963; Kapp, 1961). Notable exceptions to this trend are found in the St. Hilaire syenite suite, which shows a reverse sequence to the above, and in the carbonate rock suite at Oka, where ferromagnesian components increase with increasing SiO_2.

3. Possible mechanisms of differentiation. In order to consider possible differentiation mechanisms, we will have to speculate on the composition of the parent magma. The average Monteregian rock should be similar to the average St. Hilaire rock (Table 9.2, column 10) (see also Section B-3-g), and have an approximate modal composition of: augite 40 per cent, plagioclase 30 per cent, hornblende 5 to 10 per cent, olivine 0 to 10 per cent, biotite 0 to 10 per cent, titanomagnetite 5 to 10 per cent, apatite 5 per cent. By inference this should represent the parent magma. It corresponds closely to the commonly accepted parental alkali basalt magma (Schairer and Yoder, 1964), which could be represented by the minerals clinopyroxene, plagioclase, and olivine. This composition lies close to the Di-Ab-Fo plane, the plane of critical undersaturation (see Fig. 9.2). Other parental liquids lying close to the Di-Fo-Ne plane (olivine nephelinites) and the Di-Fo-Ak plane (melilite basalt) could fractionate to produce the okaite and ijolitic rocks at Oka (see flow sheet of Schairer and Yoder, 1964).

Representing the calcic gabbros with the compositional tetrahedron Ca Tsch-Fo-Mo-Qz,—i.e., calcium tschermak molecule ($CaAl_2SiO_6$) and anorthite replace nepheline and albite in Fig. 9.2—Beall (1962) shows that the location of the thermal divide, which lies on a plane slightly inclined (Schairer and Yoder, 1964) to the Fo-Di-Ab plane, shifts through a "zone of

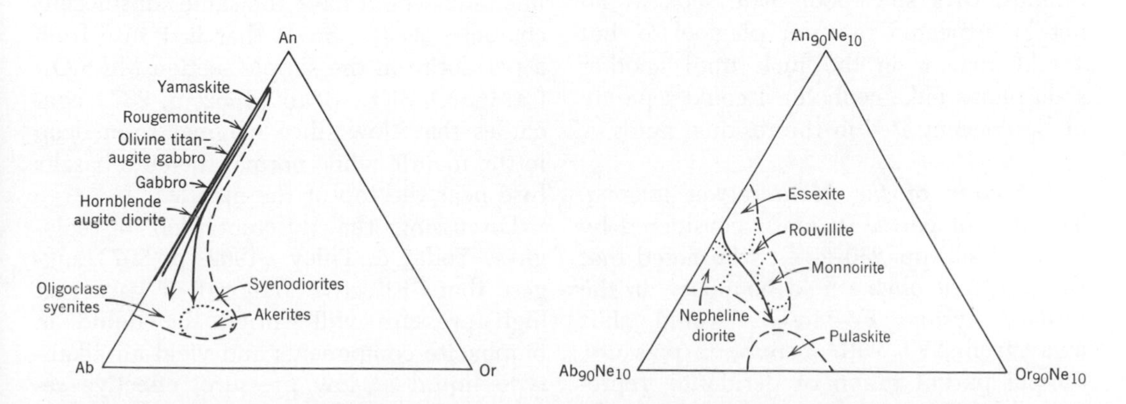

Fig. 9.4 Differentiation trends in the central Monteregian plutons as depicted by the change in composition of the feldspars. (*left*) The nepheline-free trend; (*right*) the nepheline-bearing trend (after Pouliot, 1962).

residual uncertainty" in a generally predictable manner. The region of compositions capable of differentiating to an undersaturated alkali residua is decreased by dissolved anorthite and/or volatiles (steam) in the melt, and by extensive substitution of alumina in pyroxenes (Beall, 1962). Wet conditions would favor the early crystallization of hornblende, which lies on the subsiliceous side of the An-Di-Fo plane, thus enriching the melt in SiO_2. Bulk compositions falling either side of this zone would differentiate towards their respective types, whereas those within this zone could go either way depending on the above conditions.

From thermodynamic considerations of the ternary system Ne-An-Qz (Beall, 1962, especially p. 225) predicted an extensive solid-liquid field for plagioclase in low silica regions, favoring early crystallization of high calcic plagioclase. For a melt of 43 per cent SiO_2, in which the ratio of $NaAlO_2/CaAl_2O_4$ components is unity, the first plagioclase to precipitate is An_{92}, whereas for a 77 per cent SiO_2 melt the first plagioclase is An_{71}. Limited crystallization would cause a marked increase in the soda content of the melt, and a corresponding spread of plagioclase compositions in equilibrium with the melt during continued crystallization. Disequilibrium conditions and zoning will result unless crystallization is unusually slow and continuous. In a silica-poor melt, soda would not be expected to enter plagioclase, but would remain in the melt until another soda phase (like nepheline) could separate or be concentrated in the residual fluids.

4. Source of the Monteregian magma. The role of partial fusion is considered by Beall (1962, pp. 230–237), who noted that the pyroxene-olivine field boundary, in the ternary system Fo-Mo-Qz, would shift away from SiO_2 with increase in pressure. Simple partial fusion of peridotite, represented by this system, would produce subsiliceous magmas under high pressure conditions and normal basalt magmas under lower pressure conditions. Multiple partial fusion, with transport of the melt, would give similar rocks to those crystallizing from residual liquids developed from fractional crystallization of a peridotite. Beall (1962, p. 231) notes:

"Repetition of the partial fusion process is an effective means of forming liquids whose compositions differ greatly from the rock from which they developed. It would be expected to be very important in nature, because solids which have resulted from complete crystallization of liquids which previously had fused fractionally from a host rock always will have lower solidus temperature than the host rock, and hence are very susceptible to refusion."

The effect of iron appears to be minimal, as replacement of half Mg by Fe would cause the Ol liquidus to expand slightly from Opx to Qz, and contract from Cpx to Ol. As already noted, the An component in the melt would cause the Ol field to shrink. However, the appearance of garnet (Ga) on the liquidus in the quarternary system Fo-Di-An-Qz, would expand with increasing pressure so that Ga, Py, and Fo are the only phases occurring on the liquidus in the low silica, low alumina region of the tetrahedron. Partial fusion at high pressure (approximately 50 kb) of compositions lying in the Fo liquid volume, would produce melts on the Fo-Py, Fo-Ga boundary surfaces, Fo-Py-Ga boundary line, and would have the same subsiliceous character as the fluids that first fuse from a peridotite in the simple section Mg_2SiO_4-$CaMgSiO_4$-SiO_2. Beall (1962, p. 237) concludes that "low silica magmas form deep in the mantle while normal tholeiite basalts fuse near the top of the mantle."

Discussing the differentiation of eclogites, Yoder & Tilley (1962, p. 507) suggest that "Effective removal of garnet at high pressure will enrich the liquid in omphacite components and yield an alkali-type liquid at low pressure; effective removal of omphacite at high pressure will enrich the liquid in garnet components and yield a tholeiite-type liquid." Shift of the boundary curve towards garnet at low pressure and omphacite at high pressure indicate that the liquid which "would produce alkali basalt at the surface would come from greater depths than those liquids which would produce tholeiite at the surface."

A simple Monteregian magma can be represented in the system Fo-Di-An-Qz by adding soda-plagioclase and iron oxide. It is suggested that it formed by simple or repetitive partial fusion of peridotite within the mantle.

5. Implications from isotopic and geochemical data. A mean Sr^{87}/Sr^{86} ratio of 0.7040 has been established for nine Monteregian plutons (Fairbairn et al., 1963). Ratios for individual localities are recorded on Fig. 9.1. The carbonatite at Oka (0.7032) conforms to the mean established for carbonatites in general (Powell et al., 1963) and the associated silicate rocks. Monteregian rocks correspond in ratio to oceanic basalts (0.7040); they are lower than those for continental basalts (0.7050), and the 0.7090 for sedimentary carbonate rocks, supporting the belief that this ratio decreases in the mantle (Faure et al., 1963). Carbon and oxygen isotope ratios, and trace element content of the Oka carbonatite conform to those established for carbonatites in general (Gold, 1964b). Inasmuch as Rb^{87} decays to Sr^{87}, low Sr^{87}/Sr^{86} ratios imply high K/Rb ratios, Thomp-

TABLE 9.3 Comparison of K/Rb Ratios of Some Monteregian Rocks and Minerals with Other Major Rock Types (See Tables 11.9 and 11.10)

Samples	Number of Samples	Mean K/Rb	Standard Deviation	Reference
Mixed layer chlorite-biotite from Palaeozoic limestone, included in or adjacent to Monteregian silicate rocks from Mt. Royal and St. Hilaire	14	225	57	Thompson, 1964
Hornfels, St. Hilaire	1	236	...	Gold, 1963
Biotite from alnoite, Oka Complex	1	290	...	Thompson, 1964
Biotite from okaite, Oka Complex	1	212	...	Thompson, 1964
Biotite from carbonatite, Oka Complex	3	121.7	4.5	Thompson, 1964
Biotite from carbonatite, Oka Complex	1	94.7	...	Fairbairn et al., 1963
Biotite from essexite, Mt. Johnson	1	94.8*	...	Fairbairn et al., 1963
Biotite from granite, Mt. Megantic	1	50.5*	...	Fairbairn et al., 1963
Biotite from nordmarkite, Brome Mtn.	1	279*	...	Fairbairn et al., 1963
Gabbroic rocks ($<2\%$ K_2O), St. Hilaire	8	264.5	68.9	Gold, 1963
Essexitic rocks ($>2\%$ K_2O), St. Hilaire	5	291.6	58	Gold, 1963
Syenite, St. Hilaire	3	301.6	79.8	Gold, 1963
Syenite porphyry, St. Hilaire	4	245	96.6	Gold, 1963
Tawite, St. Hilaire	1	75.6		Gold, 1963
Crust (sedimentary, metamorphic and igneous rocks)		250		Thompson, 1964
Upper oceanic mantle (low potash tholeiites and Hawaiian alkali lavas)		512		Lessing et al., 1963
High potash ($>2\%$ K_2O) Hawaiian alkali lavas		260		Lessing et al., 1963
Upper continental mantle		310		Gast, 1960

* K and Rb measurements were not made on the same sample.

son (1964) measured K/Rb ratios in biotite from some Monteregian rocks and found the environment so indicated to be at variance with that inferred from the Sr^{87}/Sr^{86} data (see Table 9.3).

6. Other considerations. The presence of calcite and apatite, in varying amounts, in Monteregian rocks, necessitates consideration of the role of CO_2 and P_2O_5 in the evolution of these rocks. That the magma was dry is demonstrated by the lack of pneumatolytic and/or hydrothermal effects in the country rocks around all plutons (except Oka), the intermediate structural state of the plagioclase feldspars (wet conditions, i.e., dissolved volatiles in the melt, would facilitate unmixing), by analogy with the differentiation mechanisms suggested by the synthetic systems (Section D-3). Outgassing obviously had taken place (assuming that all magmas have a real volatile content) before emplacement in the local chambers, probably in the western part of the province (beneath the Oka region). Where favorable structural traps were available, volatiles collected and carbonatites formed (Gold, 1963). The change in character of the Monteregian rocks from west to east (Sections A-1, B-3), suggest migration of the magma along a plunging conduit—up from the west (deep) to the east (shallow)—being tapped in transit to form local essentially vertical magma chambers at fairly regular intervals.

IV. A COMPARISON OF SWEDISH, AFRICAN, AND RUSSIAN KIMBERLITES

H. von Eckermann

A. Introduction

In the Krishnan volume of the Indian Geological Survey (von Eckermann, 1964c) I described the Swedish kimberlites, their relation to the associated carbonatites, and their composition in comparison with the African and Russian kimberlites. Since that paper was written (1962), I have read several other papers that deal with the latter two groups of kimberlites and have extended my own research on the problems of the Swedish group. Therefore, I have deemed it appropriate to rewrite my earlier paper, making it more complete and bringing it up to date.

B. Nomenclature

According to Shand (1934) the endogenous minerals of the kimberlitic magma are olivine, serpentine, phlogopite, ilmenite, and perovskite, with a little augite in some rocks. As this assemblage contains very little lime, and all chemical analyses of kimberlite show much lime, Shand concluded that "in the earlier stage of its history kimberlite must have contained some easily decomposed lime-mineral." Shand found melilite the only known mineral to fit, and suggested an alteration of melilite-basalt into kimberlite. Shand considered enstatite, diopside, and pyrope-garnet to be foreign bodies, picked up and enclosed in the kimberlitic magma. The original name "kimberlite," proposed by Lewis, stood for a porphyritic peridotite carrying all these minerals. Today kimberlite is also used for porphyritic peridotites containing only Shand's endogenous minerals, and that is the sense in which it is used in this paper. In the Swedish kimberlites, however, the porphyritic texture is not always in evidence megascopically and sometimes even not microscopically, due to the gravitative settling of the olivine crystals towards the bottoms of the dikes, leaving the upper parts of the dikes even-grained. Along contacts and in narrow dikes the reduction of grain size of the chilled borders also makes the porphyritic texture megascopically unapparent even if it is evident microscopically. Some chrome-spinel is generally present.

C. The Swedish Kimberlites

Shand's description of the kimberlites of South Africa agrees fairly well with some rocks termed kimberlites that occur as dikes and fragments in volcanic and tuffitic breccias at Alnö Island and the surrounding mainland on the Baltic west coast, and as dikes on the islands and promontories at the northern end of the Baltic. In these Swedish rocks, however, the phlogopite is occasionally replaced by more biotitic micas. Enstatite, diopside, and pyrope-garnet are absent, but some melanite occurs occasionally as a secondary mineral within pseudomorphs of melilite. Fresh melilite is very rare, but pseudomorphs of melilite occur frequently. The rocks are illustrated in Figs. 9.5, 9.6, and 9.7.

The term "kimberlite" was first used for Swedish rocks by Geijer (1928) when describing dikes from the coast region of the northern Baltic. He wrote: "What is called in South Africa a micaceous kimberlite is a rock identical in all essential features with the reconstructed character of the Skogsudden dikes, only that such a high content of augite as in the latter is not common." These dikes were later mapped and described in detail by Larsson (1943) who subdivided them into three groups: alnöitic, picrite-porphyritic, and carbonatitic kimberlites. The first group is characterized by phenocrysts of biotite and olivine pseudomorphs, the second by olivine pseudomorphs alone, and the third by a small amount of olivine pseudomorphs (within a dolomitic groundmass) and vesicles filled by later crystallized carbonate, around which mica and aegirine crystals are tangentially oriented.

The use of the term "alnöite" for the rocks of the first group is, according to Geijer, questionable "without straining to a considerable degree the limitations of this term." The alnöite, when first discovered on the Alnö island, was called by Törnebohm (1882, p. 240) melilite-basalt and its mineralogy was stated to be phenocrysts of biotite, augite, olivine, and apatite in a matrix of melilite, perovskite, apatite, and some calcite. Eichstädt (p. 194) later added anomite phenocrysts and Högbom

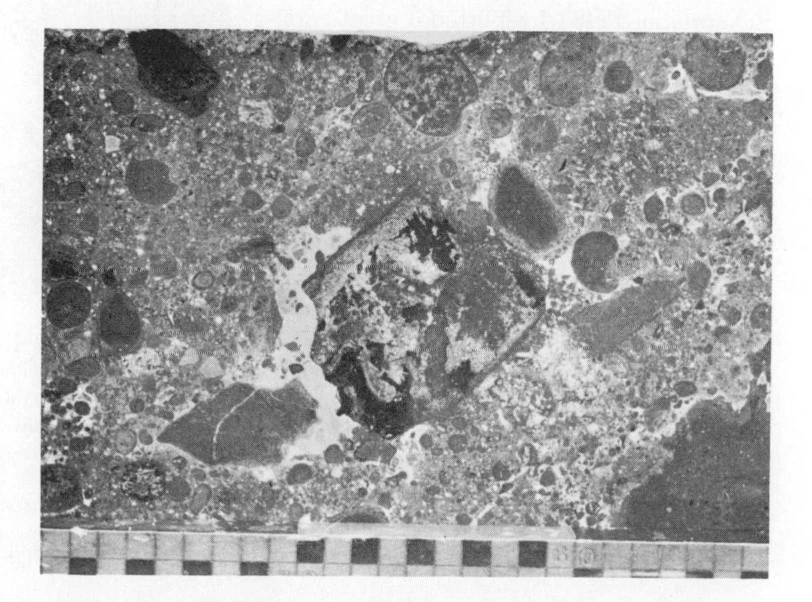

Fig. 9.5 Tuffitic boulder from the mainland west of the Alnö Island. The central fragment is alnöitic, the one down to the left kimberlitic, while the one immediately to the upper right of the alnöite is sandstone. White areas are secondary calcite. Scale: 1:1.14.

Fig. 9.6 Kimberlite from center of a dyke with well-crystallized olivines and a fine-grained ground mass of melilite, mica (phlogopitic), ilmenite and chrome-spinel. Ordinary light. Magnif.: ×91.

(1895, p. 235) phenocrysts of titaniferous magnetite and yellowish garnet occasionally surrounding the melilite crystals. In 1948 in lectures as well as in a paper (von Eckermann, 1948) I reported a great variation of the melilite content of the alnöites and the discovery of an alnöite at Stavreviken on the mainland northwest of Alnö which contained no melilite.

The name "alnöite" was first proposed by Rosenbusch for a group of melilite-bearing dike rocks, not belonging to the basalts of later epochs but closely related to older "elaeolith"-syenites. This relationship, however, as far as Alnö is concerned is not a direct one, the nepheline syenites being the metasomatic product of the surrounding gneiss-granite caused by the interaction between the latter and magmatic carbonatite. As further discussed below, the carbonatite is believed to be a byproduct of the transformation of melilite-basalt into kimberlite, as already suggested by Shand. The mineral composition of the original alnöite was also microscopically determined and excellently described by Berwerth (1893, p. 440). In my Alnö Memoir I suggested a nomenclature based on percentages of the constituent minerals, in which alnöite, kimberlite, and intermediary rocks could be clearly defined (von Eckermann, 1948, pp. 14–15).

Geijer (1928, p. 14) emphasized the intimate relation between alnöite and micaceous kimberlite, quoting the available literature of Wagner, Rimann, and Brögger. He found it improbable that such small quantities of kimberlite magma as represented by the Kalix dikes "have

Fig. 9.7 Kimberlite from margin of a great dyke. The big olivine crystal is partly serpentinized and the original crystal faces ground away, as if the crystal has moved in a crystal mush. The melilite laths of the matrix are mostly altered into minute garnet grains, clay minerals, and carbonate. The three dark spots in the upper part of the olivine are pyrochlore or perovskite crystals. Ordinary light. Magnif.: ×91.

travelled alone from the great depth" and suggested an accompanying igneous body of larger dimensions. He assumed its position to be hidden below the waters of the Bothnian Gulf and not necessarily at the present rock surface. Larsson (1943), on the other hand, believed the emplacement of the dikes to suggest a tectonic connection with a regional deformation of the earth crust. This, in turn, would exclude the necessity of a central alkaline area comparable with that of Alnö. The mineralogical and chemical characteristics of the Kalix dikes, however, are so closely related to those of the Alnö area, that there could hardly be any doubt whatever of a very close relationship between the two as well as of a common age and genetic descent. The conformity is illustrated by Table 9.4.

TABLE 9.4 Comparison of Melilite-basalt and Alnöite

	1	2
SiO_2	31.17	29.25
TiO_2	2.96	2.54
Al_2O_3	6.25	8.80
Fe_2O_3	3.22	3.92
FeO	9.64	5.42
MgO	19.19	17.66
CaO	17.76	17.86
K_2O	2.51	2.45
Na_2O	2.03	0.77
P_2O_5	1.69	2.86
H_2O	2.05	2.61

1. Melilite basalt, Sutherland, analysis No. 60 in *Geology of South Africa*, A. L. du Toit (1954).
2. Alnöite at Norrvik, Alnö Island, analysis No. 73 in *The Alkaline District of Alnö Island*, H. von Eckermann (1948).

I therefore support Geijer's view of the existence of a larger body, or perhaps several, of kimberlitic or alnöitic composition, from which the dikes were intruded along tension fissures formed by the fracturing of the overlying rocks when the internal gas pressure of the carbonatite-capped ascending lava exceeded the lithostatic load; but I also agree with Larsson's suggestion that a surrounding aureole of metasomatically formed alkaline rocks may not necessarily have been formed. The kimberlites of Kalix in the Alnö-nomenclature are more or less kimberlitic beforsites and alvikites. They represent the basal parts of the carbonatites formed at the top of the lava column by the rise from below of a stream of carbon fugitives, and probably squeezed out in the tension fissures in the wake of the preceding, even more purely carbonatitic liquids. At Alnö, their grouping into dominantly calcitic and dominantly dolomitic carbonates suggest at least two different high-pressure centers of high tension carbonates (von Eckermann, 1948).

Recently, support for Geijer's view has been obtained by Professor F. E. Wickman and L. Söderstrom during his search for evidence of Swedish craters formed by the impact of meteors. Two possible submarine circular depressions with central elevated parts have been located, one east of the islands outside Luleå and south of Kalix, confirming Geijer's suggestion, and another in Åviken Bay east-northeast of Alnö Island, confirming the presence of another alkaline intrusion foretold by the present author (1948, pp. 126–127).

Since 1960 many tuffitic boulders have been discovered within the Alnö region by Åke Hörsten, S. Söderström, and myself. These represent tuffitic out-throws from an explosive diatreme whose outcrop remains unknown. So far, no inclusions of sövite or any other primary carbonatites have been discovered in any of these boulders, which led me to suggest (von Eckermann, 1966) that the supposed Åvike diatreme has been blown out by gases collected on top of a kimberlitic-alnöitic magma and mainly composed of CH_4 and H but lacking oxygen, while the origin of the earlier sövite-diatreme at Alnö was due to high-tension volcanic gases rich in carbon oxides and poor in water. The separate location of carbonatite and kimberlite diatremes may not be evidence of nonconsanguinity, but of lateral displacement of the volcanic juvenile gases that have lost their oxygen content by the formation of carbon oxides (carbonates) and water. This may explain the inflammable gases, extremely rich in methane and hydrogen, encountered during exploratory drillings in Russian kimberlite diatremes and quoted by Davidson (1964, pp. 193–194). Petersilie (1960, pp. 210–223) also discussed this very rare phenomenon in connection with the alkali rocks in the Kola peninsula, and there is no reason why similar concentrations of inflammable gases could not be found underneath the three known Swedish kimberlitic and carbonatitic diatremes.

The presence of tuffites in the glacial moraine drift all over the Alnö and Åvike regions suggest the existence of a considerable tuffitic volcanic superstructure at the beginning of the last glaciation, which remained until the very end of glacial times and as late as 7200 years ago in those parts of the country. Some outcrops *in situ* may even remain underneath the moraine. This raises the question of the age of the tuffitic diatreme. The age of the pyrochlore minerals in the sövitic intrusion lies somewhere between 560 to 570 million years (von Eckermann and Wickman, 1956). Various considerations lead me to conclude that a very long time lapsed between the formation of the carbonatite and the blowing out of the kimberlitic diatreme of Åvike Bay, which caused the formation of the volcanic superstructure. The lack of carbonatite fragments in about 60 tuffitic boulders of sizes up to several tons is notable. The calcite found in some of them is secondary. Their resemblance to Russian kimberlitic tuffs is striking (Bobrievich et al., 1964, Fig. 10).

During the accumulation of carbonic acid or any other carbon fugitive the increasing gas concentration and rising pressure leads to carbonatization of the olivines, melilites and perovskites. When the pressure is relieved, the minerals are no longer subject to this metamorphism. Especially is this noticeable for the olivines which are the last to be metamorphosed. Even strongly carbonatitic magma from levels below the fracturing center may, in consequence, rise in the wake of the one already squeezed out and produce kimberlitic dikes with quite fresh olivines. An analogous phenomenon in which carbonic acid of one dike escaped through the wall-rocks and the olivine remained fresh, while in another with impermeable walls they were metamorphosed, was recently described by the author (von Eckermann, 1963a, 1963b). Åhman (1950, pp. 207–211) found a boulder in the Kalix region that contained a kimberlitic carbonatite dike with fresh olivines. The mineral paragenesis and the texture of the rock strongly emphasize the intimate relationship between the Kalix and Alnö rocks.

According to results obtained by examination of a large number of dikes, the typical alnöite of low calcite content is typical to represent the melilite-basalt from which the kimberlite rocks derive. Shand (1934) did not discuss by which process a parent melilite-basalt lost some of its lime, thus converting into kimberlite. The discovery of globules of carbonate in the Alnö kimberlites, increasing in number in the more carbonatitic types, led me to suggest (von Eckermann, 1961) a CO_2-saturation of the kimberlite followed by a concentration at the top of the magma column of the still rising high-tensioned and now immiscible carbonate globules. The description given by Larsson of the carbonate-filled "vesicles" of his third group of Kalix dikes (1943, p. 27) leaves little doubt that they are similar globules and not ordinary *in situ* vesicles. The immiscibility of carbonate globules when passing through kimberlite magma with already completely carbonatized melilites was only a working hypothesis and I wrote: "that it may seem a wild flight of fantasy insufficiently supported by experimental and field data" (von Eckermann, 1961, p. 35). Since then some very important contribution to the problems of the geneses of both carbonatites and kimberlites have been made. Koster van Groos and Wyllie (1963, 1966) experimentally showed that an immiscibility relationship does exist between alkali carbonatite melts and silicate melts. Although the experiments were restricted to sodic carbonatite and are thus not directly applicable to the dominantly potassic Swedish carbonatites, they nevertheless make my hypothesis more credible.

D. Swedish, South African, and Russian Kimberlites

The alnöite is chemically very similar to the melilite-basalt, or olivine-melilitite, the main difference being the higher K/Na ratio of the alnöite, as shown by the comparison in Table 9.4. One may, in consequence, be justified in assuming that kimberlite derived from melilite basalt in Africa and that derived from alnöite should also be very similar. As already mentioned, the mineral compositions of the kimberlites of South Africa and of Alnö are similar if only the primary minerals are considered. The secondary minerals, however, picked up and enclosed in the magma, are different. For instance, the pink pyrope-garnet of the South-African rocks is missing in the corresponding Alnö rocks, which on the other hand may contain yellow to brownish-yellow melanite-garnet. Furthermore, this melanite is not a foreign body but generally one of the minerals formed with carbonatization of the melilite during the transition of alnöite into kimberlite. Occasionally alnöite also contains primary melanitic garnet, which may be represented in the kimberlite by garnets with melanitic kernels and grossularitic rims. Even in very strongly carbonatized kimberlites, the melilite is recognizable as pseudomorphs, but altered into garnet, carbonate of mostly dolomitic composition and clay minerals, usually montmorillonitic, or into phlogopite and illitic minerals. Sometimes the pseudomorphs consist of pure carbonate, as in the dikes of the Ruri carbonatite complexes in western Kenya (McCall, 1965, Plate XII). Occasionally the minute garnet grains of the pseudomorphs of the Swedish kimberlites seem to have recrystallized into larger melanitic crystals. If the pyrope-garnet of the South African as well as of the U.S.S.R. Siberian kimberlites could be supposed to have originated in an analogous way, the similarity between the three rocks would be even more marked.

The Alnö rocks do not contain the enstatite and diopside of the South African kimberlites; instead they contain augite and aegirine-augite. The former minerals may be picked-up "foreign bodies" (Shand, 1934), but the latter are certainly not. At two localities on the Alnö Island, but nowhere else, the alnöite contains large rounded crystals of barkevikitic hornblende, or kaersutite (Howie, 1963). Nothing comparable with this amphibole has been found in the kimberlites. A striking resemblance between Swedish and South African kimberlites is shown by Dawson's description of the second-generation mica of the Basutoland kimberlites (Dawson, 1962, pp. 545–560, Plate I, Fig. 2). An analogous phenomenon was previously discussed at some length by Larsson (1943) for the Kalix kimberlites and by me for the Alnö kimberlites (von Eckermann, 1960). I have suggested that the corrosion of the first-generation mica and the marked increase of second-generation mica with increased carbonate content may be the result of changing conditions, the temperature, pressure and concentration of carbonates and fugitive carbon varying during intrusion. Already congealed kimberlite of alnöite may have gone into solution again when through accumulation of carbonate a new pressure center was formed and a stop was called in the retreat of the fluid magma underneath the already frozen one in the upper part of the volcanic vent. Dawson also noted a marked association between calcite and second generation mica. On the other hand, the two generations of olivine in the Basutoland kimberlites, also recorded elsewhere by Wegner and Verhoogen (Dawson, 1962, p. 553) are very rare in the Alnö dikes and have only recently been definitely established in a few dikes (von Eckermann, 1964a).

Dawson compared four analyses of Basutoland kimberlites with analyses of kimberlites from South Africa and Russia (Dawson, 1962, p. 551, table 4) and wrote as follows: "Constant chemical features of the basaltic kimberlites are: low SiO_2 and Al_2O_3, high MgO and H_2O, fairly high TiO_2, CO_2 usually present, Fe_2O_3 greater than FeO, K_2O greater than Na_2O, Al_2O_3 greater then $K_2O + Na_2O$ and the constant presence of P_2O_5. . . . The micaceous kimberlites have the same general characteristics as the basaltic types, but the content of CaO, CO_2, and K_2O is usually higher, whereas H_2O+ is slightly lower. These differences in the chemistry are reflected in the increase in mica and calcite and lesser degree of serpentinization in the micaceous rocks."

Dawson's chemical characterization of the African kimberlites is valid for the Swedish kimberlites, too, subject to certain restrictions. The K_2O/Na_2O ratio of the latter is generally higher; Fe_2O_3 is not always greater than FeO and H_2O+ is comparatively low. In most cases the Fe_2O_3/FeO ratio is $\leqslant 1$, but in strongly carbonatized micaceous kimberlites and in melilite-bearing ones it rises above 1. Another unique feature is the occasional presence of free carbonic acid enclosed in tiny vesicles within the carbonates and apatites of the Swedish kimberlites. Such an occurrence has so far not been reported from any other kimberlite locality in the world, as far as I know.

In Russian kimberlites the K_2O/Na_2O ratio show variations within wide limits, but the average value is decidedly >1 (Bobrievich et al., 1964, p. 49; and Menyailov, 1962, pp. 65 and 94). In this respect they resemble the Swedish kimberlites more than the South African ones. On the other hand, the average Fe_2O_3/FeO ratio of the Jakutian kimberlites is considerably higher than its Swedish counterparts, reaching almost 2 (by weight). Its corresponding molecular values for 339 analyses range from 3.7 to 0.1 (Bobrievich et al., 1964, pp. 44–49), with an average of 0.9. The Cr_2O_3 content of the Russian kimberlites seldom exceeds 0.20 per cent, the average of 339 analyses being 0.13. The majority of Swedish kimberlites show 0.06 to 0.10 per cent, and the highest content recorded is 0.18 per cent.

E. Discussion

A chemical comparison of Swedish, South African, and Russian kimberlites may be attempted by using the Niggli reference values. When drawing this comparison among them, I propose to use all analyses, published and unpublished, from the Alnö and Kalix regions, the analyses of South African kimberlites compiled by Dawson (1962, p. 551), the analyses of Russian kimberlites published by Menyailov (1961, p. 33 and p. 66, 3m from contact), the analysis referred to by Dawson (1962, p. 551) and published by Krutojarsky in 1958, those analyses published by Menyailov (1962, pp. 65 and 94), and the average of 399 analyses published by Bobrievich et al., (1964, pp. 48–49). Recalculating all these analyses in the Niggli values Al, Fm, C, and alk and plotting them against Si or CO_2, the same reciprocity as previously observed for the Swedish kimberlites between Fm and C is immediately evident. To a high Fm corresponds a low C and vice versa (cf. von Eckermann, 1948, p. 109, Fig. 31, and von Eckermann, 1963b, p. 24, Fig. 11).

Consequently, we may plot instead the mean value $(C + FM)/2$. Keeping in mind that Al is always higher than alk, we may plot their mean value also: $(Al + alk)/2$. Because the four Niggli values in question represent molecular volume percentages, the sum of the two mean values is 50.

The resulting diagram (Fig. 9.8), in which the mean values are plotted against CO_2, indicates a complete agreement be-

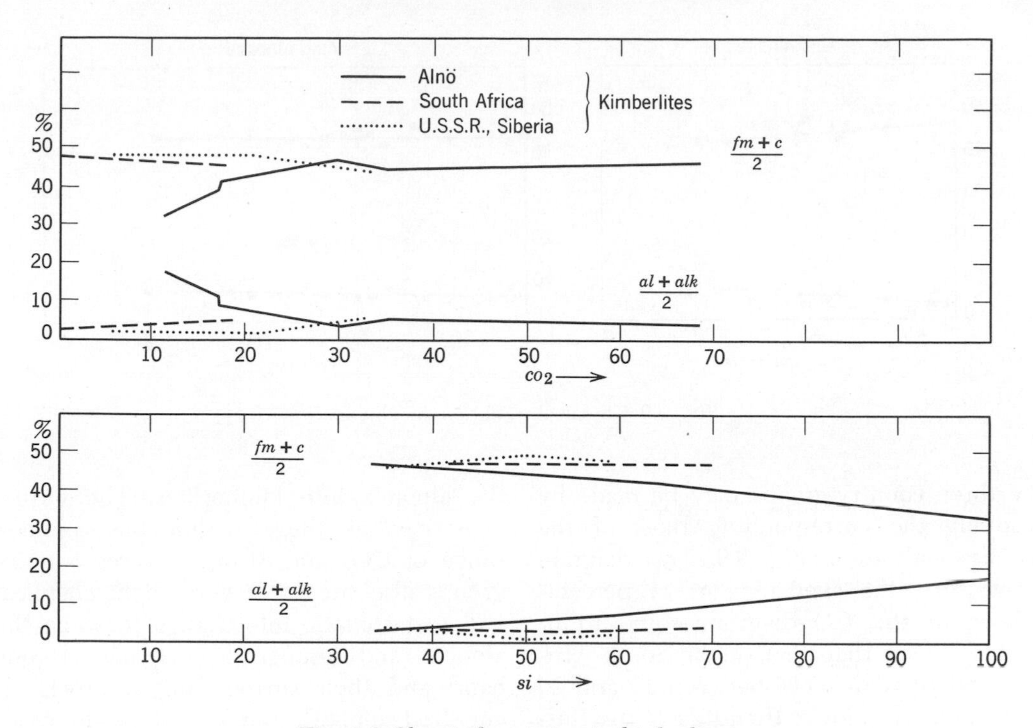

Fig. 9.8 Chemical variation in kimberlites.

tween the Swedish and Russian kimberlites at a CO_2 between 32 and 26, an increased tendency of the Fm + C of the latter between 26 and 20, a strong constant increase below 20, and a corresponding decrease of alumina and alkalies. A similar relation exists between the Swedish and the South African rocks. From $CO_2 = 32$ up to 68 the Swedish kimberlites remain almost constant with a very slight increase of Fm + C but never reach the ultimate values of the Russian and South African rocks. The sudden angular break of the Swedish diagram at CO_2 about 18 corresponds to an increased soda content and to the entering of nepheline in the mineral paragenesis. The kimberlites represented by that part of the diagram are, in consequence, not quite comparable to those of South Africa and Russia. They may be explained by the kimberlite having engulfed and digested acid wallrocks at great depth. Their quite local occurrence may correspond to an equally local brecciation of the wallrocks, of which fragments have recently been found in tuffitic kimberlitic breccias east and west of the sövite body.

The corresponding Si plot in Fig. 9.8 shows almost complete agreement of the three groups between 34 and 40 Si but a gradual decrease of Fm + C in the medial values of the Swedish group compared with both the Russian and South African ones. Above 69 this tendency increases strongly in the Swedish group due to the increased nepheline content.

The water content of the three groups varies considerably at different localities (cf. von Eckermann, 1964c, p. 274, Fig. 2) but there is a common tendency for the chemically bound water content to decrease with increased CO_2. On the other hand, with increased Si the average water content is conspicuously high in the other two groups when compared with the Swedish one, which remains almost constant irrespective of locality.

It would have been interesting to compare the Swedish alnöites and the South African melilite basalts. Unfortunately, too few analyses of the latter are available. But a comparison with the kimberlites of

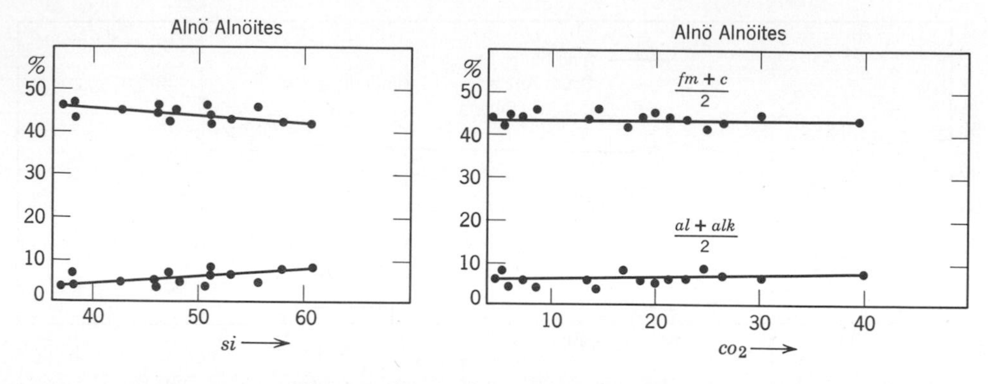

Fig. 9.9 Chemical variation in alnöites.

the three country-groups may be made by studying the corresponding plots of the alnöite analyses in Fig. 9.9. This diagram shows that the average Fm + C-percentage is in the CO_2-diagram equal to or slightly lower than that of the South African and Russian rocks between 10 and 20 CO_2, somewhat lower than that of the Russian and Swedish kimberlites between 20 and 30 CO_2 and decidedly lower than the Swedish ones between 30 and 40 CO_2. In the Si-diagram, the Fm + C-values between 38 and 55 agree fairly well with those of the kimberlites of all three groups, with slight tendency to fall towards Si = 61. The Al + alk values are, of course, in every case reciprocal. A comparison of the average water content indicates a falling tendency at higher CO_2, quite similar to the one recorded in the case of the kimberlites. The Si-diagram, on the other hand, shows a local variation but generally an almost constant average value. Even the similarity between alnöites and Swedish kimberlites is evident.

The similarity of the Niggli values of the alnöites to those of the kimberlites of the same Si- and CO_2-values is of great theoretical interest. Apparently it suggests that an eventual withdrawal of CaO and (Fe,Mg)O from the alnöite by the carbon fugitives must have occurred in about the same proportion as that found in kimberlites; namely the ratio Fm + C: Al + alk must have remained almost constant during the whole process of transformation of the alnöites into kimberlites. The virtual constancy of these within the common range of CO_2 and Si of the three country groups also suggest a very slight chemical and metasomatic interchange between the alnöitic and kimberlitic magmas on one hand and their surrounding wallrocks or engulfed xenoliths on the other. In other words, the fenitization power of these rocks is rather small as long as they do not grade into high-tensioned carbonatites.

The veracity of this conclusion is amply proved by the investigation of the Alnö dikes. Even when the energy level, established by temperature, pressure, and CO_2 concentration is fairly high permitting fenitization of the wallrocks at the contact (namely, the exchange across the border between Si of the wallrock and Ca, Mg, and Fe of the kimberlite), the relative proportions of Ca, Mg, and Fe remain virtually unaltered as do the Niggli ratios. To judge from numerous thin sections of rocks taken across the contacts very little or no carbonic acid takes part in the fenitization of the wallrocks, the latter being virtually calcite-free. Syenitization at the very contact of the gneiss-granite, to a depth of a few millimeters, nephelinitization and crystallization of aegirine-augite characterize the fenite. Occasionally, some natrolite replaces the nepheline, indicating that some water may take part in the fenitization process. This has occurred at the contacts of some Alnö kimberlites with Si-values between 40 and 50.

One problem still unsolved is the unusually high K_2O/Na_2O ratio of the Swedish kimberlites compared with the South African and most Russian corresponding rocks. One is tempted to accept a chemical interchange at the contacts, but no such evidence has been found. The genetic origin of the potassium must be very deep seated and it remains obscure.

Another problem is the question of the origin of the carbonic acid. Unfortunately, the 399 new Russian kimberlite analyses, previously mentioned, do not include any CO_2 determinations. But recently Roedder (1965) has shown that olivine-bearing nodules and phenocrysts from basalts contain liquid CO_2 inclusions, and it is therefore reasonable to assume that the melilite basalts at great depths may have contained it too.

In my comparison of the different kimberlites, I have left out of consideration a rather important component of these rocks: the fluorine. I suggested many years ago that the fluorine in cooperation with carbonic acid and water may have been the deciding factor responsible for the low temperatures at which the kimberlites and their carbonatitic derivates must have been fluid during intrusion. This suggestion is now confirmed by the experimental data, according to a private letter from Professor O. F. Tuttle of November 1961. He wrote: "It looks now as though with excess alkali plus water, with fluorine and carbon dioxide as primary anions, you can have almost any temperature you wish from 800 to 300°C." As a basis for comparison, however, the fluorine content may be of little use on account of its easy penetration of the wallrocks of the dikes, where fluorite may be found. Usually only small amounts of fluorine are left in the Swedish kimberlites, mostly bound to micas and apatites, with fluorite being rare. No influence on the $(C + Fm)/(Al + alk)$ ratios has been noticed. There are few data on the part played by fluorine in the Russian and African rocks.

In the Swedish kimberlites the radioactivity rises with increased carbonate content (von Eckermann, 1964b). This may suggest a transport of radioactive material with the previously mentioned fugitive globules. By the use of autoradiographs the radioactivity has been localized to the perovskites and to minute crystals of, probably, the dysanalyte-pyrochlore series. With increasing carbonatization of the kimberlite the perovskite is altered into ilmenite and carbonate, the ilmenite retaining the radioactivity as well as the Nb, Ta, Th, and U usually present in small quantities in the primary mineral. The lack of published data prevents a comparison of the radioactivity of South African and Russian kimberlites with the Swedish ones at present.

Finally, a new observation in the recently discovered tuffitic Alnö kimberlites is worth mentioning. In one single thin slide out of several hundreds from one of the largest boulders, I found an aggregate

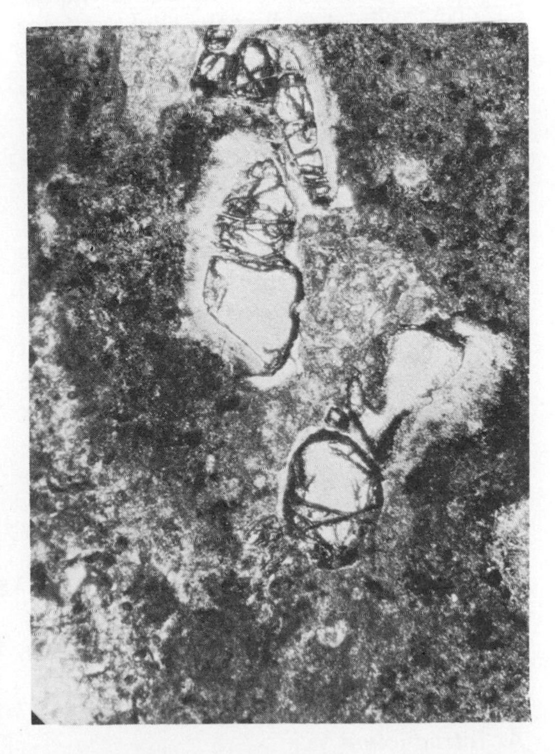

Fig. 9.10 Diamond-like crystals found in one of the tuffitic boulders and in one single thin slide. Ordinary light. Magnif.: ×310.

of some minute, perfectly clear, uncolored crystals and crystal fragments of high refraction, as shown in Fig. 9.10. They are surrounded by light-colored reaction zones, where the yellowish matrix has lost its color, indicating a chemical reduction action. By the Fedoroff method the refractive index was determined on the universal stage and found to correspond to that of diamond, about 2.40 ± 0.05. The crystals are isotropic, so the possibilities of them being some other mineral is of course limited. When I told Professor C. F. Davidson about the discovery he wrote: "The richest kimberlites as far as diamond production is concerned carry one part diamond in 10^7 of rock, and the average is one in 10^{10} or less. So the chances of finding a diamond in a thin section are somewhat around the cube of the probability of finding the needle in the haystack."

Nevertheless, I have since then crushed and pulverized about 100 kg of tuffitic boulders without finding the slightest trace of any similar crystals. And I still keep trying in order to prove definitely that they are diamonds.

F. Conclusion

The series of South African and Russian analyses used in the comparison with Swedish kimberlites are too few to allow any definite conclusion to be drawn, but they serve to suggest, nevertheless, an intimate chemical relationship. The similarity of their primary mineral parageneses support a common genetic history. They have all carried carbon fugitives, which in some rocks in South Africa and Siberia have produced diamonds and graphite, while in Sweden they partly remain as carbonic acid inclusions in the rock minerals. The discovery of a few minute diamond-like crystals in the tuffitic boulders west of Alnö may indicate that where the pressure rose above the average diamonds were formed in Sweden, too. If this is confirmed by future research the ties that unite the genesis of the three groups of kimberlite will be further strengthened.

The age of the Swedish kimberlites is not definitely established, but their accompanying carbonatites have been found to be early Cambrian. The same age applies to the Norwegian Fen carbonatites. The age determinations have been carried out on pyrochlore and mica. The South African kimberlites are considered Mesozoic and the U.S.S.R. kimberlites may be as young as 100 to 150 million years. However, recent determinations on kimberlite minerals from the Yakutian pipes by Mikheyenko and Nenashev (1960, p. 147) by the potassium-argon method led to a minimum age of about 610 million years. Now, one may well ask if this is the common age of all kimberlites before intrusion. If so, they may all be intrusions deriving from a common deep layer of melilite basalts of global extent but their intrusions may not have taken place simultaneously. This question may be resolved by new age determinations being made on mica from alnöite and sövite by the Sr-Rb method, in cooperation with Professor Niggli and Dr. Jäger at the University of Bern.

V. KIMBERLITES OF EASTERN NORTH AMERICA

K. D. Watson

A. Introduction

Kimberlite and the closely related rock alnöite occur in many places in eastern and central North America. The earliest detailed petrographic account is that describing the peridotite, now classified as kimberlite, occurring in Elliott County,

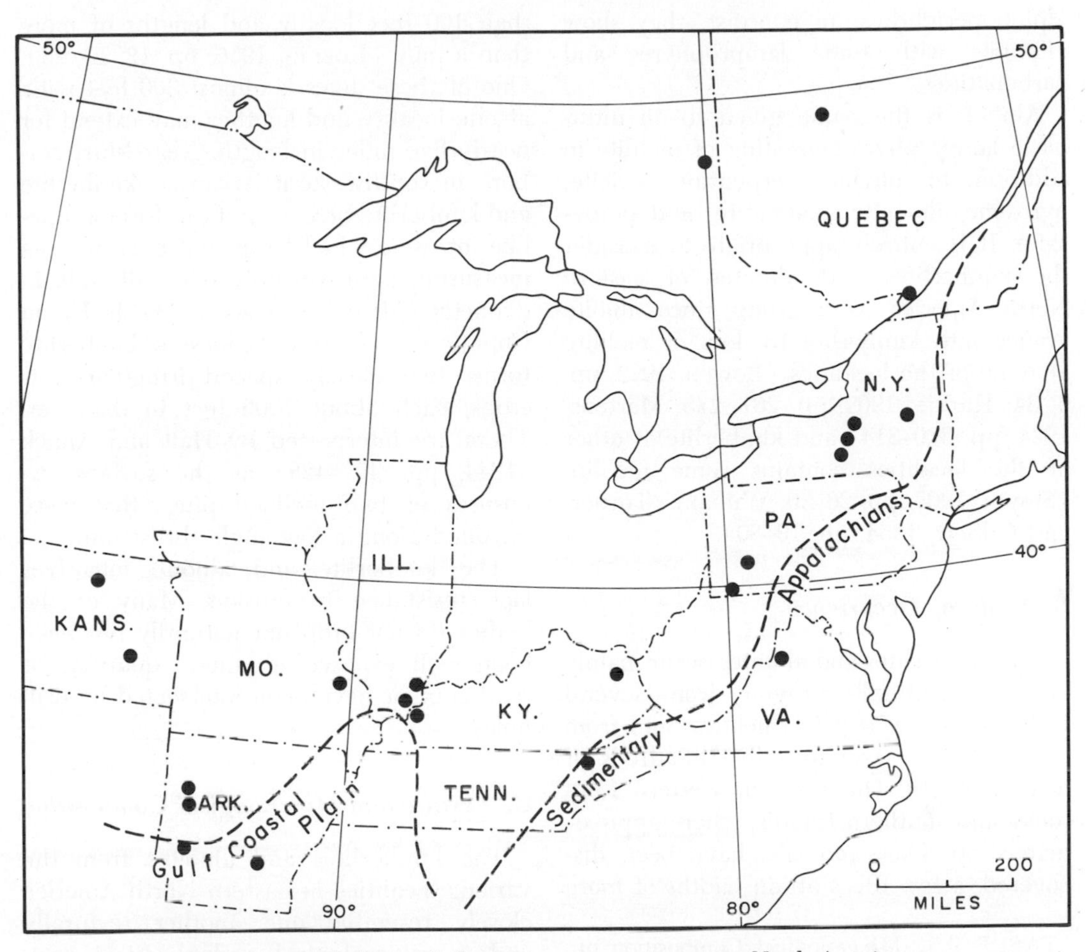

Fig. 9.11 Kimberlite and alnöite occurrences in eastern North America.

eastern Kentucky, published by J. S. Diller in 1886 (pp. 121–125). Since then, kimberlites and alnöites have been described from Ontario, Quebec, New York, Pennsylvania, Virginia, Tennessee, western Kentucky, Illinois, Missouri, Arkansas, and Kansas (Fig. 9.11).

The rock-name *kimberlite* was introduced in 1888 by Lewis (pp. 129–131) for a porphyritic peridotite from South Africa consisting of olivine, serpentine, weakly pleochroic biotite, bronzite, chrome diallage, smaragdite, perovskite, pyrope, ilmenite, chromite, carbonate, and several other minerals. Four years later, the name *mica-peridotite* was proposed by Diller (1892, pp. 286–289) for a somewhat similar rock from western Kentucky composed mainly of biotite, serpentine pseudomorphous after olivine, and perovskite with lesser amounts of apatite, talc, magnetite, chlorite, calcite, and undetermined secondary material. Since then, these names have acquired greater latitude in meaning and at present, they are used interchangeably or almost so by some petrologists (e.g., Williams, Turner, and Gilbert, 1954, pp. 79–80; Huang, 1962, p. 150). It seems preferable, however, to use only the name kimberlite for the porphyritic rocks, thereby maintaining a clear distinction from the plutonic peridotites (cf. Martens, 1924, p. 313; Tröger, 1935, pp. 292, 297; Watson, 1955, p. 566). Kimberlites differ markedly in texture, mineralogical and chemical composition, and tectonic setting from alpine peridotites; in contrast, they show affinities with some lamprophyres and carbonatites.

Alnöite is the name given to an ultrabasic lamprophyre consisting of melilite in addition to olivine, serpentine, calcite, pyroxene, ilmenite, magnetite, and perovskite. It is entirely appropriate to consider the kimberlites and alnöites of eastern North America as a group since alnöite grades into kimberlite by loss of melilite at some of the localities (Bowen, 1922, pp. 6, 34; Harvie, 1909, pp. 261, 275; Martens, 1924, pp. 310–314) and kimberlite at other of the localities contains some melilite (Smyth, 1902, pp. 26–30; Williams, Turner, and Gilbert, 1954, pp. 79–80).

B. Mode of Occurrence

The kimberlites and alnöites occur mainly as dikes and sills ranging from several inches to a few feet in thickness and from several tens of feet to a few hundreds of feet in length. However, in western Kentucky and southern Illinois, where approximately 50 dikes and sills have been discovered, a few dikes attain widths of more than 100 feet locally and lengths of more than a mile (Koenig, 1956, pp. 12, 13, 23). One of these dikes is almost 300 feet wide at one locality and another may extend for nearly five miles in length. Near Murfreesboro in southwestern Arkansas, kimberlite and kimberlite breccia and tuff form a pipelike intrusive which crops out over an area measuring approximately one half mile in diameter (Miser and Ross, 1923). In Union County, northeastern Tennessee, kimberlite forms two closely spaced irregular outcrops, each about 1000 feet in diameter. These are interpreted by Hall and Amick (1944, pp. 427–428) as the surface exposures of two inclined plugs that were intruded along a low-angle thrust fault.

The kimberlite and alnöite intrusives lack resistance to erosion. Many of the bodies do not crop out naturally but have been well exposed in mines, quarries, or road cuts, or have been intersected by drill holes.

TABLE 9.5 Mineralogical Composition of Kimberlite from Bachelor Lake, Quebec (percentage by volume)

	1	2	3	4	5
Olivine and altered olivine	48	45	29	38	41
Phlogopite	9	21	24	20	26
Calcite	18	13	39	20	17
Augite	...	0.2	0.1	6	1
Perovskite	3	7	1	1	3
Apatite	0.1	0.2	0.1	2	4
Magnetite	12	6	6	5	4
Ilmenite	7	4	1	...	3
Antigorite and calcite	...	...	...	7	...
Chlorite	3	4	...	...	1
Bowlingite (?), etc.	...	...	...	1	...

1, 2, and 3 correspond to analyses 1, 2, and 3 in Table 9.7 (Watson, 1955, p. 568).

C. Texture and Mineralogical Composition

The kimberlites and alnöites from the various localities in eastern North America closely resemble one another texturally and in mineralogical and chemical composition (Tables 9.5, 9.6, and 9.7). Accordingly, a representative rock—the kimberlite from Bachelor Lake, Quebec, with which the writer is most familiar—is selected for detailed description (Watson, 1955). This kimberlite is a medium to dark gray massive rock in which olivine, or its pseudomorphs, together with phlogopite, calcite, and, in some samples, ilmenite, are clearly evident macroscopically. Commonly, the olivine, pseudomorphs after olivine, and phlogopite are euhedral. In some parts of the dikes they occur as numerous medium- to fine-grained phenocrysts in a dark gray fine-grained to aphanitic groundmass; in others, they occur in a matrix containing abundant medium- to fine-grained white calcite; and in others, they grade seriately from medium to aphanitic. The variations in texture and mineralogical composition

TABLE 9.6 Mineralogical Composition of Kimberlite from Kentucky*
(percentage by volume)

	1	2	3	4	5	6	7
Olivine and serpentine	...	...	...	...	...	...	47
Serpentine† and chlorite	46	26	30	26	39	19	22
Phlogopite	25	27	11	29	21	2	1
Calcite	19	37	39	31	21	64	9
Opaque minerals‡	8	9	15	12	12	12	5
Pyroxene	1	...	...	1	5	...	1
Perovskite	...	...	2	...	...	...	5
Apatite	1	1	1	1	1	1	...
Pyrope	...	...	...	...	...	...	10
Quartz	...	...	1	...	...	...	...

* Compiled from Koenig, 1956.
† Mainly after olivine.
‡ Mainly ilmenite and magnetite; minor pyrite, hematite, leucoxene, limonite, and chromite (?); may include perovskite if not listed separately.

1. Claylick dike, Crittenden County; analysis 6 in Table 9.7; pyroxene is augite.
2. Hutson dikes, Livingston County.
3. Old Jim dikes, Crittenden County.
4. Glendale dike, Crittenden County.
5. Hobby dike, Caldwell County, analysis 7 in Table 9.7; pyroxene is augite.
6. Two Brothers dike, Crittenden County.
7. Elliott County; analysis 8 in Table 9.7; ilmenite 2%, magnetite 2%, chromite 1%; pyroxene is enstatite or hypersthene; may include some dolomite.

within individual dikes seem to be erratic. Reductions in grain size or in proportions of phenocrysts along contacts or in narrow apophyses are not apparent except within a millimeter or two of the margin. Abundant veinlets of white calcite occur locally in the dikes.

Microscopically, panidiomorphic texture is common. Euhedral crystals are predominant not only among the phenocrysts of olivine and phlogopite but also among the smaller grains and those of augite, perovskite, magnetite, and apatite. Poikilitic texture is also conspicuous in some thin sections. In most of these sections the oikocrysts are calcite (Fig. 9.12) but in a few, they are phlogopite. The calcite forms either anhedral crystals, reaching a few millimeters in diameter, that completely enclose euhedral crystals of other minerals, or optically continuous webs between closely spaced euhedral crystals. Near the contacts of a dike, many of the phlogopite crystals are oriented with their major dimensions parallel to the dike margin. Elsewhere in the dikes, the structure is massive except for subparallel orientation of flakes of phlogopite and laths of antigorite between some closely spaced phenocrysts of olivine and phlogopite.

Modes of representative specimens of kimberlite from Bachelor Lake are listed in Table 9.5 in percentage by volume.

Olivine (Fo_{85}) and its pseudomorphs occur as euhedral and subhedral crystals that are mainly between 0.5 and 2 mm in diameter. Unaltered olivine is present in about a fifth of the thin sections only. No relationship is apparent between the degree of alteration of olivine and the amount of calcite in the rock. A transition from almost unaltered to entirely altered olivine may occur within the width of a single thin section. In some specimens, the altered olivine crystals consist of fine-grained aggregates of fibrolamellar and fibrous serpentine containing magnetite dust; in others they consist of aggregates of fine flakes and laths of bowlingite. A few specimens contain pseudomorphs consisting of rims of bowlingite and cores of randomly oriented fine-grained talc. One specimen contains some olivine crystals partly replaced by bowlingite and others completely pseudomorphed by fine-grained calcite and bowlingite. The distribution of the calcite in these pseudomorphs suggests that it has replaced patches of relic olivine in grains that had been partly altered previously to bowlingite.

Phlogopite forms euhedral and subhedral crystals mainly 0.25 to 2 mm in major dimensions. In many specimens the crystals are distinctly zoned. They show parts in

Fig. 9.12 Photomicrograph of kimberlite, Bachelor Lake, Quebec. Poikilitic texture. Euhedral and subhedral crystals of olivine, partly serpentinized olivine, and perovskite (black), along with minor phlogopite and magnetite in calcite host (white). Crossed nicols. ×57.

which the absorption and birefringence (Y and Z = medium brown, $B = 0.045$) indicate a lower Mg to Fe ratio than in other parts in which the absorption and birefringence are lower (Y and Z = pale yellow, $B = 0.030$). In some specimens the ratio of Mg to Fe decreases from core to rim; in others, the zoning is reversed and is commonly oscillatory.

The phlogopite crystals in most specimens have narrow rims, incomplete rims, or irregular patches within them composed of a micaceous mineral that differs markedly from the phlogopite by having reverse pleochroism (X = deep orange brown, Y and Z = very pale yellow, almost colorless; $X > Y = Z$). The rims and patches have their cleavage traces and extinction positions parallel to those of the phlogopite crystal. The relief nearly matches that of phlogopite but the birefringence of the latter is about 0.010 greater. The amount of this mineral is much less than one per cent of most specimens, but in one containing 20 to 25 per cent phlogopite, it composes almost 5 per cent of the rock. Mica with reverse pleochroism has been observed in kimberlite, alnöite, and carbonatite elsewhere (Watson, 1955, pp. 569–570). Recently, Hogarth (1964, p. 136) has attributed the reverse pleochroism of some micas to the presence of Fe^{+3} in tetrahedral sites.

Calcite is abundant in the kimberlite and in a few specimens constitutes more than 50 per cent of the rock. It forms anhedral grains, most of which are between 0.1 mm and 1 mm in size, although a few reach 5 mm. Where abundant, calcite forms a matrix in which dominantly euhedral and subhedral crystals of other minerals lie embedded (Fig. 9.13). In some specimens it is poikilitic and forms either anhedral grains completely enclosing smaller euhedral crystals of other minerals or optically continuous webs a few millimeters across between closely spaced euhedral crystals (Fig. 9.12). In several specimens calcite has slightly replaced phlogopite and, less commonly, olivine, and clinopyroxene. Much of the calcite, however, shows no evidence that it originated by replacement.

Clinopyroxene is present in less than half of the thin sections examined. It forms stubby prisms and irregular granules, generally less than 0.1 mm long. The grains tend to cluster around the edges of olivine phenocrysts; some are partly enclosed in the olivine and others are included in phlogopite. Most of the clinopyroxene is a pale brownish gray variety having the optical properties of augite.

Perovskite, which is an accessory mineral in all specimens, forms equant grains that are chiefly between 0.02 and 0.1 mm across. Many crystals are euhedral and rectangular or octagonal in section. The perovskite crystals are pale purplish brown or yellow; some are isotropic and others are weakly birefringent. The rims and cores of many grains contain fine-grained ilmenite in abundance. Perovskite is included within phlogopite and calcite and in a few places is molded on olivine.

Apatite is present in minor amounts in all specimens. Most of the crystals are slender prisms 0.01 to 0.1 mm long, although a few are stout and reach 5 mm in length. Some of the slender prisms form groups that radiate into calcite from points of attachment on olivine crystals but most are completely surrounded by calcite.

Magnetite is present in all specimens and, excluding the dust formed by alteration of olivine, ranges in amount from 4 to 12 per cent (Table 9.5). Most of it forms subhedral equant crystals that are mainly 0.01 to 0.1 mm in diameter. Many of these crystals are included in phlogopite and calcite and a few are molded on olivine.

Ilmenite, which is a variety rich in magnesium, occurs in most specimens. The amounts listed in Table 9.5 do not include the minute grains enclosed in perovskite. Most of the ilmenite forms irregular grains, mainly 0.2 to 1 mm in diameter, contrasting markedly in shape and size with the magnetite. Some of the ilmenite occurs interstitially among olivine crystals and some of it has phlogopite molded on it. Many of the ilmenite anhedra are partly surrounded by irregular rims of magnetite which apparently crystallized later than ilmenite. The large ilmenite grains contain widely spaced thin lamellae of exsolved magnetite.

Antigorite, except for that which forms pseudomorphs after olivine, occurs in only a few specimens. In specimen 4, Table 9.5, it forms laths mainly 0.1 to 0.3 mm long which compose part of the groundmass and which commonly are partly or completely enclosed in phlogopite. Most of these laths consist in part of fine-grained calcite and some are almost completely pseudomorphed by it. Some laths are composed of only one crystal of antigorite; others are composite and consist in part of

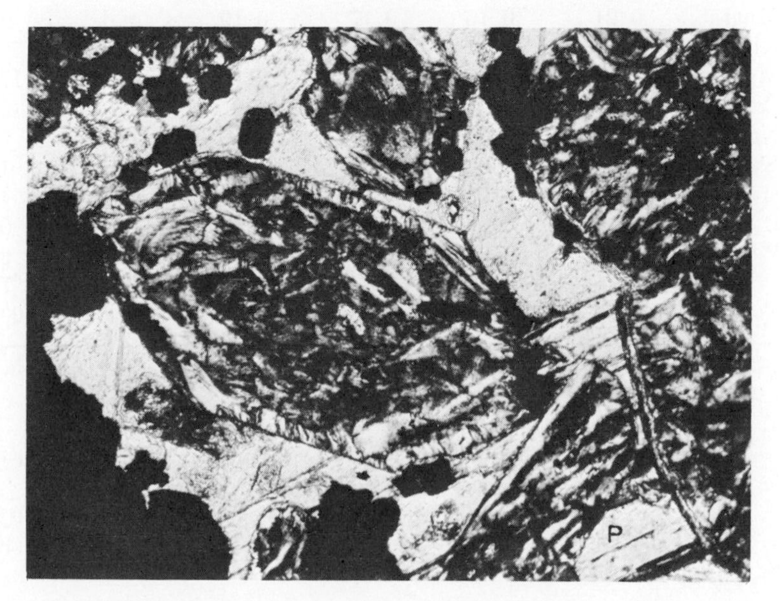

Fig. 9.13 Photomicrograph of kimberlite, Bachelor Lake, Quebec. Euhedral and subhedral crystals of serpentinized olivine, phlogopite (P), perovskite (black), and magnetite embedded in calcite (white). Crossed nicols. ×145.

many small elongate grains oriented with long axes perpendicular to a median fracture running the length of the large lath. This antigorite may be a late primary mineral that has been partly replaced by carbonate. On the other hand, the antigorite and calcite may be alteration products of a preexisting mineral. In this alternative, the original mineral could be melilite for its composition (åkermanite) would enable it to yield antigorite and calcite, its habit is commonly lathlike, and it commonly shows a combination of peg structure and a median cleavage trace reminiscent of the structure of the composite laths. Moreover, melilite has been reported to occur in kimberlite elsewhere and it is an essential constituent of the closely related rock, alnöite.

Chlorite forms rims only a few microns wide on phlogopite and on mica with reverse pleochroism in some sections. It occurs also as extremely fine-grained aggregates in the groundmass of several specimens.

D. Chemical Composition

Chemical analyses of kimberlite from Bachelor Lake, Quebec, and from localities in New York, Pennsylvania, and Kentucky are given in Table 9.7. These match closely analyses of kimberlite from Africa, Siberia, and Sweden listed in Tables 8.1, 8.4, 8.5, and 9.4. In marked contrast with other kinds of ultramafic rocks, the kimberlites contain abundant TiO_2 and P_2O_5, owing to their high content of perovskite and ilmenite and of apatite. They are, moreover, extremely rich in CO_2. Indeed, some speci-

TABLE 9.7 Chemical Analyses of Kimberlite from Quebec, New York, Pennsylvania, and Kentucky

	1	2	3	4	5	6	7	8
SiO_2	22.74	24.15	22.86	26.37	28.83	29.80	30.30	27.30
TiO_2	5.86	6.46	2.98	1.98	5.67	2.24	2.55	1.31
Al_2O_3	3.09	2.58	3.78	6.14	2.94	7.90	7.54	3.44
Fe_2O_3	8.47	7.67	4.79	3.97	3.60	6.90	3.93	3.92
Cr_2O_3	0.09	trace	0.06	0.18	n.d.	n.d.	n.d.	n.d.
FeO	7.54	8.36	5.32	4.02	5.13	4.13	6.65	5.10
MnO	0.21	0.16	0.17	0.19	n.d.	n.d.	n.d.	n.d.
NiO	trace	0.02	...	0.09	n.d.	n.d.	n.d.	n.d.
MgO	23.83	24.03	14.58	16.19	24.31	17.90	19.50	30.30
CaO	11.82	10.27	22.24	16.01	11.24	15.90	13.80	12.70
Na_2O	0.27	0.25	0.33	1.46	0.75	0.20	0.20	0.20
K_2O	0.94	1.02	1.52	0.46	1.31	1.72	2.62	0.26
H_2O^+	6.22	4.98	3.42	5.52	3.96	4.05	4.15	4.63
H_2O^-	0.76	0.90	1.65	5.90	0.83	0.94	0.82	0.48
P_2O_5	0.68	0.23	1.32	1.12	0.77	0.93	0.56	0.65
CO_2	7.24	9.02	14.84	10.70	11.64	7.04	7.33	9.23
Total	99.76	100.10	99.86	100.77*	100.98	99.65	99.95	99.52

1–3. Bachelor Lake, Lesueur Township, Quebec; specimens 1, 2, and 3 in Table 9.5 (Watson, 1955, p. 573).
4. Cascadilla Creek, Ithaca, New York (Martens, 1924, p. 312).
* Including 0.07% Cl and after correcting for the oxygen equivalent of 0.64% S.
5. Fayette County, Pennsylvania (Kemp and Ross, 1907, p. 517).
6. Claylick dike, Crittenden County, Kentucky; specimen 1 in Table 9.6 (Koenig, 1956, p. 27).
7. Hobby dike, Caldwell County, Kentucky; specimen 5 in Table 9.6 (Koenig, 1956, p. 37).
8. Elliott County, Kentucky; specimen 7 in Table 9.6 (Koenig, 1956, p. 49).

mens from Bachelor Lake and other localities, which are not included among the analyses, resemble impure carbonatites. Some of the samples included in Table 9.7 contain CO_2 in excess of CaO, thereby requiring inclusion of $MgCO_3$ in their norms (Watson, 1955, p. 573).

E. Origin of Carbonate

The presence of the carbonate, so abundant in kimberlite, if primary in origin, could explain the emplacement of kimberlite as a highly fluid material at relatively low temperature. For this reason, an attempt to determine its origin is of great importance petrogenetically. Fortunately, a study of the relationships at Bachelor Lake provides a probable answer to the question, which may be germane also to other occurrences where the evidence is less decisive.

Although the carbonate in kimberlite of some localities is assumed to be a product of weathering, it is clear that this cannot be the mode of origin at Bachelor Lake. There the bedrock surface is fresh and well scoured glacially and the specimens studied are drill cores obtained from depths of a few hundred feet or more below the surface. Moreover, no relationship exists between depth of intersection and proportion of carbonate in the rock. The alternative possibility that the calcite is a product of hydrothermal alteration by fluids derived from a source distinctly younger than the kimberlite may also be ruled out since carbonate is either absent or essentially so in all the other rocks and the ores of the area (Watson, 1957). Thus, the conclusion that the calcite is a product of the kimberlite magma itself seems inescapable. It has been suggested that calcite occurring in a kimberlite dike near Ithaca, New York (Broughton, 1950, p. 230), may have been derived from the thick section of calcareous rocks penetrated by the dike. However, since carbonate rocks are unknown in the Precambrian of northwestern Quebec, no sound reason exists for postulating that the magma that formed the kimberlite at Bachelor Lake obtained its carbonate by reaction with limestone or dolomite.

Some of the calcite in the kimberlite at Bachelor Lake is probably deuteric. This carbonate forms partial pseudomorphs of other minerals such as olivine and phlogopite; that which occurs with antigorite as well-defined laths in specimen 4, Table 9.5, may be secondary after melilite. Much of the calcite, however, shows no evidence whatsoever of a secondary origin. On the contrary, it occurs as medium- to fine-grained aggregates of *anhedral* grains which are sharply molded against or completely enclosing euhedral crystals of olivine, phlogopite, augite, perovskite, magnetite, and apatite in a manner indicating strongly that it is a late-crystallizing primary mineral (Figs. 9.12 and 9.13). One must consider the possibility that these textural relationships originated by selective replacement of a very fine-grained groundmass in preference to coarser phenocrysts by virtue of the greater reactivity of the finer aggregate. If this were the mode of origin, however, one would expect the resulting aggregate to have inherited a fine-grained texture since this has happened where fine-grained andesite and rhyolite lapilli tuff have been carbonatized immediately adjacent to the dikes. One might contend that the possibilities remain that the calcite selectively replaced a glass groundmass or a medium- to fine-grained aggregate of anhedral grains of an unstable mineral such as melilite. However, since no relics of these were observed among the calcite in the many thin sections studied, such possibilities must be considered unlikely. In contrast to the opinion of Shand (1947, pp. 444–445), Taljaard (1936, pp. 312–315), and Tröger (1935, p. 297) that the abundant calcite of South African kimberlite was derived from melilite formerly present in the rock, the weight of the positive evidence leads to the conclusion that much of the calcite in the Bachelor Lake kimberlite is a late-crystallizing primary mineral.

F. Temperature of Intrusion

Generally, the kimberlite intrusives have not produced recognizable aureoles of metamorphism. However, in a few places where they have intruded coal, oil-bearing sandstone, and salt, the wallrocks and inclusions have been affected. These contact effects yield some information regarding the temperatures of emplacement.

Sosman (1938) has estimated the intrusion-temperature of a kimberlite dike several feet in width, which cuts coal seams in Fayette County, southwestern Pennsylvania. Coal occurring as inclusions in the dike and in the seams within about a foot of the contact have been converted to coke. The results of heating inclusions of the natural coke at various temperatures in the laboratory were compared with the results of heating samples of the unmetamorphosed coal. In addition, the content of residual hydrogen, oxygen, and nitrogen in the coke was determined. From these data, Sosman concluded that the maximum temperature reached by the coke inclusions was between 440 and 520°C and that the intrusion-temperature of the dike could hardly have exceeded 600°C. The conclusion that the temperature was very low is of great interest although it does not take into consideration the possible influence of pressure. Sosman records the presence of a considerable proportion of carbonate in the dike and mentions that Honess and Graeber have shown that some of the carbonate in a similar dike at Dixonville, Pennsylvania, may be primary. He does not, however, refer to the carbonate in presenting an explanation of the low temperature of intrusion.

English and Grogan (1948) have deduced the minimum temperature at the time of intrusion of the kimberlite dikes and sills that cut oil-bearing sandstone of Mississippian age in Gallatin County, southeastern Illinois. The rocks immediately adjacent to the intrusions contain a black carbonaceous residue probably derived from the oil formerly present in the sandstone. English and Grogan (1948, p. 200) state that "Under laboratory conditions, and if sufficient time is allowed, a temperature as low as 340°C is sufficient to drive off the volatile fractions of petroleum and to decompose the remaining hydrocarbons so as to leave behind a petroleum residue" and that "For any given oil it is said that pressure has essentially no effect on the temperature of cracking." By using this information and the method of Lovering (1936), they conclude that the minimum temperature of intrusion of the kimberlite was approximately 725°C. However, the minimum temperature may be less than 725° since the model neglects the effect of latent heat of crystallization and the possibility that the increase in temperature of the wallrocks may be due in part to the prolonged flux of magma through the channel.

Broughton (1950) has described the contact relationships of a kimberlite dike, about a foot wide, that intrudes rock salt near Ithaca, New York. The relationships suggest that the salt was rendered fluid by the intrusion of the dike and that it persisted in that state until after the highly tenuous kimberlite magma had crystallized. Broughton (1950, p. 231) points out that although the melting point of anhydrous halite at one atmosphere is about 800°C, the temperature at which the salt became fluid was probably lowered by the addition of water from the kimberlite magma. That the magma contained considerable water is shown by the presence of serpentine pseudomorphs after olivine phenocrysts and of abundant serpentine and chlorite in the groundmass.

Calcite is a major constituent of the groundmass and has replaced the centers of some phenocrysts of former olivine. Broughton (1950, p. 230) believes that the calcite may have been derived from the thick section of calcareous sediments penetrated by the dike below the salt. He does not consider the possibility that the carbonate may be partly responsible for the inferred high fluidity of the kimberlite magma at relatively low temperature.

Clegg (1955) has investigated the metamorphism of Middle Pennsylvanian bituminous coal by kimberlite dikes occurring near Absher, Williamson County, southern Illinois. The coal adjacent to a dike 18 inches wide has been converted to coke in a zone four to five inches in width and has been folded, fractured, and veined by calcite at greater distances from the contact. Differential thermal analyses were made of samples of natural coke taken at measured intervals from the dike and of unaltered coal which previously had been heated to known temperatures and cooled. Comparisons of the differential thermograms yielded estimates of the temperatures reached by the coal at various distances from the dike. Clegg (1955, p. 16–17) cites reasons for believing that the effect of pressure probably was small and concludes (p. 16) that the temperature of the coal reached 600° or less immediately adjacent to the dike and decreased at a rapid rate outward therefrom.

Clegg (1955, p. 10, 16) records the presence of tension fractures and drag folds, which indicate that the intrusive material continued to flow upward even after the coking process was underway. If this flow through the channel persisted over a long period, the wallrock adjacent to the fissure might have attained a temperature almost equal to that of the magma. Indeed, the temperature of the kimberlite magma may not have exceeded that of the wallrock (600°C as a maximum) for chilled margins are entirely lacking (Clegg, 1955, p. 7).

G. Tectonic Environment

Most of the kimberlite intrusives of eastern North America occur in the Interior Lowlands subdivision of the Central Stable region and those in Ontario and northwestern Quebec are in the Canadian Shield. The kimberlites occurring in the Shenandoah Valley in Virginia (Johnson and Milton, 1955, p. 1689) and in the Norris region of Union County, northeastern Tennessee (Hall and Amick, 1944) lie within the Sedimentary Appalachians. The well-known kimberlite occurring near Murfreesboro in Pike County and the kimberlite intersected in a deep drill hole in Cleveland County, Arkansas (Moody, 1949, pp. 1415–1416) lie within, but close to the boundary of, the Gulf Coastal Plain (Fig. 9.11). Those slightly farther north, in Scott and Logan Counties, Arkansas, intrude Paleozoic rocks of the Ouachita Mountains and the adjacent Arkoma basin. Thus it is seen that most of the kimberlites occur in nonorogenic environments. Those that do not are apparently postorogenic with the possible exception of that occurring in the Sedimentary Appalachians in northeastern Tennessee. In that locality, Hall and Amick (1944, p. 428) observed in the kimberlite "a pronounced banding that conforms to the regional strike and dip, which might suggest that it was exposed to at least a part of the forces which distorted the sedimentary rocks of the region." However, it is possible that the banding is merely an igneous flow structure that developed parallel to conformable contacts of the intrusive.

Several localized areas of intensely deformed rocks, known as cryptovolcanic or cryptoexplosion structures, have been found in the Interior Lowlands. These have been interpreted by Bucher (1936) as effects of concealed magmatic activity; on the other hand, Dietz (1960, 1962, p. 500) attributes some of them to impact by meteorites, mainly because of the presence of shatter cones. Although closely coincident occurrences of cryptovolcanic structures and kimberlites are rare when their distribution is examined in detail, a spatial relationship, noted by McCall (1964, p. 253), is evident when their distribution is viewed broadly. Recently, Snyder and Gerdemann (1965) have described several cryptovolcanic structures that are aligned along an east-west trending zone, 400 miles long, extending from southern Illinois to eastern Kansas. Kimberlite has been found at three of these structures.

H. Age

All the kimberlites of eastern North America, except those in Ontario, northwestern Quebec, and Pike County, Arkansas, intrude Paleozoic sediments—the youngest rocks with which they are associated. The age of these Paleozoic sediments ranges from Cambrian in some localities to Pennsylvanian in others. The kimberlites of Pike County are narrowly dated geologically since they intrude Lower Cretaceous sediments and have provided some of the material composing the lower part of an Upper Cretaceous formation (Ross, Miser, and Stephenson, 1929, p. 189). Kimberlite in Woodson County, Kansas, which can be dated only as post-Pennsylvanian geologically, has been assigned a mid-Cretaceous age from the K-Ar ratio in its phlogopite (Paul C. Franks, 1964, personal communication). Some of the Monteregian intrusives of southeastern Quebec, to which the alnöites and kimberlites near Montreal (Fig. 9.11) probably are related, have been dated by the K-Ar and Rb-Sr ratios in biotites as Cretaceous also (Fairbairn, et al., 1963, pp. 6516–6520). The kimberlite at Portland Point, near Ithaca, New York, which intrudes Upper Devonian sedimentary rocks, has an age of 155 ± 4 million years (mid-Jurassic), based upon the K-Ar ratio of its phlogopite (Geochron Laboratories, Inc.).

Zartman, et al. (1965) have determined K-Ar and Rb-Sr ratios in biotite, phlogopite, and hornblende from several small intrusives occurring throughout the central and eastern United States. They report that diatremes of kimberlite that cut Cambrian rocks in southeastern Missouri give an Early Devonian age of 390 ± 20 million years, kimberlite from Elliott County, Kentucky, has an Early Permian age of 265 ± 15 million years, and isolated kimberlites, nepheline syenites, and alkalic lamprophyres occurring in various areas of Paleozoic rocks give Jurassic to Cretaceous ages.

The age of the kimberlite at Bachelor Lake, determined from the K-Ar ratio in phlogopite, is 1100 million years (Geochron Laboratories, Inc.). The Bachelor Lake kimberlite lies within the Superior province of the Canadian Shield, in which the principal orogeny (Kenoran) occurred approximately 2500 million years ago (Stockwell, 1964, p. 5). The kimberlite, however, is matched closely in age by two postorogenic alkaline complexes of this province—the Lackner complex at 1090 million years and the Coldwell complex at approximately 1050 million years (Stockwell, 1964, p. 18). Carbonatite constitutes part of the Lackner complex (Hodder, 1961, pp. 22–26). The coincidence in age with the carbonate-rich kimberlite may be significant genetically.

I. Summary and Conclusions

The kimberlites of eastern North America are small postorogenic intrusives occurring for the most part within the central Stable Region. Some have been dated as late Mesozoic and others as Proterozoic (Middle Neohelikian, 1100 m.y.); in spite of their disparity in age, they show great similarity in mineralogical and chemical composition. Many of the intrusions are narrow yet remarkably persistent and have extremely tenuous offshoots. These relationships suggest, as one possibility, that the kimberlite magma was highly fluid. The intrusions have induced either little or no change in their wallrocks. From the effects exerted locally on coal and oil, it is deduced that the temperature of emplacement may have been less than 600°C, or so. The kimberlites contain abundant serpentine and most of them contain abundant carbonate. The textural relationships at some occurrences indicate that much of the carbonate is a late-crystallizing primary mineral. This conclusion may apply also to other occurrences where the relationships are less definitive. In an experimental investigation of the system $CaO\text{-}CO_2\text{-}H_2O$, Wyllie and Tuttle (1960, p. 45) found that a liquid phase could exist at temperatures as low as approximately 650°C. It seems likely, considering all evidence, that the kimberlites were emplaced at relatively low temperature as an accumulation of crystals transported by a highly fluid liquid rich in carbon dioxide and water. The possible nature of such a liquid is discussed in the next section (VI) in connection with phase relationships in the system CaO-MgO-SiO_2-CO_2-H_2O.

VI. EXPERIMENTAL STUDIES IN THE SYSTEM CaO-MgO-SiO_2-CO_2-H_2O

G. W. Franz and P. J. Wyllie

A. Introduction

The field evidence that many carbonatites are intrusive and possibly magmatic was incompatible with available experimental data until Wyllie and Tuttle (1960) demonstrated that liquids in the system CaO-CO_2-H_2O precipitate calcite at temperatures down to 640°C through a wide pressure range. The problem of the origin of carbonatites has since been examined by studying the phase relationships in systems containing the "synthetic carbonatite magma" and silicate minerals occurring in rocks associated with carbonatites. The increasing awareness in recent years of possible genetic connections between carbonatites and kimberlites (von Eckermann, 1948, 1958; Saether, 1957; Dawson, 1964; Garson, 1962; Davidson, 1964; Wyllie, 1967) led to the selection of forsterite as a suitable additional mineral component, giving the five-component system CaO-MgO-SiO_2-CO_2-H_2O. Sections through this system have been investigated by Franz (1965).

B. Experimental Results

The phase fields intersected by part of the composition triangle $CaCO_3$-$Ca(OH)_2$-Mg_2SiO_4 at 1 kb pressure in the temperature interval 550°C to 950°C were delineated by studying linear TX sections containing 10, 20, and 30 weight per cent Mg_2SiO_4. Synthetic forsterite was added to commercial calcite and portlandite in appropriate proportions, and the mixtures were homogenized. Experimental details can be found in Franz and Wyllie (1966).

The phase fields intersected by the 30 per cent forsterite join are shown in Fig. 9.14. Notice that in addition to the crystalline and liquid phases listed in the diagram, a vapor phase coexists with all assemblages, albeit in very small amounts. Of particular interest in this composition join, and in the other TX sections, are the horizontal lines, labeled R_1 through R_7, which mark the isothermal, isobaric coexistence of six-phase assemblages. These assemblages represent univariant reactions. Above and below each isobaric reaction temperature, there extend a total of six five-phase assemblages. Several of these are intersected by the linear TX section shown in Fig. 9.14. From the distribution of the five-phase assemblages, and from knowledge of the composition of most of the phases involved, complete equations can be written for the seven univariant reactions. The precise compositions of the liquid and vapor phase involved in each reaction are not known, so the equations cannot be balanced. The reactions, in the direction of increasing temperature at 1 kb pressure, are:

R_6 at 605°C. Portlandite + calcite + monticellite + brucite + vapor = liquid.

R_5 at 624°C. Calcite + monticellite + brucite = periclase + liquid + vapor.

R_4 at 625°C. Monticellite + brucite
= portlandite + periclase + liquid
+ vapor.

R_3 at 655°C. Portlandite + monticellite
= calciochondrodite + periclase
+ liquid + vapor.

R_2 at 755°C. Calciochondrodite
+ monticellite + periclase
= merwinite + liquid + vapor.

R_1 at 870°C. Calciochondrodite
+ merwinite
= dicalcium silicate + periclase
+ liquid + vapor.

R_7 at 895°C. Calcite + monticellite
+ periclase + vapor
= forsterite + liquid.

The estimated composition of the liquid in reaction R_6, in weight percentage of mineral components, is 50 per cent portlandite, 40 per cent calcite, 6 per cent dicalcium silicate, and 4 per cent periclase. This liquid is regarded as a "synthetic carbonatite magma" because it is capable of precipitating calcite at moderate temperatures, although it is realized that the water

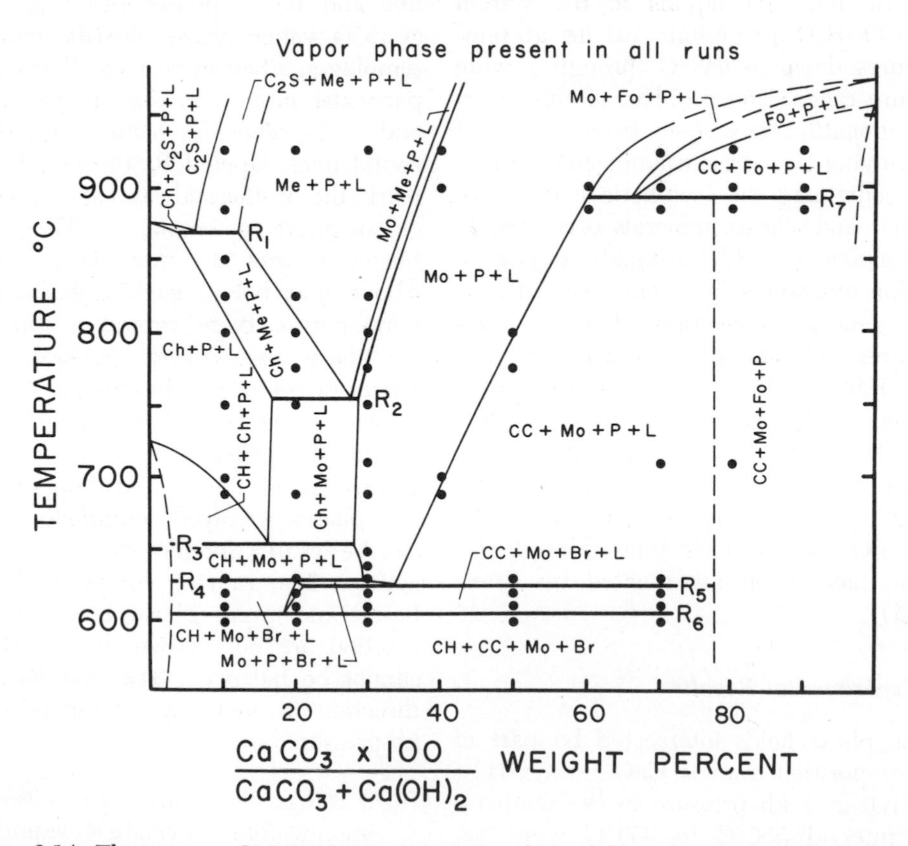

Fig. 9.14 The system $CaO\text{-}MgO\text{-}SiO_2\text{-}CO_2\text{-}H_2O$; phase fields intersected at 1 kb pressure by a linear composition join. The univariant reactions R_1 to R_7 are listed in the text. Abbreviations: CH, portlandite, $Ca(OH)_2$; CC, calcite, $CaCO_3$; Ch, calciochondrodite, $Ca_5(SiO_4)_2(OH)_2$; C_2S, dicalcium silicate Ca_2SiO_4; Me, merwinite, $Ca_3MgSi_2O_8$; Mo, monticellite, $CaMgSiO_4$; Fo, forsterite, Mg_2SiO_4; P, periclase, MgO; Br, brucite, $Mg(OH)_2$; L, liquid; V, vapor.

content and precipitation of portlandite tarnish the analogy to some extent. The composition of the vapor phase in this reaction is almost pure H_2O. Reaction R_6 is of particular interest because the "synthetic carbonatite magma" precipitates not only calcite and hydrated phases, but also monticellite, a silicate mineral normally regarded as a "high temperature" mineral.

Reactions R_6 and R_7 are of greatest interest in the present context. The composition of the liquid phase in reaction R_7 is considerably enriched in $CaCO_3$ compared to that in reaction R_6, and the vapor phase in R_7 is much richer in CO_2 than that in R_6. Forsterite appears in equilibrium with the liquid at 895°C by reaction R_7. Theoretical considerations indicate that R_7 occurs at lower temperatures with increasing pressures. The available evidence suggests that at pressures readily attained within the crust of the earth, reaction R_7 (or its equivalent with brucite instead of periclase) will intersect the reaction for the beginning of melting in the system (R_6 at 1 kb pressure). This produces a situation where the "synthetic carbonatite magma" can coexist with monticellite, forsterite, calcite, brucite, and portlandite at temperatures of the order of 600°C.

C. Discussion

Results obtained in the system CaO-MgO-SiO_2-H_2O at 1 kb pressure demonstrate that the composition plane Ca_2SiO_4-MgO-H_2O is a thermal barrier (Franz and Wyllie, 1966). Liquids with compositions on the SiO_2 side of the barrier crystallize to assemblages of anhydrous silicates and a vapor phase, whereas crystallization of liquids on the side of the barrier away from SiO_2 leads to the precipitation of hydrated phases and the evolution of vapor. The situation in the system CaO-MgO-SiO_2-CO_2-H_2O is directly analogous, although geometrical problems in representation of five-component systems prohibit a simple graphical demonstration. It can be shown that in the five-component system, only liquids that are undersaturated with respect to SiO_2 are capable of yielding residual liquids precipitating hydrated and carbonated phases. The occurrence of decarbonation reactions in this system provides an interesting extension compared to the system CaO-MgO-SiO_2-H_2O, namely, the precipitation of magnesian silicate minerals such as monticellite and forsterite along with the low-temperature, residual "synthetic carbonatite magma." The liquid phase contains only moderate amounts of dissolved MgO and SiO_2, so that crystallization would not yield very much forsterite and monticellite. However, it is significant that the carbonate-rich liquid can coexist in stable equilibrium with these "high temperature" magnesian silicate minerals at temperatures appropriate for the emplacement of kimberlites. The experimental results thus provide support for the possible genetic links between kimberlites and carbonatites, which have been discussed elsewhere in Chapters 8 and 9 (see especially Dawson, Chapter 8-V; von Eckermann, Chapter 9-IV; and Watson, Chapter 9-V).

According to Dawson (Chapter 8-II-B), kimberlite may be defined as a serpentinized and carbonated mica-peridotite of porphyritic texture, containing nodules of ultrabasic rock types. Only rarely has the carbonate in kimberlites been regarded as a primary crystalline phase, and it is more usual to consider the carbonate as a product of weathering, as a product of hydrothermal fluids from younger intrusions, as derived from xenoliths of limestones, or as a deuteric mineral. Watson (1955, and Chapter 9-V-E), after a detailed study of the Bachelor Lake kimberlite dikes, concluded that the calcite amounting to as much as 50 modal per cent of the rocks was the product of a carbonate magma; much of the calcite is a late-crystallizing primary mineral. This conclusion "may be germane also to other occurrences where the evidence is less decisive."

It is significant that there is a complete gradation in chemical composition between kimberlites and alnöites on the one hand, and carbonatites on the other (see Fig. 8.11). The phase relationships outlined in this section indicate that the calcite in the kimberlites and alnöites can no longer be classified with confidence as an alteration product (cf. Shand, 1934). It is possible that for kimberlite pipes emplaced by a fluidization process, the fluid involved may be a carbonatite magma (see Watson in Chapter 9-V-1) rather than a dense gaseous phase. A gaseous phase could coexist with the carbonatite magma. Dawson's Table 8.7 requires a gaseous phase for the fluidization process, but a carbonatite magma was involved in the earlier "skarn stage."

There are several ways in which kimberlites and carbonatites could be associated, in the light of available experimental and petrological evidence. It appears very likely that a carbonatite magma coming accidentally into contact with a crystalline kimberlite at 600 to 650°C would be in equilibrium with many minerals within the kimberlite. Crystallization of an undersaturated, carbonated kimberlite magma would probably yield a residual liquid corresponding rather closely to a carbonatite magma. Crystallization of a melilite-basalt or kimberlite magma could lead to the separation of an immiscible liquid fraction corresponding to a carbonatite magma (see von Eckermann, Chapter 9-IV-C; and Koster van Groos and Wyllie, 1966). These possibilities should be considered as alternative working hypotheses.

10. *Mafic and Ultramafic Nodules*

I. INTRODUCTION

P. J. Wyllie

The great interest in the small nodules found in alkalic lavas and kimberlite diatremes lies in the hope that they will provide information about the composition and mineralogy of the earth's mantle. They have already been discussed by several contributors, including O'Hara, Chapter 5-IV; Dawson, 8-II and 8-V; Davidson, 8-III; Watson, 8-IV; Upton, 9-II; and von Eckermann, 9-IV. The nodules have been interpreted as representative of primary mantle material; as residual mantle material after extraction of basalt; as xenoliths picked up within the earth's crust; as cumulates from primary basaltic magma formed as bottom cumulates in temporary reservoirs, or formed marginally during upward flow.

Forbes and Kuno in Section II present a world-wide review of peridotite inclusions and their host rocks. They offer the data as a regional framework for the interpretation of geochemical and petrological studies. In decreasing order of abundance, the following inclusions are found: gabbro, peridotite, basic granulites, garnet peridotite, and eclogite. Among the peridotite inclusions, spinel-lherzolite is most frequently reported, but there are at least a dozen other assemblages known, most of which are believed to be accidental. Forbes and Kuno discuss the tectonic setting of inclusion-bearing basalts in some detail. The peridotite-bearing basalts clearly define regional arcuate belts, with circumoceanic and oceanic belts prevailing. The chemical composition of the inclusion-bearing basalts from various environments are compared with their inclusions on FMA and CNK diagrams. The inclusion-bearing basalts from all three environments display a strong compositional kinship, but the intraoceanic basalts are characterized by low $K/(K + Na)$ as compared with the higher ratios in mediterranean and continental occurrences. The origin of the peridotite inclusions appears to be related to the genesis of basaltic magma within the mantle.

Following the world-wide review, Kuno in Section III describes in some detail the whole suite of nodules collected from a single crater in Japan. The nodules can be arranged according to the depth of their supposed source regions: andesite (surface), granodiorite (upper part of crust), gabbro (lower part of the crust), pyroxenite and peridotite (top of the mantle), and garnet peridotite (below the peridotite horizon in the mantle). This arrangement agrees with the seismological observations on the crustal and upper mantle structure of the region. The presence of anorthite in the ultramafic nodules is probably related to the unusually high thermal gradient of the region. Exsolution lamellae in the pyroxenes indicate that these are not simple crystal cumulates in magmas. Lineation indicates flow in the solid state, and recrystallization.

In Section IV Davidson summarizes the evidence that the eclogites and garnet peridotites among the xenoliths found in kimberlite pipes are disrupted fragments of the deep metamorphic crust. High-grade metamorphic zones are known to include rock types comparable with the inclusions found in kimberlite pipes. He suggests that it is subjective to allocate the granulites to the crust, and the peridotites and garnet peridotites to the mantle, and he questions whether the nodules in kimberlite pipes provide any basis for philosophizing on the nature of rocks beneath the crust. He illustrates the range of mineralogical composition in terms of garnet, enstatite, and diopside of 70 xenoliths of garnet-pyroxene rocks from a single kimberlite pipe in Siberia. No two modal analyses are the same. Another diagram shows modal analyses for 174 ultrabasic inclusions showing a similar wide range in mineralogy. If these inclusions represent the upper mantle, then the latter is of so varied a composition that petrogenetic studies based on a single rock-type such as garnet-peridotite must be of questionable value. This variability of rock type is a feature of high-grade metamorphism. Davidson cites apparently irrefutable evidence from Czechoslovakia that garnet peridotite and eclogite nodules do not always come from great depth.

In Section V O'Hara assumes that basalts originate in the mantle and fractionate during ascent, and that their ultramafic inclusions are related to this process. He considers the inclusion of accidental crustal xenoliths a sufficiently unlikely event to be ignored in general. He suggests a procedure that may provide criteria for the mode of origin of nodules. Nodule suites can be arranged in a geochemical sequence based on changes in chemical ratios, and the sequence can be used to predict portions of phase diagrams, from high to low temperature, if a particular process is assumed to operate in the formation of the nodules. For a given suite there will in general be a different phase diagram for each hypothesis. The alternative predictions can then be evaluated in the light of available experimental data or tested directly against suitable experiments. Some specific differences between the predictions of three hypotheses are tabulated.

Ultrabasic or ultramafic inclusions also occur in peridotites in minor and major intrusions. Drever and Johnston in Chapter 3-V-C-3 describe peridotite xenoliths in the picrite dikes of Skye; these were also described by Harker (1904) in the Skye Memoir. In Chapter 4-II-C-3 Irvine describes inclusions of peridotite in the layered ultrabasic rocks of Duke Island. The processes involved in the formation and location of the inclusions in these intrusions are almost certainly of local significance.

The geochemistry of nodules and their relationship to basalts are compared with the alpine-type ultramafic rock and with ultramafic rocks from stratiform intrusions in Chapter 11, and estimates of the depth of formation of nodules in basalts and kimberlites are made by O'Hara in Chapter 12-II.

II. PERIDOTITE INCLUSIONS AND BASALTIC HOST ROCKS

Robert B. Forbes
and
Hisashi Kuno

A. Introduction

The controversy concerning the cumulative versus exotic origin of peridotite inclusions in basaltic rocks has been continuous and spirited since the early description of olivine nodules in basaltic bombs near Eisenbühl, Germany (Reuss,

1852). A historical summary cannot be presented here, and the reader is referred to LaCroix (1893), Schadler (1913), Ross, Foster and Meyers (1954), Wilshire and Binns (1961), and Kushiro and Kuno (1963) for a more detailed appreciation of the earlier contributions.

Kuno (1959a), Kushiro and Kuno (1963) and others had previously noted that peridotite inclusions occur in *alkali-olivine* basalts rather than tholeiites; and in 1963 Kushiro and Kuno knew of over 70 confirmed occurrences of peridotite inclusion-bearing basalts. With the international cooperation of many colleagues, we initiated a continuing effort in 1963 to compile available data on previously known and newly reported peridotite inclusion localities. Over 200 localities are now known (Forbes and Kuno, 1965).

Peridotite inclusions occur in pyroclastic, flow and hypabyssal rocks, as summarized in the following:

1. *Flows.* Flows from central vents, pyroclastic cones and basaltic shield volcanoes; fissure flows from shield volcanoes; and plateau alkali basalt flows, erupted from single or multiple vents.
2. *Pyroclastics.* Tuff and scoria cones; cores in bombs and lapilli; bedded tuffs (including sub-aqueous types); and vent breccias (agglomerates).
3. *Hypabyssal.* Breccia pipes (basalt-basaltic kimberlite-kimberlite); dikes and sills (including monchiquite, lamprophyre, etc.)

B. Inclusions

Although peridotite assemblages have been the most widely discussed, several inclusion rock types other than xenoliths derived from the subvolcanic basement are found in basaltic host rocks. In approximate order of decreasing abundance, these types include: gabbro, peridotite, basic granulites, garnet peridotite, and eclogite.

1. Garnet peridotite and eclogite inclusions. It is probable that garnet peridotite, eclogite and granulite inclusions occur in more inclusion suites than currently recognized, based on reports of discrete and fragmental grains of pyrope-almandine garnet and diopsidic (omphacitic?) clinopyroxene in peridotite inclusion-bearing basalts from various localities. In some cases, inclusion types megascopically classified as gabbroic gneisses, may be hypersthene-bearing basic granulites, as recently recognized in the inclusion suite of Prindle Volcano, Yukon-Tanana Upland, Alaska (H. Foster, R. Forbes and D. Ragan, unpublished data).

In addition to the well-known kimberlite occurrences, eclogite inclusions are known to occur in basaltic rocks on Nunivak Island, Bering Sea, Alaska (J. Hoare, personal communication); in the tuffaceous nepheline basalt of the Salt Lake Crater, Oahu, Hawaii (Yoder and Tilley, 1962; Kuno, 1959a); and in basaltic host rocks at four localities in New South Wales, Australia (Lovering and White, 1964). The detailed mineralogy of the eclogite fragment from Nunivak Island is not known at this writing, but the eclogitic inclusions from the Salt Lake Crater, have peridotitic affinities, and the assemblages include hypersthene and olivine in addition to omphacitic clinopyroxene and pyrope rich garnet. (Yoder and Tilley, 1962; Kuno, 1963.)

The mineral assemblages of the eclogitic inclusions from New South Wales frequently contain calcic plagioclase and scapolite (Lovering and White, 1964). Bulk chemical analyses of the eclogitic inclusions from Salt Lake Crater (Yoder and Tilley, 1962; Kuno, 1963) show that these inclusions are more magnesian than eclogites from crystalline schist terrane (Forbes, 1965).

Eclogitic inclusions therefore occur in basaltic rocks in the continental, mediterranean and intraoceanic settings. The compositional similarity between eclogites in peridotite masses and the Salt Lake eclogite inclusions may be significant, in respect to the possible origin of the Hawaiian inclusions as eclogite masses associated with upper mantle peridotite. The New South Wales eclogite(?) inclusions (Lovering and White, 1964) occur in suites that also contain garnet-pyroxene and pyroxene granulite fragments. To our knowledge gneissic granulite inclusions have not been reported from intraoceanic localities, although a gneissic fragment believed to be an altered basic granulite was recently recovered from an alkali olivine basalt flow on St. Lawrence Island, Bering Sea, Alaska (R. Forbes and H. Matsumoto, unpublished data).

The apparent absence of basic granulite inclusions from the intraoceanic inclusion suites is also provocative, in respect to the absence of a continental crust in the oceanic basins.

2. *Peridotite inclusions.* As discussed by Ross, Foster, and Myers (1954) and many others, the assemblage forsteritic olivine-spinel-chrome diopside-enstatite (bronzite) is the most frequently reported peridotite inclusion type. Many peridotitic assemblages have been reported from various inclusion suites, including the following:

olivine-spinel,
olivine-spinel-enstatite (bronzite),
olivine-spinel-enstatite (bronzite)-chrome diopside (augite),
olivine-spinel-chrome diopside (augite),
olivine-titanaugite
bronzite-spinel,
olivine-spinel-diopside-anorthite,
garnet-diopside-olivine (transitional to olivine-bearing eclogite),
garnet-enstatite-olivine,
augite-leucite,
olivine-leucite-augite.

Most of these assemblages are believed by us to be exotic, but the following may be cognate cumulates:

olivine-titanaugite,
augite-leucite,
olivine-leucite-augite.

The inclusion assemblage olivine-titanaugite, described by Forbes (1963) from a Ross Island, Antarctica alkali-olivine basalt, contains titanaugite which is chemically similar to that in the host basalt (Forbes, unpublished data), and olivine with a Fayalite content similar to the rims of cognate phenocrysts (Forbes and Banno, 1966). The leucite-bearing assemblages previously listed, were described by Reinisch (1908), from inclusions in leucite basalts at Gaussberg, Antarctica. The occurrence of leucite in such assemblages suggests a cognate rather than an exotic and deep crustal or mantle origin.

In our brief outline of peridotite inclusion assemblages we have attempted to recognize and delete occurrences which appear to be cumulates, including olivine segregations in picritic basalts, and olivine-plagioclase or olivine-plagioclase-pyroxene aggregates.

C. Geographical Distribution and Geologic Setting of Inclusion-Bearing Basaltic Rocks

1. *Geographical distribution.* As shown in Figs. 10.1 and 10.2, peridotite inclusion-bearing basaltic rocks occur on all of the continents including Antarctica; on intraoceanic volcanic island archipelagos in the Atlantic, Pacific, and Indian Ocean basins; and on islands in the Bering, Japan and China Seas. We do not know of any occurrences in Sweden, Finland, South America, Greenland, India and the interior regions of China and the U.S.S.R.

The regional distribution of peridotite inclusion-bearing basalts, as shown on the two locality maps (Figs. 10.1 and 10.2), clearly define regional arcuate belts which occur in both oceanic and continental settings. Circumoceanic and oceanic belts prevail, and intracontinental occurrences are subordinate. Descriptions of the terms intraoceanic, mediterranean and continental, as used here, follow:

1. *Intraoceanic.* Volcanic islands or archipelagos in the deep ocean basins.

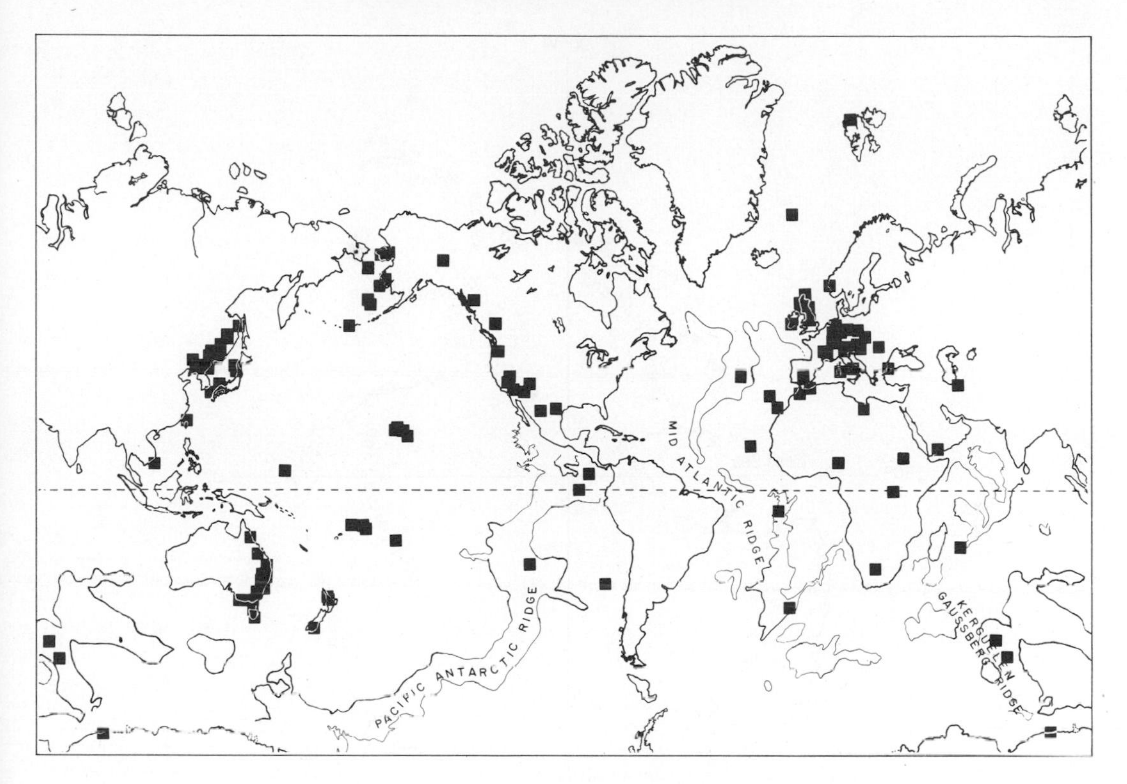

Fig. 10.1 Worldwide peridotite inclusion localities (excluding Antarctica).

2. *Coastal or Mediterranean.* Islands in shallow seas or coastal waters, including those in the hinterland areas behind island arcs.

3. *Continental.* (a) Intracontinental. Occurrences in the interior regions of the continents; (b) Circumoceanic. Occurrences along the continental margins, on the continental side of orogenic belts.

2. *Regional Geology.* The choice of terms used in the above classification reflects, in part, the difficulties which were also met by Chayes (1964) in defining circumoceanic versus intraoceanic volcanic settings. Chayes has geographically defined *circumoceanic* as "any island, island chain, peninsula, or continental area lying immediately on the shoreward side" of oceanic trenches; thereby defining provinces that are essentially characterized by orogenic volcanic activity, and tholeiitic rather than alkali-olivine basalts. Although the circum-Pacific belt of peridotite inclusion-bearing basalts is regionally circumoceanic, the two provinces are not coincident, and they rarely overlap.

It is clear that peridotite inclusion-bearing basalts occur in alkali basalt petrologic provinces. There is a high probability that peridotite inclusions will be found in Cenozoic eruptive centers or fields *wherever they occur,* if the host rocks are alkali-olivine basalts with a high TiO_2 content (> 1.75 weight per cent) and normative nepheline and/or leucite.

In the circum-Pacific regions, inclusion-bearing basalts occur on the continental side of the currently active orogenic volcanic belts, or in the hinterlands of the circum-Pacific arcs. These are the Cenozoic alkali basalt provinces as previously noted by Tomkeieff (1949), Barth (1956), Kuno (1959b), and Sugimura (1960). These provinces occur in tectonic settings characterized by epeirogenic uplift and high angle faulting during Tertiary and/or Quaternary time. Tholeiitic, not alkali

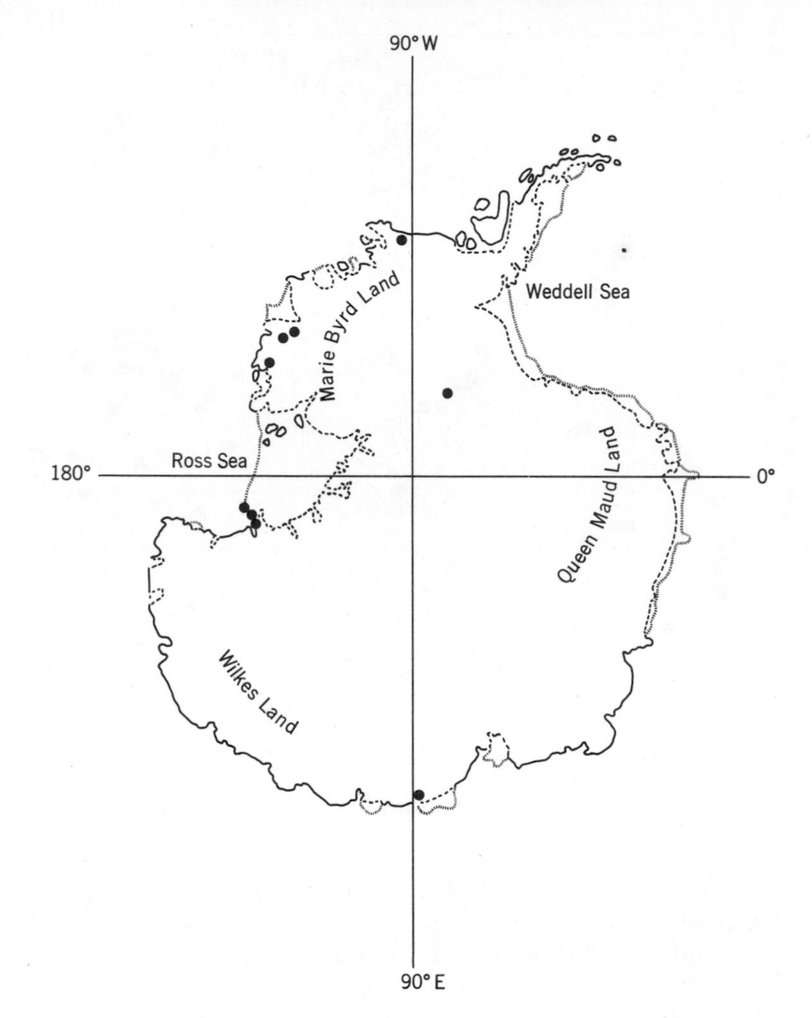

Fig. 10.2 Antarctic peridotite inclusion localities.

basalts, are members of the rock series erupted by orogenic andesitic volcanoes, thus explaining why peridotite inclusions have not been reported from basalts associated with orogenic volcanic suites. One anomaly is known, however, on Kanaga Island in the Aleutian Archipelago, Alaska (Ross, Foster and Meyers, 1954), where peridotite inclusions occur in an alkali-olivine basalt. Although the alkali basalt-peridotite inclusion association is here preserved, the occurrence of alkali basalt on an island located along the apparent axis of the Aleutian Arc is anomalous. The Kanaga anomaly appears to be a terminal occurrence in a series of inclusion-bearing basalt localities including Nunivak, St. Lawrence, and the Pribilof Islands (Barth, 1956), an arcuate belt of localities that appears to cross the hinterland to intersect the Aleutian Arc. Geophysical data compiled by Woollard and Strange (1963) indicate possible welts in the M discontinuity behind the Arc that parallel the trend defined by the above localities. The tectonic and petrologic significance of these relations remains in doubt, and the Kanaga anomaly deserves further investigation.

The circum-Pacific inclusion belt is chiefly defined by continental localities, but the regional continuity of the belt is maintained even though it also includes occurrences in the mediterranean and oceanic settings. The trend defined by inclusion localities along the west margin of North America appears to be contiguous with that established by dredged specimens of peridotite inclusion-bearing alkali basalts in the Baha Seamount Province (A. E. J. Engel, personal communication); and the Cocos (Chubb and Richardson, 1933) and Galapagos Islands (Gooch, 1876), which appear to be related to volcanic activity along the East Pacific Rise and adjacent submarine ridges and fault zones.

Recent findings suggest that the mid-oceanic ridges may maintain their integrity under the continental crust, after they plunge beneath the margins of the continental blocks. Structural provinces characterized by high-angle faulting and rifting often parallel the trends of the oceanic ridges, as projected under the continents. The compositional similarity of inclusion-bearing basalts in a belt traversing continental, mediterranean, and oceanic settings along the west margin of North America and the East Pacific rise indicates that inclusion-bearing alkali-olivine basalts are somehow petrogenetically related, regardless of geographical setting.

Brevity forbids an extended discussion of the regional geologic implications of all of the belts of peridotite inclusion-bearing basalts shown in Figs. 10.1 and 10.2 but the regional tectonic parameters outlined above appear to apply to the Atlantic, West European, circum-Mediterranean, Indian Ocean, and Antarctic belts. The circum-Mediterranean inclusion occurrences appear to be continental extensions of the Cape Verde-Madeira-Canary Island belt; and the occurrences on Kerguelen (Edwards, 1938) and Heard Islands (P. J. Stephenson, personal communication) astride the Kerguelen-Gaussberg ridge seem to be related to the contiguous occurrence of inclusion-bearing leucite basalts at Gaussberg, Antarctica (Reinisch, 1908), where the Kerguelen-Gaussberg ridge appears to intersect the continent.

Inclusion-bearing alkali basalts rarely occur in Precambrian shield terrane, but a few localities are known including several occurrences in the rift region in East Africa (Holmes and Harwood, 1932) and at Gaussberg, Antarctica (Reinisch, 1908). In these occurrences the host basalts are leucite-bearing olivine basalts.

D. Distribution in Geologic Time

Inclusion-bearing basalts are dominantly of Cenozoic age, and the inclusion producing mechanism has continued through Quaternary time up to the present. Peach (1963) and Foster, Forbes and Ragan (unpublished data) have reported post-Pleistocene inclusion-bearing pyroclastic cones and related flows in British Columbia, Canada, and Alaska, respectively. Historic Hawaiian flows contain peridotite inclusions, including the 1801 Hualalai (Macdonald, 1949) and 1950 Kaapuna (Finch and Macdonald, 1950) flows on the island of Hawaii. Ile des Cendres, a submarine volcano which was briefly exposed during the period March–May, 1923, off the east coast of Cochin China, was composed of alkali basalt containing olivine nodules and inclusions of granite, limestone, and sandstone (Patte, 1924).

The occurrence at Calton Hill, Derbyshire, England (Tomkeiieff, 1928; El D Hamad, 1963), and numerous localities in Ayreshire, Inverness-Shire, and adjacent districts in Scotland are in basalts believed to be of Carboniferous age. Lovering and Richards (1964) cite K^{40}–Ar^{40} data indicating that the inclusion-bearing breccia pipe near Delegate, New South Wales, Australia, was intruded about 168 million years ago. Peridotite inclusion bearing basalts may have been erupted with increasing frequency during Cenozoic time, as Paleozoic and Mesozoic inclusion-bearing basalts appear to be rare. Engel, Engel and Havens (1965) have recently reinforced our observations, noting that:

". . . for the first three quarters of geological time these eruptions of tholeiitic basalts appear to occur almost to the exclusion of alkali basalts."

However, continental peridotite inclusion-bearing basalts occur as pyroclastic cones, breccia pipes, and/or flows of rather limited area and volume; and many pre-Cenozoic occurrences may have been removed or obscured by destructive and constructive geological processes. It is also possible that alteration, deformation and recrystallization may have obscured the evidence in pre-Cenozoic basalts. But the survival of partially carbonatized and serpentinized peridotite inclusions in the Carboniferous basalts of Scotland, and in a metamorphosed basic dike (green schist facies) recently reported in the Alaska range (J. Hawkins and D. M. Ragan, personal communication) shows that the identity of such inclusions may persist over long periods of geologic time.

E. Regional Petrology of the Host Basalts

Known host rocks include the following basaltic rock types: olivine tholeiites, alkali olivine basalts, basanites (basanatoids), olivine-melilite basalts, olivine-nepheline-melilite basalts, olivine-leucite basalts, hawaiite, mugearite, and limburgite.

Kimberlites are notably rich in inclusions, and although there may be a genetic relationship between olivine-melilite-basalts and kimberlites, the kimberlite problem will not be discussed here (see Chapters 10-IV and 12-III). The appearance of olivine tholeiites in the above list may be questioned by those acquainted with the problem, but it is now clear that peridotite inclusions also occur in olivine tholeiites, even though such occurrences are relatively rare. Formerly, it was believed that tholeiitic basalts were not peridotite inclusion bearing (Kuno, 1959a), but three confirmed occurrences of inclusion-bearing olivine tholeiites are known in the Hawaiian Islands, including two occurrences on Maui (Macdonald and Katsura, 1964), and the 1950 Kaapuna flow of Mauna Loa (Finch and Macdonald, 1950).

If the bulk chemical analyses of the host basalts are classified in terms of the "normative tetrahedron" of Yoder and Tilley (1962), oversaturated (Qz + Hy) and saturated (Hy) tholeiites must be added to the list of host basalts. However, these rocks contain modal olivine, even though olivine does not appear in the norm, and the $K_2O/(Na_2O + K_2O)$ ratios show alkali rather than tholeiitic basalt affinities. Macdonald and Katsura (1964) have previously noted that the presence of hypersthene in the norm depends on several factors other than alkali and silica content, including the oxidation state of the iron.

Chayes (1964) reported that chemically analyzed oceanic basalts could be distinguished from circumoceanic basalts at the 92 per cent confidence level, by using the following discriminants:

"Letting A = nepheline + $acmite_{norm}$, and B = TiO_2 weight per cent 1.75, we define as *petrographically oceanic* any analysis in which either $A > 0$ or $B > 0$ and as petrographically circumoceanic any analysis in which $A = 0$ and $B \leq 0$"

When Chayes' discriminants are applied to the bulk chemical analyses of peridotite inclusion-bearing basalts in our files, 96 per cent of these rocks are *oceanic, regardless of geographical setting*. The application of Chayes' method shows that most peridotite inclusion-bearing basalts are characterized by high TiO_2 (>1.75 weight per cent) and/or silica undersaturation; but it also indicates that these parameters will discriminate alkali basalts, as defined by Yoder and Tilley (1962) regardless of geographical location. High TiO_2 content is an important factor in the definitive chemistry of peridotite inclusion-bearing basalts, as several hypersthene normative host basalts have TiO_2 contents that exceed 1.75 weight per cent, thereby qualifying these rocks as *oceanic* even though they are not nepheline normative.

The *oceanic* character of peridotite inclusion-bearing basalts, as just defined, demonstrates the compositional convergence of host basalts in all geographical settings, but for our purpose, these discriminants neglect a most important parameter: total alkali content and of more importance, the alkali ratio.

The FMA and CNK diagrams shown as Figs. 10.3*a* and 10.3*b* compare the chemical composition of inclusion-bearing basalts from oceanic, mediterranean, and continental localities to the average compositions of Pacific and Atlantic basalts as given by Green and Poldervaart (1955). These average bulk chemical compositions were calculated from analyses of basalts from island archipelagos, and analyses of low K oceanic tholeiites (Engel and Engel, 1963, 1964) were not available to the authors at that time. For our purpose, however, these averages are useful, as the compositional affinities to be here discussed chiefly involve alkali rather than low K tholeiitic basalts.

The plots in the FMA diagrams (Figs. 10.3*a* and 10.3*b*) appear to define two groups: the low and high alkali fields. Plots of the average values taken from Green

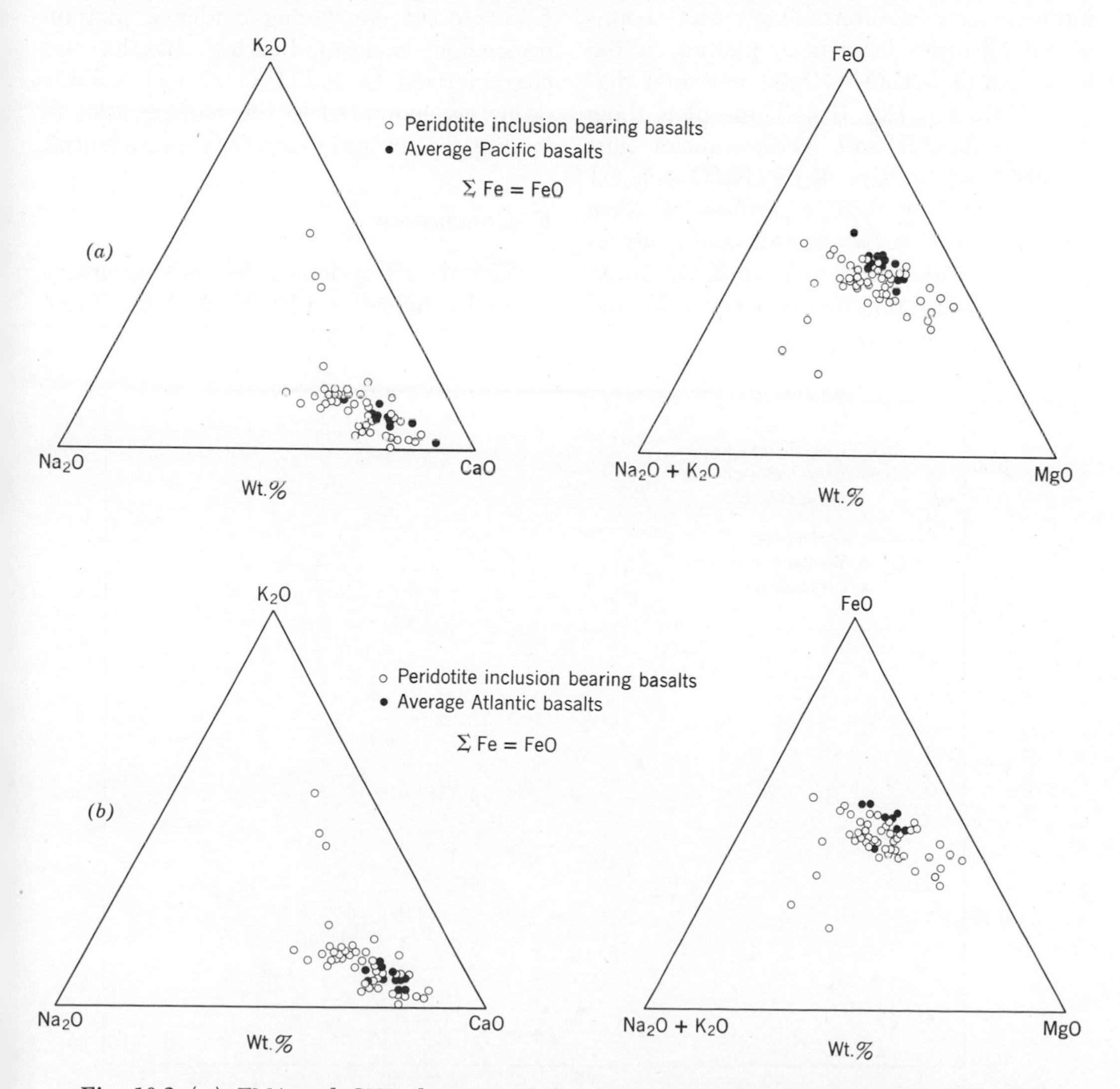

Fig. 10.3 (*a*) FMA and CNK diagrams of the comparative chemical composition of inclusion bearing basalts and average Pacific basalts as given by Green and Poldervaart (1955). (*b*) FMA and CNK diagrams of the comparative chemical composition of inclusion bearing basalts and average Atlantic basalts as given by Green and Poldervaart (1955).

and Poldervaart (1955) tend to lie in the low alkali field. Inclusion-bearing basalts from continental localities plot in both fields, but the high alkali basalt types occur more frequently on the continents than in the ocean basins. Although inclusion bearing basalts tend to be less calcic than oceanic basalts, as shown in the CNK diagrams of Figures 10.3*a* and 10.3*b*, there does not seem to be any correlation between calcium content and oceanic versus continental localities.

Peridotite inclusion-bearing basalts from intraoceanic, mediterranean, and continental localities have been plotted on the $K_2O/(Na_2O + K_2O) - SiO_2$ variation diagram shown as Fig. 10.4. These plots show that continental and mediterranean host basalts tend to have $K_2O/(Na_2O + K_2O)$ ratios exceeding 0.25, regardless of silica content; and that basalts from the mediterranean localities tend to have $K_2O/(Na_2O + K_2O)$ ratios ranging between 0.35 and 0.40, and silica contents greater than 45 weight per cent. A $K_2O/(Na_2O + K_2O)$ ratio of 0.25 also serves as a discriminant between the highly undersaturated nepheline-melilite and melilite basalts from oceanic versus continental localities (plots ranging between 35 and 39 weight per cent SiO_2). The diagram additionally shows that host basalts with SiO_2 exceeding 47 weight per cent tend to be absent in the intraoceanic regions. Although inclusion-bearing basalts from all three settings display strong compositional kinship, these data present convincing evidence that intraoceanic inclusion-bearing basalts are characterized by low $K_2O/(Na_2O + K_2O)$ ratios, as compared to the higher ratios in mediterranean and continental occurrences.

F. Conclusions

With the exception of the early summary given by Schadler (1913), and the more

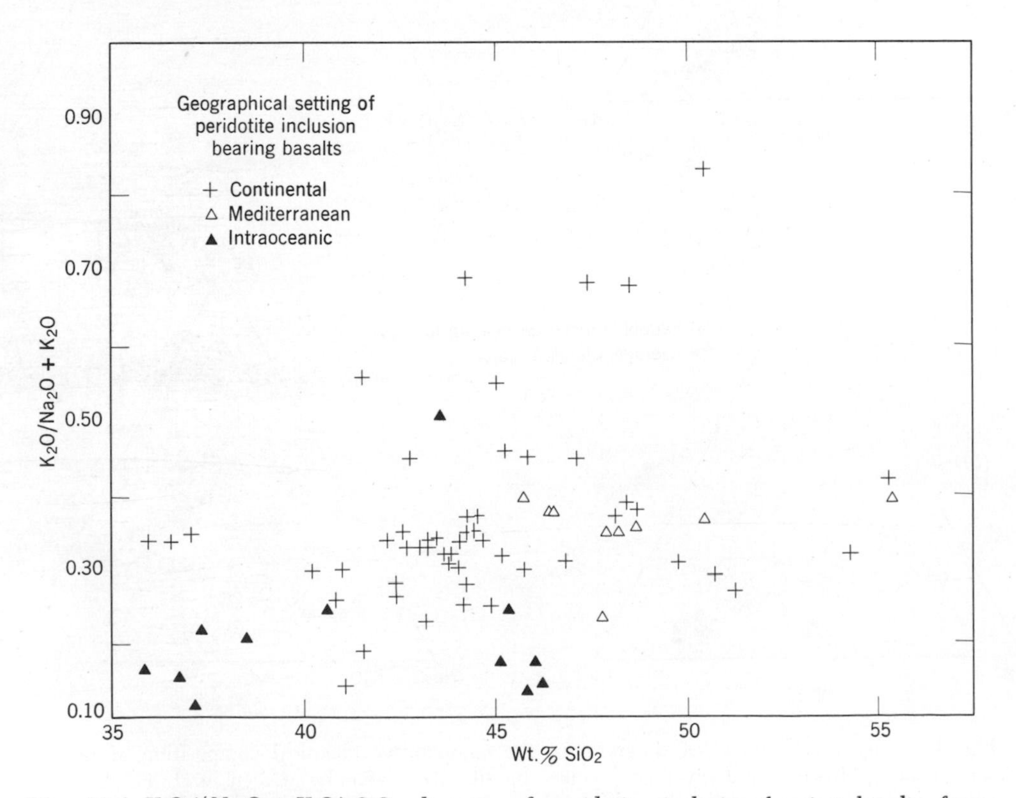

Fig. 10.4 $K_2O/(Na_2O + K_2O)$-SiO_2 diagram of peridotite inclusion bearing basalts from continental, mediterranean, and intraoceanic localities.

recent contributions of Ross, Foster, and Meyers (1954) and Kushiro and Kuno (1963), little attention has been given to the comparative petrology of the host rocks and inclusions, and the regional distribution of these occurrences. As reports of new or rediscovered localities have been added to our compilation, it has become apparent that peridotite inclusion-bearing basalts are not petrological rarities; and that Cenozoic alkali-olivine basalts that occur in the previously defined settings very frequently contain peridotite inclusions.

The contiguous nature of oceanic and continental inclusion belts, the similarity in bulk chemical composition and mineralogy of the host basalts, and the apparent association of oceanic ridges, rift zones, and inclusion-bearing basalts in both oceanic and continental settings suggests that the basaltic magmas were derived from the mantle; and that the origin of the peridotite inclusions is related to the genesis of basaltic magma in these zones. The increase in $K_2O/(Na_2O + K_2O)$ ratios observed in the continental host basalts may be due to alkali contamination from the crust and/or increased fractionation of alkalies related to the greater height of the magma column in continental regions.

Although our findings will not solve the basic arguments concerning the cumulate versus exotic origin of peridotite inclusions, or the dispute over mantle versus crustal parentage, these data offer a regional framework for the interpretation of data derived from detailed geochemical and petrological investigations.

III. MAFIC AND ULTRAMAFIC NODULES FROM ITINOME-GATA, JAPAN

Hisashi Kuno

A. Introduction

There are at least 15 localities of peridotite nodules in Japan, all included in alkali basaltic rocks of the Japan Sea coast. The nodules are associated with those of dunite, pyroxenite, and gabbros, and also with partly fused fragments of granitic and schistose rocks.

Itinome-gata is a circular crater 800 m in diameter lying in Oga Peninsula, Akita Prefecture, northeast Honshu. There are three other craters of similar size in the vicinity. Itinome-gata is surrounded by deposits of basalt lapilli and accidental tuff breccia ejected from the crater about 4000 years ago (Hayashi, 1955). They are underlain by older Miocene andesite complex.

The deposits contain fragments of the andesite and of less abundant granodiorite, gabbro, hornblende gabbro, pyroxenite, peridotite, and garnet peridotite. The granodiorite was probably derived from the one exposed to the northwest of the crater. The other rock fragments or nodules probably came from deep-seated sources, because such rocks have never been observed in the surrounding area.

The basalt lapilli contain phenocrysts of olivine, augite, andesine-oligoclase, and magnetite set in a groundmass of andesine, augite, olivine, iron oxide, and glass. A chemical analysis (Katsura, 1956) shows that it is a slightly alkalic basalt though SiO_2 is high (52.42 per cent) because of the presence of a few per cent quartz xenocrysts. The analysis quoted by Ross et al. (1954, p. 722) as that of the host rock of the Itinome-gata nodules is actually that of Meng-chien, east Manchuria nodules (Ross et al., 1954, p. 706).

B. Description of Mafic and Ultramafic Nodules

The mafic and ultramafic nodules are up to 20 cm in diameter. The constituent minerals are listed in Table 10.1.

Gabbro shows an indistinct foliation due to concentration of pyroxenes in thin lenticular masses, but no lineation is observable. Brown hornblende and magnetite (listed as spinel in Table 10.1) are present in small quantity. Pleochroic hypersthene contains exsolution lamellae of augite and ilmenite. Granular texture, foliation, and

TABLE 10.1 Constituent Minerals of Nodules from Itinome-gata

	Olivine	Ortho-pyroxene	Diopside	Spinel	Horn-blende	Garnet	Plagio-clase
Gabbro	−	+	+	+	+	−	+
Hornblende gabbro	±	±	±	+	+	−	+
Pyroxenite	±	+	+	±	±	−	±
Peridotite	+	+	+	+	±	−	+
Garnet peridotite	+	+	+	+	+	+	+

TABLE 10.2 Chemical Compositions of Hornblende Gabbro and Peridotite Nodules from Itinome-gata, Salt Lake, and Hualalai and Calculated Composition of Peridotite Left After Partial Melting

	1	2	3	4	5	6	7
SiO_2	40.73	44.02	44.59	44.39	43.29	44.08	43.9
Al_2O_3	23.16	1.03	2.98	3.26	2.36	0.47	1.5
Fe_2O_3	4.33	0.83	1.68	2.02	1.23	1.29	1.0
FeO	5.33	7.06	6.83	7.06	7.20	7.25	7.0
MgO	7.28	46.99	41.10	40.79	40.91	45.32	44.9
CaO	13.77	trace	2.22	0.94	2.84	0.76	1.5
Na_2O	1.52	0.05	0.22	0.35	0.33	0.14	0.1
K_2O	0.57	trace	0.05	0.04	0.05	<0.05	0.0
H_2O+	1.35	0.09	0.09	0.13	0.93	0.65	...
H_2O-	0.75	0.00	0.00	0.08	0.07	0.10	...
TiO_2	0.97	trace	0.06	0.13	0.20	0.06	0.1
P_2O_5	0.04	trace	0.01	0.15	0.03	<0.05	0.0
MnO	0.13	0.11	0.17	0.13	0.14	0.13	0.1
Cr_2O_3	n.d.	0.42	0.26	n.d.	0.27	0.32	...
Total	99.93	100.60	100.26	99.47	99.85	100.57	100.1

1. Olivine-bearing hornblende gabbro (HK59050801) from Itinome-gata. Analyst, H. Haramura.
2. Peridotite (HK63111602a) from Itinome-gata. Analyst, H. Haramura.
3. Garnet peridotite (HK50061804g) from Itinome-gata. Analyst, H. Haramura (Kushiro and Kuno, 1963).
4. Peridotite (HK61082601a) from Salt Lake near Honolulu, Oahu Island. Analyst, T. Saito (Japan Analytical Chemistry Research Institute).
5. Peridotite (HK57101204d) from Salt Lake near Honolulu. Analyst, H. Haramura (Kushiro and Kuno, 1963).
6. Peridotite (HK61030402) from 1801 flow of Hualalai Volcano, Hawaii Island, collected by G. A. Macdonald. Analyst, H. Haramura.
7. Calculated composition of peridotite left after partial melting of supposed mantle peridotite to produce average tholeiite magma of Japan (Kushiro and Kuno, 1963).

bending of plagioclase twinning indicate that the rock has been subjected to deformation and recrystallization.

Hornblende gabbro is coarse-grained, consisting essentially of hornblende and plagioclase (anorthite to labradorite according to Hayashi, 1955) in equal proportion, although in some specimens, one of the two minerals exceeds the other in quantity. Distinct foliation is developed owing to selective concentration of hornblende in different layers a few millimeters thick, but no lineation is observable. An analysis of a typical specimen with nearly equal proportion of hornblende and plagioclase is given in column 1, Table 10.2.

Hornblende is dark brown, including numerous pigments of an opaque mineral, possibly ilmenite, as a result of exsolution. Analyses of two such hornblendes are given in columns 1 and 2, Table 10.3.

According to calculation of constituent molecules, they are made up of 75 per cent pargasite $NaCa_2(Mg,Fe^{+2})_4(Al,Fe^{+3})_3Si_6O_{22}(OH)_2$ and 25 per cent tschermakite $Ca_2(Mg,Fe^{+2})_3(Al,Fe^{+3})_4Si_6O_{22}(OH)_2$ almost to the exclusion of other molecules. Either hypersthene or augite may be concentrated in small streaks. Magnetite (spinel of Table 10.2) is in small quantity. Judging from the presence of foliation, hornblende gabbro is a product of metamorphism of some gabbroic rock. In view of the high Al_2O_3 content, the original rock does not appear to be any kind of volcanic rock.

Pyroxenite contains more diopside than orthopyroxene. The amount of olivine (Fa_{13}) varies from nil to about 50 per cent. Exsolution lamellae and flakes of ilmenite and orthopyroxene in diopside and those of ilmenite and diopside in orthopyroxene are common. Orthopyroxene is a little more ferriferous (Fs_{10-12}) than orthopyroxenes in peridotite and garnet peridotite. Pale brown to greenish-brown hornblende ($2V_x \doteqdot 80°$), dark brown spinel, and calcic plagioclase are often present as accessories.

Peridotite (column 2, Table 10.2) has an indistinct lineation because of concen-

TABLE 10.3 Chemical Compositions and Atomic Proportions (on 23 oxygen atoms) of Hornblendes from Itinome-gata (Analyst, H. Haramura)

	1	2	3		1	2	3
SiO_2	40.02	40.91	44.21	Si	5.862	5.908	6.077
Al_2O_3	15.53	15.99	16.70	Al	2.138	2.092	1.923
Fe_2O_3	4.81	4.07	1.44	Σ	8.000	8.000	8.000
FeO	8.53	7.89	3.22	Al	0.544	0.630	0.782
MgO	12.38	13.57	18.78	Fe^{+3}	0.530	0.442	0.149
CaO	12.21	10.92	11.88	Ti	0.183	0.241	0.078
Na_2O	2.04	2.36	3.18	Fe^{+2}	1.044	0.952	0.370
K_2O	0.94	0.28	<0.1	Mn	0.021	0.021	0.012
H_2O+	1.70	1.32	0.54	Mg	2.701	2.919	3.846
H_2O-	0.00	0.15	0.07	Σ	5.023	5.205	5.237
TiO_2	1.66	2.22	0.76	Ca	1.915	1.689	1.749
P_2O_5	tr.	<0.05	0.05	Na	0.579	0.661	0.847
MnO	0.17	0.17	0.10	K	0.176	0.052	0.017
				Σ	2.670	2.402	2.613
Total	99.99	99.90	100.93				

1. Dark brown hornblende from hornblende gabbro (HK59050801, No. 1 of Table 10.2).
2. Dark brown hornblende from hornblende gabbro (51 III HH 129) collected by H. Hayashi.
3. Pale brown hornblende from garnet peridotite (HK58012403). The analyzed material contains a very small amount of spinel.

tration of spinel and orthopyroxene in tiny strings. This structure does not appear to have been produced by crystallization of magma but has been formed probably by flowage in solid state and recrystallization. Olivine (Fa_9), composing 60 to 70 per cent of the rock, also appears to show preferred crystal lattice orientation parallel to the lineation. Orthopyroxene (Fs_7) and diopside have exsolution lamellae and flakes as in pyroxenite. Plagioclase is in rare independent grains. Pale straw-yellow hornblende ($2V \doteqdot 90°$) and pale brown spinel are sometimes present as interstitial grains.

Garnet peridotite (column 3, Table 10.2) does not differ from peridotite in appearance except for the absence of lineation. The constituent minerals in the two rocks are also essentially the same. Olivine and orthopyroxene have composition ranges of Fa_{9-11} and Fs_{7-10}, respectively. The sample studied by Ross et al. (1954) belongs to this type. Pale straw-yellow hornblende ($2V \doteqdot 90°$) is invariably present as interstitial grains. From its analysis (column 3, Table 10.3) it is seen that the mineral consists of 87 per cent pargasite, 7 per cent tschermakite, and 6 per cent cummingtonite. Similar pale-colored hornblende is found in peridotite from St. Paul's Rock (Tilley, 1947).

Garnet which has been now replaced by intergrowth of spinel and pyroxenes occurs as rounded or subhedral grains. Each grain consists of irregular-shaped diopside and enstatite (the compositions determined by P. Weiblen of the University of Minnesota with an electron-probe X-ray microanalyser) enclosing numerous fibrous or vermicular colorless spinel. The transition from garnet to spinel-pyroxene intergrowth can be expressed by the following equations:

$$\underset{\text{garnet}}{CaMg_2Al_2Si_3O_{12}} \rightleftharpoons \underset{\text{diopside}}{CaMgSi_2O_6} + \underset{\text{spinel}}{MgAl_2O_4} + SiO_2$$

$$\underset{\text{garnet}}{Mg_3Al_2Si_3O_{12}} \rightleftharpoons 2\,\underset{\text{enstatite}}{MgSiO_3} + \underset{\text{spinel}}{MgAl_2O_4} + SiO_2$$

SiO_2 thus liberated should have reacted with adjacent olivine to produce enstatite. In keeping with this, enstatite is present along the boundary between the intergrowth and olivine. In some cases, the spinel-pyroxene intergrowth has been further transformed along its margin to an aggregate of calcic plagioclase, olivine, and spinel. This transformation can be expressed by the following equation:

$$\underset{\text{diopside}}{CaMgSi_2O_6} + 2\,\underset{\text{enstatite}}{MgSiO_3} + \underset{\text{spinel}}{MgAl_2O_4} \rightleftharpoons \underset{\text{anorthite}}{CaAl_2Si_2O_8} + 2\,\underset{\text{forsterite}}{Mg_2SiO_4}$$

The excess spinel originally present in the intergrowth may coexist with anorthite and forsterite in equilibrium. The observed transformation garnet—spinel + pyroxene —plagioclase + olivine + spinel was probably caused by decrease of pressure. This conclusion is in good agreement with the experimental work by Kushiro and Yoder (1964a). The pressure decrease is possibly due to convection current within the mantle. Anorthite also occurs as larger grains independent from the transformation of garnet.

C. Interpretation of Chemistry and Mineralogy of Peridotite and Garnet Peridotite

Analyses of peridotite and garnet peridotite are given in columns 2 and 3 of Table 10.2. The peridotite is lower in Al_2O_3, Fe_2O_3, CaO, and alkalis and higher in MgO than the garnet peridotite. In this respect, the latter resembles garnet-free peridotites from Salt Lake (columns 4 and 5), Ludlow (Hess, 1955), St. Paul's Rock (Tilley, 1947), and New South Wales (Wilshire and Binns, 1961), and is therefore representative of the world-wide peridotite of the mantle. On the other hand, the composition of the peridotite is similar to that of peridotite from the 1801 flow of Hualalai (column 6) and a calculated composition of peridotite left after partial melting to produce tholeiite magma (column 7). It is possible that the analyzed Itinome-gata peridotite is a residual material of partial melting which took place in the past. The absence of garnet in this peridotite may be due to a compositional effect such as the low Al_2O_3 content. If so, the rock may be isophysical with garnet peridotite.

The garnet peridotite would originally have had an assemblage olivine + pyroxenes + garnet + spinel + hornblende. As it appears to be isochemical with the garnet-free peridotites from Salt Lake etc, the original rock would represent a high-pressure modification of the latter (Ringwood et al., 1964). Some peridotite nodules from Itinome-gata, which have not been analyzed yet, may be isochemical with the garnet peridotite, and therefore, apart from the presence of plagioclase, they would represent a low-pressure modification of the garnet peridotite.

The presence of exsolution lamellae and flakes in pyroxenes of pyroxenite, peridotite, and garnet peridotite indicates that these rocks are not simple crystal accumulates in magmas. They were probably formed at some high temperatures, either through magmatic crystallization or recrystallization in solid state, but were later subjected to cooling. The presence of lineation in peridotite also indicates flowage in solid state and recrystallization.

It is suggested that pyroxenite and peridotite, characterized by olivine-pyroxene-spinel assemblage, formed a layer originally overlying that of garnet peridotite in the upper mantle. By later deformation, possibly due to convection current, some part of garnet peridotite was brought up into the pyroxenite-peridotite layer where garnet was no more stable and transformed to spinel and pyroxene, an assemblage common with that in pyroxenite and peridotite. Calcic plagioclase is probably also stable in the pyroxenite-peridotite layer, as it occurs as independent grains in all the three rock types. The plagioclase-olivine-spinel aggregate around the spinel-pyroxene intergrowth was produced either as a further readjustment according to the P-T condition of this layer or as a result of heating and release of pressure during the transportation to the surface by the magma. As plagioclase is quite uncommon in the world-wide peridotite nodules, its presence is possibly connected with unusually high thermal gradient of the Itinome-gata region as is discussed below.

D. Relation of Rock Fragments and Nodules to Crustal and Upper Mantle Structure and Heat Flow

Different rock types occurring as ejecta at Itinome-gata may be arranged according to the depth of supposed source regions: andesite (surface), granodiorite, gabbro and hornblende gabbro, pyroxenite and peridotite, and garnet peridotite (now partly included in the pyroxenite-peridotite layer).

This arrangement agrees with the result of seismological observations, and, according to explosion seismological studies (Matuzawa, 1959), the crustal thickness of the region southeast of Oga Peninsula is 20 to 25 km, within which a layer with Vp about 5.8 km/sec is underlain by another layer with Vp about 6.2 km/sec. The latter is separated by the Moho discontinuity from a layer with Vp from 7.5 to 8.0 km/sec. Kanamori (1963) estimated the depth of the Moho below Oga Peninsula as about 30 km. The granodiorite and gabbros were probably derived from the upper and lower crustal layers respectively, and the ultramafic nodules from the uppermost mantle.

Kanamori and Mizutani (oral communication by Kanamori, 1965) measured Vp of the peridotite nodule (column 2, Table 10.2) under 10 kb pressure and at room temperature. It varies from about 9 to 8 km/sec depending on the propagation direction of the elastic waves in relation to the lineation. At higher temperatures, the velocity may be a little lower. In addition, the presence of plagioclase in the ultramafic nodules may contribute somewhat to the reduction of the elastic wave velocity.

Kanamori and Mizutani's measurement was carried out on the sample with the least amount of plagioclase. Thus the layer just below the Moho may have Vp as low as 7.5 to 8.0 km/sec.

According to Horai (1964), Oga Peninsula lies in a region where observed terrestrial heat flow values are about 2.20×10^{-6} cal/cm^2 sec. From his observations, he estimated the temperature at the Moho below this region as lying between possible limits of 816 and 1146°C. Thus the thermal gradient of the region is unusually high. Owing to the high temperature in the uppermost mantle, plagioclase may be formed as a stable phase by dissociation of part of Ca-tschermak's molecule contained in pyroxene. It would be interesting to compare Al_2O_3 contents in pyroxenes of plagioclase-bearing and plagioclase-free peridotite nodules from various localities of the world and also to investigate the presence or absence of plagioclase in peridotite nodules from localities of different heat flow values.

The postulated model of the upper mantle described here agrees with that proposed by Ringwood (1962c).

IV. THE SO-CALLED "COGNATE XENOLITHS" OF KIMBERLITE

C. F. Davidson

Among the xenolithic rock-types found in kimberlite breccias, one group of inclusions, commonly referred to as eclogites and garnet-peridotites, is of much-debated origin. Many petrologists believe that these rocks are representative of the upper mantle. Others maintain that they are comagmatic with the kimberlite, formed as segregations in the subcrustal or deep-crustal hearth from which the breccias arose. Still another interpretation, that these enclaves are disrupted fragments of deep metamorphic crust, has hitherto met with little acceptance. The inclusions in question are often spoken of as nodules, since they are of an ovoid or rounded form doubtless attributable to their attrition during ascent from depth. They range in diameter from a few millimeters to 30 cm, with an average of 5–10 cm. In many pipes they are completely absent, in others they are found very sparingly, and exceptionally they may make up as much as 2 per cent of the rock.

The contribution presented here summarizes the evidence that can be adduced in favor of the least popular interpretation of these nodules, that they are metamorphic rocks of crustal origin. In the interests of brevity the arguments are listed numerically.

1. The entire range of petrographic types among these xenoliths can be paralleled in several high-grade metamorphic terrains exposed at the earth's surface—for example, in southern Norway, in central Europe, and in central Kazakhstan, where the eclogites and garnet-peridotites are accompanied by garnet- and hypersthene-granulites and their diaphthoretic derivatives. The same association with metamorphic granulites of many kinds is found in the kimberlite pipes. It is thus subjective to accept that the granulites are of crustal derivation and at the same time assign the eclogites and garnet-peridotites to a subcrustal origin.

2. Because of restrictions surrounding the diamond industry, few Western workers have been able to collect adequate samples of these xenoliths and there has been a tendency to regard as representative hand-picked specimens supplied in response to requests for eclogite and garnet-peridotite. But in representative bulk samples, the mineralogical composition of these

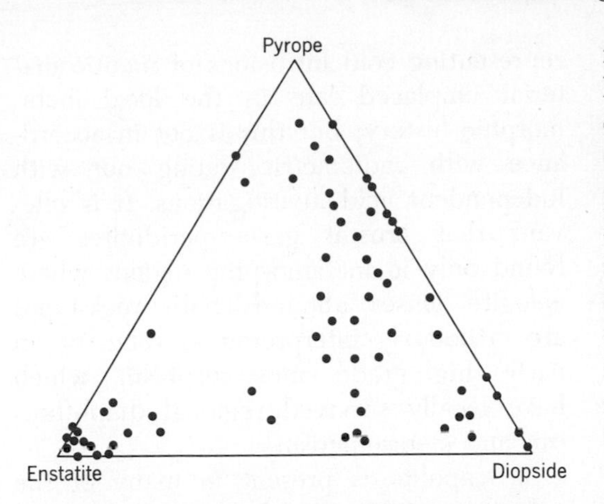

Fig. 10.5 The composition of garnet-pyroxene xenoliths from the Obnazhennaya pipe of kimberlite breccia (from Milashev, 1963).

rocks varies enormously. Figure 10.5 (from Milashev *et al.*, 1963) illustrates in terms of the contained garnet, enstatite, and diopside the modes of 70 xenoliths of garnet-pyroxene rock from a single Siberian pipe. Apart from the enstatitites, no two modal analyses are the same. This diversity is reflected in the high variability of chemical analyses of eclogites from kimberlite, no two of which are concordant. In the same manner, as shown in Fig. 10.6 which summarizes 174 modal analyses (Milashev *et al.*, 1963), the ultrabasic inclusions may range in a single pipe from dunite to peridotite, harzburgite, saxonite, lherzolite, and pyroxenite, sometimes but by no means

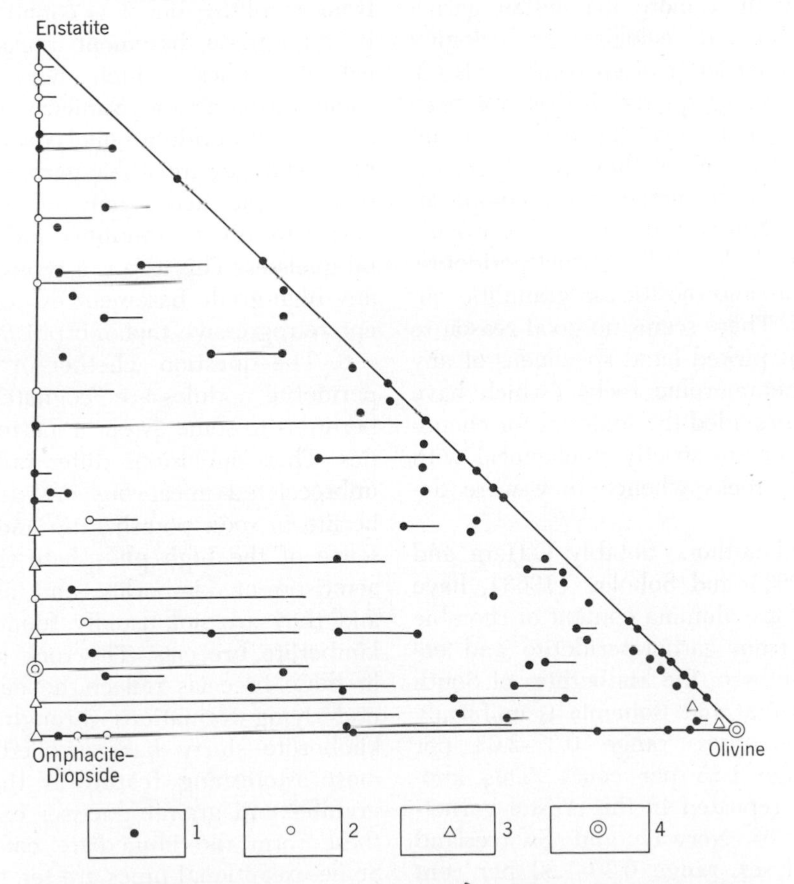

Fig. 10.6 The composition of ultrabasic xenoliths from the Obnazhennaya pipe of kimberlite breccia. 1. single specimens; 2. average of 2–3 specimens; 3. average of 4–9 specimens; 4. average of 10–12 specimens. The horizontal lines indicate the content of pyrope (from Milashev, 1963).

always with pyrope, often with a tenor of iron-magnesian chrome-spinellid far in excess of that of garnet. In addition, there are many amphibolized and phlogopitized derivatives. If these inclusions represent the upper mantle, then the latter is clearly of so varied a composition that petrogenetic studies based on a single rock-type such as garnet-peridotite must be of questionable value. This great variability is however a feature of high-grade metamorphism, subject to all the vagaries of metamorphic differentiation, and is in keeping with the interpretation that the xenoliths are of crustal origin.

3. In Russian studies, it has become customary to divide the garnet-pyroxene inclusions into two main groups: (a) "true" eclogites, with a more magnesian garnet than (b) "crustal" eclogites or "eclogite-like rocks", the latter often bearing plagioclase, kyanite, or quartz. It has not been recognized that this distinction is ill-founded, since both of these rock-types occur in high-grade metamorphic complexes (e.g. south Norway and central Europe), the former as lenses in garnet-peridotite, the latter in anorthositic or granulitic environments. There seems no good reason to believe that picked hand specimens of any of these metamorphic rocks (which have invariably provided the material for chemical analyses) are strictly isochemical with the igneous rocks whence they were derived.

4. Several authors, notably O'Hara and Mercy (1963) and Sobolev (1963), have shown that the alumina content of rhombic pyroxenes from garnet-peridotite and eclogite xenoliths in the kimberlites of South Africa, Yakutia, and Bohemia is uniformly low (15 analyses, range 0.37–2.65 per cent, average 1.25 per cent). This idiosyncrasy is repeated in the crustal garnet-peridotites of Norway and Switzerland (eight analyses, range 0.30–1.60 per cent Al_2O_3, average 1.02 per cent). It has been suggested that the garnet-peridotite assemblages exposed in metamorphic terrains are themselves of very deep origin, representing cold intrusions of mantle material emplaced late in the local metamorphic history; but this is not in accordance with radiometric dating nor with independent field investigations. It is relevant that crustal garnet-peridotites are found only in metamorphic regions where eclogite lenses abound; both rock-types are orthodoxly interpreted as relics of an early high-grade metamorphism which have locally survived regional diaphthoresis and metasomatism.

5. Scapolite is present in many of the eclogite xenoliths in Siberian pipes, and it is also noteworthy in granulite inclusions in the Siberian, Australian, and southern African diatremes. This mineral has never been recorded from kimberlite, other than from xenoliths; but it is commonly present in high-grade basement rocks, including eclogite relics, which have undergone some retrogression. Similarly the eclogite and garnet-peridotite enclaves exhibit kelyphite rims around their garnet, just as are seen in the accompanying inclusions of garnet-pyroxene-granulites and other crustal gneisses. This also is a typical feature of any high-grade basement exhibiting incipient retrogressive metamorphism.

6. The question whether or not garnet-peridotite nodules are "cognate" with kimberlite is to some extent a matter of semantics. These inclusions differ radically from unbrecciated micaceous or basaltoid kimberlite in soda:potash ratio and in the absence of the high phosphate that is characteristic of kimberlite and allied rocks; and they are not usually found except in kimberlite breccias. The rock assemblages in these breccias reflect the nature of the underlying formations through which the kimberlite slurry has travelled; but their most astonishing feature is the rarity of granites and granite-gneisses except where these form the immediate country rocks. Some exceptional pipes are ten times richer in almandine garnet than in the commonly more widespread pyrope. From this it appears that the deeper crust in platform regions must consist of granulites, with

developments of eclogite, garnetiferous anorthosite, and garnet-peridotite such as persist only as relics, if at all, under near-surface conditions. Of these, garnet-peridotite would be particularly prone to serpentinization and thus to trituration and fluidization, with release of its kelyphite-rimmed pyrope grains to the groundmass of the kimberlite mush. In this sense only it is cognate with kimberlite, in that it provided the pyrope, chrome-spinellids, and part of the serpentine in the breccia-slurry.

7. It is widely believed that the eclogite xenolith must come from great depth, since diamond has been found in them. But in the literature of the world's diamond industry only three such diamond-bearing xenoliths have been described—two found in 1897 at the Newlands pipe in South Africa (now respectively in the collections of the British Museum of Natural History and of the Mining Academy of Freiberg in Saxony) and one in 1959 at the Mir pipe in Yakutia. A mill test of 20 tons of "eclogite" (mainly griquaite) once undertaken at Kimberley did not yield a single diamond. The three known diamantiferous nodules have recently been investigated by Sobolev and Kuznetsova (1966). They show a rather wide range in chemical composition (SiO_2 43.26–46.65 per cent, Al_2O_3 9.86–15.21 per cent, MgO 11.26–18.45 per cent), and are generally comparable to metamorphic eclogites. Their almandine-pyrope garnets are chemically similar to the garnets in crustal rocks both of eclogite and pyroxene-granulite facies (cf. Sobolev, 1964); and although their pyroxenes show a high (FeO + MgO): CaO ratio (respectively, 1.00 and 1.25 in two cases), this is not a sufficient criterion to confirm a subcrustal origin. The Russian specimen carries some graphite. Further diamond-bearing eclogites (in one case with kyanite) which have not yet been described have recently been found in the kimberlite of the Belsbank fissure swarm near Kimberley (J. B. Dawson, personal communication).

8. Diamond has not yet been recorded from any xenolith of garnet-peridotite; but, as shown by rare inclusions of one mineral in another, at least some diamonds are cogenetic with the violet (chromium-bearing) pyrope of this rock type, just as some are clearly cogenetic with the olivine, enstatite, diopside, and chrome-spinellids found in this rock and in kimberlite alike. (A small proportion, 2.4 per cent, of the garnet inclusions in Siberian diamonds are orange-red pyrope, of the type present in lherzolite and eclogite). Since peridotite carries a higher content of carbon (0.01–0.10 per cent) than most igneous rocks, and is richer in nickel and platinum which may act as a catalyst in the formation of diamonds, this association is understandable. But there is no sympathetic relationship between diamond and pyrope, such as one might expect if both minerals came from great depth; and in the mines of Kimberley, Premier, and Mir the tenor of diamond in unweathered kimberlite is said to *decrease* with depth of working. These anomalies make it interesting to note that in Central Europe the Ries crypto-explosive structure of South Germany, famous for its coesite and stishovite, is contemporary with the nearby kimberlite pipes of Bohemia. Further, some of the crypto-explosive structures of Illinois, Missouri, and Kansas are accompanied by igneous rocks akin to kimberlite; and numerous "clastic pipes" in the Yakutian kimberlite province seem comparable. A genetic connexion between large near-surface crypto-explosive structures and the smaller and deeper kimberlite diatremes seems possible; and in this event it is arguable that if coesite and stishovite can be formed by shock at a high level, diamond may well have been produced within the crust at a somewhat greater depth. Perhaps this is the explanation of the several Russian records of diamond in limestone xenoliths and wall-rocks of the kimberlite diatremes. Recent Russian studies (Bezrukov *et al.*, 1966) on the artificial formation of diamonds at low temperatures and at pressures of only some

tens of kilobars are relevant in this connection, since the diamonds produced show a wide range of octahedral, cubic, and rounded forms very like natural stones.

9. Apparently irrefutable evidence that the garnet-peridotite and eclogite nodules in kimberlite pipes do not come from great depth has recently been forthcoming from researches in Czechoslovakia, conducted by Kopeský, Sattran, and Fiala (1962). In the Česke Středohoří of Bohemia a dozen occurrences of kimberlitoid pipes carrying pyrope, chrome-diopside, picroilmenite, and chrome-spinellids are now known; and three alluvial diamonds have been found. The rocks here are somewhat higher in alumina and lower in magnesia than most kimberlites, and they are locally highly carbonatized. They are associated with alnöitic lavas and tuffs. The pipe breccias, up to 400 meters in diameter, are of Neogene age; and they contain abundant xenoliths of Upper Cretaceous sediments, which in some cases form as much as 95 per cent of the rock mass, together with inclusions of granulite-facies crystalline schists and in some pipes abundant pyrope-peridotite, pyroxenite and eclogite. To explore the possible source of these inclusions, in 1959 a 20-cm-diameter diamond drill hole was sunk vertically, 80 meters from the margin of the Linhorka diatreme which is particularly rich in xenoliths of pyrope-bearing rocks. At a depth of 112 meters the drill penetrated the granulites and migmatites of the basement complex, with garnet and kyanite. From 209 to 436 meters it traversed a dark green serpentinized peridotite with pyrope and pyroxene and with zones of pyroxenite and eclogite. The pyrope crystals range up to 2 cm and are rimmed by kelyphite. After passing through the ultrabasic sheet, which is a little pyritized towards its margins, the drill re-entered the granulites and migmatites. The ultrabasic rocks encountered by drilling (which are on exhibition in the Museum of the Geological Survey in Prague) are wholly identical with the xenoliths in the pipe, and in this instance there is no doubt whatever that the garnet-peridotites and eclogites found as inclusions in a kimberlitoid diatreme were torn from a high-grade ultrabasic lens in the basement complex and not derived from the mantle. The widespread distribution of comparable garnet-peridotites and garnet-serpentinites in the basement rocks of Bohemia has been described by Fiala (1965). It is significant that the Cr_2O_3 content of the garnet in these rocks (18 analyses, range 0.56–6.85 per cent, average 1.96 per cent or 1.74 per cent if one high value is omitted) is the same as the tenor of Cr_2O_3 in the garnet of peridotite and olivinite nodules recorded by Sobolev (1964) from the kimberlite pipes of Siberia (22 analyses, range 0.27–3.77 per cent, average 1.74 per cent.

In the light of these observations, it seems fitting to ask whether the garnet-peridotite and eclogite xenoliths in kimberlite pipes provide any valid basis for philosophizing on the nature of the rocks below the crust.

V. CRYSTAL-LIQUID EQUILIBRIA AND THE ORIGINS OF ULTRAMAFIC NODULES IN BASIC IGNEOUS ROCKS

M. J. O'Hara

In this discussion it is assumed that all basalts fractionate during their ascent (O'Hara, 1965) by the precipitation of minerals at or near the cool margins of the conduit and that ultramafic nodules in basalts and other basic volcanic rocks may originate in three ways:

Hypothesis I—as crystalline residua of the upper mantle, remaining after partial melting produced the basalt in which they occur.

Hypothesis II—as crystal accumulates formed as a loose coating or as suspended nodules at the cool, slow flowing margin of the conduit.

Hypothesis III—as xenoliths of the normal upper mantle composition, which may, however, have suffered thermal metamorphism.

Hypotheses II and III envisage the possibility that a suite of nodules in a single eruption originated over a considerable range of depth (i.e., pressure).

Accidental origin of ultramafic nodules as xenoliths from unrelated crustal peridotites is judged to be a sufficiently unlikely event to be ignored when treating the origin of nodule suites *in general,* although some instances are known (e.g., Kopeskỳ and Sattran, 1962).

If a basalt formed by partial melting is to form a continuous fluid medium bearing detached crystalline residua, the volume proportion of crystalline residua must be less than $\frac{4}{3}\pi r^3 \div 8r^3 \simeq \frac{1}{2}$. Failing this, it is more likely that the basalt would be expressed from a continuous network of the residual crystalline materials. A yield of 50 per cent or more basalt on partial melting of the upper mantle greatly exceeds estimates currently acceptable to petrologists. Hypothesis I cannot therefore be favorably regarded.

When flow conditions in a magma are suitable for the elutriation of nodules formed according to Hypothesis III, those formed according to Hypothesis II must also be present. The latter can be expected to occur alone and more frequently, because of their greater availability and the smaller increase of the rate of flow necessary for the elutriation of such loosely attached materials.

All suites of nodules probably exhibit some geochemical and mineralogical variations. These will not, in general, originate by the crystal sorting mechanisms that operate in large layered intrusions (Chapter 2), such mechanisms being irrelevant in Hypotheses I and III and not applicable in Hypothesis II where layered bottom accumulation is not necessarily envisaged. Layering features apparently indicative of bottom accumulation are reported from a suite of olivine-clinopyroxene nodules from a tholeiitic volcano in Reunion (Upton and Wadsworth, personal communication) and may be present in other provinces (e.g., Yamaguchi, 1964, p. 183 and plate 24), but these might equally well be due to crystallization on the side wall of a conduit.

The nodules of a particular suite (or subsuite based upon the identification of nodules formed according to different hypotheses) may be arranged in a geochemical sequence based upon changes in the Fe^{2+}/Mg, Ni^{2+}/Mg, Cr/Al, and Na/Ca ratios in the minerals, such that one end of the series may be termed the high end, implying more refractory characteristics, and higher temperature of coexistence with liquid. The other end may be termed the low end, implying less refractory characteristics, more fractionated and hence lower temperature origin. This geochemical sequence may be produced, whatever is believed to be the origin of the nodule suite (e.g., Frechen, 1963; Yamaguchi, 1964, Table 3; J. L. Carter, personal communication). It can then be used to predict or construct a portion of the phase diagram (not necessarily isobaric) for the natural system according to Hypotheses I or II, which will in general yield a different phase diagram from the same suite of nodules. The alternative predictions may then be evaluated in the light of available experimental data, or tested directly by suitable experiments, so that knowledge of the appropriate crystal-liquid equilibria will provide criteria of origin. Examples of the use of this approach, applied principally from the point of view of Hypothesis II, have been published for nodules in kimberlite (O'Hara and Yoder, 1963; O'Hara, 1963a,b) and nodules in olivine-basalts (O'Hara, 1965;

O'Hara and Mercy, 1963). The hypothesis that eclogite nodules in kimberlite represent the upper mantle composition, while the garnet-peridotites represent residua of partial melting, predicts a quite different phase diagram from that postulated by O'Hara and Yoder (1963)—eclogite would have to begin to melt at a lower temperature than garnet-peridotite, with the appearance of both olivine and orthopyroxene among the residual crystals. Critical experiments showed that these requirements were not satisfied. Similarly, if the data of Frechen (1963) are treated according to Hypothesis I a different type of phase diagram from that postulated by O'Hara (1965) is obtained and the conclusion reached that the upper mantle must be composed of a clinopyroxene + spinel rock if the "higher" nodules in the geochemical sequence are to represent residua of partial melting. Some specific differences between the predictions of the three hypotheses are shown in Table 10.4.

If Hypothesis III is adopted for a suite or subsuite of nodules, then it might be asked why should one suppose that the upper mantle has a uniform composition? There is indeed no reason why it should be uniform, but if the chondrite model is adopted, the derivation of all such proposed "primary" variations of upper mantle composition from homogeneous starting material must be explained, probably in terms of crystal-liquid or crystal-fluid processes operating on a terrestrial rather than local scale early in geologic history. Again, inspection of a nodule suite allows construction of the requisite phase diagrams, which can then be tested. Variations in character of nodule suites from adjacent volcanoes, such as those reported by Yamaguchi (1964, Table 1) must always strengthen the case for a cognate origin.

Particular attention must be paid to the proportions of mineral phases present in nodules. The proportions in which olivine and two pyroxenes precipitate together from a fractionating magma at moderate depth probably favor the production on average of orthopyroxene-poor olivine-websterites, but any combination of the three phases (e.g., olivine-rich lherzolite) may form the average composition of crystalline residua formed during a partial melting process to produce the same magma compositions.

There is one alleged criterion of origin of nodule suites based on a misunderstanding of crystal-liquid equilibria, which nevertheless appears to command considerable respect. This is the proposition that the nodules are too rich in chromium (but it could as well be any element) to have

TABLE 10.4 Hypotheses for the Origin of Nodule Suites

Proposition	Hypothesis I	II	III
Nodules must be general multiphase assemblages that fulfill all mineralogical, geochemical, and geophysical requirements of the upper mantle			
(a) at the low end	×	×	✓
(b) at the high end	×	?	✓
(c) throughout	×	×	✓
Partial melting of low members must begin at lower temperatures than that of successively higher members	✓	?	?
(a) yielding a basaltic liquid	?	×	✓
(b) with the appearance of crystalline residua appropriate in mineral assemblage and mineral proportions to higher members of the series	✓	×	×
The original mineral assemblages (perhaps partly altered during transport) represents equilibrium at temperatures close to the beginning of melting	✓	✓	×

✓ = true, × = in general untrue, ? = not essential to be true precipitated from, i.e., been in equilibrium with, basalt (e.g., Ross et al., 1954; Vilminot, 1965), and hence the nodules, by elimination must be fragments of the mantle. The factual basis of this statement has already been challenged (O'Hara and Mercy, 1963), but if it were accepted it would follow directly that basalt could not be the partial melting product of the nodules. Hence, basalt could not be a partial melting product of the upper mantle, thereby raising great difficulties regarding the origin of basalt and the mechanism whereby nodules became incorporated in it.

Future workers on nodule suites are urged to organize the collection of data so that they permit the construction of the phase diagrams appropriate to the alternative hypotheses, allowing thereby a critical test of the possibilities.

11. *Geochemistry*

I. INTRODUCTION

P. J. Wyllie

Discussion of the chemistry and geochemistry of ultramafic rocks has been an integral part of all preceding chapters, and this chapter contains articles concerned specifically with the geochemistry of trace elements and isotopes. Several of the samples listed in tables in this chapter have locations in ultramafic complexes discussed elsewhere in the book. Trace element measurements on mantle-derived rocks have bearing on three major problems: heat production in the upper mantle, the derivation of basalts from the mantle, and the possibility of secular trends or geographic variations in mantle material.

Detailed historical reviews of the geochemistry of ultrabasic and ultramafic rocks by Turekian and Wedepohl (1961) and Vinogradov (1962) refer to data obtained by spectrochemical techniques near their sensitivity limit, the data therefore being of doubtful significance. Recent work of higher reliability has used techniques of neutron activation analysis and isotope dilution. Goles, in Section II, reviews the recent results for 23 elements plus the rare earths from lanthanum to lutetium, respectively. For many rocks the overall average abundances have only limited significance because the abundances do not constitute a single population. There are differences among trace element contents of alpine intrusions, ultramafic nodules, and their host basalts for several elements including Na, K, Rb, Sr, Co, Ni, Th, and the Rb/Sr ratio. The content of Co is insensitive to mineralogy and occurrence, whereas Ni shows a marked dependence on mineralogy and occurrence. The magnitude of the sampling problem needs further investigation; for example, the Twin Sisters dunite (Chapter 5-III) displays marked variability in both Th and U abundances. Goles concludes that alpine-type intrusions are residual in nature, and cannot give rise to basalts by any reasonable differentiation process; they do not constitute a significant fraction of the upper mantle.

In Section III Taylor tabulates data for stable isotopes of hydrogen, carbon, silicon, sulfur, and oxygen from meteorites and mafic and ultramafic igneous rocks. Ultramafic rocks and meteorites have a narrow range of isotopic variation relative to the total observed range in nature, and oxygen and carbon provide most data of interest. Terrestrial ultramafic rocks from a variety of sources have a uniform O^{18}/O^{16} ratio, which is similar to that for chondrites but quite distinct from that for achondrites. There is no difference in oxygen isotope composition between peridotite and serpentinite, which suggests that H_2O is added to peridotite during serpentinization without oxygen exchange with the adjacent crust. The water could not be meteoritic water because one would then expect drastic changes in O^{18} content to occur. The oxygen isotope fractionation among sets of minerals provides temperature estimates; most ultramafic rocks (excluding serpentinites) and meteorites formed at temperatures of 700 to 800°C, and probably higher. The trace of carbon in chondrites and basalts has a low value of C^{13}/C^{12}, whereas the major concentrations of carbon in carbonaceous chondrites, carbonatites and diamonds have higher values of C^{13}/C^{12}. The higher ratio probably relates to the earth's mantle. The oxygen isotope data for gabbros, basalts, and ultramafic rocks of various types leaves no doubt that these rocks are related genetically, but it tells nothing of the nature of the relation. The remarkable uniformity of C^{13} and O^{18} contents of carbonatites, and the similarity in O^{18}/O^{16} ratios of pyroxenes from gabbros, peridotites and carbonatites strongly suggests that these rocks also are related.

In Section IV, Hurley discusses the significance of the ratios Sr^{87}/Sr^{86} and Rb^{87}/Sr^{86} in geological materials and meteorites and the way these variables have changed relative to values when the earth was formed, assuming that the earth's mantle has been differentiated by flowing fluids. Sr^{87}/Sr^{86} should be higher in shallower source regions than in deeper source regions. Oceanic basalts therefore come from deeper (or less differentiated) sources than continental basalts. From a tabulation of Rb, Sr, and isotope abundance estimates for various mantle products Hurley reaches several conclusions. There is no contemporary relationship between alpine-type ultramafic rocks and other common materials reaching the surface from the mantle, in oceanic or continental regions. Ultramafic nodules differ from intrusive material and match modern basalts, indicating that they are genetically related to the basalts carrying them. Ultramafic zones in stratiform intrusions have basalt-like Sr^{87}/Sr^{86} as would be expected from their inferred origin. The problem of how far back in time it is necessary to go before the ratio in alpine-type ultramafic rocks drops to the level of other mantle derivatives remains unresolved, because there is an analytical discrepancy between two groups of investigators. The results of one group suggest that the alpine-type ultramafic rocks separated in the latter half of the earth's history and subsequently rose to the surface, and the results of the other group suggest that these rocks are residual accumulates from some very early Rb/Sr-enrichment process, which was followed by a separation of sialic crust in the early Archean.

In Section V Murthy and Stueber illustrate the variation of K/Rb and of K in various materials. Basalts show systematic variation of K/Rb with K. There is no systematic variation of K/Rb for eclogite inclusions, ultramafic inclusions, and alpine-type intrusions, although K varies very widely. K/Rb values scatter about the average crustal value, and the value for alkali basalt; they are lower than values for oceanic tholeiites. Murthy and Stueber conclude that the upper mantle zone is characterized by the low K/Rb values of ultramafic rocks and inclusions, which is lower than that usually assumed for primitive mantle material. Birch has suggested that the upper mantle differentiated from the primitive mantle early in the earth's history, with continental formation being a second stage differentiation. The early differentiation could have produced an alkali-enriched upper mantle with low K/Rb. The residual nature of the alpine peridotites seems almost certain, with fractionation processes having effectively drained alkalis to the crust. The genetic relationship between ultramafic nodules and host basalts is established by Sr^{87}/Sr^{86} ratios, and the low alkali abundances of the nodules implies that they are residual or crystal cumulate in origin. The low K/Rb ratio of the nodules indicates that they were probably formed in the upper mantle regions.

II. TRACE ELEMENTS IN ULTRAMAFIC ROCKS

Gordon G. Goles

A. Introduction

Everything we surmise about the constitution of the deep interior of the earth is an inference from one or the other of two kinds of information: what may have gone in (initial boundary conditions) and what has come or is coming out. Inferences based on the first of these are exemplified by the wide-ranging speculations on whether or not the overall composition of the earth resembles that of one or another class of meteorites (Hurley, 1957; Lovering, 1958; MacDonald, 1959a,b; Gast, 1960; Harris and Rowell, 1960; Ringwood, 1962a; Wasserburg et al., 1964; S. R. Taylor, 1964; Gast, 1965).

The second kind of information includes seismic data, heat flow as a function of geographical position, and the mineralogy, petrology and geochemistry of rocks that seem to have been erupted or emplaced from great depths. These fundamentally observational data have proved to be somewhat less conducive to unbridled speculation in their interpretation than have attempts to set initial boundary conditions for the earth's composition. Nevertheless, so little is known about the deep interior of the earth that there is still wide latitude for differing models of its constitution, all purporting to agree with the observations.

Those models which have been recently proposed (e.g., Ringwood, 1962b,c; Clark and Ringwood, 1964) have largely been independent of speculations on the initial composition of the earth. To the extent that such independence can be preserved, further elaboration of compositional models may help to define better the initial boundary conditions themselves. One should note that historically this has not always been the case; models of the composition of the upper mantle often have tended to rely heavily on assumed meteoritic analogs (e.g., Lovering, 1958; Gast, 1960; Harris and Rowell, 1960, have given an extensive and critical review of many such hypotheses).

An acceptable compositional model of the mantle must account not only for the observed seismic properties but also for the observed patterns of heat flow and for the petrological and geochemical properties of rocks that are derived from or closely related to the mantle. This test, which is in principle a very powerful one, is in reality applicable only to models of the upper mantle, which perhaps is a factor in its partial neglect. Efforts to obtain quantitative data of high accuracy with which to apply such a test have been limited in number and scope, although within the past few years the situation has improved markedly. This is due in part to application of techniques such as neutron activation analysis and isotope dilution to suites of ultramafic rocks and basalts. (Neutron activation analysis has been discussed in detail by Bowen and Gibbons, 1963, and a discussion of isotope dilution was given by Webster, 1960). One should keep in mind, however, that data of adequate accuracy are still so sparse that we can do little more than outline the problems.

In the context of this review of trace elements in ultramafic rocks, there are three major problems upon which we may focus our attention: heat production in the upper mantle, the derivation of basalts from the upper mantle, and the possibility of secular trends or geographic variations in mantle materials. Heat production is critically dependent upon abundances and distributions of K, Th, and U in the upper mantle, so that one may place stringent boundary conditions on compositional models by means of investigations of contents of these trace elements in alleged mantle rocks.

The very widespread oceanic and plateau basalts seem to be either partial or total melts of portions of the upper mantle (Kushiro and Kuno, 1963). In particular, tholeiitic (subalkaline) basalts dredged from the deeper portions of the ocean seem to represent mantle-derived material that has undergone only very minimal differentiation, if any at all (Engel and Engel, 1964a,b). Thus, plausible compositional models of the mantle must be such as to give rise to these basalts by simple processes. Trace element studies of ultramafic rocks and of primitive basalts may therefore be used in conjunction with mass balance arguments to limit possible mantle compositions. Provinciality, either in time or in space, would tend to indicate that available samples of mantle rocks came from circumscribed reservoirs and would thereby minimize the role which could be assigned to large-scale convection in the mantle.

Trace element data for ultramafic rocks that had been published before 1961 or 1962 have been reviewed by Turekian and Wedepohl (1961) and by Vinogradov (1962). Most of this information was obtained via spectrochemical techniques, often by working near the apparent sensitivity limit, and is of doubtful significance. In both review articles, the authors place great weight on results of analyses using more reliable techniques, to the extent that these were available to them. In the last few years much additional data of apparently high reliability has been published, so that I shall concentrate on reviewing the very recent work and commenting on: (a) how it affects the averages presented by Turekian and Wedepohl and by Vinogradov; (b) tentative conclusions which may be drawn concerning the three major problems cited above.

B. Recent Trace Element Determinations in Ultramafic Rocks

In this section I review briefly, element-by-element, results that have become available since Turekian and Wedepohl (1961), and Vinogradov (1962), presented their tabulations. I shall emphasize data obtained via activation analysis or isotope dilution, although results of other techniques and some work published prior to 1961 shall also be noted. Coverage of the English-, French- and German-language literature is, I believe, reasonably complete up to the end of 1964, with more recent data included in some cases. The Russian literature, which is very extensive, has been examined principally by reliance upon *Geokhimya* and upon English-language abstracting services; its coverage is by no means as complete as that for the other major literatures.

Table 11.1 compares data given by Turekian and Wedepohl and by Vinogradov; where there are new data, the Table includes my choice of the best values for overall average abundances in ultramafic rocks. *One should note most carefully that for many elements, abundances in ultramafic rocks do not constitute a single well-defined population.* Accordingly, in these cases (and also perhaps others of which we are ignorant as yet), the overall average abundances can have only a very limited significance.

1. Boron. Varlakov and Zhuzhgova (1964) have determined B in ultramafic rocks (principally serpentinites) via a spectrographic technique. Massifs studied varied from essentially boron-free to moderately boron-rich. They argue that B has been introduced from outside sources during serpentinization, a conclusion in agreement with that of Faust, Murata, and Fahey (1956). An average value for the B contents of dunites, from the work of Varlakov and Zhuzhgova, would be about 10 ppm B ($1 \text{ ppm} \equiv 1 \times 10^{-6}$ g/g). There is perhaps some indication that peridotites characteristically have higher B contents, so that a choice of 20 ppm as an overall average seems reasonable. This number must be considered very uncertain, however, until a survey of fresh ultramafic

TABLE 11.1 Estimates of Trace Element Abundances in "Average" Ultramafic Rock (in ppm)

Element	Turekian and Wedepohl	Vinogradov	This Chapter*
Li	0.X	0.5	...
Be	0.X	0.2	...
B	3.	1.	≈20.
C	...	100.	...
N	6.	6.	≈15.
F	100.	100.	...
Na	4200.	5700.	~1040.
Al	20000.	4500.	≈10000.
P	220.	170.	...
S	300.	100.	...
Cl	85.	50.	~150.
K	40.	300.	≈200.
Ca	25000.	7000.	...
Sc	15.	5.	~16.
Ti	300.	300.	...
V	40.	40.	...
Cr	1600.	2000.	2400.
Mn	1620.	1500.	1040.
Co	150.	200.	110.
Ni	2000.	2000.	~1500.
Cu	10.	20.	≈30.
Zn	50.	30.	...
Ga	1.5	2.	~5.
Ge	1.5	1.	...
As	1.	0.5	...
Se	0.05	0.05	...
Br	1.	0.5	...
Rb	0.2	2.	~1.
Sr	1.	10.	~20.
Y	0.X	...	≈5.
Zr	45.	30.	...
Nb	16.	1.0	...
Mo	0.3	0.2	...
Ru	...	...	...
Rh	...	...	...
Pd	0.12	0.12	...
Ag	0.06	0.05	...
Cd	0.X	0.05	...
In	0.01	0.013	...
Sn	0.5	0.5	...
Sb	0.1	0.1	...
Te	...	0.001	≈0.001
I	0.5	0.01	≈0.1
Cs	0.X	0.1	...
Ba	0.4	6.	≈0.4
La (REE)†	0.X	0.3	≈2.
Hf	0.6	0.5	...
Ta	1.0	0.02	...
W	0.77	0.1	...
Re	...	...	...
Os	...	...	...
Ir	...	...	...
Pt	...	0.2	...
Au	0.006	0.005	≈0.009
Hg	0.0X	0.01	...
Tl	0.06	0.01	...
Pb	1.0	0.1	≈0.05
Bi	...	0.001	...
Th	0.004	0.005	≈0.06
U	0.001	0.003	≈0.02

* For those elements whose estimated abundances are listed in this column, see text (section B) for data, discussion and references.

† La is used to represent abundances of all rare-earth elements, La to Lu inclusive. See Schmitt et al. (1963) and Balashov (1963) for complete data and discussion.

rocks, preferably by an isotope dilution technique, is made.

2. *Nitrogen.* Ammoniacal nitrogen in rocks has been determined by Vinogradov, Florenskii, and Volynets (1963). They find an average of 13.8 ppm N in dunites by melting the rocks in vacuo and using standard gas analysis techniques for estimating NH_3 contents. Precautions against contamination seem to have been adequate, so that their values are probably reliable. I shall use 15 ppm N as a rough estimate of the overall abundance of this element in ultramafic rocks.

3. *Sodium.* The first application of instrumental neutron activation analysis to ultramafic rocks was that by Salmon (1957), who determined Na in a dunite from Balsam Quarry, North Carolina, by this technique. This is not surprising, since Na is probably the easiest of all elements to determine by this method. Salmon also used radiochemical neutron activation analysis to determine Na and K abundances in this rock. He secured excellent agreement between the two techniques, finding 115 ppm Na via instrumental analysis and 108 ppm Na via the radiochemical method.

These values are also in excellent agreement with the Na abundances determined for dunites by Stueber and Goles (1967), who used an instrumental neutron activation technique to determine five elements in 113 ultramafic rocks. They find an average of about 105 ppm Na for dunites and about 2130 ppm Na for pyroxenites. Thus, Na contents are strongly correlated with bulk mineralogy in ultramafic rocks. There is also a correlation exhibited with the mode of occurrence: alpine-type intrusions, of varying mineralogy, average 520 ppm Na, while ultramafic inclusions in basalts or kimberlite pipes average 1490 ppm Na. The results of Stueber and Goles demonstrate that Na contents in ultramafic rocks do not constitute a single well-defined population. While it seems possible to regard the mineralogical dependence of the total Na content as a smooth function, alpine intrusions and ultramafic inclusions seem to represent two distinct populations. (See also Stueber and Murthy, 1966b, for a discussion of the genetic relations, or lack of them, between these rock types.)

Stueber and Goles find an overall average value of 1040 ppm Na (arithmetic mean of all data) in ultramafic rocks. The significance of this average is of course severely limited by the distinctions previously noted. The overall average value of 1040 ppm Na is markedly lower than those given by Turekian and Wedepohl or by Vinogradov. The average value for alpine intrusions, 520 ppm, is higher than the mean value of 210 ppm Na for alpine ultramafic rocks reported by Hamilton and Mountjoy (1965). Hamilton and Mountjoy used a modified flame-spectrophotometric method to determine Na and K in 40 samples from six different regions. Their distribution is skewed toward the low end (median: 30 ppm Na) and they appear to have selected a preponderance of dunites or serpentinites derived from dunites. Given the uncertainties introduced by sampling difficulties, the results of Hamilton and Mountjoy and of Stueber and Goles seem to be concordant.

In four cases it is possible to make more-or-less direct comparisons between the two sets of results:

1. A sample of the Twin Sisters, Washington, dunite was found to have 78 ± 8 ppm Na by Stueber and Goles; determinations on what seems to be comparable material by Hamilton and Mountjoy gave 21 and 13 ppm Na. There is some evidence that U and Th contents of different samples of this dunite are anomalously variable (Lovering and Morgan, 1963b), so that the Na values are perhaps not beyond the true range of variation.
2. Stueber and Coles determined 72 ± 6 ppm Na in a dunite from the Klamath Mountains, California; Hamilton and Mountjoy found 62 and 17 ppm Na in similar material.
3. A dunite from Trinity Alps, California, gave 9 ± 1 ppm Na (Stueber and Goles); Hamilton and Mountjoy, analyzing what may be the same rock, found 15 ppm Na.
4. Talc- and tremolite-bearing peridotites from the same locality were analyzed by both groups: 2940 ± 90 ppm Na (Stueber and Goles); 2300 and 1400 ppm Na (Hamilton and Mountjoy). In the latter two cases all samples were obtained from collections by Lipman (1964), so that comparisons stand on firm ground. It seems that the method used by Hamilton and Mountjoy is indeed capable of determining with acceptable accuracy, alkalis in ultramafic rocks. Thus for alpine-type intrusions perhaps an average value of about 400 ppm Na would be appropriate. For ultramafic rocks in general I assume the overall average of Stueber and Goles, 1040 ppm Na, to be valid.

4. Aluminum. Malakhov (1964) gives Al contents of ultrabasic rocks from the Urals. He finds 4900 ppm Al in dunites from relatively undifferentiated massifs and 18,400 ppm Al in pyroxenites. His average for ultrabasic rocks as a whole is 11,100 ppm Al, intermediate between values suggested by Turekian and Wedepohl and by Vinogradov. I shall choose 10,000 ppm Al as an overall average, but note that this does not take into consideration types of ultramafic and related rocks not represented in Malakhov's survey (e.g., eclogites). Note also that the quality of available analytical data on this element in ultramafic rocks is not very satisfactory. A wide variety of ultramafic rocks should be surveyed for Al, preferably by an instrumental analysis technique (e.g., that used by Fisher, 1964).

5. Chlorine. Hoering and Parker (1961) determined the Cl contents of two dunites (National Bureau of Standards #4999, and Jackson County, North Carolina): 140 and 170 ppm Cl, respectively. These analyses, which were apparently overlooked by Vinogradov, were done gravimetrically in the course of an investigation of the isotopic ratios of this element in natural systems. The analytical technique leaves much to be desired, especially from the standpoint of avoiding contamination, but the purpose of this work compelled them to take careful precautions against introducing Cl from other sources so that the analyses are probably reliable. Also, Hess and Otalora (1964) report Cl contents of 13 serpentinites from the Mayaguez, Puerto Rico, drill core, averaging 150 ppm Cl. Although their analyst systematically obtains much too high values for Na (Stueber and Goles, 1966), so that one is led to suspect his data on other trace elements, this average agrees well with results of Hoering and Parker. On the basis of this data, I shall assume an average of 150 ppm Cl in ultramafic rocks.

6. Potassium. Hamilton and Mountjoy's (1965) work, discussed in B-3, is the most extensive survey of this element in ultramafic rocks and seems to be trustworthy. Stueber and Murthy (1966b) have analyzed 29 ultramafic rocks, of a wide variety, by an isotope dilution technique. Their work, while it does not include as many individual rocks, is more useful in defining the K contents of the various modes of occurrence. Both sets of authors report exactly the same mean value for alpine-type intrusions, 41 ppm K. This value is also in excellent agreement with the average of 40 ppm K in ultramafic rocks reported by Holyk and Ahrens (1953), using a spectrochemical technique. Salmon (1957) found 32 ppm K in the Balsam Quarry, North Carolina, dunite via radiochemical activation analysis.

Ultramafic inclusions contain an average of 340 ppm K, according to Stueber and Murthy. Heier (1963) has studied a number of eclogites, from both metamorphic and volcanic environments, by direct gamma-ray spectrometry of the natural K^{40} and U- and Th-series activities present. His values for eclogites from volcanic environments (inclusions in the sense of Stueber and Murthy) average about 2600 ppm K. The only rock of similar type analyzed by Stueber and Murthy was an eclogite inclusion from the Visser Pipe, Tanganyika. They report 716 ppm K, which is near the lower limit of values reported by Heier. While it seems that ultramafic inclusions themselves are highly variable in their K contents, it is clear that they must average at least 340 ppm K, as given by Stueber and Murthy, or perhaps somewhat higher. Thus, an "average" for K in ultramafic rocks in some broad sense would be critically dependent upon the weighting that was employed of alpine-type intrusions versus ultramafic inclusions. Accordingly, I shall with some trepidation choose 200 ppm K as a best guess at such a general average. One should note that average K contents in specific classes of ultramafic rocks may vary from this value by more than an order of magnitude.

There are two additional determinations

of K in ultramafic rocks that are of interest. Tilton and Reed (1963) report 12 ± 4 ppm K in the Twin Sisters dunite (via isotope dilution) and Adams (1964) reports 43 ± 15 ppm K in a sample of the Mayaguez, Puerto Rico, serpentinite core (via instrumental gamma-ray spectrometry). These values are well within the ranges of those determined in the more extensive surveys previously reviewed.

7. ***Scandium.*** Stueber and Goles (1966) observed that Sc contents of ultramafic rocks were strongly dependent on the mineralogic composition (cf. results on Na discussed above) but not on the mode of occurrence. They give an overall average of 16 ppm Sc, whereas they find that dunites have an average of about 5 ppm Sc and pyroxenites, about 40 ppm Sc. These results imply that Sc is strongly concentrated in pyroxene, relative to its abundance in olivine. Thus, the value given by Vinogradov (5 ppm Sc) is indeed appropriate for dunites but is a poor representation of ultramafic rocks in a more general sense. I shall choose 16 ppm Sc as an overall average for ultramafic rocks.

Schmitt et al. (1963) have analyzed a peridotite and an eclogite from South African diamond pipes via radiochemical neutron activation analysis. Their values, 10.4 ± 0.5 ppm Sc (Wesselton peridotite) and 43 ± 2 ppm Sc (Roberts Victor eclogite), are in good agreement with those for similar inclusions analyzed by Stueber and Goles.

8. ***Chromium.*** Data for this element in 113 ultramafic rocks was reported by Stueber and Goles (1966). Neglecting some samples with anomalously high Cr contents, they found an average of about 2400 ppm Cr, somewhat higher than that of Vinogradov (2000 ppm Cr) and markedly higher than that of Turekian and Wedepohl (1600 ppm Cr). The analytical technique used by Stueber and Goles is probably superior to any other in common use for Cr in rocks, due to its insensitivity toward the mineralogic behavior of Cr and particularly toward the presence of chromite or picotite, which often cause analytical difficulties through their refractoriness. (Schmitt, Goles and Smith, 1966, discuss this problem in some detail and give examples of comparisons of various analytical methods.) The Cr contents of ultramafic rocks are not strongly dependent on mineralogic composition (in the sense of the olivine/pyroxene ratio) or mode of occurrence, so the suite of rocks studied by Stueber and Goles may be thought of as a single population in this respect. Accordingly, I shall take their value of 2400 ppm Cr as a superior estimate of the average Cr content for ultramafic rocks.

Wedepohl (1963) has employed X-ray fluorescence to determine Cr (and Mn and Ni) in a suite of 12 peridotite inclusions in basalts. He finds an average Cr content of about 2200 ppm, in excellent agreement with the average of Stueber and Goles.

Turekian (1963) has reported Cr, Ni, and Sr in minerals from three eclogites and has used these data, in conjunction with abundances in basalts, to demonstrate that tholeiitic and alkali basalt magmas could not arise in a simple way from eclogites. While direct comparisons with the results of Stueber and Goles cannot be made, Turekian's values lie in a reasonable range of Cr abundances. The Cr values of Turekian and Carr (1961) on a dunite (1840 ± 60 ppm Cr) agree in a general way with data of Stueber and Goles for similar rocks.

Hess and Otalora (1964) report an average of 2500 ppm Cr for their suite of serpentinites, in excellent agreement with the values above.

9. ***Manganese.*** Stueber and Goles found that abundances of this element were not affected in any discernible way by mineralogic composition or mode of occurrence. Their overall average, 1040 ppm Mn, is therefore a superior estimate of the abundance of this element in ultramafic rocks.

Wedepohl (personal communication)

found an average of 1090 ppm Mn in his suite of inclusions from basalts, in excellent agreement with the average of Stueber and Goles. This agreement, along with that just noted for Cr, implies that in the hands of a careful worker, X-ray fluorescence can provide data of high accuracy.

10. Cobalt. Stueber and Goles also studied this element and found that its abundances in 113 ultramafic rocks were insensitive to mineralogy or mode of occurrence, observations similar to those for Cr and Mn noted above. Their overall average of 110 ppm Co is therefore a superior estimate of the abundance of this element in ultramafic rocks.

Carr and Turekian (1961) and Turekian and Carr (1961) have reported radiochemical neutron activation determinations of Co in two samples of ultramafic rocks: a dunite (114 ± 10 ppm Co) and a kimberlite (71 ± 7 ppm Co). Smales, Mapper, and Wood (1957) used a similar technique to determine Co (and Ni and Cu) in a dunite from St. Paul's Rocks, Mid-Atlantic Ridge. They found 116 ± 3 ppm Co in this rock. These values agree well with those of Stueber and Goles for similar rocks.

11. Nickel. Edel'shtein (1963) has studied the nickel contents of ultramafic rocks, both fresh and serpentinized, from the southern Urals. He concludes that the Ni content of a serpentinite is directly related to that of the parent rock from which it was derived, a conclusion which agrees with that of Faust, Murata and Fahey (1956; see also Faust, 1963). Stueber and Goles also commented at length on the lack of any pronounced geochemical distinction between fresh and serpentinized ultramafic rocks, noting that abundances of Na, Mn, Cr, Sc, and Co all failed to exhibit any effect which could be assigned to serpentinization.

Edel'shtein (1963) reported 1700 ppm Ni as an average for a suite of dunite-peridotites with subordinate dunites; 1100 ppm Ni for a suite of peridotites, pyroxenites and subordinate dunites. Serpentinites whose parent rocks seem to have been dunites have an average of 1800 ppm Ni, those with peridotite parents, 1600 ppm Ni, those with pyroxenite parents, 1000 ppm Ni. It is clear that there is a marked dependence of Ni contents on mineralogical composition.

There also seems to be a dependence on mode of occurrence. Turekian (1963), in his study of Ni in mineral separates by radiochemical activation analysis, found 16, 295, and 460 ppm Ni in pyroxenes and 2, 57, and 46 ppm Ni in garnets from three eclogite inclusions. The values for the pyroxenes in particular are much lower than those which Edel'shtein found in alpine pyroxenites and their serpentinized equivalents. While this contrast may in fact be a reflection of mineral composition, Wedepohl's (1963) data on Ni in a suite of ultramafic inclusions from basalts support the hypothesis of a dependence on mode of occurrence. He finds an average of about 4400 ppm Ni in these inclusions, which are dunites and olivine-rich peridotites. The host basalts have much lower Ni contents, averaging perhaps 200 or 300 ppm, so that the high Ni abundances in the inclusions could not be due to simple contamination. Perhaps the ultramafic inclusions represent residual material from the partial fusion which gave rise to the basalts and as such have scavenged almost all NiO initially present in the total system. In any case, Wedepohl's average Ni content in inclusions is more than twice Edel'shtein's averages for alpine-type rocks of comparable mineralogy. Clearly, the reasons for the interesting behavior of Ni in various types of ultramafic rocks should be investigated. It is particularly puzzling that the geochemical behavior of Co and Ni should apparently be so different.

Hess and Otalora (1964) report 2600 ppm Ni as the average in their suite of serpentinites. They suggest that this would be somewhat higher than the average Ni abundance in the unserpentinized equivalents of these rocks. Their average agrees fairly well with Edel'shtein's results. Also, Smales, Mapper, and Wood (1957) found 1770 ± 20 ppm Ni in a dunite from St. Paul's Rocks, in excellent agreement with Edel'shtein's data.

Although it is clear that an "average" for ultramafic rocks in general should be between 1000 and 4000 ppm Ni, it is difficult to make a meaningful choice within this range on the basis of present information. I shall arbitrarily assume 1500 ppm Ni as an overall average.

12. Copper. Smales, Mapper, and Wood (1957) found 13.5 ± 0.5 ppm Cu in the dunite they analyzed. Using a gamma-gamma coincidence counting technique, I have determined Cu via instrumental activation analysis in two of the ultramafic inclusions studied by Stueber and Goles. The results are: 21 ± 16 ppm Cu and 90 ± 30 ppm Cu. It thus seems reasonable that an acceptable average abundance would be higher than the 10 ppm Cu given by Turekian and Wedepohl and the 20 ppm Cu given by Vinogradov. Perhaps 30 ppm Cu would not be too wildly speculative a choice.

13. Gallium. Borisenko (1963) has used a colorimetric technique to determine Ga in a suite of ultramafic rocks. His apparent sensitivity limit, about 1 ppm Ga, is adequate to outline the geochemistry of this element in alpine-type intrusions. He finds that dunites range from ⩽1 to 5 ppm Ga, peridotites from 3 to 6 ppm Ga, and pyroxenites range up to 28 ppm Ga. Thus there is a clear dependence upon mineralogical composition similar to that noted for Na and Sc above. Borisenko's overall average value of about 5 ppm Ga seems to be the best estimate available for this element in ultramafic rocks.

14. Rubidium. This element, along with Sr, is of great interest because of the potentialities of the Rb^{87}-Sr^{87} decay system for investigating the history of the relationship between the crust and the upper mantle. Faure and Hurley (1963) and Stueber and Murthy (1966b) have studied these elements by isotope dilution techniques. The former report 6.90 ± 0.09 ppm Rb for an eclogite inclusion (Roberts Victor mine) and 0.5 ppm Rb for a pyroxenite (source not given). The latter analyzed 29 ultramafic rocks, of various modes of occurrence, and reported the following averages: 0.145 ppm Rb in alpine-type intrusions, 2.07 ppm Rb in ultramafic inclusions and 1.44 ppm Rb for an overall average value, excluding a mica peridotite. As just noted in similar cases, any estimate of an overall "average" for Rb must be very sensitive to the weighting of the various rock types employed. I shall arbitrarily choose 1 ppm Rb as such an "average" value. (See Chapter 11-IV).

15. Strontium. Faure and Hurley (1963) report 149 ± 0.7 ppm Sr (eclogite inclusion) and 49 ppm Sr (pyroxenite); Rb/Sr ratios for these rocks are 0.05 and 0.01 (g/g). The average values of Stueber and Murthy (1966b) are: 6.09 ppm Sr (alpine-type intrusions), 30.5 ppm Sr (ultramafic inclusions), and 21.8 ppm Sr (overall arithmetic average). They give Rb/Sr ratios for individual rocks ranging from 0.010 to 1.32, the latter being a serpentinite from the Muskox layered intrusion, Northwest Territories, Canada. Excluding this sample, their range of Rb/Sr ratios extends to 0.165. Clearly, once again there are distinct populations present, so that an overall "average" is almost meaningless. I shall arbitrarily choose 20 ppm as an "average" Sr content for ultramafic rocks. (See also Chapter 11-IV).

16. Yttrium. Schmitt et al. (1963) analyzed for this element via radiochemical neutron activation analysis in an eclogite inclusion from the Roberts Victor mine. They found 8.8 ± 0.2 ppm Y. This is likely to be on the high rather than the low side of an appropriate average value of ultramafic rocks in general. Balashov and Turanskaya (1962) report 4.8 ppm Y in a peridotite from the Urals and Balashov (1963) found 2.1 ppm Y in a pyroxenite from the Kola Peninsula. Perhaps a more exhaustive survey would indicate mineralogical or mode-of-occurrence dependencies for this element. I shall guess that roughly 5 ppm Y would be reasonable for an overall average in ultramafic rocks.

17. Tellurium. In conjunction with their studies of meteorites via radiochemical activation analysis, Goles and Anders analyzed for Te (and I and U) in the Twin Sisters dunite (unpublished data; the analytical procedure is described by Goles and Anders, 1962). They were only able to set an upper limit of $\leqslant 5$ ppb Te (1 ppb $\equiv 1 \times 10^{-9}$ g/g). This limit agrees in a general way with Vinogradov's estimate, 1 ppb Te.

18. Iodine. Goles and Anders (unpublished data; see section B-17) found 45 ± 14 ppb I in the Twin Sisters dunite. Kuroda and Crouch (1962), using a spectrophotometric method, found 70 ± 20 ppb I in olivine from the Jackson County, New Jersey, dunite. Since these isolated values are likely to be on the low rather than the high side of an appropriate overall average, I shall guess that 100 ppb or 0.1 ppm I would be reasonable for such an average.

19. Barium. Hamaguchi, Reed, and Turkevich (1957) found 0.39 ± 0.09 ppm Ba in the Twin Sisters dunite via radiochemical neutron activation analysis. This determination was apparently overlooked by Vinogradov, although Turekian and Wedepohl place great weight on it. It is mentioned here in order to have a more nearly complete compilation of work done on trace elements in the Twin Sisters dunite. Turekian and Wedepohl's estimate of 0.4 ppm Ba is acceptable.

20. The rare earths, lanthanum to lutetium inclusive. Schmitt et al. (1963) give data and an extensive discussion of their results on the Wesselton, South Africa, peridotite and the Roberts Victor, South Africa, eclogite. I shall represent their data by listing La values only (3.3 ± 0.1 ppm La and 4.2 ± 0.1 ppm La, respectively) and refer the reader to the original paper for a complete discussion. Balashov and Turanskaya (1962) found 1.8 ppm La in a peridotite from the Urals and Balashov (1963) reports duplicate determinations of 0.65 and 1.4 ppm La on a pyroxenite from the Kola Peninsula (see original papers for complete data on lanthanides). A value of 2 ppm La is probably a reasonable guess at the overall average for ultramafic rocks.

21. Gold. DeGrazia and Haskin (1964) find 2.4 ppb Au in a peridotite from Webster, North Carolina. This value agrees well with data on Au reported by Vincent and Crocket (1960) and others (see Vinogradov, 1962, for further references). Vincent and Crocket (1960) also report Au contents in olivine inclusions from basalts, which average about 5 ppb Au. Both sets of authors used radiochemical neutron activation analysis, as did Shcherbakov and Perezhogin (1964) who find a somewhat higher average for 27 ultramafic rocks, 9.4 ppb Au. They also report averages of 14 ppb Au in olivines and 16 ppb Au in pyroxenes (both ortho- and clinopyroxenes). I shall use 9 ppb Au as an estimate of the average for ultramafic rocks in a general sense.

22. Lead. Tilton and Reed (1963) reported 19 ± 8 ppb Pb in the Twin Sisters dunite via radiochemical neutron activation and commented on the disagreement with previous isotope dilution determinations. They also determined Pb in a dunite from St. Paul's Rocks, Mid-Atlantic Ridge (110 ± 10 ppb Pb), an eclogite inclusion from Salt Lake Crater, Hawaii (210 ppb Pb), and two "nodules" (Dreiser Weiher, Germany: <10 ppb Pb; Gila, Arizona: 80 ± 30 ppb Pb). I shall assume an overall average of 50 ppb Pb for ultramafic rocks in general.

23. Thorium. This element, along with K and U, has received much attention both because of its usefulness in geochronology and its contribution to heat production in the earth. Recent work on Th abundances includes that by Lovering and Morgan (1963a,b), Heier (1963) and Adams (1964). Lovering and Morgan have concentrated their attention on eclogites, both those present as inclusions in pipes and those found as lenses in metamorphic rocks. As in the case of K contents observed by Heier (1963; also see Section B-6), eclogites from metamorphic environments have more variable Th (and U) contents than those from volcanic pipes. Lovering and Morgan (1963a) find a range in Th contents for pipe eclogites in continental areas of 0.15 to 0.29 ppm Th, with an average for these rocks of 0.22 ppm Th. One volcanic eclogite inclusion from an oceanic region (Salt Lake Crater, Hawaii) has 0.10 ppm Th, lower than any of the continental pipe eclogites. This, of course, is the reverse of what would be expected from heat-flow data if eclogites constitute an appreciable fraction of the upper mantle and if these samples are representative ones. Analysis of another specimen of Salt Lake Crater eclogite by Lovering and Morgan (1963b) confirms the relatively low Th abundance; they find 0.129 ± 0.003 ppm Th. Lovering and Morgan (1963b) also report data on a dunite inclusion from Gila, Arizona, 0.0115 ± 0.0006 and 0.0147 $\pm$ 0.005 ppm Th, and on the Twin Sisters dunite, 1.02 ± 0.42 and 5.35 ± 3.51 ppb Th. The Twin Sisters dunite displays marked variability in both Th and U abundances, as mentioned in Section B-3.

Heier (1963) finds approximately the same average Th content in pipe eclogites, 0.46 ppm Th, but observes more nearly constant Th/U ratios in these rocks than those found by Lovering and Morgan. His result for an eclogite from Salt Lake Crater, Hawaii, agrees very well with those of Lovering and Morgan. Since Heier's technique is much more direct and less subject to analytical errors, I shall assume 0.4 ppm Th to be an appropriate average for eclogite inclusions.

Lovering and Morgan's (1963b) work on dunites indicates that an average Th content of 0.001 ppm for these rocks would be a reasonable estimate. Thus, once again we are faced with distinct populations and the problems posed by them. Analyses by Adams (1964), using a technique similar to that of Heier, give 21 ± 10 ppb Th or about 0.02 ppm Th for an aggregate of serpentinite samples from the Mayaguez, Puerto Rico, drill core. This result reinforces the impression that intrusions have characteristically lower Th contents than do ultramafic inclusions. I shall make a wild guess at an overall average for ultramafic rocks: roughly 0.06 ppm Th. The reader should note that even the order of magnitude of this estimate is uncertain.

24. Uranium. Hamaguchi, Reed, and Turkevich (1957) were the first to determine U in an ultramafic rock by what has proved to be the powerful technique of neutron activation analysis. More recently, Lovering and Morgan (1963a,b), Heier (1963), and Tilton and Reed (1963) have surveyed a significant number of ultramafic rocks for U contents, using various techniques. In general, these results agree fairly well. Lovering and Morgan (1963a) find an average in continental pipe eclogites of 52 ppb U, which is a factor of about five lower than the average of 280 ppb U found by Heier (1963) for similar rocks; this seems to be the most significant disagreement among the various sets of data. All agree on values of about 30 to 50 ppb U for eclogites from the Salt Lake Crater, Hawaii. As just noted (Section B-23), this is not consistent with the idea that eclogite is a major constituent of the upper mantle, if the samples are representative ones.

Dunites, serpentinites, and olivine inclusions in basalts all seem to be significantly poorer in U than do eclogites. Goles and Anders (unpublished; see Section B-17) found 0.8 ± 0.1 ppb U in the

Twin Sisters dunite, in good agreement with the value of 1.2 ± 0.3 ppb U found in the identical specimen by Hamaguchi, Reed, and Turkevich (1957). Tilton and Reed report ≤0.4 ppb U (neutron activation) and 16 ppb U (isotope dilution) in this rock; the latter determination is almost certainly in error because of contamination. Lovering and Morgan (1963b) found 1.27 ± 0.50 and 7.57 ± 0.55 ppb U in the Twin Sisters dunite. The range of values seems very wide, as noted above, but it is clear that this rock contains much less U than do eclogites, by perhaps two orders of magnitude. Dunite of this approximate composition could be a major constituent of only those regions of the mantle either where there was no significant heat production or where the remainder was made up of something resembling an eclogite in U, K, and Th contents.

Adams (1964) found 14 ± 10 ppb U in his serpentinite aggregate (see Section B-23). Tilton and Reed (1963) found a range of values from 4 to 50 ppb U in olivine inclusions in basalts. As in the case of the Th data discussed above, it is clear that U contents in ultramafic rocks constitute several distinct populations. An estimated overall average value of 20 ppb U would be in reasonable accord with the data; the estimate is as uncertain as that for Th given in Section B-23.

C. Discussion

We may now briefly return to the three major problems mentioned in the introduction. The possibility of secular trends or geographic variations in the composition of the upper mantle may be disposed of at once. Except for such fragmentary data as that on the differences in U, Th contents among eclogite inclusions (Sections B-23 and B-24), there is no evidence of provinciality in time or space from studies of ultramafic rocks. Stueber and Goles (1966) and Stueber and Murthy (1966b) made special efforts to find such variations, without success.

Problems of heat production in the upper mantle and of the origin of basalts are best treated by examining abundances of alkali metals, Th, and U. It is immediately clear that these abundances, insofar as they are presently known, cannot be used as a test of either Lovering's (1958) compositional model, based on eclogites, or Ringwood's (1962b,c) "pyrolite" model. Either model fits the known compositional data with satisfactory accuracy. What can be concluded (see Stueber and Murthy, 1966b) is that alpine-type intrusions are residual in nature and probably do not constitute a volumetrically significant fraction of the upper mantle. Such material cannot give rise to basalts by any reasonable differentiation process.

III. STABLE ISOTOPE STUDIES OF ULTRAMAFIC ROCKS AND METEORITES

Hugh P. Taylor, Jr.

A. Introduction

Studies of stable isotope abundances in rocks and minerals have provided information on (a) genetic relationships among rock types, (b) possible chemical and physical processes that have affected rocks during or subsequent to their formation, (c) the existence or nonexistence of isotopic equilibrium during formation of mineral assemblages, and (d) the temperatures of formation of minerals and rocks. One of the most important aspects of these studies has also been the effort to ascertain any differences or similarities in isotopic ratios between terrestrial ultramafic rocks and the stony meteorites. The latter has obvious implications with regard to the composition of the entire earth.

In this chapter we review the data on stable isotope abundances in ultramafic rocks and meteorites in the light of the above questions. The most important elements showing appreciable variations in abundance of their nonradiogenic isotopes are hydrogen, carbon, oxygen, silicon, and sulfur. Other elements of low atomic weight show isotopic variations, but these have not been investigated in detail (e.g., Li, Be, B, N, etc.). The percentage mass differences between isotopic species of an element rapidly become very small as one moves to higher atomic numbers; hence, significant variations in natural isotopic abundances are not expected in the heavier elements.

Let us therefore concentrate on the five important elements named above, all of which occur in ultramafic rocks and meteorites. Variations in isotope ratio for each are reported in the δ notation (e.g., see Epstein, 1959), where

$$\delta = \left(\frac{R_{\text{sample}}}{R_{\text{standard}}} - 1\right) 1000$$

and R_{sample} is either D/H, C^{13}/C^{12}, O^{18}/O^{16}, Si^{30}/Si^{28}, or S^{34}/S^{32} in the sample and R_{standard} is the corresponding ratio in some arbitrary, convenient standard. We are not interested in the absolute abundances of the isotopic species, only in the variations; the latter can be measured very accurately with present mass spectrometric techniques. This accuracy is about 1 per mil for D/H and 0.1 per mil for the other four isotope ratios. To place the subsequent discussion in proper context, please refer to Table 11.2 where we list the commonly used isotopic standards and the general range in isotopic variations observed in the earth. It is important to note that ultramafic rocks and meteorites generally show a very narrow range of isotopic variation relative to the total range observed in nature, and it is beyond the scope of this chapter to go into the reasons for these large isotopic fractionations.

B. Isotopic Variations in Ultramafic Rocks and Meteorites

1. Deuterium-hydrogen. Deuterium-hydrogen ratios in ultramafic rocks have not been investigated in detail, but Boato (1954) has made an extensive study of

TABLE 11.2 Range of Variation in Stable Isotope Composition of Hydrogen, Carbon, Oxygen, Silicon, and Sulfur in Terrestrial Minerals, Rocks, and Waters (compiled from a variety of sources)

Element, with Accepted Isotopic Standard	Per Mil Isotopic Variation in	
	Minerals and Rocks	Natural Waters
Hydrogen SMOW, standard mean ocean water	−180 to +20	−410 to +50
Carbon Chicago PDB belemnite $CaCO_3$	−35 to +5	. . .
Oxygen SMOW, standard mean ocean water	−2 to +36	−50 to +15
Silicon Quartz vein, Mother Lode, Calif.	−2.2 to +3.2	. . .
Sulfur Canyon Diablo meteorite troilite	−45 to +60	. . .

TABLE 11.3 Deuterium-Hydrogen Analyses of Meteorites and Mafic and Ultramafic Igneous Rocks (relative to SMOW, standard mean ocean water)

Specimen	$\delta D/H$ (per mil)	Reference
Meteorites		
Ivuna—Type I carbonaceous chondrite	+270	(1)
Orgueil—Type I carbonaceous chondrite	+216	(1)
Cold Bokkeveld—Type II carbonaceous chondrite	−123	(1)
Haripura—Type II carbonaceous chondrite	− 69	(1)
Mighei—Type II carbonaceous chondrite	− 96	(1)
Murray—Type II carbonaceous chondrite	+ 42	(1)
Nawapali—Type II carbonaceous chondrite	−103	(1)
Santa Cruz—Type II carbonaceous chondrite	− 47	(1)
Lance—olivine-pigeonite chondrite	−108	(1)
Mokoia—olivine-pigeonite chondrite	+174	(1)
Indarch—enstatite chondrite	−134	(1)
Iron meteorites (average)	−113	(2)
Terrestrial rocks and minerals		
Hawaii volcanic bomb, 1955 Kilauea eruption	− 85	(3)
Hawaii glassy spatter, 1954 Kilauea eruption	− 78	(3)
Mihara volcanic bomb, 1951 eruption, Japan	− 62	(3)
Olivine basalt, Imazu, Hukuoka, Japan	− 64	(3)
Huzi basalt, Japan	− 94	(3)
Hatizyozima basalt, Seven Izu Islands, Japan	− 62	(3)
Average hornblende, Sierra Nevada granitic rocks (35)	− 87	(4)
Average biotite, Sierra Nevada granitic rocks (36)	− 88	(4)
Biotite, biotite-soevite, Alno, Sweden	− 62	(5)
Biotite, type Alnoite dike, Alno, Sweden	− 67	(5)
Biotite, Iron Hill carbonatite complex, Colorado	− 77	(5)
Biotite, biotite pyroxenite bomb, Laacher See, Germany	− 73	(5)
Biotite, Pt. Frederick pyroxenite, Southeast Alaska	− 71	(5)
Serpentinite, Mayaguez, Puerto Rico, mohole test site	− 68	(6)
Serpentinite, mid-Atlantic ridge	− 60	(6)
Serpentinized peridotite, Tinaquillo, Venezuela	− 78	(6)
Serpentinized peridotite, Bay of Islands, Newfoundland	−101	(6)
Serpentinized peridotite, Octoraro Creek, Pennsylvania	− 67	(6)
Serpentinized peridotite, Thetford Mines, Quebec	−122	(6)

(1) Boato (1954)
(2) Edwards (1955)
(3) Kokubu et al. (1961)
(4) Godfrey (1962)
(5) Taylor and Epstein (1966)
(6) Epstein (1966)

D/H ratios in meteorites, principally the carbonaceous chondrites. The available data are given in Table 11.3, and because isotopic analyses of terrestrial ultramafic rocks are sparse we also include some D/H values obtained on basalts, and on hornblende and biotite separates from granitic igneous rocks.

The accuracy of the meteoritic data is low because of problems of contamination with terrestrial H_2O (Boato, 1954), but the large variation is certainly real. The D/H ratios of Ivuna, Orgueil, and Mokoia are larger than in any known terrestrial sample, and on this basis alone their hydrogen content must be extraterrestrial. The H_2O contents of the iron meteorites and of Indarch are very low, and contamination problems are correspondingly more serious.

The D/H ratios of terrestrial mafic and

TABLE 11.4 Carbon Isotope Analyses of Meteorites and Mafic and Ultramafic Igneous Rocks (relative to Chicago PDB belemnite $CaCO_3$)

Specimen	$\delta C^{13}/C^{12}$ (per mil)	Reference
Meteorites		
Ivuna—Type I carbonaceous chondrite	−6.6	(1)
Orgueil—Type I carbonaceous chondrite	−11.4	(1)
Cold Bokkeveld—Type II carbonaceous chondrite	−7.3	(1)
Haripura—Type II carbonaceous chondrite	−3.7	(1)
Mighei—Type II carbonaceous chondrite	−9.9	(1)
Murray—Type II carbonaceous chondrite	−3.9	(1)
Nawapali—Type II carbonaceous chondrite	−10.0	(1)
Santa Cruz—Type II carbonaceous chondrite	−4.3	(1)
Felix—olivine-pigeonite chondrite	−16.4	(1)
Lance—olivine-pigeonite chondrite	−15.7	(1)
Mokoia—olivine-pigeonite chondrite	−18.1	(1)
Indarch—enstatite chondrite	−12.9	(1)
Richardton—ordinary chondrite (olivine-bronzite)	−24.6	(1)
Forest City—ordinary chondrite (olivine-bronzite)	−24.3	(1)
Canyon Diablo, iron (octahedrite)—graphite	−6.3	(2)
Canyon Diablo, iron (octahedrite)—cohenite (Fe_3C)	−17.9	(2)
Terrestrial rocks and minerals		
Olivine basalt, Hawaiian Islands (2 samples)	−25.1	(2)
Andesite, Hawaiian Islands	−24.8	(2)
Basaltic andesite, Hawaiian Islands	−25.2	(2)
Melilite-nepheline basalt, Hawaiian Islands	−26.0	(2)
Columbia River basalt, Picture Gorge, Oregon (6)	−24.3	(2)
Basalt, Kaersut, Greenland	−21.8	(2)
Kimberlite, Transvaal, South Africa (non-diamond bearing)	−23.8	(2)
Diamonds, Kimberley Mines, South Africa (average of 6 specimens)	−3.4	(2)
Calcite, augite soevite, Laacher See, Germany (2)	−7.7	(3)
Calcite, biotite soevite, Laacher See, Germany (5)	−6.9	(3)
Calcite, soevite, Alno, Sweden (6 samples)	−5.9	(3)
Dolomite carbonatite, Iron Hill, Colorado	−5.9	(3)
Calcite vein in kimberlite, Transvaal, South Africa (2)	−5.3	(4)
Calcite, soevite, Stjernoy Island, Norway (2)	−6.8	(5)
Calcite, albite soevite, Seiland area, Norway	−8.0	(5)

(1) Boato (1954)
(2) Craig (1953)
(3) Taylor et al. (1966)
(4) Baertschi (1957)
(5) Von Eckermann et al. (1952)

ultramafic rocks are very uniform, if one excludes serpentines. Only limited data are available, but the observed range in δ values is only —94 to —62. This is insignificant compared to the range observed in meteorites, but is nevertheless similar to the range of D/H ratios obtained for the Type II carbonaceous chondrites. Most of the H_2O in these meteorites is present in a serpentine-like layer lattice silicate of exceedingly fine grain size. It is noteworthy that several serpentine samples from terrestrial ultramafic rocks have D/H ratios similar to the Type II carbonaceous chondrites, particularly in view of the wide range of D/H observed in terrestrial waters (Craig, 1963).

2. ***Carbon isotopes.*** The available data on C^{13}/C^{12} variations in meteorites and in terrestrial mafic and ultramafic rocks and carbonatites are given in Table 11.4. As with D/H, the variation of C^{13}/C^{12} in meteorites is very large; however, no samples lie outside the terrestrial range. The major groups of meteorites seem to be clearly delineated by their C^{13}/C^{12} ratios. In terms of increasing C^{13} content, one goes from ordinary chondrites through olivine-pigeonite chondrites to the carbonaceous chondrites. The Type I and Type II carbonaceous chondrites cannot be distinguished on the basis of C^{13}/C^{12} ratios.

The tiny amounts of carbon in terrestrial basalts are uniformly very low in C^{13}, and they are almost identical to the carbon in ordinary chondrites. However, igneous carbon in carbonatites is also very uniform and is much richer in C^{13} (by 15 to 20 per mil), as is the carbon in diamonds from ultramafic kimberlite pipes. The latter show a relatively wide range in C^{13}/C^{12}, but average about 3 to 4 per mil lower than the PDB belemnite standard. The δ values of carbonatites and diamonds are similar to the values measured in Type I and Type II carbonaceous chondrites.

3. ***Silicon isotopes.*** Only very limited data are available on Si^{30}/Si^{28} variations in natural samples. Data of interest to the present work are given in Table 11.5. Terrestrial dunites and ordinary chondrites are identical in their silicon isotopic composition, and are similar to basalts and gabbros. Biotite from several granitic igneous rocks from the Sierra Nevada, California, shows a range of Si^{30}/Si^{28} of —0.5 to +0.8 (Tilles, 1961). It must be remembered that the total range of isotopic variation is smaller for silicon than for the other elements considered in this chapter.

4. ***Sulfur isotopes.*** Sulfur isotope data on meteorites and terrestrial mafic and ultramafic rocks are presented in Table 11.6.

TABLE 11.5 Silicon Isotope Analyses of Meteorites and Mafic and Ultramafic Igneous Rocks (relative to vein quartz, Mother Lode, Calif.)

Specimen	$\delta Si^{30}/Si^{28}$ (per mil)	Reference
Meteorites		
Richardton olivine-bronzite chondrite	−0.3	(1)
Melrose olivine-hypersthene chondrite	−0.3	(2)
Terrestrial rocks and minerals		
Dunite, Jackson Co., North Carolina	−0.3	(1)
Dunite, Mt. Dunn, New Zealand	−0.3	(1)
Augite from picrite basalt tuff, Mauna Kea, Hawaii	0.0	(2)
Lower gabbros, Skaergaard intrusion, Greenland (2)	−0.5	(1)
Average biotite, Sierra Nevada granitic rocks (9)	+0.1	(1)

(1) Tilles (1961)
(2) Reynolds and Verhoogen (1953)

TABLE 11.6 Sulfur Isotope Analyses of Meteorites and Mafic and Ultramafic Igneous Rocks (relative to Canyon Diablo troilite)

Specimen	$\delta S^{34}/S^{32}$ (per mil)	Reference
Meteorites		
Average meteoritic troilite (14 samples)	0.0	(1)
Elemental sulfur, Orgueil carbonaceous chondrite	+1.5	(2)
Sulfate, Orgueil carbonaceous chondrite	−1.3	(2)
Iron sulfide, Orgueil carbonaceous chondrite	+2.6	(2)
Weighted average, Orgueil carbonaceous chondrite	+0.4	(2)
Terrestrial rocks and minerals (sulfides)		
Insizwa sill, South Africa, weighted average (19)	+1.0	(3)
Palisades sill, New York, weighted average (13)	+1.0	(3)
Cobalt sill, Ontario, weighted average (6)	+0.7	(3)
Leitch sill, Ontario, average of two composite samples	+0.1	(3)
Sudbury Cu-Ni ore bodies, Ontario (17 samples)	+1.3	(4)
Stillwater complex Ni ore body, Montana (2)	+0.4	(4)
Aldan pyroxenite, U.S.S.R.	+0.4	(5)
Rai-iz dunite, U.S.S.R.	+0.4	(5)
Peridotite, Union, Maine	−0.9	(6)
Peridotite, Marie Pond, Maine	−0.4	(6)

(1) Thode et al. (1961)
(2) Monster et al. (1965)
(3) Shima et al. (1963)
(4) Thode et al. (1962)
(5) Vinogradov et al. (1957)
(6) Kulp et al. (1956)

Meteoritic troilite is remarkably uniform in its S^{34}/S^{32} content; 14 samples analyzed by Thode et al. (1961) showed a total range of only −0.3 to +0.2. Isotopic fractionations have been observed among the various sulfur-bearing phases of Orgueil carbonaceous chondrite, but the average S^{34}/S^{32} in this meteorite is very similar to the average meteoritic troilite.

The isotopic compositions of sulfides from differentiated mafic sills show considerable variation, but the weighted mean average of S^{34}/S^{32} in any given sill is very uniform. Shima et al. (1963) observed variations of −3.1 to +3.3 (Insizwa sill), −0.3 to +5.3 (Palisades sill), and +0.1 to +2.8 (cobalt sill), but the average S^{34}/S^{32} in the three sills varied only from +0.7 to +1.0, only slightly more S^{34}-rich than meteoritic troilite. Sulfides from Cu-Ni ore bodies at Sudbury, Ontario, and the Stillwater complex, Montana, are also only slightly enriched in S^{34} relative to meteorites. Sulfides from four ultramafic rocks (Table 11.6) have an average δ value almost identical to Canyon Diablo troilite.

*5. **Oxygen isotopes.*** Oxygen isotope ratios of meteorites and terrestrial ultramafic rocks are discussed last because they represent a much larger number of analyses than the stable isotope determinations previously discussed. These data are given in Table 11.7. Taylor et al. (1965) have shown that most meteorites other than the carbonaceous chondrites and the olivine-pigeonite chondrites and achondrites (which also are carbonaceous) can be divided into two distinct groups on the basis of their δO^{18} values in pyroxene. One group, with pyroxene δ values of +5.3 to +6.3, includes the ordinary chondrites, the

TABLE 11.7 Oxygen Isotope Analyses of Meteorites and Ultramafic Igneous Rocks (relative to SMOW, standard mean ocean water)

Specimen	$\delta O^{18}/O^{16}$ (per mil)	Reference
Meteorites		
Orgueil—Type I carbonaceous chondrite	+12.2	(1)
Al Rais—Type II carbonaceous chondrite	+11.3	(1)
Murray—Type II carbonaceous chondrite—whole rock	+ 9.5	(1)
Murray—Type II carbonaceous chondrite—olivine	− 2.1	(1)
Murray—Type II carbonaceous chondrite—pyroxene	− 0.5	(1)
Mokoia—olivine-pigeonite chondrite	+ 5.5	(1)
Vigarano—olivine-pigeonite chondrite	+ 3.0	(1)
Felix—olivine-pigeonite chondrite	− 0.8	(1)
Olivine–hypersthene chondrites (14 samples)	+5.0 to +5.9	(2)
Olivine–hypersthene chondrites—pyroxene (4 samples)	+5.8 to +6.2	(1)
Olivine–bronzite chondrites (13 samples)	+4.8 to +5.4	(2)
Olivine–bronzite chondrites—pyroxene (3 samples)	+5.4 to +5.8	(1)
Enstatite chondrites (2 samples)	+6.0 to +6.3	(1)
Enstatite achondrites (2 samples)	+5.9 to +6.0	(1)
Mesosiderites—pyroxene (3 samples)	+4.0 to +4.4	(1)
Hypersthene achondrites—pyroxene (3 samples)	+3.7 to +4.3	(1)
Basaltic achondrites—pyroxene (7 samples)	+3.8 to +4.2	(1)
Basaltic achondrites—whole rock (5 samples)	+4.2 to +4.5	(1)
Diopside–olivine achondrites—pyroxene (2 samples)	+5.3 to +5.5	(1)
Goalpara—olivine pigeonite achondrite—pyroxene	+ 8.6	(1)
Steinbach stony-iron—pyroxene	+ 4.3	(1)
Bondoc stony-iron—pyroxene	+ 3.9	(1)
Pallasite stony-irons—olivine (2 samples)	+3.5 to +4.0	(2)
Terrestrial rocks and minerals		
Pyroxenes from gabbros and basalts (8 samples)	+5.5 to +6.6	(3,4)
Pyroxenes from ultramafic complexes (12 samples)	+5.1 to +6.3	(3,4)
Enstatite from dunite bomb, Peridot, Arizona	+ 6.4	(3)
Dunites from Calif., Southeast Alaska, and N. Carolina (4)	+5.4 to +5.7	(2)
Dunite bombs from Arizona, Calif., and Hawaii (3)	+5.3 to +5.5	(2)
Dunite, Mt. Dunn, New Zealand	+ 5.8	(2)
Dunite, Kranbat, Styria	+ 6.6	(2)
Olivine pyroxenite, Kane Peak, Southeast Alaska	+ 6.4	(2)
Olivine pyroxenite, Duke I., Southeast Alaska	+ 6.0	(3)
Hornblende pyroxenite, Annette I., Southeast Alaska	+ 5.7	(4)
Hornblende pyroxenite, Klukwan, Southeast Alaska	+ 5.5	(4)
Hornblende pyroxenite, Union Bay, Southeast Alaska	+ 5.9	(4)
Hornblende pyroxenite, Duke I., Southeast Alaska	+ 5.5	(4)
Hornblende pyroxenite, Duke I., Southeast Alaska—hornblende	+ 5.2	(4)
Hornblende pyroxenite, Duke I., Southeast Alaska—pyroxene	+ 5.7	(4)
Hornblende pyroxenite, Duke I., Southeast Alaska—magnetite	+ 0.6	(4)
Massive magnetite, pyroxenite, Klukwan, Southeast Alaska	+ 3.3	(4)
Massive magnetite, pyroxenite, Snettisham, Southeast Alaska	+ 4.4	(4)

TABLE 11.7 (*continued*)

Specimen	$\delta O^{18}/O^{16}$ (per mil)	Reference
Hornblendite, Pt. Frederick, Southeast Alaska—biotite	+ 7.1	(3)
Hornblendite, Pt. Frederick, Southeast Alaska—hornblende	+ 6.9	(3)
Mafic pegmatite, Duke I., Southeast Alaska—hornblende	+ 5.9	(3)
Mafic pegmatite, Duke I., Southeast Alaska—plagioclase	+ 7.4	(3)
Mafic pegmatite, Duke I., Southeast Alaska—magnetite	+ 0.9	(4)
Mafic pegmatite, Duke I., Southeast Alaska—hornblende	+ 6.9	(4)
Clinopyroxenite (layer 16), Muskox complex, Canada	+ 6.3	(4)
Orthopyroxenite (layer 18), Muskox complex, Canada	+ 6.6	(4)
Bronzite gabbro (layer 22), Muskox complex, Canada	+ 7.3	(4)
Chilled marginal gabbro, Muskox complex, Canada	+ 6.8	(4)
Serpentinite, Mayaguez, Puerto Rico, mohole test site	+ 6.8	(5)
Serpentinite, mid-Atlantic ridge	+ 4.6	(5)
Serpentinized peridotite, Tinaquillo, Venezuela	+ 5.2	(5)
Serpentinized peridotite, Bay of Islands, Newfoundland	+ 6.8	(5)
Serpentinized peridotite, Octoraro Creek, Pa.	+ 5.2	(5)
Serpentinized peridotite, Thetford Mines, Quebec	+ 5.1	(5)
Serpentinized dunite, Annette I., Southeast Alaska	+ 2.8	(4)
Biotite pyroxenite bomb, Laacher See area, Germany	+ 5.9	(6)

(1) Taylor et al. (1965)
(2) Reuter et al. (1965)
(3) Taylor and Epstein (1962)
(4) Taylor (1966)
(5) Epstein (1966)
(6) Taylor et al. (1966)

enstatite chondrites, the enstatite achondrites, and the diopside-olivine achondrites. In terms of number of actually observed meteorite falls, this group represents by far the most abundant meteorite types. A second group contains no chondrules and hence is made up entirely of achondritic types; these include the mesosiderites, the hypersthene achondrites, and the basaltic achondrites, all of which have pyroxene δ values of +3.7 to +4.4. This group also contains a number of stony-irons such as Bondoc and Steinbach.

All of the above meteorite types except the basaltic achondrites properly qualify as true ultramafic rock types, and it is proper to compare and contrast them with terrestrial ultramafic rock types. Even the basaltic achondrites are unusual in that they contain anorthite instead of labradorite as do terrestrial gabbros. As is readily seen in Table 11.7, terrestrial ultramafic rocks from a very wide variety of sources are exceedingly uniform in O^{18}/O^{16} ratio. Olivine-bearing ultramafic rocks, pyroxenites, and pyroxenes from gabbros and basalts all lie in the range +5.1 to +6.6 per mil. This includes 40 separate samples from all over the world; their O^{18}/O^{16} ratios are so similar to those of the chondritic group of meteorites discussed above (which vary from +4.8 to +6.3) as to suggest a genetic relationship between the two. The terrestrial ultramafic rocks are clearly distinct in O^{18}/O^{16} ratio from the achondritic group of meteorites, which have δ-values 1 to 3 per mil lower in O^{18}. The basaltic achondrites also have O^{18}/O^{16} ratios at least 2 per mil smaller than basalts and gabbros on the Earth (Taylor et al., 1965).

The carbonaceous chondrites and the olivine-pigeonite chondrites and achondrites have highly variable O^{18}/O^{16} ratios. Their whole-rock analyses vary from −0.8

to +12.2, their pyroxene analyses from −0.5 to +8.6, and one of them (Murray) contains olivine with a δO^{18} of −2.1; the latter is much lower in O^{18} than terrestrial olivine from mafic and ultramafic rocks. The carbonaceous meteorites are thus very different from other types of meteorites as well as from ultramafic rocks of the earth, and their olivine and pyroxene must have originated in different ways from the latter.

Several serpentines and serpentinized peridotites have δO^{18} values similar to unserpentinized ultramafic rocks. Six samples show a range of only +4.6 to +6.8, indicating that serpentinization has taken place without markedly changing the oxygen isotopic composition of the original peridotite or dunite. One sample with a δ-value of +2.8 has clearly been depleted in O^{18} during serpentinization. If meteoric or groundwaters were commonly responsible for serpentinization, or if cycling and recirculation of H_2O between country rock and ultramafic intrusive usually occurred, one would expect drastic changes in O^{18} content of the ultramafic rocks to occur during serpentinization. This suggests that much serpentine may form by simple addition of H_2O to the ultramafic body, without appreciable oxygen exchange with adjacent parts of the crust. Also, this H_2O must have an O^{18}/O^{16} ratio not too dissimilar from that of the ultramafic rock itself; this essentially eliminates meteoric water as a possibility except under special circumstances.

In a coexisting assemblage of minerals in an ultramafic rock or meteorite, the O^{18} content invariably increases in the sequence: magnetite-olivine-pyroxene-plagioclase. The differences in O^{18}/O^{16} content between a given set of minerals are temperature-dependent, assuming that the minerals formed in isotopic equilibrium with one another and that the O^{18}/O^{16} ratios have not subsequently been altered. This temperature-dependence must be calibrated for each mineral pair through laboratory equilibration experiments (e.g., see O'Neil and Clayton, 1964), and this has not yet been done for the mineral pairs of meteorites or ultramafic rocks. Nevertheless, the difference in O^{18}/O^{16} ratio generally decreases with increasing temperature, so relative temperature estimates among rock types are sometimes possible. Such estimates suggest that, excluding the serpentines and the carbonaceous chondrites, most ultramafic rocks and meteorites formed at temperatures at least as high as 700 to 800°C and probably considerably higher. This is particularly true if the measured fractionations of 1.5 to 2.2 per mil between clinopyroxene and magnetite at Klukwan and Snettisham, southeast Alaska, represent attainment of isotopic equilibrium. These fractionations are comparable to those measured in the lower zone gabbros at the Skaergaard intrusion (Taylor and Epstein, 1963), and probably indicate temperatures of at least 1000°C.

Massive magnetite ore segregations consistently give higher O^{18}/O^{16} ratios than finer grained, disseminated magnetite in the ultramafic complexes of southeastern Alaska (Chapter 4-III). This has also been observed by Anderson (1966) in his studies of the Quebec anorthosites, and he suggests it is due to post-crystallization oxygen exchange between the magnetite and its environment during oxidation of ulvöspinel solid solution in the magnetite; this exchange would be expected to take place more readily in the finer-grained magnetite, and except in very "dry" environments only massive ore segregations may preserve their original O^{18}/O^{16} ratio. This post-crystallization oxygen exchange is a much less serious problem in most silicate minerals.

C. Conclusions

The most significant aspect of the stable isotope abundance data on meteorites and terrestrial ultramafic rocks is that to a first approximation the isotopic compositions of these materials are the same. This is particularly true for silicon and sulfur, for which the observed variations are less than 1 per mil. The similarity is remarkable in the case of sulfur, inasmuch as fractionation processes have produced variations in S^{34}/S^{32} ratios in terrestrial samples of more than 100 per mil.

The above conclusion is least firm for hydrogen, as some carbonaceous meteorites are much higher in deuterium content than any known terrestrial material. This is the only example yet reported in which the meteoritic abundance of a nonradiogenic isotope lies outside the terrestrial range. Other meteorites analyzed by Boato (1954) and Edwards (1955) have D/H ratios similar to those in mafic and ultramafic rocks on earth.

The O^{18}/O^{16} ratios of the chondritic group of meteorites (excluding the carbonaceous ones) are strikingly similar to the ratios in ultramafic rocks. The small amounts of carbon in the ordinary chondrites are also nearly identical in C^{13} content to the trace amounts of carbon in terrestrial basalts. Hence, for every one of the five elements under discussion, the chondritic meteorites and their terrestrial counterparts in the ultramafic rocks are isotopically indistinguishable.

Other workers have suggested earth models based upon analogies with chondrites, principally because (a) the chondritic meteorites are the most abundant extraterrestrial objects which strike the earth, and (b) terrestrial ultramafic rocks and chondrites are both essentially olivine-pyroxene rock types with relatively similar Fe/Mg ratios. The stable isotope data simply are another line of evidence that is in agreement with such models. There are many difficulties in such hypotheses, however, particularly because the alkali element contents of chondrites and ultramafic rocks are so dissimilar.

Another very serious question arises in regard to the C^{13}/C^{12} contents of these rock types. Basically, there appear to be two distinct groupings: (a) trace amounts of carbon in chondritic meteorites and terrestrial basalts, including one kimberlite, in which very low C^{13}/C^{12} ratios are observed (−25 to −22), and (b) major concentrations of carbon in carbonaceous chondrites, terrestrial carbonatites, and diamonds from kimberlite pipes, including also graphite from Canyon Diablo iron meteorite, in which considerably higher C^{13}/C^{12} ratios are measured (−11 to −3). Which of these should be taken as most representative of carbon in ultramafic rocks, or of the earth's mantle? Diamonds must have formed at great depths in the earth at relatively high temperatures, and their C^{13}/C^{12} ratios have clearly not been altered by post-crystallization isotopic exchange. As discussed later, igneous carbonatites show isotopic similarities to mafic and ultramafic rocks in terms of O^{18}/O^{16} ratio. Both of these observations indicate that carbon in the earth's mantle belongs to the C^{13}-rich group, but this must remain an unresolved problem of major importance. It is possible that the tiny amounts of carbon in basalts and ordinary chondrites form by some type of reaction between CO and H_2 in which kinetic isotope fractionation effects could play a role.

A final word should be said about possible isotopic relationships among terrestrial rock types. The O^{18}/O^{16} ratios of minerals in gabbros and basalts are so similar to those in corresponding minerals from ultramafic rocks, that there can be little doubt that these rock types are genetically related. This is obvious of course for the stratiform ultramafic complexes which appear to have crystallized from gabbroic magma, but it is less definite for ultramafic intrusive bodies in orogenic belts and for peridotite bombs. Large variations in O^{18} can occur through magmatic differentiation and fractional crystallization of gabbroic magma (Taylor and Epstein, 1962, 1963) and the fact that such differences are not observed between mafic and ultramafic rocks implies a genetic relationship. Of course, this says nothing about the nature of the relationship, which might have existed as far back as the primordial differentiation of the earth. The remarkable uniformity of C^{13} and O^{18} contents of igneous carbonatites (Taylor et al., 1966), and the similarity in O^{18}/O^{16} ratios of pyroxenes from gabbros, peridotites, and carbonatites strongly suggests that these rock types are related in some fashion, also.

IV. Rb^{87}-Sr^{87} RELATIONSHIPS IN THE DIFFERENTIATION OF THE MANTLE

P. M. Hurley

Rubidium 87 decays radioactively to Sr^{87} with a half-life of about 50 billion years. This is long compared to the age of the earth. Strontium 87, consequently, has continued to increase in abundance relative to the other isotopes of strontium at a rate dependent upon the amount of rubidium that has been associated with the strontium throughout its history in any system. This has turned out to be of significance in the study of the evolution of the earth into its present chemical complexity.

In practice we are concerned with the two measured ratios Sr^{87}/Sr^{86} and Rb^{87}/Sr^{86} in geological materials and meteorites, and the way these two variables have changed relative to the values when the earth was formed. At this time Sr was isotopically homogeneous, as far as we can tell, from the evidence found in meteorites. Chondritic meteorites contain Sr in which the ratio Sr^{87}/Sr^{86} is linearly related to the ratio Rb^{87}/Sr^{86} in them (Gast, 1960; Pinson et al., 1965; Shields, 1964). The extrapolation of this relationship to zero Rb indicates that the initial, or primordial, value of Sr^{87}/Sr^{86} was 0.698 ± 0.001 at the time of origin of the meteorites, and the actual increase of the Sr^{87} relative to Rb^{87} in these materials yields an age value close to 4.5 b.y., if the decay rate of Rb^{87} is taken as 1.39×10^{-11} yr^{-1}.

If this primordial value of 0.698 is assumed to be also the initial ratio of Sr^{87}/Sr^{86} for the earth, we may examine the increases in this ratio in materials that come to the surface of the earth from the mantle. From geochemical reasoning the differentiation of the earth's mantle by the migration of fluid phases will mean a continuing enrichment of minor elements in these fluid phases as they move radially outward, assuming that equilibrium is established in the process. In other words, partition of most minor elements between solid phases left behind, and the liquid phase moving upward, is strongly in favor of concentration in the liquid phase. As these minor elements for the most part never reach saturation in the fluid phase, the level of their enrichment may indicate the extent to which a particular fluid phase has "swept out" the mantle column from which it came. These fluid phases appear close to the surface as magmas, or if effusive, as volcanic lavas.

In oceanic basalts, which rapidly reach the surface from a depth of a hundred kilometers or so, the material probably represents the fluid phase in equilibrium with a small number of mineral phases which may include olivine, pyroxene, garnet, jadeite, or amphibole. In magmas reaching shallow depths in continental regions it is possible that the equilibria at depth involve plagioclase in addition to the other essential phases mentioned. In such systems as these it is probable that the chemical potential of rubidium continues to increase in the fluid phases, whereas the strontium will increase until it can follow calcium into Ca-bearing phases such as diopside or plagioclase. Above this point it appears that strontium may even decrease in residual fluid phases, so that the strontium is left somewhat concentrated in intermediate or mafic rocks at depth. The net result is that the ratio of Rb/Sr probably increases rather slowly or not at all during the separation of fluid phases in the mantle up to the level of the first phases that carry calcium. Above that level the Rb/Sr may increase rapidly because of the depletion of strontium and continue to increase until it peaks in the final acid magmas typical of rhyolites or obsidians.

If this process of geochemical differentiation took place reasonably early in the history of the earth, the isotopic abundance in strontium would be quite variable in the various source regions, but generally the Sr^{87}/Sr^{86} ratio should be higher in the shallower regions than in the deeper, with the possible exception discussed below. From this reasoning it may be estimated that oceanic basalts come from either deeper or less differentiated sources in the mantle than many of the continental basalts, which show higher values of Sr^{87}/Sr^{86}.

The Rb, Sr, and isotopic abundance estimates in the various products from the mantle, are given in the partial listing of work by various analysts in Table 11.8. In general it is seen that the alpine-type ultramafics contain a fraction of a ppm of Rb and at most a few ppm of Sr. St. Paul's Islands peridotites are about 5 times higher, the low-alkali oceanic tholeiites are 10 to 20 times higher, and the alkali basalts 100 times higher than the alpine-type ultramafics. These materials cover the principal range of direct derivatives from the mantle in the oceanic areas, from solid residual phases or accumulates to fractionated melt phases. Despite the small sampling, it is still possible to draw several conclusions from the data.

The modern oceanic island basalts are grouped about an average value of 0.703

TABLE 11.8 Rb and Sr Contents of Ultramafic Rocks

Number of Samples, Ultramafic Rocks and Region	Av Rb,ppm	Av Sr,ppm	Rb/Sr	Sr^{87*}/Sr^{86}	References†
Alpine-type intrusions					
8 dunites	0.12	6.1	0.020	0.712	Stueber and Murthy, 1966
2 serpentinites	0.67	7.6	0.088	0.713	
2 peridotites	0.12	4.7	0.026	0.709	
5 dunites	0.09	0.5	0.19	0.711	Roe, 1964; Roe, et al., 1965
6 serpentinites	0.14	4.2	0.033	0.707	
3 peridotites	0.34	4.3	0.08	0.710	
Ultramafic inclusions					
10 samples, mixed	2.1	30	0.07	0.705	Stueber and Murthy, 1966
St. Paul's Islands, peridotites					
8 samples	0.6	27	0.026	0.704	Hart, 1964
Oceanic Basalt Range					
From low-alkali tholeiites to alkali basalts, with few exceptions.	1–20	100–1000	0.01–0.04	0.702–705*	

* Normalized to Sr^{86}/Sr^{88} = 0.1194, and relative to Eimer and Amend $SrCO_3$ Standard = 0.708.
† References for basalts include: Gast, 1960; Faure and Hurley, 1963; Hedge and Walthall, 1963; Lessing and Catanzaro, 1964; Gast, Tilton and Hedge, 1964; McDougall and Compston, 1965; Powell, Faure and Hurley, 1965; Tatsumoto, Hedge, and Engel, 1965; and personal communications.

to 0.704 for the ratio Sr^{87}/Sr^{86}. The initial strontium in the most ancient volcanic sediments (about 3 billion years old) shows a ratio of about 0.701. If these points are extrapolated backward in time to 4.5 billion years, the value of the ratio will quite closely match the value of 0.698 ± 0.001 found for the stony meteorites. Thus it is a reasonable assumption that the earth and the meteorites started with the same strontium isotopic abundance, and we can draw primary growth lines for the Sr^{87}/Sr^{86} ratio in the source regions of oceanic basalt as shown in Fig. 11.1.

Using this rate of increase, we find that the ratio Rb/Sr in the source regions of oceanic basalt must have been about 0.02 on the average. In the common oceanic alkali basalts this ratio is found to vary upward from 0.02 to as much as a factor of 2 higher showing that the process of separation of alkali-rich basaltic magma may involve a slight enrichment of rubidium relative to strontium. However, a study of primitive tholeiites (Tatsumoto, Hedge, and Engel, 1965) is beginning to show that these rocks have Rb/Sr ratios of 0.01 and concomitantly low Sr^{87}/Sr^{86} ratios of 0.702. In general, therefore, it may be concluded that the present Sr^{87}/Sr^{86} ratio ranges from 0.702 to 0.705 in the source regions of oceanic basalt, with a growth of about 0.004 in 4.5 b.y., and a ratio of Rb/Sr of about 0.02.

The Sr^{87}/Sr^{86} ratio in the alpine-type intrusions is higher than any other oceanic rock type, and actually higher than the Sr^{87}/Sr^{86} ratios at time of emplacement found in almost all continental magma types. Clearly there is no contemporary relationship between alpine-type ultramafics and other common materials reaching the surface from the mantle, in oceanic or continental regions. Possible exceptions to this statement are the Tasmanian dolerites, which had an initial Sr^{87}/Sr^{86} ratio of 0.711 (Heier, Compston, and McDougall, 1965), and a small scattering of granitic rocks found by various investigators.

Ultramafic inclusions differ distinctly from the intrusive ultramafic materials, and closely match modern basalts. As pointed out by Stueber and Murthy (1966b), it is probable that the ultramafic inclusions in continental basalts, oceanic basalts, and kimberlite are genetically related to the materials that carry them, and that both the inclusions and their associated magmas are derived from source regions, which have rather similar histories of the relative

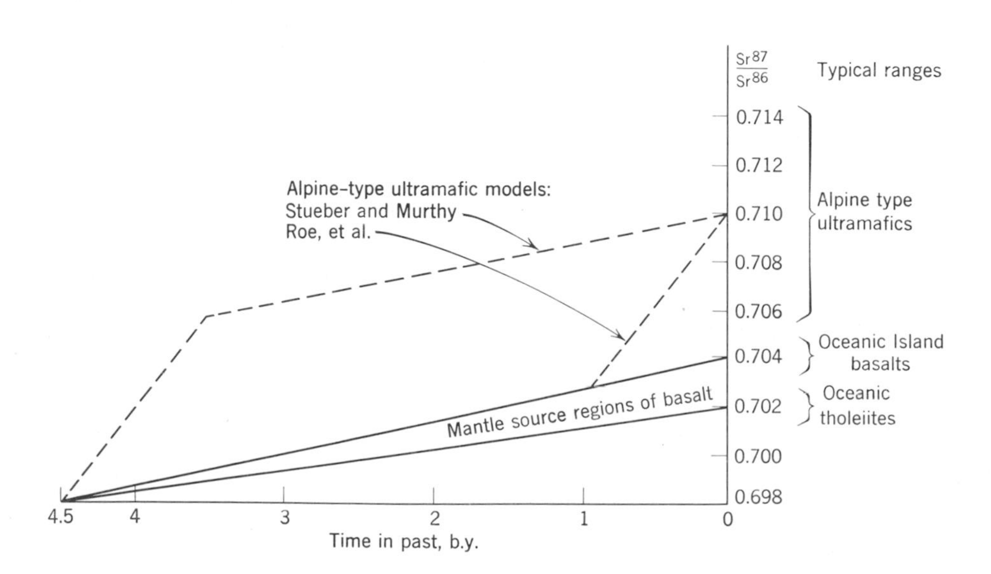

Fig. 11.1 Sr^{87}/Sr^{86} growth with time for some mafic and ultramafic rocks.

enrichment of Rb and Sr. These authors also placed the ultramafic zones in stratiform igneous complexes in this grouping, on the basis of basalt-like Sr^{87}/Sr^{86} ratios.

If we include mantle derivatives from continental areas also, we find a general grouping (with some overlap and deviations), based on the ratio Sr^{87}/Sr^{86}, as follows:

Materials	Common Range in Sr^{87}/Sr^{86} at Time of Intrusion
1. Low-alkali oceanic tholeiites, carbonatites	0.702–0.704
2. Oceanic alkali basalts, some continental basaltic intrusives, ultramafic inclusions	0.703–0.705
3. Some continental basalts, more differentiated oceanic volcanics, most plutonic sialic magmas	0.705–0.710
4. Alpine-type ultramafic intrusives	0.707–0.725 (averaging .711)

In addition to the level of the Sr^{87}/Sr^{86} ratio, it is possible to draw some information from calculated Sr^{87}/Sr^{86} regression lines. When a rock is analysed for total Rb and Sr, as well as Sr^{87}/Sr^{86} it is possible to calculate the growth of this ratio in the past. This may be plotted as in Fig. 11.1. The slope of the lines is proportional to the ratio Rb/Sr in the rock. These regression lines must extend back to the time of last change in Rb/Sr ratio, and may give information on the age of the material with its present composition as opposed to its time of rise to the earth's surface.

How far into the past is it necessary to go before the Sr^{87}/Sr^{86} ratio in the alpine-type ultramafics drops to the levels found in other mantle derivatives? The answer to this question is complexed by an analytical discrepancy between the different groups of investigators. Stueber and Murthy (1966b) obtained values for the Sr content more than 10 times higher than Roe et al. (1965) for the dunites, despite close agreement on serpentinites and peridotites, and close agreement on the Rb contents of all the rock types. The samples were from different localities, but the discrepancy is too uniform in all of the samples to be due to chance in random sampling. Both groups have worked with good agreement on meteorites, so are well versed in the techniques of low-level Sr analysis.

Unfortunately, this discrepancy must remain unresolved until further work, but in the meantime a different picture of mantle differentiation is obtained by selecting extremes from the two sets of measurements. The lower Sr values and therefore higher Rb/Sr ratios in the dunites from the work of Roe et al. (1965) would requre that the ultramafic masses became isolated generally in the latter half of earth history and subsequently rose to the surface. The higher Sr values and therefore lower Rb/Sr ratios measured by Stueber and Murthy (1966b) suggested to these authors that these rocks are the residual accumulates from some very early enrichment in Rb relative to Sr followed by a separation of a sialic crust in the upper mantle, in the early Archean. The plots of the two models are shown in Fig. 11.1.

A third and interesting possibility is that the alpine-type ultramafic masses were accumulates from the partial fusion of downdragged blocks of ancient crustal material, involved in mantle motions.

V. POTASSIUM-RUBIDIUM RATIOS IN MANTLE DERIVED ROCKS

V. Rama Murthy and Alan M. Stueber

Potassium and rubidium are strongly lithophile elements which are concentrated in highly differentiated material of the earth's crust, in contrast to material derived from the mantle, such as basalts and ultramafic rocks. The ionic radius of Rb is larger than that of K. Contrary to potassium, rubidium does not form minerals of its own and its abundance in silicate minerals is dependent on the extent of substitution for K or admission to vacant lattice sites. Therefore, it would appear that in either a partial melting or fractional crystallization differentiation, Rb is preferentially enriched in the liquid relative to K and that $[K/Rb]_{liquid}$ would always be less than $[K/Rb]_{crystal}$. On this simple reasoning, we should expect that the K/Rb ratio decreases with increasing differentiation. Evidence of such a relationship, wherein the K/Rb ratio decreases with increasing K content (as an index of increased differentiation) is found in a number of differentiated bodies as recently discussed by Taubeneck (1965).

A similar systematic variation of the K/Rb ratio with K content is also found in basalts (Gast, 1965; Tatsumoto, Hedge, and Engel, 1965). In the low potassic oceanic tholeiites, the K/Rb ratios reach up approximately to 1900 and trend down approximately to 300 in high potassic alkali basalts. This relationship has been interpreted by Gast to be in accord with the behavior of K and Rb in crystallization of basalts. Furthermore, the high K/Rb ratios of oceanic tholeiites are similar to those of achondrite meteorites. Based on this, as well as other compositional similarities, Gast suggested that the composition of the upper mantle is similar to that of the basaltic achondrites. This argument requires that oceanic tholeiites are total or nearly total melts of upper mantle material, a point which has also been stressed in other detailed studies (Engel, Engel, and Havens, 1965).

An alternative explanation for the variation of K and K/Rb ratios in oceanic basalts is suggested by Hart and coworkers (1964, 1965). In a detailed study of some of the mylonitized peridotites from St. Paul's rocks Hart (1964) has shown that some samples containing amphibole have K/Rb ratios as high as 1000. These rocks also show a systematic variation of the K/Rb ratio with K content, but contrary to the trend found in basalts the K/Rb ratio increases with a rise in the K content. Based on studies that show many amphiboles with K and K/Rb ratios similar to those of oceanic tholeiites, these workers suggest that the variations seen in oceanic tholeiites could be due to variations in the amounts and the chemical composition of the amphibole in a parent hornblende peridotite. Thus hornblende peridotite is suggested as the parent material from which basalts can be produced by partial fusion, similar to a suggestion made by Oxburgh (1964). To what extent hornblende peridotite is an important mantle constituent is not known, but under mid-ocean ridges this may well be important (Nicholls, 1965).

Regardless of the correct interpretation, the variations in K/Rb ratios in basalts bring up the importance of determining these ratios and the K contents of the ultramafic rocks presumably derived from the upper mantle. Such material is available in the form of alpine peridotites and the various types of inclusions found in basalts and kimberlite pipes. On the reasonable assumption that these ultramafic rocks and basalts are related in some manner to liquid-crystal separation in the differentiation history of the upper mantle, the K/Rb ratios may help clarify some of the relationships between basalts and ultramafic rocks.

TABLE 11.9 K/Rb Ratios in Ultramafic Rocks (see Table 9.3)

Number of Samples, Types of Rocks and Regions	Range of K Content (ppm)	Range of Rb Content (ppm)	Range of K/Rb Ratio	Reference
Alpine-Type Intrusions				
Wide Geographic Coverage				
8 dunites	19–61	0.07–0.30	200–340	Stueber and Murthy (1966a)
2 serpentinites	120–240	0.3–1.0	228–420	
2 peridotites	26–59	0.09–0.16	280–375	
Shikoku, Japan				
2 dunites	10–21	0.03–0.10	210–330	Hart and co-workers (1965)
1 pyroxenite	18	0.045	400	
2 eclogites	38–120	0.095–0.30	400–600	
1 diopside in eclogite	56	0.065	862	
Ultramafic Inclusions				
7 peridotites	31–730	0.4–4.5	140–450	Stueber and Murthy (1966a)
1 eclogite	716	7.5	95	
3 garnet–peridotites	940	1.7	540	
13 eclogites	700–17,700	3–83	176–433	Heier and Compston (1966)
St. Paul's Rocks				
6 peridotites	99–1450	0.25–1.70	400–1000	Hart (1964)

The K contents and the K/Rb ratios in a number of ultramafic rocks derived from the mantle are shown in a summary form in Table 11.9, which includes alpine peridotites and ultramafic inclusions (Stueber and Murthy, 1966a), a suite of eclogites from volcanic environments (Heier and Compston, 1966), a series of mylonitized peridotites from St. Paul's rocks (Hart, 1964), and an alpine peridotite from Japan (Hart and coworkers, 1965).

If we include the data on basalts, meteorites, and the average K/Rb ratio for the crust, for comparison, a general grouping of the K/Rb ratios in the various types of samples is as given in Table 11.10.

With the exception of some samples from St. Paul's rocks, the K/Rb ratios in a variety of mantle-derived ultramafic rocks and eclogitic inclusions range from about 200 to 500. Comparison of these ratios with those of basalts brings out two important features regarding the K/Rb ratios in ultramafic rocks and eclogites.

TABLE 11.10 K/Rb Ratios in Terrestrial Rocks and Meteorites

Samples	General Range of K/Rb Ratio
Mantle Derivatives	
Alpine type ultramafic rocks	200–500[a]
Ultramafic inclusions in basalts, Kimberlite pipes, etc.	100–550[b]
Oceanic tholeiites	1400[c]
Alkali basalts and continental tholeiites	$\lesssim$500[c]
Meteorites	
Chondrites	300[c]
High calcium achondrites	1650[c]
Carbonaceous chondrites	250[d]
Average for the crust	230[e]

[a] Hart et al. (1965); Stueber & Murthy (1966a).
[b] Stueber and Murthy (1966a); Heier and Compston (1966); Hart et al. (1965).
[c] Data summarized in Tatsumoto, Hedge and Engel (1965).
[d] Murthy and Compston (1965).
[e] Heier and Adams (1964).

Firstly, their K/Rb ratios are not as high as those found in oceanic tholeiites. In general, the ultramafic and eclogitic K/Rb ratios scatter about the value for alkali basalts and the average crustal value. Secondly, no systematic variation of the K/Rb ratio is found although the K contents range over three orders of magnitude. These relations are shown in Fig. 11.2 wherein the K/Rb ratios are plotted against K content for alpine peridotites, ultramafic inclusions, and eclogite inclusions as well as basalts and meteorites.

The fact that the K/Rb ratios in a number of eclogitic inclusions are similar to those of ultramafic rocks is probably significant. Eclogites have a gross composition similar to that of basalts whereas the alpine peridotites as well as the ultramafic inclusions are generally regarded as residuals or crystal accumulates. The overall similarity in the K/Rb ratios of many types of mantle-derived ultramafic rocks has been interpreted by Stueber and Murthy (1966a) to mean that there is a zone in the upper mantle characterized by low K/Rb ratios somewhat similar to those found in ultramafic rocks. If the primitive mantle material is characterized by K/Rb ratios of the order of 1500 or greater as suggested by Gast, what is the nature of the differentiation process that led to the formation of the zone in the upper mantle with much lower K/Rb ratios?

The answer to the above question can in principle come from chemical and isotopic studies on various mantle materials, despite our ignorance of specific initial boundary conditions for the chemical composition of the earth's mantle. Based on the crustal abundances of K, U, Th and certain other elements, and material balance considerations, Birch (1965) suggested that the upper mantle must have been differentiated from the primitive mantle material very early in the history of the earth, concomitant with core formation and associated fractional melting of the primitive mantle. The upper mantle material enriched in various lithophile and radioactive elements is considered to have been produced in this primitive differentiation process. Continental crust formed by further fractionation of some elements from such an upper mantle.

The formation of the upper mantle in this primitive differentiation process was presumably by the upward migration of low-temperature melting fluid phases of the original mantle material. If the geo-

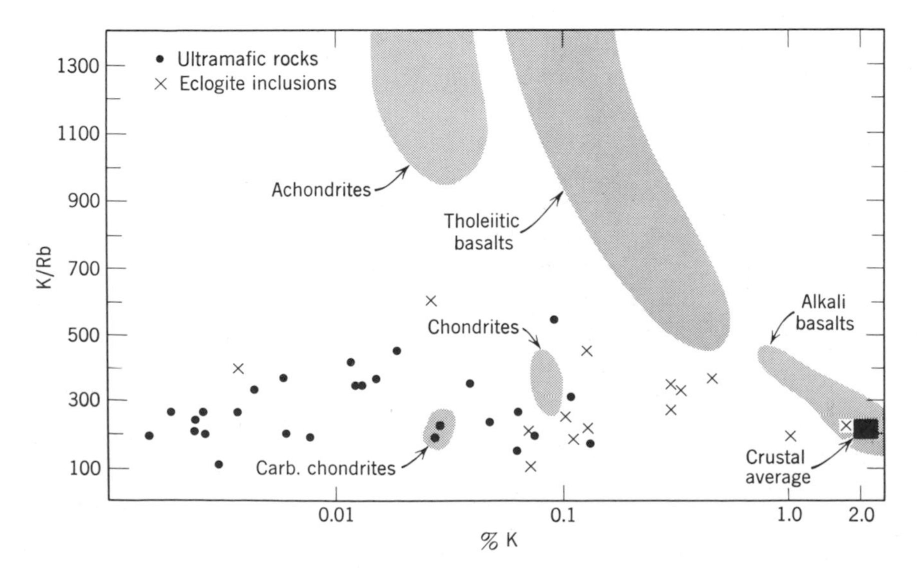

Fig. 11.2 K/Rb ratios in rocks and meteorites.

chemical considerations with respect to the distribution of K and Rb discussed earlier are generally valid, we can expect that an overall K/Rb ratio lower than that of the original mantle will be established in the upper mantle. Admittedly, this is an oversimplified picture and there might well be many deviations from it, but the general idea of an alkali element enriched upper mantle with lower K/Rb ratios and a lower mantle with high K/Rb ratios may be a reasonable one.

The Rb-Sr isotopic relations in alpine peridotites have been discussed by Hurley (Chapter II-IV). The Sr^{87}/Sr^{86} ratios in alpine peridotites are higher than those of basalts and require an association with higher Rb/Sr ratios than those of basalts. Whether such higher Rb/Sr ratios were established before or after these rocks were isolated as residuals is still an open question. But the residual nature of the alpine peridotites appears almost certain. Stueber and Murthy (1966b) explicitly suggested that alpine peridotites are residual in an upper mantle of the type proposed by Birch (1965) and that fractionation processes have effectively drained the alkalies from these rocks into the sialic crust. The low K/Rb ratios in alpine peridotites are considered to reflect the low K/Rb ratios established in the upper mantle by the primitive differentiation process.

The Sr^{87}/Sr^{86} ratios in ultramafic inclusions are generally similar to those of the materials in which they occur. This evidence permits a genetic relationship between basalts and these inclusions, but the alkali abundances in the ultramafic inclusions are so low that it is doubtful that they could be representative of basaltic parent material. Rather, these inclusions are probably material that is either residual or crystal cumulate in origin. Their K/Rb ratios, which are similar to those of alpine peridotites, seem to indicate that ultramafic inclusions formed in the upper mantle regions, subsequent to the primitive differentiation processes discussed earlier.

The close relationship between the continental crust and the alkali element enriched upper mantle was mentioned in connection with the origin of alpine ultramafic rocks. On the point of view that alpine peridotites are residuals in an upper mantle from which effectively a total upward removal of alkalies has taken place, a rough idea of the K/Rb ratio in such an upper mantle may be given by the K/Rb ratio of the average crust. Stueber and Murthy (1966a) suggested that the scatter of the K/Rb ratios in common igneous rocks of the crust in the range of 200 to 300 is probably a result of their derivation from an upper mantle with approximately similar K/Rb ratios. The oceanic tholeiites with high K/Rb ratios are derived, in this point of view, from less differentiated and presumably deeper sources in the mantle. The lower Sr^{87}/Sr^{86} ratios of oceanic tholeiites compared to other basalts (Hurley, Chapter II-IV) are also consistent with this interpretation.

If these generalized relationships between the various types of ultramafic rocks, eclogites, basalts, and the differentiation history of the upper mantle regions are reasonably valid, we should expect to find confirming evidence from other isotopic relations as well as fractionation patterns in some trace elements. In particular, we should expect that the alpine ultramafic rocks, ultramafic inclusions, and eclogites should show more radiogenic Pb and Sr isotopes as well as fractionation patterns towards enrichment of the light rare earth elements, compared to the oceanic tholeiites with high K/Rb ratios. Isotopic analyses of lead in these ultramafic rocks are not yet available in any measure, but the Sr^{87}/Sr^{86} ratios of these rocks are definitely more radiogenic than those of oceanic tholeiites. Similarly, Haskin and Frey (1966) found that many peridotites are relatively richer in the light rare earth elements than oceanic tholeiites. The need for more data of this kind is obvious in this connection. Even more important, the use of K/Rb ratio as a tracer for differentiation history needs to be investigated by studies of the type undertaken by Hart and co-workers (1965) to determine the effects of *P* and *T* on the fixation of K/Rb ratio, as well as the variations of K/Rb ratios in individual mineral phases from mantle-derived rocks. Whether the K/Rb ratios in ultramafic rocks and eclogites should be considered characteristic of an upper mantle differentiated early in the history of the earth, and, whether the basaltic K/Rb ratio variations reflect the extent of differentiation of these basalts from a grossly homogeneous mantle rather than partial fusion effects from heterogeneous mantle materials remains at present a moot question. Also, whether the close similarity between the K/Rb ratios of ultramafic rocks, eclogites, carbonaceous chondrites, chondrites and a variety of crustal rocks is simply fortuitous remains to be explored.

12. *Petrogenesis of Ultramafic and Ultrabasic Rocks*

I. INTRODUCTION

P. J. Wyllie

Confident statements and cautious deductions about the petrogenesis of ultramafic and ultrabasic rocks are scattered throughout this book, and in this chapter many of these are compared and tested against each other, and against O'Hara's pyroxene grid (Fig. 12.4). Before we consider the rocks themselves, MacGregor, in Section II, considers the phase relationships in the system CaO-MgO-Al_2O_3-SiO_2 as a guide to the mineralogy of the upper mantle from which the ultramafic and ultrabasic rocks are derived. His approach is necessarily similar to that used by O'Hara in Chapter 1-II-B-1, and his Fig. 12.2 bears comparison with O'Hara's Fig. 1.3. He also refers to the other sources of information about the composition and mineralogy of the upper mantle, including heat flow and the K, U, and Th contents of rocks (Chapter 11-II); petrological evidence from materials derived from the upper mantle such as basalts, alpine-type ultramafic rocks (Chapters 5, 6, and 7), and nodules in basalts and kimberlites (Chapter 10); and meteorites which have been omitted from this book except for the isotope review by Taylor in Chapter 11-III and brief considerations by Murthy and Stueber in Chapter 11-V. He concludes that the upper mantle is composed of a two-pyroxene peridotite with a spinel facies overlying a garnet facies. A plagioclase facies appears to be unlikely except in regions of unusually high heat flow, as suggested by Kuno in Chapter 10-III. MacGregor concludes that phase boundaries between the peridotite facies cannot account for the seismic discontinuities in the upper 200 km of the mantle, and he suggests that variations in the Al_2O_3 content of the pyroxenes may provide adequate explanation. A recent review of the mineralogy of the mantle has been given by Ringwood (1966).

In Section III O'Hara develops in more detail some aspects of the mineral facies described in Chapter 1-II and considers its application to mantle mineralogy. He shows how the mineralogy of two fixed ultrabasic compositions vary with pressure and temperature as a result of the changing solubility of Al_2O_3 in the pyroxenes, and the changing solubility of coexisting pyroxenes in each other. The mineralogy of the upper mantle may be quite sensitive to changes in bulk composition. O'Hara has devised a petrogenetic grid using two compositional parameters of clinopyroxenes coexisting with orthopyroxene and olivine in an Al_2O_3-saturated environment. Any analyzed clinopyroxene satisfying these conditions can be plotted on the grid giving an estimate of the pressure and temperature of equilibration. O'Hara plots the compositions of 65 analyzed clinopyroxenes from ultramafic rocks of two groups: peridotites from layered intrusions and alpine-type intrusions; and peridotites occurring as nodules in basalt, kimberlite, and other breccia pipes. From the estimated pressures and temperatures so derived, O'Hara enumerates a number of important conclusions in Section III-D.

In Section IV, Wyllie reviews the petrogenesis of ultrabasic rocks with particular reference to the conclusions reached by contributors to this volume.

II. MINERALOGY OF MODEL MANTLE COMPOSITIONS

I. D. MacGregor

A. Introduction

At present, there is no direct means of sampling the earth's mantle. Thus, conclusions bearing on its composition and phase assemblages are indirect. However, seismological, heat flow, geochemical, and petrological studies converge to the conclusion that the mantle is ultramafic. High-temperature and pressure-experimental petrology allows an evaluation of the ultramafic model. The degree of correspondence between interpretations from the geophysical, geochemical, petrological, and experimental approaches serves as an estimate of the validity of any chosen composition.

B. Indirect Studies of Mantle Composition

There are currently four independent methods of obtaining an estimate of the composition of the mantle. These are seismology, terrestrial heat flow, cosmic and terrestrial geochemistry, and field and experimental petrology.

Seismological studies (Gutenberg, 1959) have made it possible to define the gross boundaries of the mantle and indicate its structure in terms of density variations (Birch, 1964). Assuming that the mantle is compositionally homogeneous, any chosen composition should show density discontinuities with increasing pressure corresponding to those shown by the seismic model. The number of rock compositions that have seismic velocities equal to those observed for the upper mantle is limited to ultramafic and eclogitic compositions (Birch, 1960; Simmons, 1964b). Further, Birch (1964) indicates that ordinary dunites, bronzitites, diabases and eclogites, with from 8 to 10 weight per cent FeO, roughly follow the expected density distribution in the lower mantle. A compositionally zoned mantle could also account for the observed seismic discontinuities, but phase changes would still result in density variations within any single unit.

Empirical observation of the earth's surface heat flow indicate a rough equality for the heat flow in the oceanic and continental areas (Birch, 1964). This requires an equivalent heat generation beneath continental and oceanic areas and thus, an equivalence of the average content of the radioactive nuclides beneath a section of continental and oceanic crust. Since the concentrations of radioactive nuclides in the continental crust account for nearly all the continental heat flow, and their concentration in the oceanic crust accounts for from 5 to 10 per cent of the oceanic heat flow, the K, U, and Th content of the subcontinental and suboceanic mantle are different. The more differentiated subcontinental mantle is probably also more impoverished in the low melting silicates rich in Na_2O, K_2O, CaO, FeO, Al_2O_3, and H_2O than its suboceanic counterpart. The absolute heat flow values say little about the major element chemistry of the mantle.

Making the assumption that the chondritic meteorites are representative of the average cosmic material, Urey (1952), MacDonald (1959a), and Ringwood (1959) have proposed a carbonaceous chondrite composition as a reasonable model for the composition of the earth (see Taylor, Chapter 11-III). This conclusion is supported by the observation that the rate of heat loss at the earth's surface does not differ significantly from the rate of heat production of a chondritic earth (MacDonald, 1959b). Further support is given by Kovach and Anderson's (1965) conclusion that the astronomical data on the terrestrial planets may be satisfied, assuming that they have a gross chemical similarity. Limitations to this hypothesis are that the minor element distribution in the crust of the earth are not entirely consistent with a chondritic model (Gast, 1960). In particular, the crust and upper mantle do not contain K, Rb, Cs, U, Ba, and Sr in the proportions found in chondrites. The alkali metals are depleted with respect to U, Sr, and Ba. This leads to one of two conclusions. Either the earth is not chondritic, or dfferentiation of a chondritic parent into the crust, mantle, and core has resulted in the concentration of U, Sr, and Ba in the crust with K, Rb, and Cs being concentrated in the lower mantle. The latter conclusion is supported by MacDonald (1959b) who finds that, for a differentiated chondritic earth, approximately one third of the radioactive heat sources must be deeper than 600 km. The differentiation of a chondritic earth to give a crust, mantle and metallic core would yield a mantle close to a peridotite in composition (Ringwood, 1959). Birch (1965) argues that large-scale melting is the process whereby a homogeneous chondritic earth has evolved into the three main divisions now seen. The effectiveness of the separation process would determine the degree of chemical homogeneity of the mantle. Assuming that the present mantle is the solid residuum from partial melting, the mantle may vary in composition with depth to reflect the dependence of the minimum melting composition on pressure.

A further method of estimating mantle compositions is by the study of rocks thought to have been derived from subcrustal depths. Spinel peridotites are found in the cores of large mountain belts (Hess, 1955a), in deep fault zones, and as nodules in alkali basalts (Chapter 10). Their wide distribution, the evidence of solid intrusion (Smith and MacGregor, 1962; Green, 1964a) and their world-wide chemical homogeneity (Ross, Foster and Myers, 1954) has led to the conclusion that they are samples of the upper mantle. Moreover, their gross compositional similarity to the garnet peridotite nodules in kimberlite pipes, believed to have come from depths in excess of 120 km (Davis and Boyd, 1965), and to the chondrites has lent further support to this hypothesis. However, recent studies (Carter, 1965; Frechen, 1963; Challis, 1965a) have indicated that the spinel peridotites are probably the solid products of fractional crystallization from a mafic magma and are, thus, not primary. Green and Ringwood (1963) constructed a model mantle composition on the basis that it is composed of the sum, of some proportion, of the liquid (basalt) and crystal precipitate (dunite) phase assemblage. Although the approach is valid, the choice of the correct ratio is difficult, and correlation of the composition of the chosen ratio with other peridotites, themselves likely differentiates, does not constitute proof for that ratio. However, the petrological approach does limit the composition of the upper mantle to lie between a basalt and a peridotite, primarily within the five-component system MgO-CaO-FeO-Al_2O_3-SiO_2. The proportion of these oxides is, at present, not clear nor is their variation laterally or with depth.

An understanding of the chemistry of the mantle as it is today, thus, depends on estimates of the original nature of the primordial earth and of the differentiation processes that have resulted in its present structure. In terms of the major components, it would appear that a chondritic model for the primitive earth is, at present, the most acceptable. Birch (1964) proposes a model for the evolution of the earth and discusses the main processes resulting in the presently observed structures. Differentiation of the primordial earth by partial melting is the most important process. The homogeneity of the mantle depends on the nature and efficiency of this process. In general, there would be a tendency for the low-melting fraction, richer in Na_2O, K_2O, CaO, Al_2O_3, CO_2 and H_2O, to be concentrated toward the surface, leaving behind a refractory residue of Mg/Fe silicates or oxides. Local irregularities may result where trapped magmas have not migrated completely to the surface.

C. The Subsolidus System $CaO\text{-}MgO\text{-}Al_2O_3\text{-}SiO_2$

Experimental investigations are usually restricted to only a few components of the real mantle system. The choice of components has been such as to approximate natural peridotites and basalts. The components MgO, FeO, CaO, Al_2O_3, and SiO_2 are the most abundant oxides in these rocks. Experiments in this five-component system would, thus, be valid for a chondritic or petrological model. Variations in the abundance of these oxides may account for all compositions from a basalt to a peridotite and, presumably, the parental material. Since the number of high-pressure experiments including FeO as a component are limited, a summary of the four-component system $MgO\text{-}CaO\text{-}Al_2O_3\text{-}SiO_2$ will be given. For most silicate minerals, FeO and MgO may then be regarded as isomorphic components.

Because the apparatus presently available is limited to experiments below 200 kb, the following discussion is limited primarily to the upper mantle. In this depth zone, rocks of peridotite and gabbro composition will be composed of varying proportions of the following minerals: olivine, orthopyroxene, clinopyroxene, garnet, plagioclase, and spinel. For all but a few compositions, olivine will always be present as a phase. Thus, portrayal of the four-component system as a ternary projection from olivine (Fig. 12.1) will adequately display the phase relationships of likely mantle compositions under varying conditions.

Green and Ringwood (1963) have indicated that natural peridotites occur in three distinct mineral facies:

1. Olivine and/or orthopyroxene and/or clinopyroxene + plagioclase (plagioclase peridotite)
2. Olivine and/or orthopyroxene and/or clinopyroxene + spinel (spinel peridotite) and
3. Olivine and/or orthopyroxene and/or clinopyroxene + garnet (garnet peridotite).

Because of limited solid solution between ortho- and clinopyroxene at pressures and temperatures believed to occur in the upper mantle, compositions having both clino- and orthopyroxene as coexisting phases are the most likely representatives. The mineral facies in ultrabasic rocks are considered in more detail in Chapter 1-II.

A number of important reactions are critical in defining the boundaries between the three main peridotite types, and in defining the effects of temperature and pressure on the mutual solid solubility of components in the constituent minerals. These may be listed as follows. The important reactions defining the break between the plagioclase (Figs. 12.1*b* and 12.1*c*) and spinel peridotite (Fig. 12.1*d*) are:

$$\begin{aligned} 2\,Mg_2SiO_4 + 2\,CaAl_2Si_2O_8 &= CaMgSi_2O_6{\cdot}nCaAl_2SiO_6 \\ &+ 2\,MgSiO_3{\cdot}nMgAl_2SiO_6 \\ &+ (1-n)\,MgAl_2O_4 \\ &+ (1-n)\,CaAl_2Si_2O_8\ (n < 1) \quad (1) \end{aligned}$$

(Kushiro and Yoder, 1964c; 1965)

and

$$2\,Mg_2SiO_4 + CaAl_2Si_2O_8 = CaMgSi_2O_6 + 2\,MgSiO_3 + MgAl_2O_4 \quad (2)$$

(Kushiro and Yoder, 1964c; 1965)

and for more siliceous compositions

$$2\,CaAl_2Si_2O_8 + 4MgSiO_3 = CaMgSi_2O_6 \cdot CaAl_2SiO_6 + 2\,MgSiO_3 \cdot MgAl_2SiO_6 + 2\,SiO_2 \quad (3)$$

(Kushiro and Yoder, 1964d)

The critical reactions defining the boundary between the spinel and garnet peridotite (Figs. 12.1*d* and 12.1*e*) are

$$4\,MgSiO_3 + MgAl_2O_4 = Mg_3Al_2Si_3O_{12} + Mg_2SiO_4, \quad (4)$$

(MacGregor, 1964)

$$2\,CaMgSi_2O_6 + MgAl_2O_4 = Ca_2MgAl_2Si_3O_{12} + Mg_2SiO_4 \quad (5)$$

(MacGregor, 1965a)

and the suite of reactions for varying ratios of enstatite and diopside. An important result of this experiment was that for all compositions within the four-phase spinel peridotite field, the first garnet to appear has the molecular composition $Pyrope_{87}$ $Grossular_{13}$. This garnet shows little variation of composition with temperature or pressure. The small range of garnet chemistry is reflected in the small range of compositions found in natural garnet peridotites (O'Hara and Mercy, 1963). The wide stability field of this garnet results in the formation of the two four-phase assemblages forsterite + enstatite solid solution + garnet + spinel and forsterite + diopside solid solution + garnet + spinel (Figs. 12.1*e* and 12.1*f*). Complete solid solution along the garnet join must occur at pressures in excess of 50 kb at temperatures of about 1000°C (Fig. 12.1*h*). It is also important to note that for all compositions within the four-phase spinel peridotite field, five phases occur at the boundary between the garnet and spinel peridotite field. In a four-component system, this represents a univariant situation so that for a fixed temperature the transition from a spinel to a garnet peridotite occurs at a fixed pressure for all compositions in the field.

The control of temperature and pressure on the solubility of Al_2O_3 in the pyroxenes is governed by different reactions in the three different peridotite facies. In the plagioclase peridotite field, solid solution of Al_2O_3 in the pyroxenes is indicated by reactions of the Type (1) and (3). Kushiro (1965) has shown that on the join diopside-anorthite, the Al_2O_3 solubility of the diopside increases with increasing pressure at constant temperature. This trend probably applies to both pyroxenes in the four-phase plagioclase peridotite field.

Solid solution of Al_2O_3 in pyroxenes of the four-phase spinel peridotite are governed by combinations of the following two reactions:

$$CaAl_2SiO_6 + Mg_2SiO_4 = CaMgSi_2O_6 + MgAl_2O_4 \quad (6)$$

(MacGregor, 1965b)

and

$$MgAl_2SiO_6 + Mg_2SiO_4 = 2\,MgSiO_3 + MgAl_2O_4 \quad (7)$$

Both reactions have a negative Δv and go to the right with increasing pressure, so that the Al_2O_3 content of pyroxenes in the spinel peridotites will decrease with increasing pressure, at constant temperature. In the four-phase garnet peridotite, reactions of the type (8) govern the Al_2O_3 solubility in the pyroxenes

$$3\,MgSiO_3\chi Al_2O_3 = \chi Mg_3Al_2Si_3O_{12} + 3(1-\chi)\,MgSiO_3 \quad (8)$$

This reaction also has a negative ΔV and proceeds to the right with increasing pressure (Boyd and England, 1964a). Reaction (8) is significantly more pressure-dependent than reactions (6) or (7).

The mutual solubility of enstatite in diopside has been investigated at 1 atmosphere (Boyd and Schairer, 1964), 20 kb (Kushiro, 1964a) and 30 kb (Davis and Boyd, 1965). For the temperatures and pressures expected in the upper mantle, it is evident that pressure has very little effect

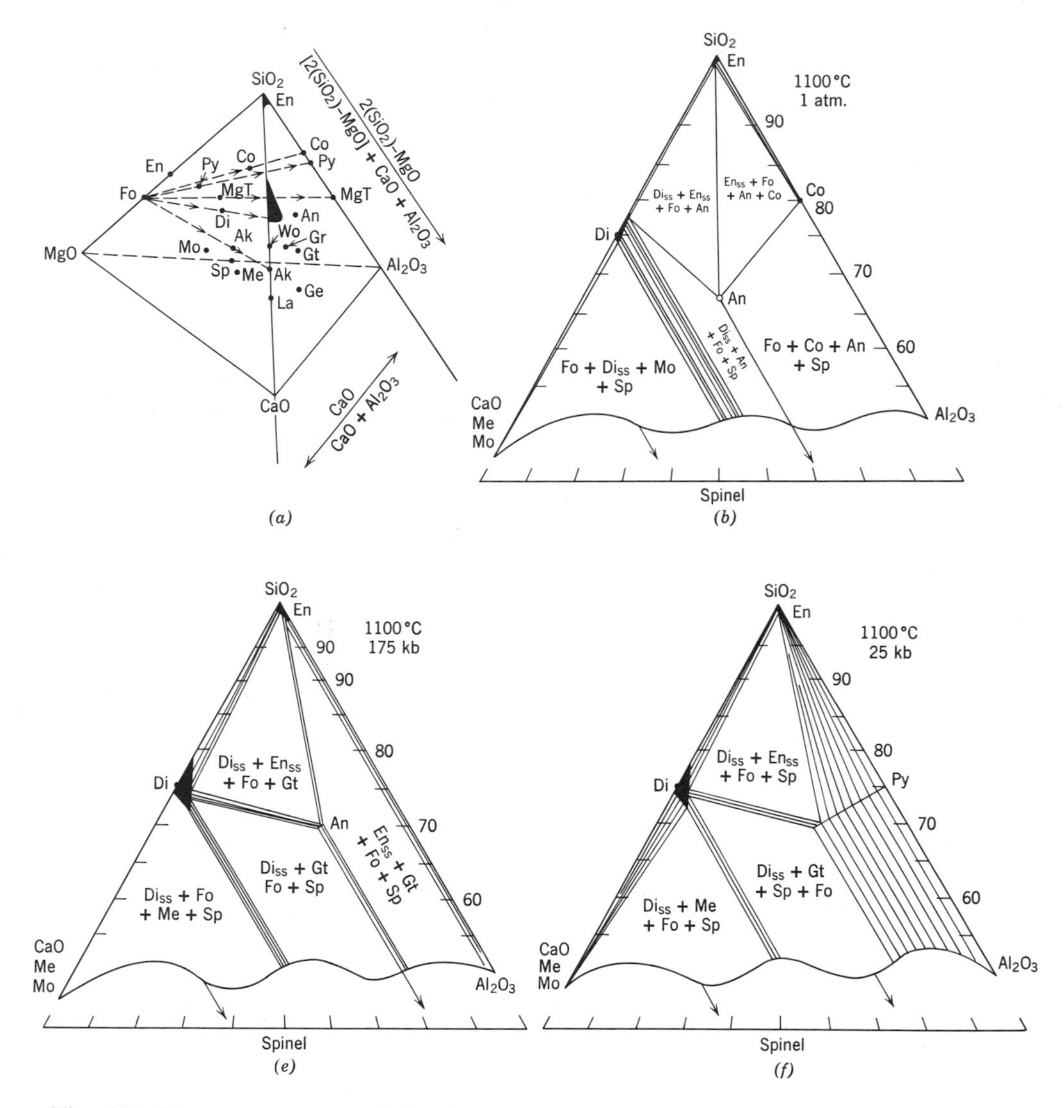

Fig. 12.1 Ternary projection of the four-component system CaO-MgO-Al_2O_3-SiO_2 onto the CaO-Al_2O_3-SiO_2 plane from forsterite (Mg_2SiO_4) composition. Figures (*b*) to (*h*) give a series of isothermal sections, at 1100°C, to indicate the variations of phase assemblages with pressure. Figures (*b*) and (*d*) will require modification as a result of work in progress (personal communications from Kushiro and Yoder, and from J. F. Hays).

on the pyroxene mutual solubility, and solid solutions on the join enstatite-diopside are primarily a function of temperature. It should be added that an increasing Al_2O_3 content of the coexisting pyroxenes results in a continuous decrease of their mutual solubility.

The upper pressure limit of the garnet peridotite has not yet been experimentally determined. However, a number of experiments on analogous systems, such as the germanates, have been conducted. It has been shown that, with increasing pressure, the isomorphic changes that might occur involve the formation of coesite (Boyd and England, 1960d), stishovite (Stishov, 1963; Sclar, Young, Carrison and Schwartz, 1962), spinel structures (Da-

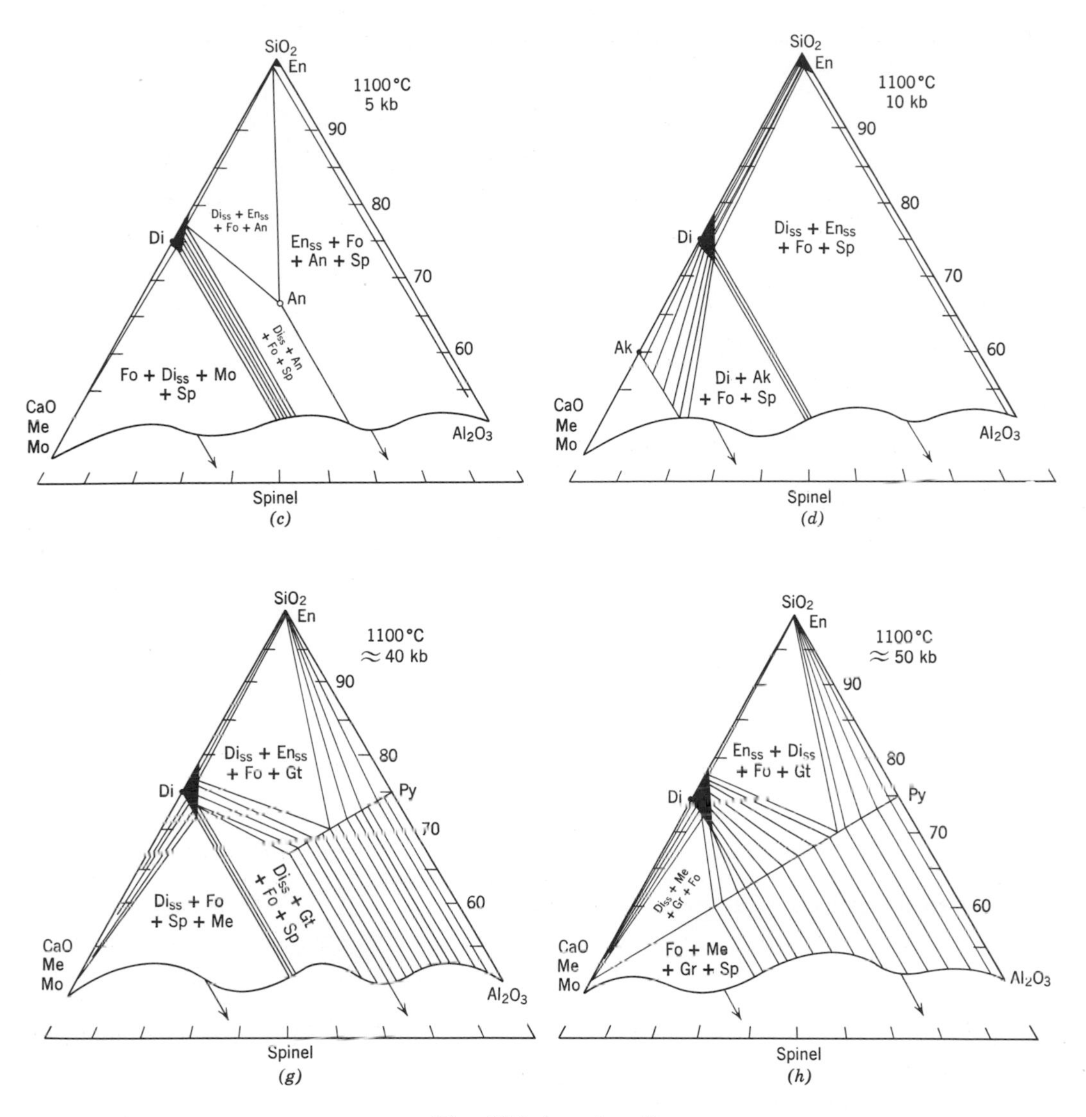

Fig. 12.1 (*continued*)

chille and Roy, 1960a; Ringwood and Seabrook, 1962; Akimoto, Fujisawa, and Katsura, 1965), R_2O_3 structures, and garnet structures (Ringwood and Seabrook, 1963).

Ringwood and Seabrook (1963) present a discussion of the likely sequence of reactions for Mg-silicates with increasing depth beyond the garnet peridotite facies involving the formation of these phases. Solid solution effects will spread these reactions rather continuously over a large depth zone. Ringwood and Seabrook (1963) suggest that reactions of this type are responsible for the steep seismic velocity gradient between 400 and 900 km. Ringwood (1966) has presented a detailed review of the problem.

From the presently available experimental data in the system CaO-MgO-Al_2O_3-SiO_2, it is possible to construct the stability limits of the three main peridotite facies (Fig. 12.2). The variation of the mineralogy of an ultramafic mantle at any single locality with depth depends upon the am-

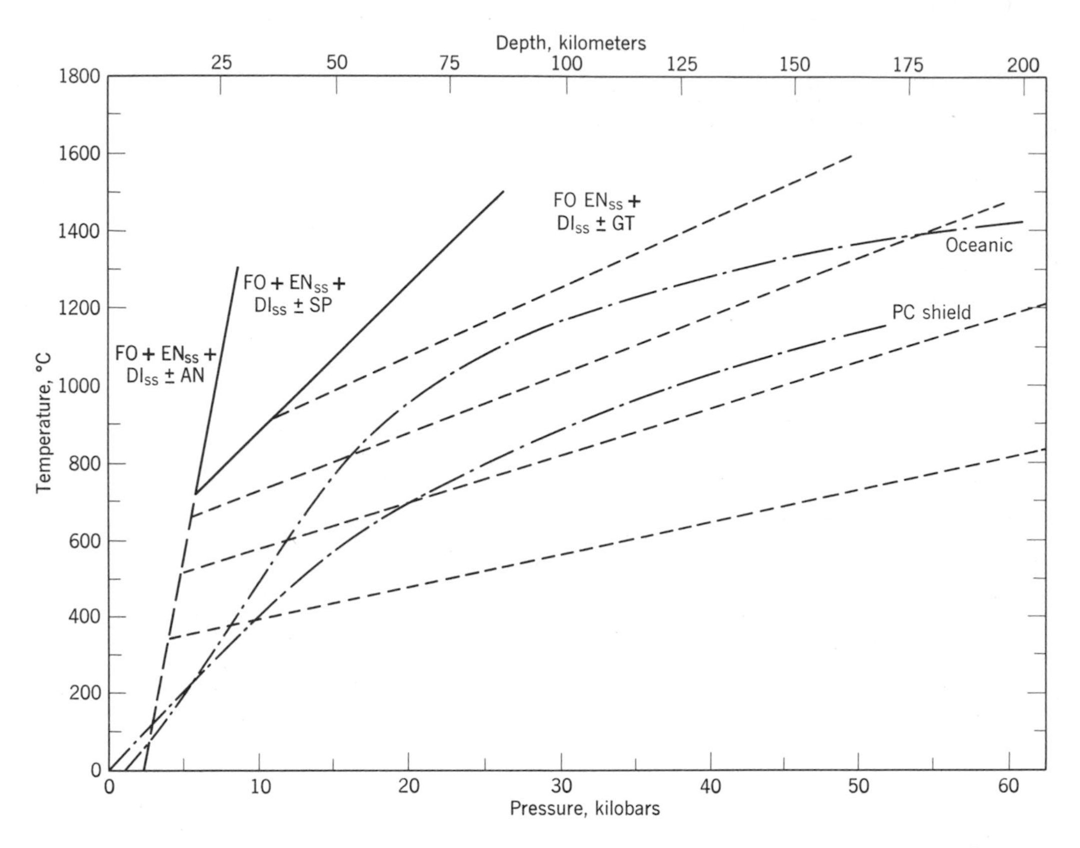

Fig. 12.2 Temperature-pressure section illustrating the variation of the phase assemblages for two-pyroxene peridotite with depth (cf. Fig. 1.3). Continuous lines: experimentally determined boundaries; dashed lines: suggested phase boundaries; dash (small) lines: Al_2O_3 isopleths; dash-dot lines: geothermal gradients.

bient geothermal gradient and with the assumed composition. Because of the intersection of the equilibrium curves for the reactions (1) and (2) and pyroxene + spinel reactions of the type (4) and (5) in the two pyroxene field, at an invariant point (Fig. 12.2), all compositions in the volume occupied by the intersection of the three four-phase volumes:

1. Forsterite + enstatite solid solution + diopside solid solution + plagioclase.
2. Forsterite + enstatite solid solution + diopside solid solution + spinel.
3. Forsterite + enstatite solid solution + diopside solid solution + garnet will be governed by the equilibrium curves shown in Fig. 12.2.

It should be added that the following reaction

$$Mg_2SiO_4 + CaAl_2Si_2O_8 = CaMg_2Al_2Si_3O_{12} \quad (9)$$

(Kushiro and Yoder, 1965)

also intersects this invariant point. The main body of ultramafic rocks fall within the above compositional volume so that the equilibrium curves of Fig. 12.2 may be used as a guide to expected phase changes in an ultramafic mantle. There still remains a question as to the slope of the reaction boundary between the plagioclase and garnet peridotites on the low temperature and pressure side of the invariant point (Fig. 12.2). Kushiro and Yoder (1965) have suggested that it follows an extension of the plagioclase to spinel peridotite boundary. However, a linear extension of curves 1 or 2 is not possible and some other slope must be postulated.

The most significant point in Fig. 12.2 is the small stability field of the spinel peridotites at high temperatures and moderately high pressures. Further, relative to expected geothermal gradients spinel peridotite is not likely to exist as a stable assemblage in the lower crust or mantle. Its presence in the cores of old mountain belts (Hess, 1955a) requires either excessively high thermal gradients during the period of active orogeny, or direct formation of spinel peridotite by fractional crystallization from basaltic magmas in large, lower, and subcrustal magma chambers. Additional evidence that the spinel peridotites are crystal fractionates (Carter, 1965; Challis, 1965a) would support the latter alternative. In this view, neither the spinel peridotite intrusions or inclusions are samples of a primitive upper mantle. The primitive composition should be more gabbroic than the average spinel peridotite.

Other compositions outside the four-phase peridotite volume will have different stability relationships. On the CaO-poor side close to the ternary $MgO-Al_2O_3-SiO_2$, the data given by Boyd and England (1963b), Fawcett (1963), and MacGregor (1964) apply. At low pressures, cordierite is a stable phase and the three- and four-phase assemblages forsterite + enstatite solid solution + cordierite (or cordierite peridotite) and forsterite + enstatite solid solution + cordierite + anorthite are stable. The stability curve for the reaction

$$5\ Mg_2SiO_4 + Mg_2Al_4Si_5O_{18} = 10\ MgSiO_3 + 2MgAl_2O_4 \quad (10)$$

(Fawcett, 1963) indicates that dry, CaO-poor peridotites should lie in the cordierite peridotite field at pressures less than 3 kb. The absence of cordierite in most diopside-free peridotites results from either a lack of equilibrium, high P_{H_2O} or a change of the stability relationships with additional components. With increasing pressure, pyrope becomes stable (Boyd and England, 1962) giving rise to the three-phase assemblage enstatite solid solution + pyrope + spinel. The coexistence of pyrope and forsterite occurs at higher pressures as the result of reaction (4). The equilibrium boundary between the CaO-poor spinel and garnet peridotites occurs at higher pressures than that for compositions in the four-phase peridotite field (MacGregor, 1965a). Increasing pressure results in the replacement of the four-phase field forsterite + enstatite solid solution + garnet + spinel by two smaller three-phase fields forsterite + enstatite solid solution + garnet and forsterite + garnet + spinel (Fig. 12.1*e* and 12.1*f*).

Compositions such as the melilite basalts on the CaO-rich side of the four-phase peridotite will exhibit a new set of relationships. In this field the phases monticellite, merwinite, melilite solid solutions, Ca-tschemak molecule, anorthite, wollastonite, and grossular are present and may coexist in different combinations with the normal peridotite phases, forsterite, diopside solid solution, garnet, and spinel.

Considering an isothermal section at 1100°C (Figs. 12.1*b* and 12.1*c*), forsterite + diopside solid solution + spinel will coexist with monticellite at low pressures (<7 kb); increasing pressure results in the breakdown of monticellite (Kushiro and Yoder, 1964) with the formation of the two four-phase volumes forsterite + diopside solid solution + spinel + melilite solid solution and forsterite + spinel + merwinite + melilite solid solution (Fig. 12.1*d*). At higher pressures (greater than 15 kb), melilite solid solutions break down by the following reactions:

$$2\ Ca_2MgSi_2O_7 = CaMgSi_2O_6 + Ca_3MgSi_2O_8 \quad (11)$$

(Kushiro, 1964a)

and

$$CaAl_2Si_2O_8 + Ca_2Al_2SiO_7 = Ca_3Al_2Si_3O_{12} + CaAl_2SiO_6 \quad (12)$$

(J. F. Hays, personal communication)

New phase fields that arise are forsterite + diopside solid solution + merwinite and forsterite + diopside solid solution + spinel + merwinite (Fig. 12.1*e*). The complete breakdown of the pyroxene spinel join (above approximately 50 kb) gives rise to the two-phase assemblages forsterite + diopside solid solution + garnet + merwinite and forsterite + garnet + spinel + merwinite (Fig. 12.1*h*). Experimental data bearing on diopside solid solutions in this volume are given by Clark, Schairer, and de Neufville (1962) and Kushiro (1964c, 1965). At 20 kb, diopside forms a continuous solid solution series with Ca-tschermak molecule (Clark, Schairer and de Neufville, 1962). The Ca-tschermak molecule has a stability field restricted to high temperatures at low and high pressures with a minimum temperature stability of 1045°C at approximately 15.5 kb (J. F. Hays, personal communication). Thus, continuous solid solution between diopside and the Ca-tschermak molecule may only be expected in this field. Experimental data on the join enstatite-wollastonite (Kushiro, 1964c) indicate discontinuous solid solution between diopside and wollastonite at 20 kb.

Compositions on the SiO_2 and Al_2O_3-rich side of the four-phase peridotites are important in the understanding of gabbroic compositions. At low pressures, the phase relationships for the normal four-phase peridotites prevail. At temperatures in excess of the invariant point (Fig. 12.2), reactions (1), (2), and (3), which mark the boundary between the plagioclase and spinel peridotite, result in the division of the tetrahedra, by the plane diopside solid solution + enstatite solid solution + spinel, into forsterite free and forsterite-bearing assemblages. On the forsterite free side, the assemblage diopside solid solution + enstatite solid solution + spinel + anorthite exists till the first appearance of garnet [reaction (9)]. At this stage, the assemblage diopside solid solution + enstatite solid solution + spinel + garnet is stable. At temperatures below the invariant point (Fig. 12.2), the plagioclase peridotite passes directly into the diopside solid solution + enstatite solid solution + garnet + spinel field. For compositions close to the diopside solid solution-garnet join the latter change is analogous to the basalt-eclogite transition. At higher pressures, enstatite reacts with anorthite (3), resulting in the formation of the new phase assemblage diopside solid solution + enstatite solid solution + garnet + quartz.

D. Additional Components

The composition of peridotites is not restricted to the four-component system CaO-MgO-Al_2O_3-SiO_2. Other components such as FeO, Cr_2O_3, Na_2O, K_2O, and TiO_2 are present. Generally all these components may be treated as dilute solutes in phases already present and no new phases will appear. In general the compositions lie within solid solution volumes which allow a wide range of compositional substitution without the addition of new phases. Exceptions that may occur are the presence of ilmenite and phlogophite in a few kimberlitic peridotite nodules. FeO is the only additional component that occurs in other than minor or trace amounts.

The effect of the addition of FeO to the four-component system is not known and no general predictions can be made from the currently available experimental work. Assuming an ideal solution, the stability of almandite (Yoder, 1955) indicates that a pyrope-almandine solid solution should be stable to lower pressure with increasing FeO (Yoder and Chinner, 1960b). Similarly, the addition of FeO as fayalite to the olivine solid solution series, results in a decrease of the pressure of the isomorphic inversion from the olivine to the spinel structure (Akimoto, Fujisawa and Katsura, 1965). However, FeO solid solution has little effect on the ortho- to clino-inversion in the enstatite-ferrosilite series (Lindsley and Boyd, 1965), and solid solution of ferrosilite in enstatite results in an increase of the lower pressure stability limit of the pyroxene solid solution (Lindsley, MacGregor and Davis, 1964). Unfortunately, it is not possible at present to indicate the effect of FeO on the subsolidus phase relationships in the quaternary CaO-MgO-Al_2O_3-SiO_2.

Little work has been done on the other additional components. However, their presence in only small amounts in ultramafic rocks suggests that they have little effect on the use of CaO-MgO-Al_2O_3-SiO_2 as a peridotite model, although reactions (4) and (5) are affected.

Little work has been done on the high pressure subsolidus relationships of natural assemblages. Kennedy (1959), Yoder and Tilley (1962), and Ringwood and Green (1964) have all worked on the basalt-eclogite transition. In each case, the transition was determined at only one temperature, and was found to occur at higher pressures than indicated by the boundary between the spinel and garnet peridotite (at high temperatures) and between the plagioclase and garnet peridotite (at low temperatures) in the synthetic system. In this case, it would appear that the effect of additional components has been to increase the pressure at which a transition occurs. The relative importance of different additional components is not readily assessed, and at present, the experimental results on synthetic systems should only be used as a model for probable relative relationships rather than for obtaining absolute values of the conditions of their formation.

E. Correlation of Phase Changes in the Four-Component System with the Seismic Model

We now investigate a subsolidus peridotite model; for example, a pyrolite or a four-phase peridotite in the four-component system (Green and Ringwood, 1963) in terms of its capability to explain observed seismic discontinuities in the mantle. The seismic model indicates the following major compressional velocity discontinuities in the mantle (Gutenberg, 1959):

1. A velocity change from approximately 7 km per second to approximately 8 km per second—the Mohorovičić Discontinuity.
2. A low-velocity zone followed by a rapid increase of about 3 per cent in the *P*-wave velocity. The depth to the low-velocity zone and its seismic characteristics are not uniform over the earth (Clark and Ringwood, 1964). In general, it may be said that, beneath the oceans and continental margins, there is a slight decrease in seismic velocity in the depth range from 50 to 220 km with a subsequent velocity increase at greater depths. Beneath the Precambrian shields, the low-velocity zone is not recorded.
3. A sharp increase in seismic velocity from 400 to 900 km.

At present, it is only possible to check the petrological model to depths of approximately 200 km. The phase changes for a pyrolite model are shown in Fig. 12.2 on which are superimposed the oceanic and Precambrian shield geothermal gradients proposed by Clark and Ringwood (1964). The extrapolated boundary (Kushiro and Yoder, 1964a) between the plagioclase and garnet peridotite may possibly account for a sharp seismic break at the Mohorovičić Discontinuity beneath the oceans. This result would be true for all compositions from a two-pyroxene peridotite to a gabbro, in the latter case being the transition from a gabbro to an eclogite. Beneath continental areas, a phase change either for a peridotite or a gabbroic composition does not account for the Mohorovičić Discontinuity. It appears that a compositional boundary is called for.

The simplified model used by Ringwood, MacGregor, and Boyd (1964) to explain the increase of seismic velocities between 150 and 200 km is not valid for CaO bearing compositions. Fig. 12.2 indicates that, for a pyrolite composition, the oceanic geothermal gradient will fall below the spinel to garnet peridotite boundary curve. Factors which are now important in determining the variation of the seismic velocities with depth will be the thermal expansion and compressibility of the constituent minerals and solid solution of Al_2O_3 in the pyroxenes.

In an isochemical system there are a number of factors that may result in a variation of the seismic velocity with depth. The thermal expansion of the minerals results in a decrease of density and seismic velocity and compressibility in an increase of the seismic velocity. Using the data supplied by Birch, Schairer, and Spicer (1942), for the thermal expansion of a dunite and the compressibility of forsteritic olivine, it may be calculated that the net result of these two factors will be a continuous increase of the seismic velocity, with depth, along either a continental shield or oceanic geotherm. The increase of seismic velocity will be less pronounced where steeper thermal gradients prevail. Other factors that affect the seismic velocity are phase changes and solid solution. In the present discussion, increased solid solution of Al_2O_3 in the pyroxene will result in the disappearance of the dense garnet phase, and hence a decrease of the seismic velocity.

Data on the solid solution of Al_2O_3 in enstatite in the garnet peridotite field is given by Boyd and England (1964a). Though their absolute values are not directly applicable to a "pyrolite" model, the slopes of the Al_2O_3 isopleths are probably similar and are used in Fig. 12.2. The intersection of an oceanic thermal gradient with the Al_2O_3 isopleths (Fig. 12.2) indicate a decrease of the modal abundance of garnet, (or increased Al_2O_3 solubility in the pyroxenes) and hence, a decrease in the density and compressional seismic velocity to a depth of approximately 90 km where the Al_2O_3 isopleths and thermal gradient reach tangency. In the depth zone from 30 to 90 km, thermal expansion of the minerals and disappearance of dense garnet as a result of solution of the Al_2O_3 in pyroxenes act to decrease the seismic velocity. Beyond 90 km the decrease of the slope of the thermal gradient and the increased modal proportion of garnet with depth will result in a large, but continuous increase of the seismic velocity. The absolute values of the Al_2O_3 isopleths will define the importance of the pyroxene solid-solution effects since they control the modal proportion of garnet and will indicate the transition from a garnet peridotite to a pyroxene pyrolite field for any one composition. Beneath Precambrian shields, a similar sequence of events prevails. However, any decrease in the seismic velocity will not be quite as marked, since it is probable that only small amounts of Al_2O_3 are soluble in the pyroxenes under these conditions. Tangency between the thermal gradient and Al_2O_3 isopleth is not reached till approximately 125 km so that any increase of the seismic velocity gradient would only be expected at greater depths.

The relative and absolute relationships of this model correlate closely with the observed distribution of seismic velocities with depth. It would thus appear that on the basis of phase relationships in the system CaO-MgO-Al_2O_3-SiO_2, an ultramafic composition in the four-phase peridotite volume may be an adequate composition for the upper mantle. The effects of the additional components FeO, TiO_2, and Na_2O would then appear to be slight.

F. Conclusions

Geophysical, geochemical, and petrological arguments lead to the conclusion that the mantle is ultramafic and probably corresponds closely to a four-phase spinel or garnet peridotite in composition. The system CaO-MgO-Al_2O_3-SiO_2 has been used as an experimental model of the stability relationships of the different peridotite phase assemblages. The effect of the other additional components is not, at present, fully understood.

It was found that for a wide range of two pyroxene peridotite compositions, the reactions governing the boundaries between the different phase assemblages occur at the same temperatures and pressures. Thus phase changes in an ultramafic upper mantle are governed by a limited number of reactions. The relationship of these reaction boundaries to the earth's thermal gradient indicate the following important conclusions. For the two pyroxene peridotites, the geothermal gradient for a Precambrian shield of oceanic region does not intersect the spinel peridotite field. Spinel peridotites may only be formed as precipitates from basaltic or picritic magmas or exist in regions with an exceptionally high geothermal gradient. Phase boundaries between the different peridotite facies do not account for the seismic discontinuities observed in the upper 200 km of the mantle. However, the variation of the solid solution of Al_2O_3 in the pyroxenes, as a function of temperature and pressure, and its effect on the seismic velocity does correspond with observed seismic variations in the depth zone from 30 to 200 km. The latter correlation would indicate that a two pyroxene peridotite is an adequate representation of the composition of the upper mantle.

III. MINERAL PARAGENESES IN ULTRABASIC ROCKS

M. J. O'Hara

A. Introduction

The contents of this section develop in more detail some aspects of mineral facies in ultrabasic rocks, described earlier in Chapter 1-II. The mineralogy of a selection of natural peridotites is then used to provide estimates of pressures and temperatures of equilibration of the rocks and to locate these on the facies diagram. Figure 1.3 outlines the mineral facies as they would be for rocks with compositions in the system CaO-MgO-Al_2O_3-SiO_2, and Fig. 1.4 shows the more complex situation with H_2O present as an additional component. In order to take into account the presence of additional components in the natural rocks the univariant equilibria become multivariate transition zones; the lines in Figs. 1.3 and 1.4 are replaced by the pairs of lines (short dashes) in Figs. 12.4 and 12.6. It was pointed out in Chapter 1-II-C, that the transition zones between ultrabasic facies will be relatively narrow and only slightly displaced relative to the univariant equilibria of the simple system. Even in the simple system CaO-MgO-Al_2O_3-SiO_2, however, the effects of solid solution provide some interesting variations in mineral parageneses developed in different bulk compositions.

B. Harzburgitic, Lherzolitic (Pyrolitic), and Wehrlitic Conditions

It is an instructive exercise to draw up P-T projections similar to Fig. 1.4 for special bulk compositions in the system CaO-MgO-Al_2O_3-SiO_2 in order to illustrate certain mineralogical effects of particular interest in upper mantle studies. Fig. 12.3 represents the situation for two distinct bulk compositions. At lower temperatures these compositions crystallize as four-phase lherzolites composed of olivine, two pyroxenes, plus an Al_2O_3-rich phase. Figure 12.3 shows the facies succession from plagioclase-lherzolite, spinel-lherzolite, to garnet-lherzolite with increasing pressure. At higher temperatures, the four-phase lherzolites may become three-phase assemblages as a result of solid solution effects.

Figure 12.3*a* represents the situation for a composition: Mg_2SiO_4, 63 per cent; $MgSiO_3$, 32 per cent; $CaMgSi_2O_6$, 3 per

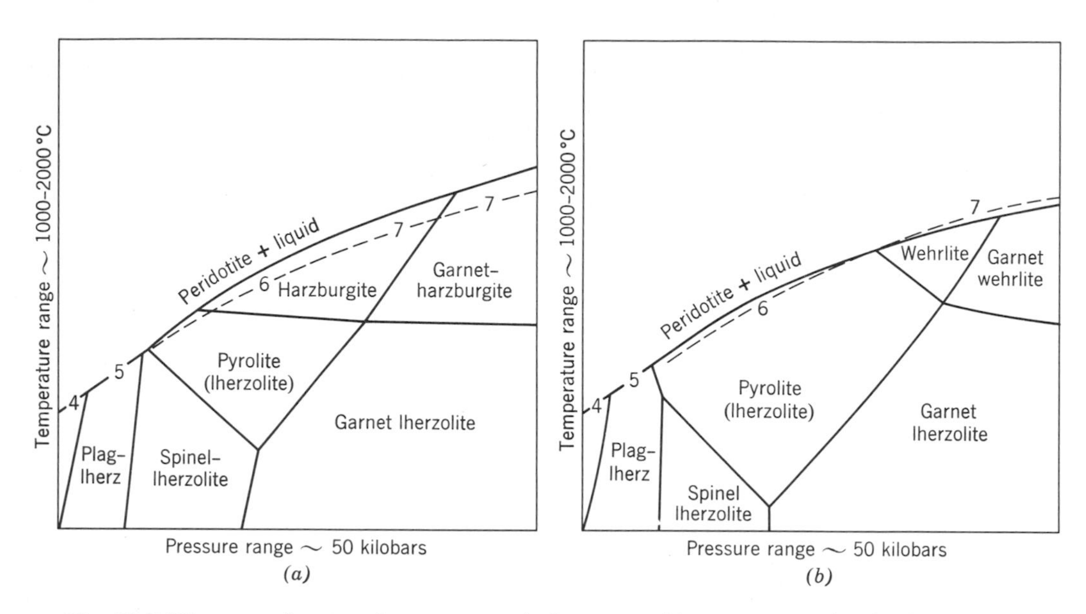

Fig. 12.3 Diagrams showing the variation of phase assemblage in particular fixed ultrabasic compositions with variations in pressure and temperature. (*a*) The composition: Mg_2SiO_4—63 per cent; $MgSiO_3$—32 per cent; $CaMgSi_2O_6$—3 per cent; Al_2O_3—2 per cent. (*b*) The composition: Mg_2SiO_4—40 per cent; $MgSiO_3$—28.5 per cent; $CaMgSi_2O_6$—28.5 per cent; Al_2O_3—3 per cent.

cent; Al_2O_3, 2 per cent (weight percentages). In this particular bulk composition at high temperatures, the independent Al_2O_3-rich phase may disappear due to the high solubility of Al_2O_3 in pyroxenes in the intermediate pressure range (discussed further in Section C) yielding a three-phase lherzolite (the "pyrolite" condition of Green and Ringwood, 1963). At higher temperatures a "harzburgitic" condition due to the solution of all potential clinopyroxene in the orthopyroxene is encountered. Figure 12.3*b* shows a similar treatment for a bulk composition Mg_2SiO_4, 40 per cent; $MgSiO_3$, 28.5 per cent; $CaMgSi_2O_6$, 28.5 per cent; Al_2O_3, 3 per cent. In suitable pressure and temperature conditions, this bulk composition shows the disappearance due to solid-solution effects, either of the independent Al_2O_3-rich phase yielding a three-phase lherzolite or "pyrolite" condition, or of the orthopyroxene, or of both the Al_2O_3-rich phase and the orthopyroxene (attainment of "wehrlitic" condition). It is vital to stress that the P-T curves bounding these conditions are not univariant facies boundaries but are critically dependent upon the bulk composition considered, and that the amounts of the phases that appear at a given boundary increase progressively away from that boundary. It is the variation in proportions of the densest phases with depth on a particular geothermal gradient, assuming a fixed upper mantle composition, which has been advanced (Ringwood et al., 1964) as an explanation of the low seismic velocity horizon at shallow depth in the upper mantle.

The attainment of pyrolitic, harzburgitic, or wehrlitic conditions has another important effect in that it raises or lowers the temperature at which melting of the ultrabasic rock will commence relative to those of equilibria 4–7 (lowers in the case of "wehrlitic" conditions at high pressures only). It also changes the composition of the first liquid to appear. This liquid now appears in a divariant or trivariant equilibrium instead of univariant equilibrium, and there is no guarantee that it will pass through the univariant composition on fractional crystallization, or that it will yield the same ultimate products of differentiation that would be obtained by similar treatment of a four-phase peridotite. Such considerations may be relevant to the problems of basalt genesis and evolution and the interpretation of ultramafic nodules in basalts. For example, if pyrolite, harzburgite, or wehrlite conditions are attained in a fixed or varying upper mantle composition at a particular depth, true xenoliths of upper mantle should reflect this, four-phase lherzolites being absent or relatively scarce in some provinces, abundant in others. Note also that "websteritic" conditions may occur at high temperatures in some pyroxenites poor in potential olivine.

C. Coexisting Pyroxenes in Four-Phase Lherzolites

Many authors have attempted to utilize the distribution of calcium, or aluminum, or of both elements together, in and between pyroxenes as a guide to their conditions of equilibration. References to much of the relevant literature are given by Onuki (1965) but other treatments have been presented by O'Hara and Mercy (1963), Green (1964a), Boyd and Macgregor (1964), and Ringwood et al., (1964). Each of these treatments appears now to be incomplete or to oversimplify the position in some respect, and the discussion given below is believed to represent a distinct advance in the basis of interpretation of these distributions.

The compositions of coexisting pyroxenes in ultrabasic assemblages in the system CMAS may be expressed as:

$$X_x\square_{1-x}{}^{[8]\text{ or }[6]}Y_y\square_{1-y}{}^{[6]}Z_z\square_{2-z}{}^{[4]}O_6$$

Where $\square$ indicates a vacant cation site. Presence of small amounts of excess MgO in the pyroxenes is then expressed as a small percentage of vacant sites in the Z position while X and Y are filled. In fact departures from the ideal formulae X. Y. Z. O_6 are small and the pyroxene compositions lie approximately in the section $CaSiO_3$-$MgSiO_3$-Al_2O_3 (CS-MS-A) of the system CMAS.

1. *$CaSiO_3$ and Al_2O_3 contents of pyroxenes.* Figure 12.5*a* illustrates the range of pyroxene solid solutions stable in the plane CS-MS-A at 30 kb at solidus temperatures (O'Hara, 1963b). At fixed temperature and pressure there are unique compositions C and P for the clinopyroxene and orthopyroxene that coexist with forsterite and the alumina-rich phase (garnet at this temperature and pressure). In the absence of the alumina-rich phase clinopyroxenes C–D may coexist with orthopyroxenes P–Q, precise compositions depending upon the bulk composition of the system. The purpose of this section is to explore the variation of the composition C with varying temperature, pressure and mineral facies, and to use this variation to further subdivide the P–T diagram of mineral facies already derived.

Two parameters of the composition of the clinopyroxene will be considered. Orthopyroxene composition variation is ignored here owing to its lower sensitivity to changes of physical conditions.

These parameters are:

$$\alpha_c = \frac{\text{wt.\% } CaSiO_3 \times 100}{\text{wt.\% } (CaSiO_3 + MgSiO_3)} \quad \text{in clinopyroxene}$$

$$\beta_c = \frac{\text{wt.\% } Al_2O_3 \times 100}{\text{wt.\% } (CaSiO_3 + MgSiO_3 + Al_2O_3)} \quad \text{in clinopyroxene}$$

Equivalent parameters in orthopyroxene are α_p and β_p. Before α and β are calculated the pyroxene composition is projected into the plane CS-MS-A from or toward SiO_2. Compositions of natural pyroxenes should be converted into this system by the convention used by O'Hara (1963a).

Figure 12.4 is a provisional projection of mineral facies and their bounding equilibria including the melting interval for natural four-phase aluminous peridotites. The P-T fields for the different mineral facies are left unlabelled for clarity, but they may be determined from Figs. 1.3 and 1.4. Superimposed on this facies diagram is a provisional grid of values of the functions α_c and β_c referring to chemical properties of the clinopyroxenes in equilibrium with olivine, orthopyroxene, and an Al_2O_3-rich phase.

In Figs. 12.5*b* and *c* natural pyroxenes are plotted on the CS-MS-A diagram (Fig. 12.5*a*) with pyroxene compositions recalculated according to the convention $CaSiO_3$ = wt $CaSiO_3$ equivalent to all CaO present in the analysis; $MgSiO_3$ = wt $MgSiO_3$ equivalent to all MgO, MnO, NiO, and FeO present; Al_2O_3 = wt Al_2O_3 equivalent to all Al_2O_3, Cr_2O_3 and Fe_2O_3 present, less an amount equivalent to any Na_2O or K_2O present. The pairs of pyroxene compositions projected in Figs. 12.5*b* and *c* are believed to be from alumina-saturated and two-pyroxene environments, and in each case their compositions correspond to the pyroxenes C and P in Fig. 12.5*a*. The wide range in their compositions

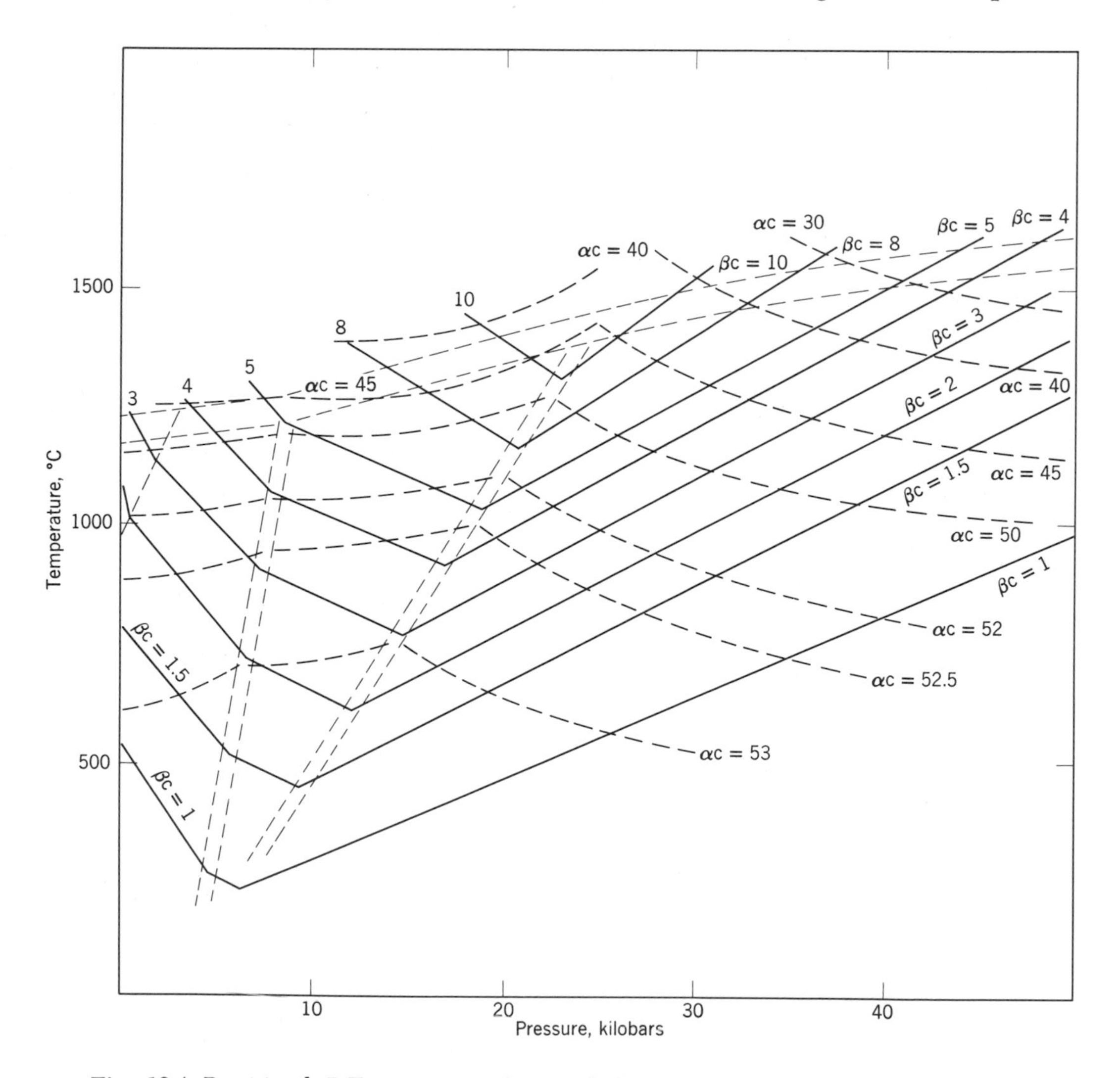

Fig. 12.4 Provisional P-T projection of mineral facies and their bounding equilibria including the melting interval, for natural aluminous four-phase peridotites (see Fig. 1.3). Superimposed is a provisional grid of values of the functions α_c and β_c (defined in text) referring to chemical properties of the clinopyroxenes in equilibrium with olivine, orthopyroxene, and an Al_2O_3-rich phase.

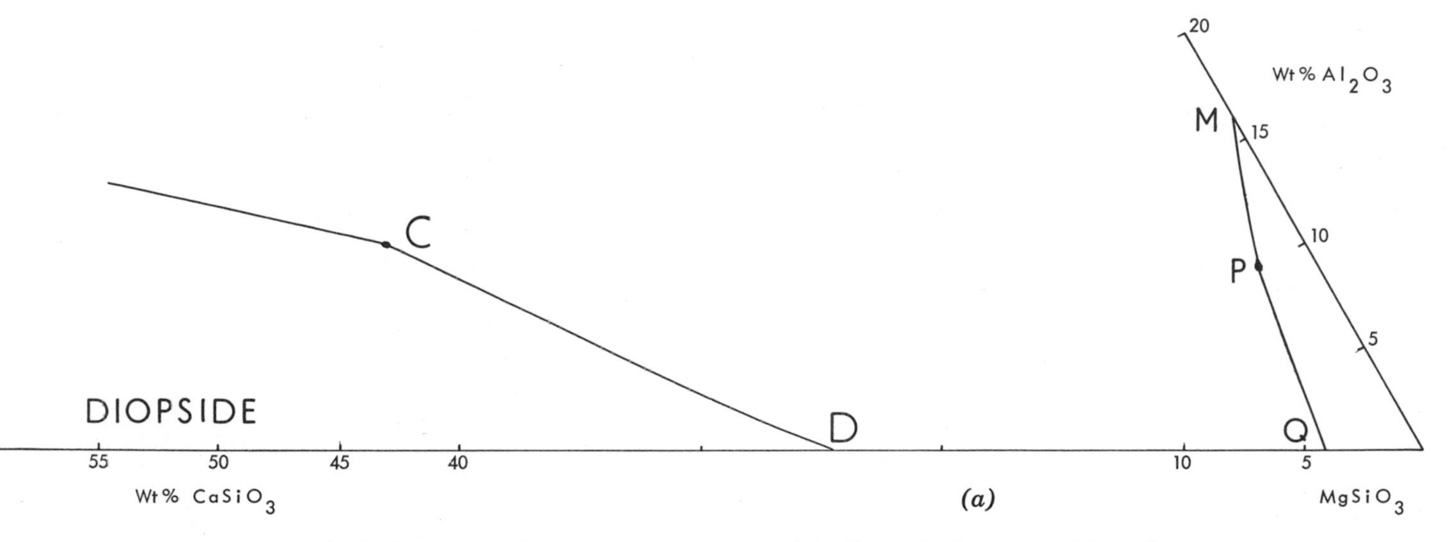

Fig. 12.5 Compositions of coexisting pyroxenes. (*a*) Part of the composition plane $CaSiO_3$-$MgSiO_3$-Al_2O_3 showing the limits of pyroxene solid solution at 30 kb and 1600°C (from O'Hara, 1963b). (*b*) and (*c*) Recalculated compositions of pyroxenes believed to be from alumina-saturated two-pyroxene rocks. Group (*b*) consists of peridotites forming parts of layered igneous masses, some of them in orogenic environments, and other alpine type peridotites. Group (*c*) consists of peridotites occurring as nodules in basalts, kimberlites, or other breccia pipes. The same symbol is applied to both clinopyroxene and orthopyroxene.

Key to projected pyroxenes:
Group (*b*) BV—Bushveld, Africa (Hess, 1949, 1952). JP—Horoman mass, Japan, primary spinel-plagioclase peridotite assemblages (Onuki, 1965, samples HM–8, 10, 11, 12). JR—Horoman mass, Japan, ?recrystallized assemblage (Onuki, 1965, sample HM–2). G—Shikoku, Japan, pyroxene of garnet-chrome diopside rock in spinel peridotite (Miyashiro

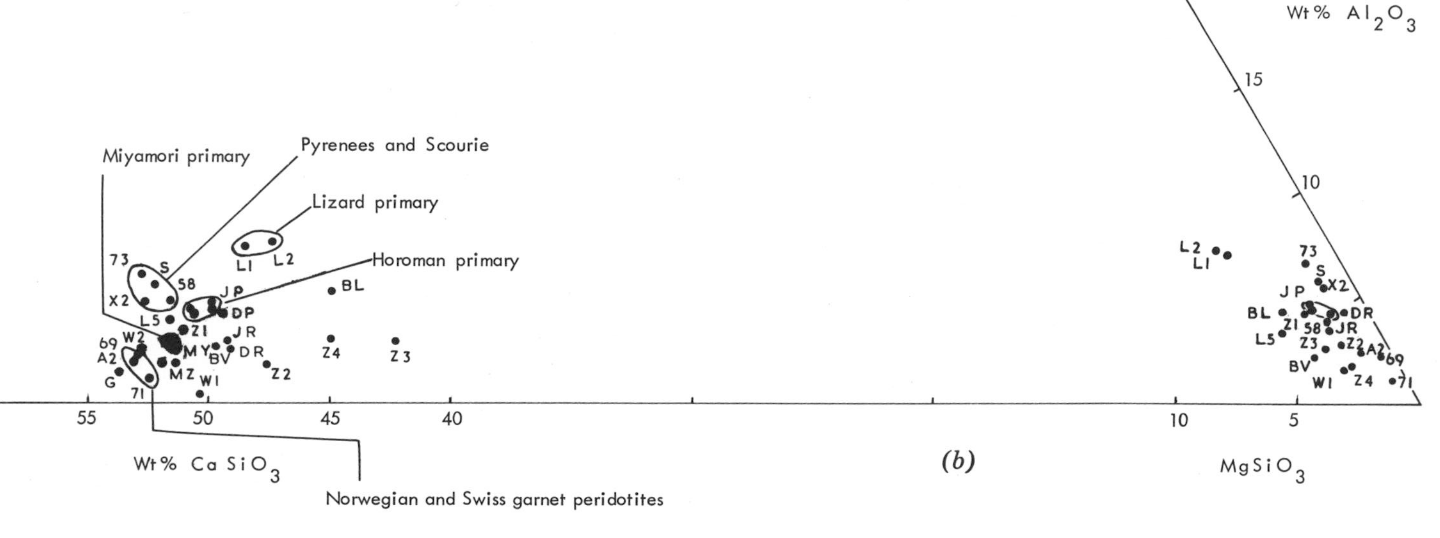

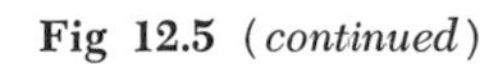

(*b*)

Fig 12.5 (*continued*)

and Seki, 1958). W1—Webster, North Carolina (Ross et al., 1954). W2—Webster, North Carolina (Hess, 1949, sample WEB).

Group (*c*) R. 1, 2, 3, 4, 7—in basalts, various sources (Ross et al., 1954, samples 1–4 and 7). F. 4, 5, 6, 8—in basalt, Dreis Weiher, Germany (Frechen, 1963, samples 4, 5, 6, 8). WA—in basalt, Australia (Wilshire and Binns, 1961, sample 1). WB—in basalt, Australia (Wilshire and Binns, 1961, sample 2). HM—in basalt, Derbyshire (Hamad, 1963, sample 15). YM (websterite)—in basalt, Japan (Yamaguchi, 1964). YT (eclogite)—in basalt tuff, Hawaii (Yoder and Tilley, 1962). NJ—in eclogite and pyrope-bearing diatreme, Navajo reservation (O'Hara and Mercy, 1966). A3, A17—in kimberlite, South Africa (O'Hara and Mercy, 1963). E.3, E.4—in kimberlite, Basutoland (Nixon et al., 1963). DTP 2—in kimberlite, South Africa (Macgregor and Ringwood, 1964). BL—Belhelvie, Scotland, felspathic peridotite, some primary spinel in associated rocks (Rothstein, 1962). DP—Dawros, Ireland; spinel-plagioclase peridotite, primary pyroxene (Rothstein, 1958, sample N). DR—Dawros, Ireland, recrystallized pyroxene assemblage of deformed peridotite (Roth-

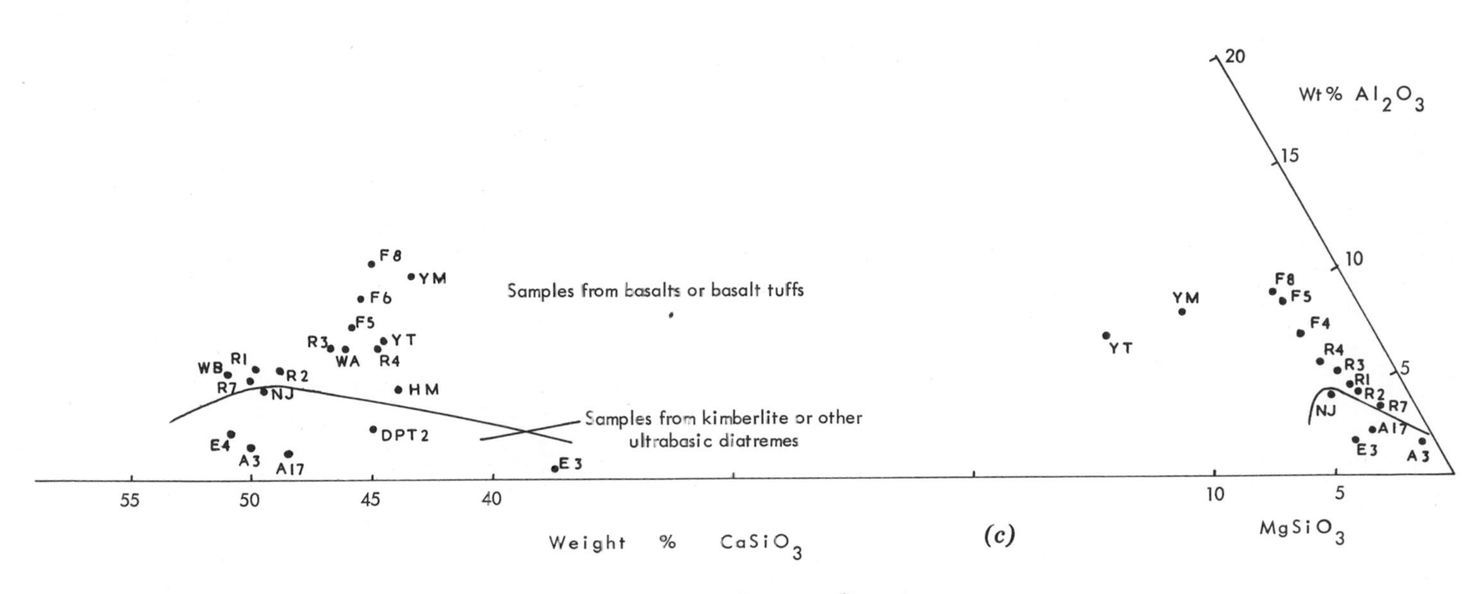

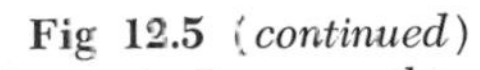

Fig 12.5 *(continued)*

stein, 1958, samples R). MY—Miyamori, Japan, orthopyroxene-poor peridotites, associated with hornblendic rocks and allegedly a crystal mush intrusion. Primary pyroxene assemblages (Onuki, 1965, samples MY–153, 52, 31L, 152, 31S). MZ—Miyamori, Japan, ?recrystallized assemblages (Onuki, 1965, samples MY–9, 10). Z1, Z2—Red Hills, New Zealand (Challis, 1965a samples 1–5 and 2–6). Z3—Dun Mountain, New Zealand (Challis, 1965a samples 3–8). Z4—Red Mountain, New Zealand (Challis, 1965a samples 4–9). L1, L2—Lizard, England, primary pyroxenes in spinel peridotite (Green, 1964a samples $O_1 - C_1$, and $O_2 - C_2$). L5—Lizard, England, recrystallized assemblage (Green, 1964a samples $O_5 - C_5$). 58, 73—Etang de Lherz, Pyrenees, spinel-lherzolite and spinel-websterite (O'Hara and Mercy, unpublished data, samples 10458 and 10473). X2,S—Scourie, Scotland, spinel-amphibole lherzolite (O'Hara, 1961, sample X.282). 69, 71—Almklovdalen, Norway, garnet lherzolite and garnet websterite (O'Hara and Mercy, 1963, samples N.69, N.71). A2—Bellinzona, Switzerland, garnet-lherzolite (O'Hara and Mercy, 1963, sample A2).

presumably reflects crystallization under widely varying pressure and temperature conditions.

The points plotted in Fig. 12.5*b* are from peridotites forming parts of layered masses, some of them in orogenic environments, and other alpine type peridotites (Group *b*). Those plotted in Fig. 12.5*c* are from peridotites occurring as nodules in basalts, kimberlites, or other breccia pipes (Group *c*). Each pair of coexisting pyroxenes is given the same symbol, and the key to the symbols is in the figure legend. Pyroxenes not plotted in Fig. 12.5, and not used in constructing Fig. 12.6, include pyroxenes recorded by Bloxam and Allen (1959) and Oosterom (1963), which either have incomplete analyses or are not guaranteed to come from appropriate assemblages, and a sample from Pyrenean lherzolite (Collée, 1963) that is apparently not saturated in Al_2O_3. Two pyroxenes from pyrope-chrome diopside nodules in kimberlite (Nixon et al., 1963) are not plotted in Fig. 12.5 but have been used to obtain points in Fig. 12.6; as sample G, these pyroxenes may yield values of α_c and β_c that are slightly high.

Note that α_c and β_c are very different parameters from α_d (which can be obtained approximately from data by Boyd and Schairer, 1964; Davis, 1963) and the maximum Al_2O_3 content of orthopyroxene in the system $MgSiO_3$-Al_2O_3, β_m (which can be obtained from data by Boyd and England, 1964a). There is virtually no experimental data to fix the values of α_c, β_c except that of O'Hara (1963b) and O'Hara and Schairer (1963) at 30 kb and 1600°C, and 1 atmosphere and 1238°C respectively. In preparing Fig. 12.4, therefore, estimates of β_c have had to be made on the basis of available data for β_m, knowing that in natural assemblages β_c is usually slightly greater than β_p, which in turn is found to be about half the value of β_m (O'Hara, 1963b). Macgregor and Ringwood (1964) obtained a higher result in experiments with natural orthopyroxenes and garnet. However, since the pyroxenes produced were not saturated with clinopyroxene, the values obtained may represent some figure between β_p and β_m (see Fig. 12.5*a*). Their results suggest that higher values of β_p may be observed in natural rather than simple synthetic systems. Estimates of the way in which β_c varies within the facies other than the garnet lherzolite facies to which the experimental data relate are based on a single item of information by Fawcett and Yoder (1963) for β_m at 900°C, 10 kb, the data of Kushiro and Yoder (1964a), and the assumptions that β_c, β_p and β_m all increase rapidly with increasing pressure at fixed temperature in the protohypersthene-plagioclase-lherzolite and orthopyroxene-plagioclase-lherzolite facies, but less rapidly in the spinel-lherzolite facies, before decreasing rapidly in the garnet-lherzolite facies (these assumptions are guided by the volume changes involved in replacing a low-Al_2O_3 pyroxene + Al_2O_3-rich phase + olivine assemblage by aluminous pyroxenes only in the different facies). This hypothesis represents a considerable modification of the simple model discussed previously (O'Hara and Mercy, 1963) which it replaces.

The estimated variation in α_c is based on knowledge of α_d and β_c, and observation of the orientation of the C-D boundary of Fig. 12.5*a* in experimentally investigated systems cited above. An allowance has been made for the effect of replacement of FeO for MgO. The general form of variation of α_p, β_p must be similar to that of α_c, β_c shown in Fig. 12.4.

Obviously temperatures and pressures derived from Fig. 12.4 can only be approximate, although relative temperatures and pressures derived for natural peridotites are probably reliable.

Boyd and Macgregor (1964) concluded that compositions of coexisting pyroxenes in peridotite nodules in basalts indicated improbably low temperatures of equilibration, but they did not take into account the effect of the relatively large Al_2O_3 contents of these pyroxenes. Elsewhere their conclusions based on alumina-poor pyroxenes from Norwegian garnet-peridotites and nodules in kimberlite are valid, substantiating previous estimates (O'Hara and Mercy, 1963).

2. Distribution of Fe^{2+}, Mg^{2+} between pyroxenes. Kretz (1961, 1963) suggested that coefficients calculated from the distribution of Fe^{2+} and Mg^{2+} between coexisting pyroxenes could be used to estimate temperatures of formation. The use of this method suffers from several complications (O'Hara and Mercy, 1963). Changing mutual solubility of two pyroxenes will influence the distribution coefficient between them (O'Hara, 1964) unless compensating changes occur. Because Al_2O_3 content influences mutual solubility even at fixed temperature and pressure, the distribution coefficient may be expected to be a function of Al_2O_3 content unless Al_2O_3-saturated pyroxenes are considered, and even then may still be a function of Cr_2O_3: Fe_2O_3:Al_2O_3 ratios, and the jadeite and aegirine contents of the pyroxene. When comparing distribution coefficients of Al_2O_3-saturated pyroxenes, the influence of varying Al_2O_3 content may complicate the manner in which the distribution coefficient varies with temperature and pressure, invalidating any treatment based on the assumption of ideal thermodynamic behavior. The interpretation of distribution coefficients for pyroxene assemblages presents too many difficulties to be judged superior at present to the calcium-aluminum distribution method used above, but may ultimately become a useful tool because these coefficients undoubtedly exhibit variations as important as those exhibited by α_c in Fig. 12.4, K_D values increasing with temperature from about 0.5 in the lowest temperature parageneses to about 0.9 in the highest temperature parageneses.

D. Conditions of Equilibration of Some Peridotites

In Fig. 12.6 points have been inserted representing approximately the conditions of equilibration implied by the mineral assemblages of some natural peridotites for which clinopyroxene analyses are available. Figures 12.4 and 12.6, therefore, contain a postulated petrogenetic grid and mineral facies system for natural terrestrial ultrabasic rocks and embody conclusions about the relative and absolute temperatures and pressures of equilibration of various groups of nodules in basalts and kimberlites, and a wide range of "alpine-type" peridotites. Data for 65 analyzed clinopyroxenes are embodied in Fig. 12.6. The websterite sample W1 yields nonintersecting parameters in Fig. 12.4 and is, therefore, omitted, as is one New Zealand sample (Challis, 1965a, sample 6) for the same reason. Note that in the low-temperature region especially, Fig. 12.6 is extremely sensitive to discrepancies arising from analytical error or impure separations of minerals to be analyzed.

The important observations arising from Fig. 12.6 are:

1. The apparent equilibration of nodules in basalts from conditions close to or within the melting interval (dry basic magmas in equilibrium with four phase peridotite), at moderate pressures in most cases, implies derivation from the uppermost mantle. If correct, this inference is inconsistent with the hypothesis that nodules occur most frequently in alkali basalts because they have travelled greater distances through the mantle. It is, however, consistent with a cognate igneous origin in the "intermediate pressure regime" as required by O'Hara (1965).
2. The apparent derivation of nodules in kimberlite from an environment consistent with equilibration at depths of 100 to 140 km on the Precambrian shield geothermal gradient (see Chapter 10-IV). The absence of materials equilibrated on the geothermal gradient at lower pressures strongly suggests that sampling is as yet incomplete. The pyroxene of E.3 (Nixon et al., 1963) presents anomalous features (Fe/Mg ratio higher than associated orthopyroxene) but

taken at face value it implies equilibration at pressures greater than 60 kb.

3. The conditions of equilibration of xenolithic garnet peridotites from kimberlite (Chapter 10-IV) and crustal garnet peridotites from Norway and Switzerland (Chapters 5-IV and 6-III) are greatly different.

4. Three groups of alpine-type peridotite from the European orogenic belts appear to have equilibrated at approximately the same pressure (15 to 20 kb), but at greatly different temperatures. The implied depth of about 50 km is consistent with derivation from basal crust or uppermost mantle in an orogenic region.

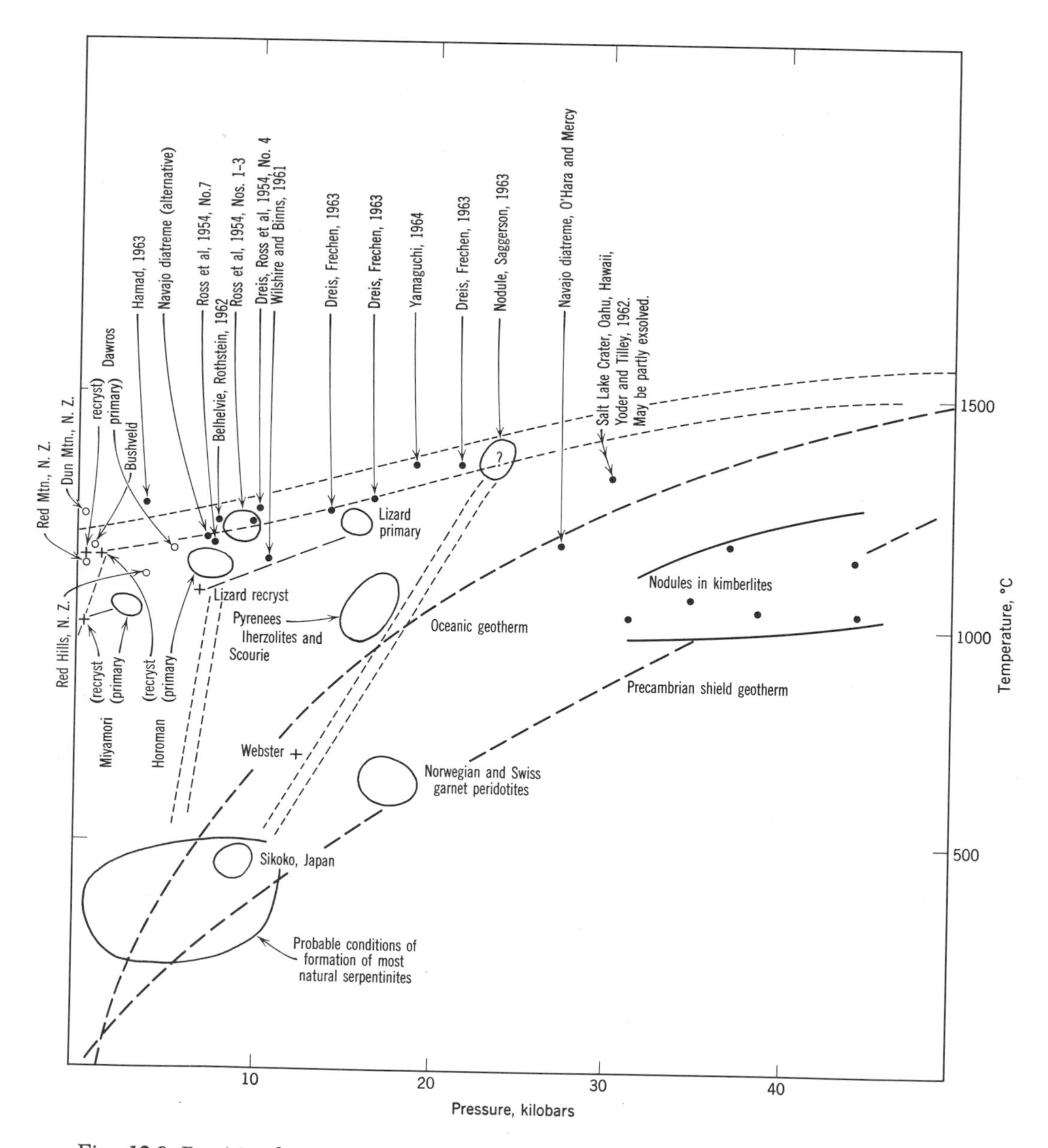

Fig. 12.6 Provisional assignment of conditions of equilibration to some natural ultrabasic assemblages on the basis of the hypothesis embodied in Fig. 12.4. Data sources may be traced through the caption to Fig. 12.5. The geothermal gradients, anhydrous facies boundaries and melting interval are transferred from Figs. 1.1, 1.4, and 12.4.

5. The conditions of crystallization of the Pyrenean lherzolites and their associated ariégites are quite different from those of the crustal and xenolithic garnet-peridotites, or the eclogite nodule from Hawaii. This accords poorly with suggestions by Ravier (1964).

6. The Pyrenean lherzolites appear to have equilibrated under conditions which are quite distinct from those represented by peridotite nodules in basalts, contrary to many published opinions.

7. Inferred conditions of crystallization of the Horoman and Miyamori intrusives in Japan are in excellent agreement with Onuki's (1965) conclusions about their genesis.

The Dawros, Lizard, Horomon, and Miyamori masses all yield evidence of possible tectonic emplacement as hot crystalline bodies with some anhydrous high temperature recrystallization (Chapters 7-III and 7-IV). This conclusion is consistent with the environment of each of the masses and was required by Rothstein (1958) and Green (1964a) for the first two masses. The Dawros primary assemblage does not fall in the spinel-peridotite facies as required by Rothstein (1962).

The conditions of crystallization deduced for the New Zealand ultramafic masses are in accord with Challis' (1965a) conclusions but differ greatly from a previous inference (O'Hara and Mercy, 1963) which is probably incorrect.

8. Alpine-type peridotites appear to have equilibrated under widely varying conditions in the range 0 to 20 kb, 400 to 1200°C, thus reinforcing the conclusion that the special tectonic conditions necessary for their transport and emplacement may be the only feature which alpine-type peridotites have in common.

9. Two alternative conditions of equilibration are satisfied by data for a peridotite nodule from a Navajo diatreme (Chapter 8-IV). The peridotite has textural features more similar to those of nodules in kimberlite than those in basalts, and is associated with eclogite nodules and pyrope xenocrysts (O'Hara and Mercy, 1966) and possible chlorite pseudomorphs after garnet are reported. The high pressure solution is, therefore, to be preferred over the lower pressure, higher temperature solution which groups it with the peridotite nodules in basalts.

10. It is possible to infer that the conditions of the "intermediate pressure regime" of basalt evolution (O'Hara, 1965) are realized in the approximate pressure range 8 to 20 kbs.

11. Melting of the upper mantle under wet conditions to yield andesitic magmas (O'Hara, 1965) or crystal accumulation from such magmas at depth, should yield peridotites equilibrated at pressures of 10 to 20 kbs and temperatures of 800 to 900°C. Such peridotites might reasonably be expected to be prominent among alpine-type peridotites and their apparent scarcity might then be a pointer to the relative unimportance of this mechanism in the generation of andesite provinces. Further sampling of alpine-type peridotites may settle this question.

IV. REVIEW

P. J. Wyllie

A. *Introduction*

The introductions to each of the preceding chapters (Sections I) have reviewed the conclusions reached, and provided some cross references to other chapters. This final contribution reviews in general and historical terms some of the problems of the petrogenesis of ultramafic and ultrabasic rocks. The greater part of the review deals with the petrogenesis of the alpine-type ultramafic rocks, because these have served as a focus of controversy for many years. The variety of ultramafic rock associations in different tectonic environments, and of the processes involved in their formation, have been emphasized throughout the book. Both are important in considering petrogenesis. Although interpretation of processes may require extensive study, rock associations are more easily distinguished; but the distinctions have not always been made. Hess (1955, p. 394) drew attention to this with the following statement: "Gross errors have probably resulted from applying conclusions drawn from facts related to mica peridotites to alpine peridotites and vice versa. If mica peridotite had been called humpty-dumptyite, these probably would not have arisen."

A preliminary classification of rock associations is given in Chapter 1-I-B. In this broad discussion of petrogenesis the associations may be considered in three groups:

1. Layered, stratiform and other intrusions involving gabbro or diabase together with crystal accumulations or concentrations.
2. The alkalic rocks of the continental regions, including kimberlites, mica peridotites, members of ring complexes, and ultrabasic lava flows.
3. The several peridotite-serpentinite associations of the orogenic belts that have been classified together, in the past, as alpine-type intrusions.

Most members of the second group are distinguished from those of the other two by their chemistry, mineralogy, and tectonic setting. Criteria for separating the other two groups, (1) from (3), have been proposed by Hess (1938, 1955) and Thayer (1960, and in Chapter 7-IV). However, contributions to this volume and other recent literature indicate that some alpine-type intrusions are not readily distinguished from layered rocks of group (1), and that several associations of ultramafic rocks occur in the alpine tectonic environment.

B. Petrogenesis of Ultramafic Rocks: General Remarks

Important factors to be considered in connection with the petrogenesis of all three groups of ultramafic intrusions include the source of the material, its variation in physical state and temperature (from its source to its position of intrusion), and its post-intrusion history. It is generally agreed that the source of ultramafic rocks is the upper mantle. The only ultramafic rocks that are composed of crustal material are those formed by metamorphic differentiation or metasomatic processes (Chapter 7-II).

When it is first derived from the upper mantle, ultramafic material could be in one of several physical states. Complete, or nearly complete fusion of upper mantle material would yield an ultrabasic liquid magma (Chapters 4, 8, and 9). Partial fusion of the upper mantle material could yield basaltic magma from which mafic minerals such as olivine and pyroxene may later be concentrated to form ultramafic rocks (Chapters 2, 3, and 9-III). Partial fusion of the upper mantle could also yield a crystal mush composed of basaltic or picritic liquid and residual olivine crystals; transportation of the mush and subsequent crystallization of the liquid would yield an ultramafic rock (Chapter 7). Similar crystal mushes could develop within the crust from original basaltic magma separated from the mantle, with subsequent crystallization and concentration of mafic minerals (Chapters 2 and 3). A crystal mush could range from a fluid assemblage containing much liquid and few crystals to a crystalline assemblage lubricated by a small proportion of liquid. An ultramafic rock could be derived directly from the upper mantle in the solid state, either by plastic flow or by tectonic transport (Chapters 5 and 6). The upper mantle itself could be exposed directly by uplift in suitable tectonic environments (Chapter 4-IV; Hess, 1960).

The temperature and physical state of ultramafic material when it is intruded will depend upon its state when derived from its upper mantle source and upon the processes operating during its upward movement. An original ultrabasic liquid magma would be emplaced within the crust as a high temperature magma (Chapter 4-III) containing a proportion of suspended olivine crystals whose amount depends upon the extent of cooling and crystallization during transportation. Emplacement of crystal mushes either derived directly from the mantle or from crystal cumulates in basic magma chambers would occur at a temperature closely approaching that of basaltic magma (Chapter 7-III). Emplacement of ultramafic rocks derived from the mantle in the solid state could occur at various temperatures, depending upon the time and distance of migration (Chapter 6). Tectonic emplacement of serpentinized peridotite (Chapter 5-II) could occur at low temperatures (Chapter 6-IV-A-2). Some kimberlites are emplaced as fluidized solid-gas assemblages, at moderate to low temperatures (Chapter 8-V). Representatives of these ultramafic and ultrabasic materials may form subaerial or submarine extrusions with physical states ranging through essentially liquid ultrabasic lavas or crystal mush lava flows with ultrabasic or basic liquids (Chapter 1-I-B-8), solid-gas pyroclastic material (Dawson, 1964), to crystalline serpentinite (Dickinson, 1966).

The more complex the post-intrusion history of an ultramafic rock, the more difficult is its petrogenetic interpretation. At one extreme are the stratiform gabbro-peridotite complexes that crystallized slowly under stable conditions and were not subsequently metamorphosed. At the other extreme are those peridotites of the alpine suite that have been subjected to several episodes of deformation and metamorphism, serpentinization, and tectonic transportation. These later events may destroy many or all of the features that permit reconstruction of the early history of their undeformed counterparts. Metasomatism or explosive activity arising from the late concentration of alkalis and volatiles in alkalic ultramafic complexes also tends to destroy the evidence of the conditions during and immediately after emplacement.

The petrogenesis of ultramafic rocks is best determined in the associations where the evidence is least modified by later events. It is therefore desirable to consider first the petrogenesis of group (1), including the stratiform intrusions; then group (2), the alkalic associations; and finally group (3), the alpine-type intrusions.

C. Petrogenesis of Stratiform Intrusions

There is general agreement that the parent magma of the stratiform intrusions in group (1) is tholeiitic basaltic magma derived by partial fusion of the upper mantle, and that gravity settling of early-formed crystals is the dominant process (Chapter 2). Irvine and Smith (Chapter 2-III) conclude that gravitational settling of mineral grains in plutonic basaltic magma is almost inevitable, and that this must be a prime consideration in studies of the origin of ultramafic rocks. Other processes cause the cyclic features of the gravity layering: periodic convection of a single cell appears satisfactory for the Skaergaard intrusion; in larger bodies such as the Bushveld intrusion a complex system of convection cells could exist; and for the Muskox intrusion, Irvine and Smith (Chapter 2-III) conclude that the cyclic units were produced by repeated intrusions of fresh basaltic liquid flowing through the whole width of the magma chamber. Gravity settling of crystals in place has proved inadequate to explain the formation of picrites in the lower parts of many basic sills

(Chapter 3). It now appears that gravity effects are superimposed on the dominant process of flow differentiation of basaltic liquid containing suspended olivine crystals, possibly in tholeiitic sills as well as in those with alkalic affinities. The crystals could have been derived directly from the mantle, or from an olivine cumulate formed by gravity differentiation during a halt in a deeper reservoir. The crystals could also have been precipitated during ascent of basaltic liquid; if so, then the mass balance of many sills (Chapters 3-II and 3-III) requires the presence elsewhere of large quantities of basaltic material. Drever and Johnston (Chapter 3-II) appeal to a process of "liquid differentiation" to accentuate the physical processes involving gravity and flow, this process perhaps becoming significant in the more volatile-rich alkalic sills. Since Bowen's (1928) study, the small picrite and peridotite sills and dykes of Skye have been widely cited as examples of the intrusion of a crystal mush lubricated by basaltic liquid, but Drever and Johnston (Chapter 3-V) conclude that these and similar rocks in Greenland were emplaced as liquid picritic magmas containing suspended olivine crystals.

D. Petrogenesis of Alkalic Ultrabasic Rocks

Parent magmas proposed for the ultrabasic rocks of group (2) in the alkalic associations of the stable continental regions include undersaturated alkalic basalts and alkalic ultrabasic liquid magmas (Chapters 8 and 9), evidence for the latter including the existence of alkalic ultrabasic lavas [Chapter 1-I-B-8(2) and (3)]. Although the upper mantle is usually considered to be the source of these magmas, contamination with crustal material is often invoked to explain their unusual chemistry (e.g., Turner and Verhoogen, 1960, p. 249 and 396). Reaction of a primary carbonatite magma from the mantle with "granitic" crustal rocks to form some alkalic ultrabasic rocks has also been proposed but not generally accepted (Chapters 8-V and 9-II). The processes involved in the formation of the gabbro-peridotite associations of group (1) occur also in the plutonic alkalic associations, with gravity settling of crystals and convective circulation being dominant in the early stages of crystallization (Chapters 2-I, 9-I, 9-II, and 9-III). Now that flow differentiation has been recognized as an important igneous process (Chapters 3-III and 3-IV), its effects will probably be discovered in the alkalic associations. The petrogenesis of the alkalic ultrabasic rocks is further complicated by additional processes involving the concentration of alkalis and volatiles in residual liquids. Retention of these components facilitates differentiation in the liquid phase by diffusion of materials along temperature and concentration gradients (Chapter 9-II); produces extreme differentiates including the volatile-rich, low-silica ultrabasic rocks such as carbonatite and okaite (Chapters 9-II and 9-III); and leads to metasomatism (fenitization) and recrystallization that may obliterate previous textures as well as forming metasomatic ultrabasic rocks (Chapter 9-II). Explosive exsolution of volatile components from basic or ultrabasic magmas causes eruption of fragmental volcanic rocks with complementary crystalline residues remaining in some volcanic conduits (Chapter 9-II). It also causes brecciation of previously crystallized rocks and the formation of diatremes (Chapter 8). The effects of volatile components are well illustrated by kimberlites: the deep-seated massive rock crystallizes from an ultrabasic magma, and higher level rocks are emplaced in diatremes as fluidized solid-gas systems, xenocrysts and xenoliths of wall rocks being mixed with the fragmented and usually greatly altered kimberlite (Chapter 8). Some kimberlites and mica peridotites may be emplaced as crystal aggregates transported by a carbonatite magma and gases at temperatures of 600 to 700°C (Chapters 9-V and 9-VI).

E. Petrogenesis of Ultramafic Rocks in Orogenic Belts

The petrogenesis of the dunites, peridotites and serpentinites occurring in zones of alpine deformation, group (3), can not be reviewed as succinctly as the rocks of groups (1) and (2). The origin of these rocks involves metamorphic as well as igneous processes (Chapters 5-II, 5-IV, 6-II, 6-III, 7-II, and 7-IV). Indeed, den Tex (1965) discussed these rocks in terms of their metamorphic lineages rather than their igneous origin. The problems of interpretation introduced by metamorphism, deformation, and reintrusion have contributed to what Hess in 1955 (p. 391) termed a "magnificent argument" concerning the possible existence of liquid ultrabasic magmas. He summarized the situation thus (1955, p. 401):

"There has been a debate for the past 35 years between the field geologist and the laboratory investigator on how ultramafic rocks are emplaced. The field man has invariably drawn the conclusion that they appear to have been very fluid—liquid—at the time of injection (Hess, 1938). Repeatedly the laboratory investigator has ruled out each new suggestion as to how such materials could be magmas at any reasonable temperature."

The debate has not been limited to the petrogenesis of the alpine-type ultramafic associations, but it has centered around these. An outline history of this debate conveniently introduces the problems, and provides an introduction for recent petrogenetic considerations of the ultramafic associations commonly classified together as alpine. The topic is presented in three portions: the historical debate up to 1955 when Hess' review paper was published, an appraisal of the situation in 1955, and a review of the additional experiments and field interpretations published after 1955.

1. The "Magnificent Argument"

At one time petrologists did not hesitate to invoke the existence of ultrabasic magmas, often proposing that these were formed by remelting of olivine crystals accumulated near the floor of a basic magma chamber (e.g., Harker, 1904, 1909). The high melting temperature of forsterite, 1890°C (Bowen and Andersen, 1914), indicated that ultrabasic liquids rich in dissolved forsterite could exist only at very high temperatures, and this led Vogt (1921) to predict a hypothetical phase diagram for the system forsterite-fayalite, showing that addition of fayalite to forsterite might cause a marked lowering of liquidus temperatures. He contended that dunites and peridotites were emplaced as liquid magmas with temperatures as high as 1500 to 1600°C (Vogt, 1923), although the generally minor thermal effects around peridotite masses makes such high intrusion temperatures very unlikely. Bowen (1928) marshalled experimental and petrological arguments against the existence of liquid magmas more basic than basalt and advanced the crystal mush hypothesis for the intrusion of peridotites as an alternative to liquid ultrabasic magmas. Much of the evidence was based on rocks of minor intrusions of group (1) in Skye [Chapters 1-I-B-2(3) and 3-V] rather than on rocks of alpine type. Experimental study of the system MgO-FeO-SiO_2 by Bowen and Schairer (1935) disproved Vogt's predicted phase diagram, by showing that 20 mole per cent of fayalite lowered the olivine liquidus temperature by less than 100°C. Additional experimental evidence from simplified rock systems tended to confirm Bowen's (1928) conclusions about the basic composition limit of liquid magmas. In the system diopside-anorthite-forsterite, for example, Osborn and Tait (1952) found that although some liquid developed at 1270°C for crystalline mixtures rich in forsterite, the liquid remained basic in composition until excessively high temperatures were reached. However, there remained the possibility that water and other volatile components would lower the liquidus temperatures of ultrabasic compositions, and Harker suggested that addition of volatiles would aid the liquefaction of accumulated olivine crystals at moderate temperatures (oral communication to Bowen, 1928, p. 166). Hess (1938) also appealed to volatiles to account for the low intrusion temperatures of many alpine-type peridotites. He proposed that at the onset of orogeny the upper mantle peridotite was fused to form a water-rich serpentinite liquid, and that this magma was emplaced in the crust at low temperatures to crystallize as a peridotite or serpentinite. Experimentalists denied the existence of such a magma when Bowen and Tuttle (1949) found no silicate melt in the system MgO-SiO_2-H_2O at temperatures below 1,000°C at pressures up to 2 kilobars. Kitahara et al. (1966) recently confirmed this conclusion and extended the pressure range to 30 kb.

Thus by 1955 two key experimental studies by Bowen and Schairer (1935) and Bowen and Tuttle (1949) weighed against the existence of "dry" or "wet" liquid ultrabasic magmas rich in dissolved olivine, at temperatures low enough to satisfy the field requirements of little or no contact metamorphism, and Bowen's (1928) crystal mush hypothesis had become widely accepted (Turner and Verhoogen, 1960, p. 321). However, in the abstract of his 1955 paper Hess "casts his vote with the field geologist and believes that the field evidence takes precedence," affirming his belief that most peridotites and serpentinites of alpine mountains "were intruded in a fluid state, as magmas," although he agreed that some peridotites could have been emplaced by essentially solid flow. He added that "Probably there is some factor or constituent missing in the laboratory investigation." Experimental studies are valuable for demonstrating that a particular petrological process is possible, but it is difficult to prove by experimental studies that a proposed petrological process is impossible. Since 1955, additional negative experimental evidence against the existence of low-temperature ultrabasic liquids has been obtained. However, experiments have also provided positive evidence that high-temperature ultrabasic liquid magmas could exist at temperatures lower than previously suspected from available experimental data (e.g., Chapter 4-III-D-4). Other experiments have elucidated the flow of crystalline peridotite (Chapter 6-IV). In the same period, detailed field and petrological studies have shown that some ultramafic rocks in alpine belts were emplaced at temperatures equal to or higher than temperatures of basic magmas (Chapters 4-III, 7-III, and 12-III). If this had been established earlier, the apparent field requirements for the existence of ultrabasic liquid magmas at low temperatures would have seemed less significant.

2. Experimental Data since 1955

The additional experimental data involve liquidus temperatures in parts of the system CaO-MgO-FeO-Fe_2O_3-SiO_2, and melting studies in the presence of the volatile components H_2O and CO_2. In an unpublished doctoral thesis Ricker (1952) presented results of a reconnaissance liquidus study in the "olivine join," Mg_2SiO_4-Fe_2SiO_4-Ca_2SiO_4, at 1 atmosphere pressure, and Wyllie (1960) later noted that the intersection of the ternary liquidus surface with the composition join Mg_2SiO_4-$CaFeSiO_4$ has the general shape predicted incorrectly by Vogt (1921) for the binary join Mg_2SiO_4-Fe_2SiO_4. Thus addition to forsterite of calcium orthosilicate as well as fayalite does produce a marked lowering of liquidus temperatures, although in relevant parts of the system CaO-MgO-FeO-SiO_2 they remain higher than estimated intrusion temperatures of those ultramafic rocks containing appreciable amounts of FeO and CaO; a mixture on the composition join Mg_2SiO_4-$CaFeSiO_4$ containing 60 weight per cent forsterite is completely liquid only at about 1500°C. Presnall (1966) completed a systematic study of the join forsterite-diopside-iron oxide in this system, at various oxygen fugacities. He showed that an original liquid representing an ultrabasic magma (CaO-rich) can precipitate a sequence of mineral assemblages equivalent to the ultramafic rocks in the Alaskan zoned complexes, at high but reasonable temperatures (Chapter 4-III-D-4). However, ultrabasic liquids in the system capable of precipitating a high proportion of forsteritic olivine still require prohibitively high temperatures (see Fig. 4.13). Clark and Fyfe (1961) described preliminary experiments on the melting temperatures of a natural serpentinite at 500–1000 bars of water pressure, and found that at 1400°C "it was clear that most of the material was liquid during the experiment. Residual olivine was coarse-grained." The composition of the liquid phase and the proportion of residual olivine were not reported. They concluded that an ultrabasic lava could flow in a submarine environment at temperatures only 100 to 200°C above observed surface lava temperatures. Franz and Wyllie (Chapter 9-VI) concluded that ultrabasic liquids in the system CaO-MgO-SiO_2-CO_2-H_2O can precipitate forsterite at temperatures of the order of 600°C at pressures attained within the earth's crust, and preliminary results of A. L. Boettcher and Wyllie indicate that this liquid may precipitate serpentine at about 500°C and estimated pressures of 10 to 20 kb. The ultrabasic liquids, however, are CaO-rich "synthetic carbonatite magmas," and although the results are applicable to the kimberlite-carbonatite association they do not solve the problem of low temperature peridotite or serpentinite liquid magmas.

If the intrusion temperature of an alpine peridotite is lower than that of basaltic magma there is little alternative to the conclusion that the material was essentially crystalline when emplaced (Chapters 5-II, 5-III, 5-IV, 6-II, and 6-III), and the hypothesis of solid intrusion for the emplacement of ultramafic rocks in alpine belts was widely accepted by 1960 (Turner and Verhoogen, 1960, p. 321). Recent experiments on the deformation of ultramafic rocks and minerals have provided valuable information on the mechanism of plastic flow of peridotite minerals (Chapter 6-IV), and the experimentally observed weakening and embrittlement of serpentinite at dehydration provides a satisfactory explanation for the field conclusion that many serpentinites were emplaced by block tectonic transport (Chapters 5-II, 6-II, and 6-IV).

3. *Field Interpretations since 1955*

The controversy concerning the existence of low-temperature ultrabasic liquid magmas tended to ignore the gabbros and basic volcanic rocks almost invariably associated with the peridotites and serpentinites (Chapter 5-II), or to relate them to a different stage of the orogenic and magmatic activity. However, the alpine-type igneous association traditionally includes these basic rocks, and discussions of their relevance to the origin of ultramafic rocks in orogenic environments have reappeared in the literature since 1955. Thayer (1960, chapter 7-IV-A) discusses and deplores the conceptual divorce of the ultramafic and mafic rocks, and he lists six criteria that characterize the intrusive peridotite-gabbro complexes of alpine type.

Reconsideration of the petrogenesis of ultramafic and mafic rocks together has contributed to the formulation or revival of several hypotheses. As a basis for discussion, the petrogenetic hypotheses are summarized and grouped in Table 12.1. Emplacement temperatures of the rocks are divided into four ranges: very high temperatures (VH), which are higher than that of basalt liquids; high temperatures (H), which correspond to the crystallization interval of anhydrous basalt liquids; medium temperatures (M), which are between the anhydrous basalt solidus and about 500°C, the temperature of formation of serpentine; and low temperatures (L), which are those within the serpentine stability field. The column widths are approximately in scale to the temperature intervals.

The hypotheses are arranged in four groups. Varying degrees of fusion of the mantle may produce basic liquids, and a range of liquid compositions that are ultrabasic. The hypotheses involving ultrabasic liquid magmas form group 1. Hypotheses involving the formation of ultramafic rocks by concentration of mafic minerals from a basic liquid form group 2. Group 3 includes the hypotheses which imply that some ultramafic rocks, or peridotite-gabbro associations, constitute representative samples of a portion of the mantle. Group 3 is considered separately from group 1; it is very unlikely that the ultrabasic liquid formed by complete fusion of a portion of the mantle would crystallize completely in the crust without differentiation, to produce an ultramafic rock with the same composition as the mantle source of the liquid. The same, or similar processes occur in each of these three groups, but this fact is not emphasized here; processes were discussed in general terms early in the review. The processes involved in Stage III of Table 12.1 represent deformation and metamorphism of the ultramafic rocks produced in Stages I and II. Hypothesis 4 refers to the ultramafic rocks that have become an integral part of a terrane of regional metamorphism.

Descriptions and interpretations of the zoned ultramafic complexes of Alaska have appeared since 1951. These constitute a distinctive group of very high temperature intrusions with pronounced metamorphic and metasomatic effects at their margins. Taylor's review (Chapter 4-III) concludes that they were formed by the successive intrusion of liquid ultrabasic magmas of different compositions, all with high contents of FeO, CaO, and H_2O. This is hypothesis 1A in Table 12.1. Onuki (1965, 1966) described ultramafic rocks from Japan that are petrographically similar to the Alaskan rocks, and he concluded that intrusion and differentiation of a parent ultrabasic liquid magma produced the "ultramafic rocks series" formed from essentially liquid magmas, crystal mushes, and residual basic magmas. This is hypothesis 1B in Table 12.1.

Following reiteration of his belief in the existence of low temperature ultrabasic liquid magmas in 1955, Hess (1960) suggested that the serpentinites of Puerto Rico represented uplifted oceanic crust, which "may be altered mantle rocks exposed at the surface" (p. 235). Such rocks were neither magmatic nor fluid (hypothesis 3B in Table 12.1). However, arguments for the existence of fluid peridotites were strengthened in the same paper when Hess reported the discovery of a high temperature metamorphic aureole around the Tinaquillo peridotite (Mackenzie, 1960).

The Tinaquillo peridotite, and other similar intrusions with high-temperature aureoles, have recently been recognized as a distinctive group of high temperature intrusions reviewed by Green in Chapter 7-III. He considers their source to be either mantle or deep-seated cumulate, and mode of intrusion to be as a crystal mush followed by diapiric flow after complete crystallization. The alternatives correspond to hypotheses 3A (with gabbro removed) or 2A in Table 12.1. Thayer (Chapter 7-IV-B-3) questions the interpretation, doubting "the presence of such aureoles, per se, as evidence that the intrusions were unusually hot when intruded." Challis (1965a, 1965b) reported pyroxene granulite facies metamorphism at the unfaulted contact of the Red Hills ultramafic intrusion of New Zealand, which has long been classified as a typical alpine-type intrusion, and she interpreted the ultramafic rocks in terms of hypothesis 2B in Table 12.1.

Representatives of the high temperature rocks discussed above have been plotted on O'Hara's pyroxene grid (Fig. 12.6, Chapter 12-III) giving estimated conditions of equilibration at temperatures greater than 1100°C, with one exception at about

TABLE 12.1 Current Hypotheses for the Origin of Alpine Ultramafic Rocks

Hypothesis Number		Chapter or Reference	Material from Mantle	Process in Mantle	Successive Stages I	Successive Stages II	Successive Stages III	Stage	Temperature Ranges* (VH, H, M, L)
1	A	4-III	Ultrabasic liquid magma, with or without suspended crystals	Complete(?) or partial fusion	Successive intrusions	Reintrusion of crystal mushes	Plastic flow, serpentinization, tectonic block transportation, and solid extrusion of serpentinite	I II III	
	B	Onuki 1965			Differentiation of parent magma				
2	A	7-III	Basic liquid magma, with or without suspended crystals	Partial fusion	Gravity differentiation forming stratiform intrusions	Reintrusion of cumulate mush		I II III	
	B	Challis 1965a				Removal of basic magma above cumulate			
	C	7-II-C-1 7-IV-B-5			Differentiation in magma chambers(?)	Submarine extrusion and differentiation		I II III	
3	A	7-III 7-IV-E	Representative mantle sample: Peridotite mush with basic liquid	Mobilization by partial fusion	Mush intrusion with flow layering	Plastic flow of layered complex		I II III	
	B	Hess 1960	Representative mantle sample: Partly serpentinized mantle peridotite in Layer 3 of oceanic crust	?	Tectonic uplift	Erosion exposing mantle		I II III	
	C	6-IV-B-2		Downward movement of convection current	Depression & heating of serpentinite	Tectonic emplacement in overlying sediments		I II III	
4		5-IV 12-III-D	Regional metamorphism of peridotites and serpentinites						

*VH—very high temperatures above basalt liquidus. H—high temperatures within crystallization interval of anhydrous basalt. M—medium temperatures between anhydrous basalt solidus and serpentine stability. L—low temperatures in serpentine stability field.

1000°C, and at pressures corresponding to depths ranging from near-surface to 50 or 60 km. These conditions correspond quite closely to the crystallization interval of anhydrous basaltic liquid.

Consideration of the genesis of alpine peridotites and gabbros together leads to comparison with the stratiform complexes of group (2). The six criteria proposed by Thayer to characterize the alpine peridotite-gabbro complexes also distinguish them from the stratiform complexes (Thayer, 1960; Chapter 7-IV-A). Thayer discusses evidence supporting hypothesis 3A in Table 12.1, with the anhydrous crystal mushes from the upper mantle (perhaps already gravity stratified) developing flow layering, and entraining masses of chromitite; associated quartz diorite and granophyre complete the calcalkaline "alpine mafic magma stem." Hess (1938, 1955) also distinguished the alpine-type ultramafic rocks from cumulates in stratiform intrusions, but Smith (1958) suggested that there is a continuous series of peridotite-gabbro associations between the stratiform types and the alpine types. Several alpine peridotites have recently been interpreted as gravity stratified crystal cumulates, following hypotheses 2A or 2B in Table 12.1 (Chapters 5-IV; 7-III-A and E).

The possible connection of volcanic activity with stratiform and other gravity-layered intrusions (Chapters 2-III, 4-II, and 4-III) led Irvine and Smith (Chapter 2-III) to suggest that other ultramafic bodies may have formed in subvolcanic reservoirs. Comagmatic lava flows could thus be associated with alpine-type ultramafic rocks formed from ultrabasic magmas (hypothesis 1), or from crystal concentrates derived from intrusive basic magmas or stratiform intrusions (hypotheses 2A and 2B). Certainly, the close association of metamorphosed basic volcanic rocks with gabbros, peridotites and serpentinites in alpine orogenic belts (Chapter 5-II) is compatible with the conclusion that these are all genetically related. The ophiolite hypothesis, 2C in Table 12.1, interprets the whole assemblage as massive, differentiated submarine lava flows ranging in composition from basic to ultrabasic, together with some intrusive rocks. If liquid ultrabasic flows have occurred, then there should be a hypothesis 1C in Table 12.1, directly comparable with 2C. Discussions of the ophiolite hypothesis in Chapters 7-II-C-1 and 7-IV-B-5 confirm that tectonic, metamorphic and metasomatic processes complicate the petrogenesis, as in most other alpine associations. There appears to be a revival of interest in the hypothesis (Maxwell and Azzaroli, 1963; Moores et al., 1966; Miyashiro, 1966), although Thayer presents reasons for concluding that ophiolite complexes are essentially identical with normal, intrusive alpine complexes (Chapter 7-IV-B-5).

According to Table 12.1, the only alpine peridotites not genetically related to gabbroic rocks are the partly serpentinized rocks derived from the mantle by hypotheses 3B and 3C; 3C is an integral part of the "spreading ocean-floor" hypothesis discussed by Raleigh in Chapter 6-IV-B-2.

The increased range of possibilities introduced by considering the petrogenesis of peridotites and gabbros together has inevitably led to conflicts of opinion. Some examples follow with the hypotheses of Table 12.1 given in parentheses. Green (Chapter 7-III) reviews the high-temperature alpine peridotites with pyroxene-hornfels metamorphic aureoles as a distinctive group (2A or 3A without associated gabbro), but Thayer (Chapter 7-IV-D) proposes, with specific reference to the Lizard intrusion, that the "contact granulites" are alpine-type norites, contemporaneous and comagmatic with the peridotites, and that the associations are normal alpine intrusive complexes (3A). Hopson (1964) interpreted the Baltimore Gabbro-State Line complex as a contemporaneously deformed stratiform complex (2A, Stages I and III), but Thayer (Chapter 7-IV-D-1) concludes that it is a normal alpine complex with most of the layering produced by magmatic flowage rather than gravity settling

(3A). Onuki (1965) concluded that the Horoman body was formed by the differentiation of a liquid ultrabasic magma (1B), whereas Miyashiro (1966) referred to unpublished conclusions of Nagasaki that the complex is composed of several units each resembling a gravity-stratified basic intrusion (2A or 2B, Stages I and III). Thayer's conclusion that ophiolite complexes (2C) are typical intrusive alpine complexes (3A) has already been mentioned.

Table 12.1 shows that alpine-type ultramafic rocks could have several origins. This conclusion, along with the wide range of conditions under which alpine ultramafic rocks have equilibrated (Fig. 12.6), has led some petrologists to suggest that the only feature that the rocks have in common is an alpine setting that causes tectonic transport and reintrusion (e.g., Chapter 12-III-D). Reintrusion of high-temperature ultramafic rocks through several kilometers is illustrated in Fig. 12.6. Hypothesis 4 in Table 12.1 implies that a peridotite of any origin becomes an alpine type if it is involved in regional metamorphism with the associated processes of deformation being represented by Stage III.

The present uncertainty about the origin of many alpine ultramafic rocks is illustrated by Challis' (1965a, 1965b) recent study of the ultramafic bodies in New Zealand. These are usually cited as typical examples of low-temperature alpine-type intrusions (e.g., Turner and Verhoogen, 1960). The high-temperature aureole at the unfaulted contact of one intrusion has been mentioned, and O'Hara's pyroxene grid (Fig. 12.6) indicates that the pyroxenes in three intrusions equilibrated at temperatures between 1100 and 1250°C at pressures corresponding to depths ranging from near-surface to about 12 km. Challis (1965a) also concluded that the masses contained igneous layering produced by gravity settling of crystals from gabbroic or possibly picritic magma. She suggested further that the ultramafic masses represent the deep-level magma-chambers of a line of Permian volcanoes, and that the less basic differentiate from the stratiform material was removed as olivine-poor lava flows. This classic example of a low-temperature alpine ultramafic intrusion is thus reinterpreted as the ultramafic part of a high-temperature stratiform intrusion which supplied basic lava flows to the surface (hypothesis 2B); some elements of the ophiolite hypothesis (2C) are therefore included. This example is a timely warning that much published field and petrological information that has become accepted as fact was based on what would be regarded today as reconnaissance work.

The shortage of suitably detailed field and petrographic studies of alpine ultramafic intrusions and associated igneous rocks, and especially their country rocks and the contact effects induced in them, is probably one of the reasons for the earlier failure to recognize high-temperature contact effects. Another reason is the probability that contact metamorphic zones may be obliterated, or left behind at the site of initial intrusion, by the effects of Ca-metasomatism and the combined processes of deformation, metamorphism, and reintrusion represented by Stage III and hypothesis 4 in Table 12.1.

Metamorphism makes interpretation of the origin of many alpine ultramafic rocks extremely difficult, although the methods of structural petrology do help to unravel the later processes involved in their formation (Chapters 6-II, 6-III, and 6-V). The difficulties are illustrated by recent discussions of the origin of ultrabasic and basic masses in the Lewisian of Scotland. Bowes et al. (1964) proposed that these rocks were derived from a layered intrusion (hypotheses 2A and 2B to Stage I in Table 12.1) that had been broken up and incorporated into the Lewisian metamorphic series, thus becoming intrusions of alpine type (Stage III and hypothesis 4 in Table 12.1). O'Hara (1965) contended that the basic gneisses are not related to the ultrabasic gneisses by an igneous mechanism. Discussions followed by Bowes et al.

(1966) and by O'Hara (1966), using geochemical data to further their respective arguments, but they were unable to resolve the problem to their mutual satisfaction.

F. Geochemical Results

In view of the difficulties of interpretation for so many ultramafic rocks in alpine regions, geochemical data may prove to be particularly useful for distinguishing among the various associations. But first it is necessary to characterize the different associations in chemical terms, and this has not been completed, even for the major elements. A comment by Smith (1962, p. 162) is relevant: "The mineral olivine is a major component of ultramafic intrusions and therefore variations in its composition may be considered most indicative of fundamental differences . . . although optical methods of determining the composition of olivine grains have been known for many years, there is now much more data on the isotopic composition of Precambrian sulphides (a recent technique) than there is on the composition of Precambrian olivines."

Some comparative data are available. Thayer, in Fig. 7.9, uses A-F-M diagrams to illustrate chemical trends for specific alpine intrusive complexes, and for alpine differentiation in general. Bowes et al. (1966) used a similar diagram to compare the chemical trends of alpine-type rocks, rocks of the Bushveld intrusion, and the ultrabasic and basic gneisses in the Lewisian; they also compared these three groups of rocks in terms of Ca, Fe, and Mg. O'Hara (1966), discussing these trends, emphasized the importance of examining the geochemical sequence in successive layers, as well as for random specimens collected to illustrate the overall range of chemical variation.

Only recently have advances in technique made possible the accurate measurement of trace element concentrations in olivine-rich rocks. The thesis study of Stueber (1965) has produced significant new data for ultramafic rocks, and much of this is discussed in Chapters 11-II, 11-IV, and 11-V. Isotope studies are presented in Chapters 11-III and 11-IV.

The reviews of trace element abundances in ultramafic rocks confirm that trace elements may be useful as genetic guides. The extremely low concentrations of Na, K, Rb, Sr, and a low value for K/Rb in the alpine ultramafic rocks indicate that they are residual in nature, and therefore they could not represent mantle material suitable as a source for the derivation of basalts. The Sr^{87}/Sr^{86} values indicate no contemporary relationship between alpine-type ultramafic rocks and other materials such as stratiform intrusions, modern basalts, and ultramafic nodules in basalt, which indicates that the alpine ultramafic rocks can represent neither the residual refractory residue of mantle material from which basalts have been derived, nor the ultramafic portions of stratiform intrusions. On the other hand, the O^{18}/O^{16} ratios of minerals in basalts and gabbros are so similar to those in alpine-type ultramafic rocks that they must be genetically related. However, Taylor (Chapter 11-III) points out that the relationship could go as far back as the primordial differentiation of the earth. Hurley (Chapter 11-IV) discusses how far back in time the growth lines for strontium isotopes in alpine ultramafic rocks must be followed before the value drops to the level of other mantle derivatives, but an analytical discrepancy between two sets of investigators complicates the situation (Fig. 11.1).

The concentration of many trace elements and the oxygen isotopic composition of peridotites appear to be unaffected by serpentinization. This suggests that serpentinization occurs simply by the addition of water, and it essentially eliminates meteoritic water except in special circumstances. This is relevant to the question of whether serpentinization occurs without much change in volume, which requires considerable migration of material, or with a large increase in volume. This question has been discussed recently by Hotstetler et al. (1966) and Thayer (1966).

The main conclusion arising from the geochemical data reviewed in Chapter 11 is that the alpine ultramafic rocks are derived from a portion of the mantle that attained its residual character during an early period of mantle differentiation. This implies that of the current hypotheses based on field and petrological studies that are shown in Table 12.1, only hypotheses 3B and 3C appear to be capable of providing suitable material.

However, I believe that the geochemists will admit that it is too soon to rule out hypotheses 1 and 2, because the available data are so sparse. There is a sampling problem that may be severe in some associations. For example, the Th and U contents of the Twin Sisters dunite (Chapters 6-III, and 11-II) show marked variation from one specimen to another, and the concentrations of Rb, Sr, and K in ultramafic rocks are very sensitive to the distribution of small proportions of amphibole. Goles emphasizes in Chapter 11-II that what is urgently needed is a detailed investigation of the trace element contents of a single alpine-type body, preferably one that has not been subjected to extreme deformation and metamorphism, showing the distribution of trace elements among the minerals within the body and in different parts of the same body. This should be compared with a similar study for a typical stratiform intrusion.

This historical review indicates that what Hess (1955) called a "magnificent argument" for and against low-temperature ultrabasic liquid magmas is being resolved as our knowledge of experimental systems and of the rocks increases. But geology has never been a dull subject, and the review of post-1955 developments indicates that the magnificent two-sided argument may degenerate into a bar-room brawl among rival groups of petrologists (Table 12.1) and geochemists; this augurs well for new discoveries as each group strives to persuade the others.

There is no doubt at all that if the petrogenesis of ultramafic rocks in alpine and other associations is to be worked out, then both the hammer and black-box approaches must be followed. The geologist needs the information that can only be obtained by the use of sophisticated chemical techniques, and the geochemist can apply his data with maximum effect only if his samples can be located within an adequate petrological framework, which requires a detailed field map of the ultramafic association and the country rocks.

G. The Upper Mantle

This completes the review of ultramafic rock petrogenesis, but some concluding remarks are required about applications to upper mantle studies. The topic has been considered in Chapters 10, 11, and 12-II. The ultramafic materials usually regarded as possible representatives of the upper mantle include the stony meteorites, the alpine ultramafic rocks, and the nodules in basalts and kimberlites.

Meteorites and terrestrial ultramafic rocks have a narrow range of stable isotope variation compared to the total observed range (Chapter 11-III). The isotope data are consistent with the chondrite analogy for earth composition, but terrestrial ultramafic rocks are distinct in O^{18}/O^{16} ratio from the achondrites. On the other hand, it has been suggested that the upper mantle composition is similar to that of the basaltic achondrites because their K/Rb ratios are similar to those of oceanic tholeiites.

Despite the uncertainties in alpine ultramafic rock petrogenesis (Table 12.1), it does appear certain that some of the rocks are residual mantle material. However, they are not related genetically to modern basalts or intrusive gabbros (Chapter 11-IV) and they are therefore unlikely to represent a significant proportion of the mantle (Chapter 11-V).

The geochemistry of ultramafic nodules and their host basalts confirms a genetic connection between them, and implies that the nodules are residual or cumulate in origin (Chapters 10 and 11); they have no genetic relationship to alpine ultramafic rocks. According to Fig. 12.6, they equilibrated in the uppermost mantle, within the crystallization interval of anhydrous basaltic liquids. The eclogite and garnet peridotite nodules in kimberlites are a potential source of basaltic liquids. Figure 12.6 indicates that they equilibrated in the mantle at depths of 100 to 140 km on the thermal gradient for shield regions. In a recent review of the chemistry of ultramafic rocks and nodules, Harris (1966) proposed that the nodules represent mantle fragments from a pyroxene-peridotite layer and deeper garnet-peridotite (see Chapter 10-III). The variable composition of pyroxene-peridotite nodules corresponds to various stages of depletion of basaltic components, the original mantle pyroxene-peridotite probably being chemically equivalent to the deeper garnet-peridotite. Harris (1966) pointed out that the few garnet-peridotite nodules so far analyzed may not be representative. Davidson (Chapter 10-IV) suggests that the nodules in kimberlites are derived not from the upper mantle but from crustal metamorphic rocks. Although the chemical variation of garnet-peridotite nodules is inadequately known, a wide variation of mineralogical composition in garnet-pyroxene nodules is established (Figs. 10.5 and 10.6 in Chapter 10-IV), and this variation encompasses rock types developed in high grade regional metamorphism. Even if these rocks are mantle fragments, as indicated by Fig. 12.6, Davidson's comment demands attention: "If these inclusions represent the upper mantle, then the latter is clearly of so varied a composition that petrogenetic studies based on a single rock-type such as garnet-peridotite must be of questionable value."

As more information is obtained about the upper mantle the more complex and heterogeneous it appears to be. Petrological and geochemical studies of ultramafic rocks and nodules undoubtedly will continue to provide data for more refined speculations about the composition and mineralogy of the upper mantle, but we must remind ourselves occasionally that it is a long extrapolation to the upper mantle in most locations, and that the method of multiple working hypotheses has always worked well in the earth sciences.

References

Adams, F. D., 1903. The Monteregian Hills—A Canadian petrographical province. *J. Geol.*, **11**, 239–282.

———, 1913. "The Monteregian Hills." Excursion in the neighbourhood of Montreal and Ottawa, 1913. *Geol. Surv. Can., Guide book 3, Excursion A7*, 29–80.

Adams, J. A. S., 1964. "Nondestructive gamma-spectrometry of serpentinite cores from Mayaguez, Puerto Rico," in Burk, C. A., ed., *A study of serpentinite.* Natl. Acad. Sci.—Natl. Res. Council Publ. **1188**, 145–148.

Afanassiev, V. A., 1939. Alkaline rocks of the Ozernaya Varaka of the Khabozero region (south-western part of the Kola peninsula). *Dokl. Akad. Nauk SSSR*, **25**, 508–512.

Åhman, E., 1950. Ett fynd av frisk olivin i kimberlit fran Kalix skärgard i Norrbotten. *Geol. Fören. Stockholm Forh.*, **72.**

Aho, A., 1956. Geology and petrogenesis of ultrabasic nickel-copper-pyrrhotite deposits at the Pacific Nickel property, Southwest British Columbia. *Econ. Geol.*, **51**, 444–481.

Akimoto, S., H. Fujisawa and T. Katsura, 1965. The olivine-spinel transition in Fe_2SiO_4 and Ni_2SiO_4. *J. Geophys. Res.*, **70**, 1969–1977.

Allan, J. A., 1914. Geology of Field map-area, British Columbia and Alberta. *Geol. Surv. Can. Mem.* **55**, 312p.

Allen, J. B., and T. Deans, 1965. Ultrabasic eruptives with alnöitic-kimberlitic affinities from Malaita, Solomon Islands. *Mineral. Mag.*, **34**, 16–34.

Allen, J. E., and R. Balk, 1954. Mineral resources of Fort Defiance and Tohatchi quadrangles, Arizona and New Mexico. *New Mex. Bur. Mines Mineral Resources, Bull.*, **36**, 192p.

Allison, A., 1936. The Tertiary dykes of the Craignish area, Argyll. *Geol. Mag.*, **73**, 73–87.

Allsopp, H. L., 1965. Rb-Sr and K-Ar age measurements on the Great Dyke of Southern Rhodesia. *J. Geophys. Res.*, **70**, 977–984.

Anderson, A. T., 1966. Iron-titanium oxide deposits in Quebec anorthosites. *Geol. Soc. Am., Spec. Paper* **87**, Abstracts of Kansas City meeting, 1965. In press.

Anderson, Don L., 1964. "Recent evidence concerning the structure and composition of the Earth's mantle." in *Physics and Chemistry of the Earth,* **6**, Pergamon Press, New York and London, 1–129.

Andreyeva, Ye. D., 1959. Gabbroic pegmatite in Sinyaya Mountain pyroxenite, the middle Urals. *Izv. Akad. Nauk SSSR Geol. Ser.* (English trans.), **9**, 29–40.

Argand, E., 1922. La tectonique de l'Asie. *Intern. Geol. Congr.*, **2**, 91.

Armstrong, J. E., 1949. Fort St. James Map-area, British Columbia. *Geol. Surv. Can. Mem.* **252.**

Arseniev, A. A., and E. A. Necheva, 1955. Olivine leucitites from the River Molbo (Siberian Platform). *Dokl. Akad Nauk SSSR*, **1104**, 910–911.

Avias, J., 1949. Note préliminaire sur quelques observations et interprétations nouvelles concernant les péridotites et serpentines de Nouvelle-Calédonie (secteur central). *Bull. Soc. Géol. Franc.* **19**, 439–451.

———, 1955. Relations minéralogiques et géochimiques entre les serpentines et péridotites de Nouvelle Calédonie, leurs inclusions, leur enclaves, les roches encaissantes. *Coll. Pétr. Sci. Terre*, nr. hors série, 213–237.

Backlund, H. G., 1936. Zur genetischen Deutung der Eklogite. *Geol. Rundschau*, **27**, 47–61.

Backström, J. W. von, 1960. Die geologie van Rustenburg en die omliggende gebied. *S. Africa Dept. Mines Geol. Surv., Toel.* Blad **4** (Rustenburg), 93p.

Baertschi, P., 1957. Messung und Dessung relativer Haufigkeitsvariationen von O^{18} und C^{13} in Karbonatgesteinen und Mineralien. *Schweiz. Mineral. Petrog. Mitt.*, **37**, 73–158.

Bain, G. W., 1934. Serpentinization: origin of certain asbestos, talc, and soapstone deposits. *Econ. Geol.*, **29**, 397–400.

———, 1936. Serpentinization of Vermont ultrabasics. *Bull. Geol. Soc. Am.*, **47**, 1961–1979.

Balashov, Yu. A., 1963. Regularities of the rare-earth distribution in the crust of the Earth. *Geokhimiya*, **1963**, 99–114.

———, and N. V. Turanskaya, 1962. Rare earth elements in a peridotite from the Polar Urals. *Geokhimiya*, **1962**, 377–378.

Balk, R., 1954. Kimberlitic tuff plugs in northeastern Arizona. *Trans. Am. Geophys. Union*, **35**, 381.

Balk, R., and M. S. Sun, 1954. "Petrographic description of igneous rocks," in Allen, J. E., and R. Balk, eds., Mineral resources of Fort Defiance and Tohatchi quadrangles, Arizona and New Mexico. *New Mex. Bur. Mines Mineral Resources Bull.*, **36**, 100–118.

Bancroft, J. A., and W. V. Howard, 1923. The essexites of Mount Royal, Montreal, P.Q. *Trans. Roy. Soc. Can.*, **17**, 13–42.

Baragar, W. R. A., 1960. Petrology of basaltic rocks in part of the Labrador trough. *Bull. Geol. Soc. Am.*, **71**, 1589–1644.

Barbosa, O., 1951. Contribuicao a origem do diamante em Diamantina, Estado de Minas Gerais. *Bull. Brasil Dep. Nac. da Prod. Mineral.* **136**, 35p.

Bardet, M. G., 1963. Controle géotectonique de la repartition des venues diamantifères dans la monde. *Chronique Mines Rech. Miniere.*, **328–329**, 67–89.

———, 1965. Les gisements de diamant d'U.R.S.S. *Chronique Mines Rech. Miniere,* 40.

———, and M. Vachette, 1966. Déterminations d'âges de kimberlite del'Ouest Africain, et essai d'interprétation des datations des diverses venues diamantifères dans le monde. *Abstracts, 3rd Symposium on African Geology,* Brussels-Tervuren.

Barth, T. F. W., 1947. The nickeliferous Iveland-Evje amphibolite and its relations. *Norges Geol. Undersökelse,* **168a**, 1–71.

———, 1950. Intrusion relations of bahiaite from Southern Norway. *Am. Mineral.* **35**, 622–627.

———, 1956. Geology and petrology of the Pribilof Islands, Alaska. *U.S. Geol. Surv. Bull.* **1028-F**, 101–160.

———, 1962. *Theoretical Petrology,* 2nd ed. John Wiley and Sons, New York, 416p.

Bartholomé, P., 1962. "Iron-magnesium ratio in associated pyroxenes and olivines," in *Petrologic studies: Buddington Vol. Geol. Soc. Am.*, 1–20.

Bartrum, J. A., and F. J. Turner, 1928. Pillow lavas, peridotites, and associated rocks of northernmost New Zealand. *Trans. New Zealand Inst.*, **59**, 98–138.

Battey, M. H., 1960. The relationship between preferred orientation of olivine in dunite and the tectonic environment. *Am. J. Sci.*, **258**, 716–727.

———, 1962. The relationship between preferred orientation of olivine in dunite and the tectonic environment. Reply to a discussion by R. N. Brothers. *Am. J. Sci.*, **260**, 313–315.

Beall, G. H., 1962. Differentiation controls in subsiliceous gabbros. Ph.D. thesis, Mass. Inst. Technol., 271p.

Bear, L. M., 1960. The geology and mineral resources of the Agros-Apsiou area. *Cyprus Geol. Surv. Dept., Mem.* **7**, pt. 1, 1–50.

Bell, P. M., 1964. High-pressure melting relations for jadeite composition. *Carnegie Inst. Wash. Yearbook,* **63**, 171–174.

———, and B. T. C. Davis, 1965. Temperature-composition section for jadeite-diopside. *Carnegie Inst. Wash. Yearbook,* **64**, 120–123.

Bennett, W. A. G., 1940. Ultrabasic rocks of the Twin Sisters Mountains. *Bull. Geol. Soc. Am.*, **51**, 2019.

Bennington, K. O., 1956. Role of shearing stress and pressure in differentiation as illustrated by some mineral reactions in the system $MgO\text{-}SiO_2\text{-}H_2O$. *J. Geol.*, **64**, 558–577.

———, 1959. Energy transfer from differentiation in a differential pressure system under non-equilibrium conditions. *J. Geol.*, **67**, 171–197.

Benson, W. N., 1918. The origin of serpentine, a historical and comparative study. *Am. J. Sci.*, **46**, 693–731.

———, 1926. The tectonic conditions accompanying the intrusion of basic and ultrabasic igneous rocks. *Nat. Acad. Sci. Mem.*, **19**, mem. **1**, 90p.

Berg, J. J. van den, 1946. Petrographic analysis of the Bushveld gabbro from Bon Accord. *Trans. Geol. Soc. S. Africa,* **49**, 155–208.

Berthelsen, A., 1960. Structural studies in the Pre-Cambrian of Western Greenland. Pt II: Geology of Tovqussaq Nuna. *Medd. Grønland,* **123,1**, 1–226.

———, 1962. Structural studies in the Pre-Cambrian of Western Greenland. Pt III: Southern Sukkertoppen District. *Medd. Grønland,* **123,2**, 1–46.

Berwerth, F., 1893. Annalen d. K.K.Naturhist. Hofmuseum, Bd. **VIII**, 440.

Bezrukov, V. A., *et al.*, 1966. The morphology of crystals of diamond, synthesized at wide intervals of temperature and pressure. *Zapiski Vsesoyuz. Mineral. Obshch.*, **95**, 1–9. (Russian.)

Bhattacharji, S., 1964. Fluid mechanics model for the mechanics of differentiation of basaltic magma during flowage. *Geol. Soc. Am. Spec. Paper* **76**, 14–15. (Abstr.)

———, 1965. Crystal settling in basaltic magma. *Geol. Soc. Am., Spec. Paper,* **82**, 11–12. (Abstr.)

———, 1966. Experimental scale model studies on flowage differentiation in sills. *Geol. Soc. Am. Spec. Paper* **87**, 11. (Abstr.)

———, and P. Savic, 1965. "Real and apparent non-Newtonian behavior in viscous pipe flow of suspensions driven by a fluid piston," in Cherwat, A. F., et al, eds., *Proc. 1965 Heat Transfer Fluid Mech. Inst.* Stanford University Press, Stanford, 248–262.

Bhattacharji, S., and C. H. Smith, 1963. Experimental studies of flowage differentiation applied to the "feeder dike" of the Muskox intrusion. *N.W.T., Can., 13th I.U.G.G. Meeting, (Upper-Mantle Symp.)* **1**, 42.

Bhattacharji, S., and C. H. Smith, 1964. Flowage differentiation. *Science,* **145,** 150–153.

Biljon, S. van, 1949. The transformation of the upper part of the Pretoria Series in the Bushveld Igneous Complex. *Trans. Geol. Soc. S. Africa,* **52,** 1–198.

Billings, M. P., and W. S. White, 1950. Metamorphosed mafic dikes of the Woodsville quadrangle, Vermont and New Hampshire. *Am. Mineral.* **35,** 629–643.

Birch, F., 1955. "Physics of the crust," in Poldervaart, E., ed., Crust of the Earth. *Geol. Soc. Am., Spec. Paper,* **62,** 101–118.

———, 1960. The velocity of compressional waves in rocks to 10 kilobars. *J. Geophys. Res.,* **65,** 1083–1102.

———, 1964. Density and composition of mantle and core. *J. Geophys. Res.,* **69,** 4377–4388.

———, 1965. Speculations on the Earth's thermal history. *Bull. Geol. Soc. Am.,* **76,** 133–154.

———, and P. LeCompte, 1960. Temperature-pressure plane for albite composition, *Am. J. Sci.,* **258,** 209–217.

Birch, F., J. F. Schairer, and H. C. Spicer, 1942. Handbook of Physical Constants. *Geol. Soc. Amer., Spec. Paper,* **36.**

Bishopp, D. W., 1952. Some new features of the geology of Cyprus. *Compt. Rend. XIX Intern. Geol. Congr.,* **15,** 13.

Bloxam, T. W., and J. B. Allen, 1959. Glaucophane schist, eclogite and associated rocks from Knockormal in the Girvan-Ballantrae complex, South Ayrshire. *Trans. Roy. Soc. Edinburgh,* **64,** 1–28.

Blumenthal, M. M., 1941. Un aperçu de la geologie du Taurus dans les vilayets de Nigde et d'Adana. *Meteae,* Ser. B, 6.

Boato, G., 1954. The isotopic composition of hydrogen and carbon in the carbonaceous chondrites. *Geochim. Cosmochim. Acta,* **6,** 209–220.

Bobrievich, A. P., M. N. Bondarenko, *et al.,* 1957. *The diamonds of Siberia.* Gosgeoltekhnizdat, Moscow, 159p. (Russian.)

———, 1959. *The diamond deposits of Yakutia.* Gosgeoltekhnizdat, Moscow, 527p. (Russian.)

Bobrievich, A. P., V. A. Kalyuzhnyi and G. I. Smirnov, 1957a. Moissanite in the kimberlite of the eastern Siberian platform. *Dokl. Akad Nauk SSSR,* **115,** 1173–1176. (Russian.)

Bobrievich, A. P., I. P. Lupin, *et al.,* 1964. *Petrography and mineralogy of the kimberlitic rocks of Yakutia.* Nedra, Moscow, 190p. (Russian.)

Bobrievich, A. P., and V. S. Sobolev, 1962. "Kimberlite formations of the north part of the Siberian platform," in *The Petrography of Eastern Siberia.* Acad. of Sci. Moscow, **i,** 341–416. (Russian.)

Borg, Iris, and John Handin, 1966. Experimental deformation of crystalline rocks. *Tectonophys.,* **3,** 249–368.

Borisenko, L. F., 1963. Some characteristics of the distribution of gallium in ultramafic rocks. *Geokhimiya,* **1963,** 746–753.

Botkunov, A. T., 1964. Some regularities of distribution in the diamond pipe Mir. *Zap. Vsesoyuz. Mineral. Obshch.,* **93,** 424–435, (Russian.)

Bovenkerk, H. P., F. P. Bundy, H. T. Hall, M. Strong, and R. H. Wentorf, 1959. Preparation of diamond. *Nature,* **184,** 1094–1098.

Bowden, F. P., and P. H. Thomas, 1954. The surface temperatures of sliding solids. *Proc. Roy. Soc.* London, Ser. A, **223,** 29–40.

Bowen, H. J. M., and D. Gibbons, 1963. *Radioactivation Analysis.* Oxford Univ. Press, New York and London. 295p.

Bowen, N. L., 1914. The ternary system: diopside-forsterite-silica, *Am. J. Sci.,* **38,** 207–264.

———, 1915. Crystallization-differentiation in silicate liquids. *Am. J. Sci.,* **39,** 161–185.

———, 1922. Genetic features of alnoitic rocks at Isle Cadieux, Quebec. *Am. J. Sci.,* 5th ser., **3,** 1–34.

———, 1928. *The Evolution of the Igneous Rocks,* Princeton Univ. Press, Princeton, 332p.

Bowen, N. L., and O. Andersen, 1914. The binary system MgO-SiO_2. *Am. J. Sci.,* 4th ser., **37,** 487–500.

Bowen, N. L., and J. F. Schairer, 1935. The system MgO-FeO-SiO_2. *Am. J. Sci.,* **29,** 151–217.

———, 1936. The problem of the intrusion of dunite in the light of the olivine diagram. *16th Intern. Geol. Congr. Repts. Washington, D.C.,* **1,** 391–396.

Bowen, N. L., and O. F. Tuttle, 1949. The system MgO-SiO_2-H_2O. *Bull. Geol. Soc. Am.,* **60,** 439–460.

Bowes, D. R., A. E. Wright, and R. G. Park, 1961. Field relations of rocks containing coexisting pyroxenes. *Geol. Mag.,* **98,** 530–531.

———, 1964. Layered intrusive rocks in the Lewisian of the North West Highlands of Scotland. *Quart. J. Geol. Soc. London,* **120,** 153–192.

———, 1966. Origin of ultrabasic and basic masses in the Lewisian. *Geol. Mag.,* **103,** 280–283.

Boyd, F. R., Jr., 1959. "Hydrothermal investigations of amphiboles" in *Researches in Geochemistry,* P. H. Abelson, ed., 377–396.

———, and J. L. England, 1959. Pyrope. *Carnegie Inst. Wash. Yearbook,* **58,** 83–87.

———, 1960a. The fayalite-Fe_2SiO_4 spinel transition. *Carnegie Inst. Wash. Yearbook,* **59,** 48–49.

———, 1960b. Aluminous enstatite. *Carnegie Inst. Wash. Yearbook,* **59,** 49–52.

Boyd, F. R., Jr., 1960c. Minerals of the mantle. *Carnegie Inst. Wash. Yearbook,* **59,** 47–52.

———, 1960d. The quartz-coesite transition. *J. Geophys. Res.,* **65,** 749–756.

———, 1962. Effects of pressure on the melting of pyrope. *Carnegie Inst. Wash. Yearbook,* **61,** 109–112.

———, 1963a. Effect of pressure on the melting of diopside, $CaMgSi_2O_6$, and albite, $NaAlSi_3O_8$ in the range up to 50 kb. *J. Geophys. Res.,* **68,** 311–323.

———, 1963b. Some effects of pressure on phase relationships in the system MgO-Al_2O_3-SiO_2, *Carnegie Inst. Wash. Yearbook,* **62,** 121–124.

———, 1964a. The system enstatite-pyrope. *Carnegie Inst. Wash. Yearbook,* **63,** 157–161.

———, 1964b. System enstatite-pyrope and its bearing on the genesis of kimberlite. *Geol. Soc. Am. Ann. Meeting 1964 program,* 17–18. (Abstr.)

———, and B. T. C. Davis, 1964. Effects of pressure on the melting and polymorphism of enstatite, $MgSiO_3$. *J. Geophys. Res.,* **69,** 2101–2109.

Boyd, F. R., Jr., and I. D. MacGregor, 1964. Ultramafic rocks. *Carnegie Inst. Wash. Yearbook,* **63,** 152–157.

Boyd, F. R., Jr., and Schairer, J. F., 1964. The system $MgSiO_3$-$CaMgSi_2O_6$. *J. Petrol.,* **5,** 275–309.

Bridgwater, D., 1965. Isotopic age determinations from South Greenland and their geological setting. *Medd. Grønland,* **179,4,** 1–56.

Brière, Y., 1920. Sur une amphibolite à grenat, olivine et hypersthène. *Bull. Soc. Franc. Mineral. Crist.,* **43,** 300–303.

Brothers, R. N., 1959. Flow orientation of olivine. *Am. J. Sci.,* **257,** 574–584.

———, 1960. Olivine nodules from New Zealand. *21st Intern. Geol. Congr.,* Copenhagen, *Repts.* **13,** 68–81.

———, 1962. The relationship between preferred orientation of olivine in dunite and the tectonic environment: A discussion. *Am. J. Sci.,* **260,** 310–312.

Broughton, J. C., 1950. Observations on the intrusion of rock salt by peridotite. *Trans. Am. Geophys. Union,* **31,** 229–233.

Brown, G. M., 1956. The layered ultrabasic rocks of Rhum, Inner Hebrides. *Phil. Trans. Roy. Soc.* London, Ser. B, **240,** 1–53.

———, 1957. Pyroxenes from the early and middle stages of fractionation of the Skaergaard intrusion, East Greenland. *Mineral. Mag.,* **32,** 511–543.

———, and E. A. Vincent, 1963. Pyroxenes from the late stages of fractionation of the Skaergaard intrusion, East Greenland. *J. Petrol.,* **4,** 175–197.

Brune, J. and J. Dorman, 1963. Seismic waves and earth structure in the Canadian Shield. *Bull. Seism. Soc. Am.,* **53,** 167–210.

Brunn, J. H., 1956, Contribution a l'étude géologique du Pinde Septentrionale et d'une partie de la Macedoine Occidentale. *Ann. Géol. Pays Helleniques,* 1st ser., **7,** 358p.

———, 1960. Mise en place et différenciation de l'association pluto-volcanique du cortège ophiolitique. *Rev. Géog. Phys. et Géol. Dyn.,* s. 2, **3,** 115–132.

Bucher, W. H., 1936. Cryptovolcanic structures in the United States. *Rept. 16th Intern. Geol. Congr.,* **2,** 1055–1083.

Buddington, A. F., and T. Chapin, 1929. Geology and mineral deposits of southeastern Alaska. *U.S. Geol. Surv. Bull.,* 800.

Buddington, A. F., and D. H. Lindsley, 1964. Iron-titanium oxide minerals and synthetic equivalents. *J. Petrol.,* **5,** 310–357.

Buerger, M. J., and E. Washken, 1947. Metamorphism of minerals. *Am. Mineral.* **32,** 296–308.

Buie, B. F., 1941. Igneous rocks of the Highwood Mountains, Montana, III Dike and related intrusives. *Bull. Geol. Soc. Am.,* **52,** 1754–1807.

Burk, C. A., 1964, Ed. *A study of serpentinite, the AMSOC core hole near Mayaguez, Puerto Rico.* Natl. Acad. Sci.—Natl. Res. Council Publ. **1188,** Washington, D.C.

Burkov, V. V. and E. K. Podporina, 1965. On the rare elements of kimberlitic rocks. *Dokl. Akad. Nauk SSSR* **163,** 197–200.

Burri, C. and P. Niggli, 1945. *Die Jungen Eruptivgesteine des mediterranen Orogens.* Guggenbühl and Huber, Zürich.

———, 1945. "Die Monteregian Hills," in Burri, C., and Niggli, P., eds., *Die Jungen Eruptivgesteine des mediterranen Orogens.* Guggenbühl and Huber, Zürich, 536–545.

Butakova, E. L., and L. S. Egorov, 1962. "The Meimecha-Kotui complex of alkalic and ultrabasic rocks" in *The Petrography of Eastern Siberia,* Acad. Sci., Moscow, **1,** 417–489. (Russian.)

Butler, J. R., 1964. Contact metamorphism along the base of the Stillwater Complex, Montana. *Geol. Soc. Am. Spec. Paper* **82,** 24. (Abstr.)

Cady, W. M., 1945. Stratigraphy and structure of west-central Vermont. *Bull. Geol. Soc. Am.,* **56,** 515–588.

———, 1956. Bedrock geology of the Montpelier quadrangle, Vermont. *U.S. Geol. Surv. Geol. Quad. Maps U.S.,* Map GQ 79.

Cameron, E. N., 1963. Structure and rock sequences of the Critical Zone of the Eastern Bushveld Complex. *Mineral. Soc. Am. Spec. Paper,* **1,** 93–107.

———, and H. E. Abendroth, 1956. Occurrence of chromite deposits in the eastern part of the Bushveld Complex. *Bull. Geol. Soc. Am.,* **67,** 1678–1679.

Cameron, E. N., and G. A. Desborough, 1964. Origin of certain magnetite-bearing pegmatites in the eastern part of the Bushveld Complex, S. Africa. *Econ. Geol.,* **59,** 197–225.

Cameron, E. N., and M. E. Emerson, 1959. The origin of certain chromite deposits of the eastern part of the Bushveld Complex. *Econ. Geol.,* **54,** 1151–1213.

Campbell, F. A., 1961. Differentiation trends in the Ice River complex, British Columbia. *Am. J. Sci.,* **259,** 173–180.

Campbell, R., and A. G. Stenhouse, 1907. The geology of Inchcolm. *Trans. Edinburgh Geol. Soc.,* **9,** 121–134.

Camsell, C., 1913. Geology and mineral deposits of the Tulameen District, British Columbia. *Geol. Surv. Can. Mem.* **26,** 188p.

Carey, S. W., 1954. The orocline concept in geotectonics. *Trans. Roy. Soc. Tasmania,* **89,** 255–288.

Carr, J. M., and L. M. Bear, 1960. The geology and mineral resources of the Peristerona-Lagoudhera area. *Geol. Surv. Cyprus Mem.,* **2,** 1–79.

Carr, M. H., and K. K. Turekian, 1961. The geochemistry of cobalt. *Geochim. Cosmochim. Acta,* **23,** 9–60.

Carter, J. L., 1965. The origin of olivine bombs and related inclusions in basalts. Ph.D. thesis, Rice University, Houston, Tex.

Carter, N. L., J. M. Christie, and D. T. Griggs, 1964. Experimental deformation and recrystallization of quartz. *J. Geol.,* **72,** 688–733.

Challis, G. A., 1965a. The origin of New Zealand ultramafic intrusions. *J. Petrol.,* **6,** 322–364.

———, 1965b. High-temperature contact metamorphism at the Red Hills ultramafic intrusion—Wairau Valley—New Zealand. *J. Petrol.,* **6,** 395–419.

Chayes, F., 1964. A petrographic distinction between Cenozoic volcaniçs in and around the open oceans. *J. Geophys. Res.,* **69,** 1573–1588.

Chenevoy, M., 1950. Les enclaves de serpentine dans les gneiss du Massif Central Français. *Bull. Soc. Franç. Mineral. Crist.,* **73,** 13–26.

———, 1958. Contribution a l'étude des schistes cristallins de la partie nord-ouest du Massif Central Français. *Mem. Carte Géol. France,* 428p.

Chidester, A. H., 1962. Petrology and geochemistry of selected talc-bearing ultrmafic rocks and adjacent country rocks in north-central Vermont. *U.S. Geol. Surv. Profess. Paper* **345,** 207p.

———, M. P. Billings, and W. M. Cady, 1951. Talc investigations in Vermont, preliminary report. *U.S. Geol. Surv. Circ.* **95,** 33p.

Choubert, B., 1946. Sur la prèscence du diamant au Gabon (A. E. F.) en rélation avec des kimberlites et des roches carbonatés metamorphiques. *Compt. Rend. Sce. Acad. Sci.,* **223,** 638–640.

Christie, J. M., D. T. Griggs, and N. L. Carter, 1964. Experimental evidence of basal slip in quartz. *J. Geol.,* **72,** 734–756.

Chubb, L. J., and C. Richardson, 1933. Geology of Galapagos, Cocos & Easter Islands. *Bernice P. Bishop Museum, Bull.* **110,** 45–67.

Chudoba, K. F. and J. Frechen, 1950. Über die plastische Verformung von Olivin. *Neues Jahrb., Abhand., Abt. A,* **81,** H.2, 183–200.

Clark, R. H., and W. S. Fyfe, 1961. Ultrabasic liquids. *Nature,* **191,** 158–159.

Clark, S. P., Jr., 1961. A redetermination of equilibrium relations between kyanite and sillimanite. *Am. J. Sci.,* **259,** 641–650.

———, and A. E. Ringwood, 1964. Density distribution and constitution of the mantle. *Rev. Geophys.,* **2,** 35–88.

Clark, S. P., Jr., J. F. Schairer, and J. de Neufville, 1962. Phase relations in the system $CaMgSi_2O_6$-$CaAl_2SiO_6$-SiO_2 at low and high pressure. *Carnegie Inst. Wash. Yearbook,* **61,** 59–68.

Clark, T. H., 1952. Montreal area. *Quebec Dept. Mines, Geol. Rept.* **46,** 159p.

———, 1955. St. Jean–Beloeil area. *Quebec Dept. Mines, Geol. Rept.* **66,** 83p.

———, 1964a. Upton area. *Quebec Dept. Nat. Resources, Geol. Rept.* **100,** 37p.

———, 1964b. St. Hyacinthe area (west half). *Quebec Dept. Nat. Resources, Geol. Rept.* **101,** 128p.

———, 1964c. Yamaska–Aston area. *Quebec Dept. Nat. Resources, Geol. Rept.* **102,** 192p.

Clegg, K. E., 1955. Metamorphism of coal by peridotite dikes in southern Illinois. *Ill. Geol. Surv. Rept. Investigations,* **178,** 1–18.

Cloos, H., 1941. Bau und Tätigkeit von Tuffschloten. Untersuchungen an den Schwabischen Vulkan. *Geol. Rundschau,* **32,** 709–800.

Coertze, F. J., 1958. Intrusive relationships and ore-deposits in the western part of the Bushveld Igneous Complex. *Trans. Geol. Soc. S. Africa,* **61,** 387–392.

———, 1960. Anorthosite emplaced in a shear-zone in gabbro of the Bushveld Igneous Complex. *Trans. Geol. Soc. S. Africa,* **63,** 75–81.

———, 1963. The relationship between the Pretoria Series and Bushveld Igneous Complex northeast of Pretoria. *S. Africa Dept. Mines Geol. Surv. Ann.,* **1,** 67–70.

———, and F. W. Schumann, 1962. The basic portion and associated minerals of the Bushveld Igneous Complex north of Pilanesberg. *S. Africa Dept. Mines Geol. Surv. Bull.,* **38,** 48p.

Coes, L., 1955. High pressure minerals. *J. Am. Ceram. Soc.,* **38,** 298.

Coleman, R. G., D. E. Lee, L. B. Beatty, and W. W. Brannock, 1965. Eclogites and eclogites:

Their differences and similarities. *Bull. Geol. Soc. Am.*, **76**, 483–508.

Collée, A. L. G., 1963. A fabric study of lherzolites, with special reference to ultrabasic nodular inclusions in the lavas of Auvergne, (France). *Leidse Geol. Meded.*, **28**, 3–102.

Cooke, H. C., 1937. Thetford, Disraeli, and eastern half of Warwick map-areas, Quebec. *Geol. Surv. Can. Mem.* **211**, 160p.

———, 1950. Geology of a southwestern part of the Eastern Townships of Quebec. *Geol. Surv. Can. Mem.*, **257**, 142p.

———, 1957, Coaticook–Malvina area. *Quebec Dept. Mines, Geol. Rept.* **69**, 37p.

Cottrell, A. H., 1948. "Effect of solute atoms on the behaviour of dislocations," in Report of a conference on strength of solids. *Phys. Soc. London,* 30–38.

Coulter, N. A., and J. R. Pappenheimer, 1949. Development of turbulence in flowing blood. *Am. J. Physiol.*, **159**, 401–408.

Cousins, C. A., 1959. The structure of the mafic portion of the Bushveld Igneous Complex. *Trans. Geol. Soc. S. Africa,* **62**, 179–189.

Cox, K. G., R. L. Johnson, L. J. Monkman, C. J. Stillman, J. R. Vail, and D. N. Wood, 1965. The geology of the Nuanetsi igneous province. *Phil. Trans. Roy. Soc.* London, Ser. A, **257**, 71–218.

Craig, H., 1953. The geochemistry of the stable carbon isotopes. *Geochim. Cosmochim. Acta,* **3**, 53–92.

———, 1963. The isotopic geochemistry of water and carbon in geothermal areas. *Conf. Nuclear Geol. Geothermal Areas,* Spoleto, Italy, 17–53.

Cross, W., 1897. The igneous rocks of the Leucite Hills and Pilot Butte, Wyoming. *Am. Mineral.*, **4**, 115–141.

Currier, L. W., and R. H. Jahns, 1941. Ordovician stratigraphy of central Vermont. *Bull. Geol. Soc. Am.*, **52**, 1487–1512.

Dachille, F. and R. Roy, 1960a. High pressure studies of the system $Mg_2GeO_4Mg_2SiO_4$ with special reference to the olivine-spinel transition. *Am. J. Sci.*, **258**, 225–246.

———, 1960b. High pressure phase transformations in laboratory mechanical mixers and mortars. *Nature,* **186**, 34.

———, 1962. "Opposed anvil pressure devices," in *Modern Very High Pressure Techniques.* R. H. Wentorf, ed., Butterworth and Co., London, 163–180.

Dal Vesco, E., 1953. Genesi e metamorfosi delle rocce basische e ultrabasiche nell ambiente nesozonale dell' orogene Pennidico (Contone Ticino). *Schweiz. Mineral. Petrog. Mitt.*, **33**, 173–480.

Daly, R. A., 1911. Magmatic differentiation in Hawaii. *J. Geol.*, **19**, 289–316.

———, 1925. Carbonate rocks of the Premier Mine, Transvaal. *J. Geol.*, **33**, 659–684.

———, 1928. Bushveld igneous complex of the Transvaal. *Bull. Geol. Soc. Am.*, **39**, 703–768.

Davidson, C. F., 1943. The Archaean rocks of the Rodil district, South Harris, Outer Hebrides. *Trans. Roy. Soc. Edinburgh,* **61**, 71–112.

———, 1957. The diamond fields of Yakutia. *Mining Mag. (London),* **97**, 329–337.

———, 1964a. On diamantiferous diatremes. *Econ. Geol.*, **59**, 1368–1380.

———, 1964b. The chemical history of the earth. *Advancing Frontiers in Geology and Geophysics.* Indian Geophys. Union, Hyderabad.

———, 1965. Diamantiferous diatremes: a reply. *Econ. Geol.*, **60**, 1735–1739.

———, 1966. Diamantiferous diatremes. *Econ. Geol.*, **61**, 786–790.

Davies, K. A., 1952. The building of Mount Elgon (East Africa). *Geol. Surv. Uganda. Mem.* **7**, 62p.

———, 1956. The geology of part of South-East Uganda with special reference to the alkaline complexes. *Geol. Surv. Uganda. Mem.* **8**, 76p.

Davis, B. T. C., 1963. The system enstatite-diopside at 30 kilobars pressure. *Carnegie Inst. Wash. Yearbook,* **62**, 103–107.

———, 1964. The system diopside-forsterite-pyrope at 40 kilobars. *Carnegie Inst. Wash. Yearbook,* **63**, 165–171.

———, and F. R. Boyd, 1965. The system $Mg_2Si_2O_6$-$CaMgSi_2O_6$ and its bearing on the origin of kimberlite. *J. Geophys. Res.*, **71**, 3567–3576.

Davis, B. T. C., and J. L. England, 1964. Melting of forsterite up to 50 kilobars. *J. Geophys. Res.*, **69**, 1113–1116.

Dawson, J. B., 1960. A comparative study of the geology and petrography of the kimberlites of the Basutoland province. Ph.D. thesis, University of Leeds.

———, 1962. Basutoland kimberlites. *Bull. Geol. Soc. Am.*, **73**, 545–560.

———, 1962. Sodium carbonate lavas from Oldoinyo Lengai, Tanganyika. *Nature,* **195**, 1075–1076.

———, 1962. The geology of Oldoinyo Lengai. *Bull. Volcanol.* **24**, 349–387.

———, 1964. Carbonate tuff cones in northern Tanganyika. *Geol. Mag.*, **101**, 129–137.

———, 1967a. "Oldoinyo Lengai, an active volcano with sodium carbonatite lava flows," in O. F. Tuttle and J. Gittins, eds., *The Carbonatites.* Wiley Interscience, New York.

———, 1967b. The kimberlite/carbonatite relationship. *Proc. 4th Gen. Meeting Intern. Mineral. Assoc.*, New Delhi, 1964, (*Indian Mineral.*, in press).

Day, T. C., and A. G. Stenhouse, 1930. Notes on

the Inchcolm anticline. *Trans. Edinburgh Geol. Soc.,* **12,** 236–251.

DeGrazia, A. R., and Haskin, L., 1964. On the gold contents of rocks. *Geochim. Cosmochim. Acta,* **28,** 559–564.

Derby, O. A., 1891. On the magnetite ore districts of Jacupiranga and Ipanema, Sao Paulo, Brazil. *Am. J. Sci.,* 3rd Ser., **41,** 311–321.

DeRoever, W. P., 1957. Sind die Alpinotypen peridotitmassen vielleicht tektonisch verfrachtete Bruchstücke der Peridotitschale?. *Geol. Rundschau,* **46,** 137–146.

de Vaumas, E., 1960. Further contributions to the geomorphology of Cyprus. *Ann. Rep. Geol. Surv. Cyprus,* 24.

De Waard, D., 1965. A proposed subdivision of the granulite facies. *Am. J. Sci.,* **263,** 455–46.

Dickinson, W. R., 1966. Table Mountain serpentinite extrusion in California coast ranges. *Bull. Geol. Soc. Am.,* **77,** 451–472.

Dietz, R. S., 1960. Meteorite impact suggested by shatter cones in rock. *Science,* **131,** 1781–1784.

———, 1961. Vredefort ring structure: meteorite impact scar? *J. Geol.,* **69,** 499–516.

———, 1963. Alpine serpentinites as oceanic rind fragments. *Bull. Geol. Soc. Am.,* **74,** 947–952.

Diller, J. S., 1886. Notes on the peridotite of Elliot County, Kentucky. *Am. J. Sci.,* 3rd Ser., **32,** 121–125.

———, 1892. Mica-peridotite from Kentucky. *Am. J. Sci.,* 3rd Ser., **44,** 286–289.

Donnelly, T. W., 1964. Evolution of eastern Greater Antillean island arc. *Am. Assoc. Petroleum Geologists Bull.,* **48,** 680–696.

Douglas, J. A. V., 1964. Geological investigations in east Greenland, Pt. VII. The Basistoppen sheet, a differentiated basic intrusion into the upper part of the Skaergaard Complex, east Greenland. *Medd. Grønland,* **164,** 5.

Dow, D. B., and H. L. Davies, 1964. The geology of the Bowutu Mountains, New Guinea. *Australia Bur. Min. Res., Geol. Geophys. Rept.* **75,** 31p.

Drake, C. L., and H. P. Woodward, 1963. Appalachian curvature, wrench faulting, and offshore structures. *Trans. N.Y. Acad. Sci.,* Ser. II, **26,** no. 1, 48–63.

Draper, D., 1911. The diamond-bearing deposits of Bagagem and Agua Suja in the state of Minas Gerais, Brazil. *Trans. Geol. Soc. S. Africa,* **14,** 8–20.

———, 1923. Additional evidence regarding the origin of the high-level diamond-bearing breccias of Diamantina, Brazil. *Trans. Geol. Soc. S. Africa,* **26,** 7–13.

Drescher, F. K., and H. K. E. Kruger, 1927. Der Peridotit von Kaersut (Grønland) und sein Ganggefolge als Beispeil einer Sekretions-differentiation. *Neues Jahrb. Mineral. Petr.* (B)—Bd. **57,** (Mugge-Festschrift) Abt. A., 569–616.

Dresser, J. A., 1901. A hornblende lamprophyre dyke at Richmond, P.Q. *Can. Record Sci.,* 315–320.

———, 1903. The geology and petrology of Shefford Mountain, Quebec. *Geol. Surv. Can., Ann. Rept.,* 1900, **13,** pt. L, 35p.

———, 1906. The Geology of Brome Mountain, Quebec. *Geol. Surv. Can., Ann. Rept.,* 1904, **16,** pt. G, 22p.

———, 1910. Geology of St. Bruno Mountain, Province of Quebec. *Geol. Surv. Can., Mem.* **7,** 33p.

Drever, H. I., 1952. The origin of some ultramafic rocks. A preliminary survey of the evidence for and against gravitative accumulation of olivine. *Medd. Dansk Geol. Foren.,* **12,** 227–229.

———, 1953. A note on the field relations of the Shiant Isles picrite. *Geol. Mag.,* **90,** 159–160.

———, 1956. The geology of Ubekendt Ejland, west Greenland: pt. II. The picritic sheets and dykes of the east coast. *Medd. Grønland,* **137,** 1–41.

———, 1958. Geological results of four expeditions to Ubekendt Ejland, west Greenland. *Arctic,* **11,** 198–210.

———, 1960. Immiscibility in the picritic intrusion at Igdlorssuit, west Greenland. *21st Intern. Geol. Congr.,* Copenhagen, *Repts.* **13,** 47–58.

———, 1964. An experiment in the use of light drilling techniques in petrological research. *Proc. Geol. Soc. London,* **1615,** 50–52.

———, and R. Johnston, 1957. Crystal growth of forsteritic olivine in magmas and melts. *Trans. Roy. Soc. Edinburgh,* **63,** 289–315.

———, 1958. The petrology of picritic rocks in minor intrusions—a Hebridean group. *Trans. Roy. Soc. Edinburgh,* **63,** 459–499.

———, 1959. The lower margin of the Shiant Isles sill. *Quart. J. Geol. Soc. London,* **114,** 343–365.

———, 1965. New petrographic data on the Shiant Isles picrite. *Mineral. Mag.,* **34,** 194–203.

———, and C. M. Thomas, 1961. Ultrabasic liquids. *Nature,* **192,** 157–158.

Drever, H. I., and D. F. Livingstone, 1948. Some basaltic rocks from west Greenland. *Proc. Roy. Soc. Edinburgh,* B, **63,** 97–114.

Drever, H. I., and J. G. MacDonald, 1967. Some new data on 'kylitic' sills and associated picrites in Ayrshire, Scotland. *Proc. Roy. Soc. Edinburgh,* B, **70,** 31–47.

Dubertret, L., 1955. Géologie des roches vertes du nord-ouest de la Syrie et du Hatay (Turquie). *Notes Mém. sur le Moyen-Orient,* **6,** 1–224.

Duparc, L., and M. Tikonovich, 1920. *Le platine et les gîtes platinifères de l'oural et du monde,* Geneve, 542p.

Du Reitz, T., 1935. Peridotites, serpentines and

soapstones of northern Sweden. *Geol. Foren, Stockholm Förhandl.*, **56**, 133–260.

Durrell, C., 1940. Metamorphism in the southern Sierra Nevada northeast of Visalia. *California Univ. Pub. Geol. Sci.*, **25**, 74–94.

Du Toit, A. L., 1954. *The Geology of South Africa* 3rd ed. Oliver and Boyd, Edinburgh, 611p.

Ebert, H., 1936. Bemerkung zu den Vorträgen Backlund und Eskola. *Geol. Rundschau*, **27**, 74–75.

Eckermann, H. von, 1948. The alkaline district of Alnö Island. *Sveriges Geol. Undersökn, Arsbok, Ser. Ca: Arhandl. Uppsat.*, **36**, 176p.

———, 1958. The alkaline and carbonatitic dikes of the Alnö formation on the mainland northwest of Alnö Island. *Kungl. Svenska Vetensk. Akademiens handlingar*, 4th series, **7**, no. 2.

———, 1960. Contributions to the knowledge of the alkaline dikes of the Alnö regions, I–III. *Arkiv. Mineral. Geol.*, **2**, no. 41.

———, 1961. The petrogenesis of the Alnö alkaline rocks. *Bull. Geol. Inst. Univ. Upsala*, **40**, 25–36.

———, 1963a. Contributions to the knowledge of the alkaline dikes of the Alnö region, V–VIII. *Arkiv. Mineral. Geol.* **3**, no. 12.

———, 1963b. Contributions to the knowledge of the alkaline dikes of the Alnö region, IX. *Arkiv. Mineral. Geol.* **3**, no. 19.

———, 1964a. Contribution to the knowledge of the alkaline dikes of the Alnö region, XI–XII. *Arkiv. Mineral. Geol.*, **3**, no. 29.

———, 1964b. Distribution of radioactivity in minerals and rocks of the Alnö alkaline area. *Arkiv. Mineral. Geol.*, **3**, no. 27.

———, 1964c. The Swedish kimberlites and a comparison with South African and Russian rocks. *Advancing Frontiers in Geology and Geophysics.* Indian Geophys. Union, Hyderabad.

———, 1966. Age relationship between the Alnö dykes and the sövite pegmatite. *Arkiv. Mineral. Geol.*, In press.

———, H. von Ubisch, and F. E. Wickman, 1952. A preliminary investigation into the isotopic composition of carbon from some alkaline intrusions. *Geochim. Cosmochim. Acta* **2**, 207–210.

Edel'shtein, I. I., 1963. Petrology and nickel content of ultrabasic intrusions in the Tobol-Buryktal area of the Southern Urals. Magmatizm, Metamorfizm, Metallogeniya Urala. *Akad. Nauk SSSR, Ural'sk Filial, Gorn.-Geol. Inst. Tr. Pervogo Ural'sk. Petrogr. Soveshch.*, Sverdlovsk, **1961**, 319–323.

Edwards, A. B., 1938. Tertiary lavas from the Kerguelen Archipelago. *B.A.N.Z. Antarctic Expedition (D. Mawson) 1929–1931. Rept.*, Ser. A, pt. **5**, no. 2, 72–100.

———, 1941. The crinanite laccolith of Circular Head, Tasmania. *Proc. Roy. Soc. Victoria*, **53**, 403–415.

———, 1953. Crinanite-picrite intrusions in the Nebo district of New South Wales. *Proc. Roy. Soc. Victoria*, **65**, 9–29.

Edwards, C. B., and Howkins, J. B., 1966. Kimberlites in Tanganyika. *Econ. Geol.* **61**, 537–554.

Edwards, G., 1955. Isotopic composition of meteoritic hydrogen. *Nature*, **176**, 109–111.

Eichstadt, F., 1884. Anomit fran Alnö. *Geol. Fören.* Stockholm *Förh.* **7**.

El-Hinnawi, E. E., 1964. Petrochemical characters of African volcanic rocks. *New Jahrb. Miner. Mh.*, **6**, 166–187.

Eller, J. P. von, 1961. Les gneiss de Sainte-Marie-aux-Mines et les séries voisines des Vosges moyennes. *Mém. Serv. Carte Géol. d'Alsace et de Lorraine*, **19**, 1–160.

Engel, A. E. J., and C. G. Engel, 1963. Basalts dredged from the northeastern Pacific Ocean. *Science*, **140**, 1321.

———, 1964a. Composition of basalts from the Mid-Atlantic Ridge. *Science*, **144**, 1330–1333.

———, 1964b. Igneous Rocks of the East Pacific Rise. *Science*, **146**, 477–485.

———, and R. G. Havens, 1965. Chemical characteristics of oceanic basalts and the upper mantle. *Bull. Geol. Soc. Am.*, **76**, 719–734.

English, R. M., and R. M. Grogan, 1948. Omaha pool and mica-peridotite intrusives, Gallatin County, Illinois. *Ill. Geol. Surv. Rept. Investigations*, **130**, 189–212.

Epshteyn, Ye. M., and L. I. Anikeyeva, 1965. Problems in geology and petrology of ultrabasic alkalic intrusive rock complexes (trans. by V. P. Sokolof). *Intern. Geol. Rev.*, **7**, 307–324.

Epstein, S., 1959. "The variations of the O^{18}/O^{16} ratio in nature and some geologic applications," in *Researches in Geochemistry*, ed. P. H. Abelson, John Wiley and Sons, New York, 217–240.

———, 1966. Oxygen and hydrogen isotope studies of serpentine. In preparation.

Eric, J. H., A. A. Stromquist, and C. M. Swinney, 1955. Geology and mineral deposits of the Angels Camp and Sonora quadrangles, Calaveras and Tuolumne Counties, California. *Calif. Div. Mines Spec. Rept.* **41**, 55p.

Erickson, R. L., and L. V. Blade, 1963. Geochemistry and petrology of the alkalic igneous complex at Magnet Cove, Arkansas. *U.S. Geol. Surv., Profess. Paper*, **425**, 1–95.

Erlich, E. N., 1964. A new province of alkaline igneous rocks in the north of the Siberian platform. *Zap. Vsesoyuz. Mineral. Obshch.*, **93**, 682–692. (Russian.)

Ernst, T., 1935. Olivinknollen der Basalte als Bruchstücke alter Olivinfelse. *Nachr. Ges. Wiss.*

Göttingen, Math-Phys. Kl., Gruppe IV, Band **1**, no. 13, 147–154.

Eskola, P., 1921. On the eclogites of Norway. *Skr. Vidensk. Selsk. Kristiania,* **8,** 1–118.

Faessler, C., 1962. Analyses of rocks. *Quebec Dept. Nat. Resources, Geol. Rept.* **103,** 251p.

Fairbairn, H. W., G. Faure, W. H. Pinson, P. M. Hurley, and J. L. Powell, 1963. Initial ratio of strontium 87 to strontium 86, whole-rock age, and discordant biotite in the Monteregian igneous province, Quebec. *J. Geophys. Res.,* **68,** 6515–6522.

Faure, G., and P. M. Hurley, 1963. The isotopic composition of strontium in oceanic and continental basalts: application to the origin of igneous rocks. *J. Petrol.,* **4,** 31–50.

Faust, G. T., 1963. Minor elements in serpentine—additional data. *Geochim. Cosmochim. Acta,* **27,** 665–668.

———, K. J. Murata, and J. J. Fahey, 1956. Relation of minor-element content of serpentines to their geological origin. *Geochim. Cosmochim. Acta,* **10,** 316–320.

Fawcett, J. J., 1963. The upper stability limit of magnesian chlorites to 10 kilobars P_{H_2O}, *Carnegie Inst. Wash. Yearbook,* **62,** 140–143.

———, 1964. Upper stability limits of magnesian chlorites. *Carnegie Inst. Wash. Yearbook,* **63,** 136–137.

———, and H. S. Yoder, Jr., 1963. The liquidus region at 10 kilobars $P.H_2O$. *Carnegie Inst. Wash. Yearbook* **62,** 143–145.

Feringa, G., 1959. The geological succession in a portion of the northwestern Bushveld (Union section) and its interpretation. *Trans. Geol. Soc. S. Africa,* **62,** 219–232.

Fiala, J., 1965. Pyrope of some garnet peridotites of the Czech massif. *Krystalinikum.* Acad. Sci., Prague **3,** 55–74.

Finch, R. H., and G. A. Macdonald, 1950. Hawaiian volcanoes during 1950. *U.S. Geol. Surv. Bull.* **996-B,** 72.

Findlay, D. C., 1964. Petrology of the Tulameen ultramafic complex, British Columbia. *Geol. Soc. Am., Spec. Paper,* **76,** 58. (Abstr.)

———, and C. H. Smith, 1965. The Muskox drilling project. *Geol. Surv. Can., Paper* **64-44,** 1–170.

Fisher, D. E., 1964. The aluminum content of chondritic meteorites as determined by activation analysis. *Geochim. Cosmochim. Acta,* **28,** 743–749.

Fisher, D. J., 1963. Ed. of "Symposium on layered intrusions," *Mineral. Soc. Am. Spec. Paper* **1,** 1–134.

Flett, J. S., 1930. The teschenite of Easter Dalmeny. *Sum. Prog. Geol. Surv. G. Britain,* 1929, **3,** 59–74.

———, 1931a. The Saline No. 1 teschenite. *Sum. Progr. Geol. Surv. G. Britain,* 1930, **2,** 44–51.

———, 1931b. The Blackness teschenite. *Sum. Progr. Geol. Surv. G. Britain,* 1930, **3,** 39–45.

———, 1932. The Stankards sill. *Sum. Progr. Geol. Surv. G. Britain,* 1931, **2,** 141–156.

———, 1934. Geological map of Lizard. *Geol. Surv. Engl. Wales,* sheet 359, scale 1:63,360.

———, 1946. Geology of the Lizard and Meneage (explanation of sheet 359). *Geol. Survey G. Britain Mem.,* 208p.

———, and J. B. Hill, 1912. Geology of the Lizard and Meneage (explanation of sheet 359). *Geol. Surv. Engl. Wales Mem.,* 280p.

Flinn, D., 1965. "Deformation in metamorphism," in Pitcher, W. S., and G. W. Flinn, eds., *Controls of Metamorphism.* Oliver and Boyd, Edinburgh and London, 46–72.

Flint, D. E., J. F. de Albear, and P. W. Guild, 1948. Geology and chromite deposits of the Camagüey district, Camagüey Province, Cuba. *U.S. Geol. Surv. Bull.* **954-B,** 39–63.

Forbes, R. B., 1963. Ultrabasic inclusions from the basalts of the Hut Point area, Ross Island, Antarctica. *Bull. Volcanol.,* **26,** 13–21.

———, 1965. The comparative chemical composition of eclogite and basalt. *J. Geophys. Res.,* **70,** 1515–1521.

———, and S. Banno, 1966. Nickel-iron content of peridotite inclusion and cognate olivine from an alkali-olivine basalt. *Am. Mineral.,* **51,** 130–140.

Forbes, R. B., and H. Kuno, 1965. The regional petrology of peridotite inclusions and basaltic host rocks. *Proc. 22nd Intern. Geol. Congr., Upper Mantle Symp.,* New Delhi (1964), 161–179.

Forestier, F. H., 1962. Les péridotites serpentinisées en France: *Bull. B.R.G.M.,* **2,** 43–75.

Forgacs, O. L., A. A. Robertson, and S. G. Mason, 1958. The hydrodynamic behaviour of paper-making fibres. *Pulp Paper Mag. Can.,* **59,** 117–128.

Fortier, Y. O., 1945. Orford, Eastern Townships, Quebec. *Geol. Surv. Can., Paper* **45-8,** 5p.

Fourie, G. P., 1959. The chromite deposits in the Rustenburg area. *S. Africa Dept. Mines Geol. Surv. Bull.* **27,** 45p.

Fox, H., and J. J. H. Teall, 1893. Notes on some coast sections at the Lizard. *Quart. J. Geol. Soc. London,* **49,** 199–210.

Fozzard, P. M. H., 1956. Further notes on the volcanic rocks of Igwisi. *Records Geol. Surv. Tanganyika,* **6,** 69–75.

Frankel, J. J., 1942. Studies on Karroo dolerites. 2. Some younger intrusions of olivine basaltic dolerite. *Trans. Geol. Soc., S. Africa,* **45,** 1–25.

Franz, G. W., 1965. Melting relationships in the system CaO-MgO-SiO_2-CO_2-H_2O: a study of synthetic kimberlites. Ph.D. thesis, The Pennsylvania State University.

———, and P. J. Wyllie, 1966. Melting relationships in the system $CaO-MgO-SiO_2-H_2O$ at 1 kilobar pressure. *Geochim. Cosmochim. Acta,* **30,** 9–22.

Frechen, J., 1962. Führer zu volkanologisch-petrographischen Exkursionen im Siebengebirge am Rhein, Laacher Vulkangebiet und Maargebiet der Westeifel. Stuttgart, 151p.

———, 1963. Kristallisation, Mineralbestand, Mineralchemismus und Forderfolge der Mafitite vom Dreiser Weiher in der Eifel. *Neues Jahrb. Mineral. Monatsh.,* **1963,** 205–225.

Fredriksson, K., and A. E. Ringwood, 1963. Origin of meteoritic chondrules. *Geochim. Cosmochim. Acta.,* **27,** 639–641.

Freedman, J., D. U. Wise, and R. D. Bentley, 1964. Pattern of folded folds in the Appalachian Piedmont along Susquehanna River. *Bull. Geol. Soc. Am.,* **75,** 621–638.

Fuller, R. E., 1939. Gravitational accumulation of olivine during the advance of basaltic flows. *J. Geol.,* **47,** 303–313.

Fyfe, W. S., F. J. Turner, and J. Verhoogen, 1958. Metamorphic reactions and metamorphic facies. *Geol. Soc. Am. Mem.* **73,** 259p.

Game, P. M., 1942. Optical properties of olivines from Ubekendt Ejland, west Greenland. *Mineral. Mag.,* **26,** 11–15.

Garson, M. S., 1962. The Tundulu carbonatite ring-complex in southern Nyasaland. *Nyasaland Geol. Surv. Mem.* **2,** 248p.

Gass, I. G., 1958. Ultrabasic pillow lavas from Cyprus. *Geol. Mag.,* **95,** 241–251.

———, and D. Masson-Smith, 1963. The geology and gravity anomalies of the Troodos Massif, Cyprus: *Phil. Trans. Roy. Soc.* London, Ser. A, **255,** 417–467.

Gast, P. W., 1960. Limitations on the composition of the upper mantle. *J. Geophys. Res.,* **65,** 1287–1297.

———, 1961. The rubidium strontium method. *Ann. N.Y. Acad. Sci.,* **91,** 181–184.

———, 1965. Terrestrial ratio of potassium to rubidium and the composition of Earth's mantle. *Science,* **147,** 858–860.

———, G. R. Tilton, and C. Hedge, 1964. Isotopic composition of lead and strontium from Ascension and Gough islands. *Science,* **145,** 1182–1185.

Gaudette, H. E., 1963. Geochemistry of the Twin Sisters ultramafic body, Washington. Ph.D. thesis, University of Illinois.

Geijer, P., 1928. Alnöitic dikes from the coast region of Lulea and Kalix in northern Sweden. *Fennia,* **50,** no. 11.

Gerling, E. K., and I. I. Matveeva, 1964. "K-Ar ages of basic rocks" in Absolute age of geological formations. *Dokl. Sovet. Geol. Intern. Geol. Congr.,* **3,** 329–341. Moscow, Nauka. (Russian.)

Gevers, T. W., 1933. Alkali rocks in the Auas mountains, south of Windhoek, South-West Africa. *Trans. Geol. Soc., S. Africa,* **36,** 77–89.

Gill, J. E., and D. P. Gold, 1962. Mounts St. Hilaire and Johnson: *54th N.E.I.G.C. guidebook,* ed. T. H. Clark. McGill University, Montreal, 67–79.

Gillson, J. L., 1927. Origin of the Vermont talc deposits. *Econ. Geol.,* **22,** 246–287.

Gilluly, J., 1933. Replacement origin of the albite granite near Sparta, Oregon. *U.S. Geol. Surv., Profess. Paper* **175-C,** 65–81.

———, 1937. Geology and mineral resources of the Baker quadrangle, Oregon. *U.S. Geol. Surv. Bull.* **879,** 119p.

Gjelsvik, T., 1951. Oversikt over bergartene in Sunnmøre og tilgrensende deler av Nordfjord. *Norg. Geol. Undersøkelse,* **179,** 1–45.

Godfrey, J., 1962. The deuterium content of hydrous minerals from the east-central Sierra Nevada and Yosemite National Park. *Geochim. Cosmochim. Acta,* **26,** 1215-1245.

Gold, D. P., 1962. The Oka Complex: *54th N.E.I.G.C. guide book,* T. H. Clark ed., McGill University, Montreal, 7–14.

———, 1963a. Average chemical composition of carbonatites. *Econ. Geol.,* **58,** 988–991.

———, 1963b. The relationship between the limestones and the alkaline rocks of Oka and St. Hilaire, Quebec. Ph.D. thesis. McGill University, Montreal, 354p.

———, 1967a. The minerals of the Oka carbonatite and alkaline complex, Oka, Quebec. *Proc. 4th Gen. Meeting Intern. Mineral. Assoc.,* New Delhi, 1964. *Indian Mineral.* In press.

———, 1967b. The average and typical chemical composition of carbonatites. *Proc. 4th Gen. Meeting Intern. Mineral. Assoc.,* New Delhi, 1964. *Indian Mineral.* In press.

Goldsmith, H. L., and S. G. Mason, 1961. Axial migration of particles in Poiseuille flow. *Nature,* **190,** 1095–1096.

———, 1962. The flow of suspensions through tubes. I. Single spheres, rods, and discs. *J. Colloid Sci.,* **17,** 448–476.

———, 1964. Some model experiments in haemodynamics. *Bibliotheca Anat.,* **4,** 462–478.

———, 1967. "The microrheology of dispersions," in Eirich, F. R., ed., *Rheology: Theory and Applications.* Academic Press, New York, **IV,** 152p.

Goles, G. G., and E. Anders, 1962. Abundances of iodine tellurium and uranium in meteorites. *Geochim. Cosmochim. Acta,* **26,** 723–737.

Gooch, F. A., 1876. Über vulkanishe Gesteine der Galapagos Inseln. *Mineral. Petrog. Mitt.,* 133–140.

Goranson, R. W., 1940. Physics of stressed solids. *J. Chem. Phys.,* **8,** 323–334.

Graham, R. P. D., 1944. "The Monteregian Hills," in Dresser, J. A., and T. C. Denis, eds., *Geology of Quebec*. Quebec Dept. Mines, Geol. Rept. 20, **2**, 455–482.

Grantham, D. R., and J. B. Allen, 1960. Kimberlites in Sierra Leone. *Overseas Geol. Mineral. Res.,* **8,** 6–25.

Green, D. H., 1961. Ultramafic breccias from the Musa Valley, Papua. *Geol. Mag.,* **98,** 1–26.

———, 1963. Alumina content of enstatite in a Venezuelan high-temperature peridotite. *Bull. Geol. Soc. Am.,* **74,** 1397–1402.

———, 1964a. The petrogenesis of the high-temperature peridotite intrusion in the Lizard area, Cornwall. *J. Petrol.,* **5,** 134–188.

———, 1964b. The metamorphic aureole of the peridotite at the Lizard, Cornwall. *J. Geol.,* **72,** 543–563.

———, 1964c. "A re-study and re-interpretation of the geology of the Lizard Peninsula, Cornwall," in K. F. G. Hosking and G. J. Shrimpton, eds., *Present views of some aspects of the geology of Cornwall.* Roy. Geol. Soc. Cornwall, Truro, Cornwall.

———, and A. E. Ringwood, 1963. Mineral assemblages in a model mantle composition. *J. Geophys. Res.,* **68,** 937–945.

———, 1964. Fractionation of basalt magmas at high pressures. *Nature,* **201,** 1276–1279.

———, 1966. An experimental study of the gabbro to eclogite transformation and its petrological applications. *Geochim. Cosmochim. Acta,* **31.** In press.

Green, J., and A. Poldervaart, 1955. Some basaltic provinces. *Geochim. Cosmochim. Acta,* **7,** 177–188.

Greenwood, H. J., 1963. The synthesis and stability of anthophyllite. *J. Petrol.,* **4,** 317–351.

Gregory, H. E., 1917. Geology of the Navajo country, a reconnaissance of parts of Arizona, New Mexico, and Utah. *U.S. Geol. Surv. Profess. Paper* **93,** 1–161.

Greninger, A. B., and A. R. Troiano, 1949. *Trans. AIMME,* **185,** 590.

Griggs, D. T., M. S. Paterson, H. C. Heard, and Anomalous weakness of synthetic crystals. *Science,* **147,** 292–295.

———, 1965b. Water-weakening of silicates. *Trans. Am. Geophys. Union,* **46,** 163. (Abstr.)

Griggs, D. T., M. S. Patterson, H. C. Heard, and F. J. Turner, 1960. "Annealing recrystallization in calcite crystals and aggregates," in Griggs, D. T., and J. Handin, eds., *Rock deformation. Geol. Soc. Am. Mem.* **79,** 21–38.

Griggs, D. T., F. J. Turner, and H. C. Heard, "Deformation of rocks at 500° to 800°C," in Griggs, D. T., and J. Handin, eds., rock deformation, 1960. *Geol. Soc. Am. Mem.,* **79,** 39–104.

Griscom, Andrew, and D. L. Peterson, 1961. Aeromagnetic, aeroradioactivity, and gravity investigations of Piedmont rocks in the Rockville quadrangle, Maryland. *U.S. Geol. Surv., Profess. Paper,* **424-D,** D267-D271.

Grubenmann, U., 1908. Der granatolivinfels der Gordunotals, und seine Begleitgesteine. *Vischr. naturf. Ges. Zürich.,* **53,** 129–156.

Guilbert, J. M., 1962. The origin of the chromites below the Steelpoort Main Seam of the Bushveld Complex. Ph.D. thesis, Univ. of Wisconsin, Madison, Wisconsin, 153p.

Guild, P. W., 1947. Petrology and structure of the Moa chromite district, Oriente Province, Cuba. *Trans. Am. Geophys. Union,* **28,** 218–246.

———, and Balsley, J. R., 1942. Chromite deposits of Red Bluff Bay and vicinity, Baranof Island, Alaska. *U.S. Geol. Surv. Bull.,* **936-G,** 171–187.

Gunn, B. M., 1963. Layered intrusions in the Ferrar dolerites, Antarctica. *Mineral. Soc. Am., Spec. Paper* **1,** 124–133.

Gutenberg, Beno, 1959. *Physics of the Earth's Interior,* Academic Press, New York, 240p.

Hack, J. T., 1942. Sedimentation and volcanism in the Hopi Buttes, Arizona. *Bull. Geol. Soc. Am.,* **53,** 335–372.

Hall, A. L., 1930. Asbestos in the Union of South Africa. *Geol. Surv. S. Africa, Mem.* 12.

———, 1932. The Bushveld Igneous Complex of the Central Transvaal. *S. Africa Dept. Mines Geol. Surv. Mem.* **28,** 560p.

Hall, G. M., and H. C. Amick, 1944. Igneous rock areas in the Norris region, Tennessee. *J. Geol.,* **52,** 424–430.

Hamad, S. el. D., 1963. The chemistry and mineralogy of the olivine nodules of Calton Hill, Derbyshire. *Mineral. Mag.,* **33,** 483–497.

Hamaguchi, H., G. W. Reed, and A. Turkevich, 1957. Uranium and Barium in Stone Meteorites: *Geochim. Cosmochim. Acta,* **12,** 337–347.

Hamilton, D. L., C. W. Burnham, and E. F. Osborn, 1964. The solubility of water and effects of oxygen fugacity and water content on crystallization in mafic magmas. *J. Petrol.,* **5,** 21–39.

Hamilton, W., 1965. Diabase sheets of the Taylor Glacier region, Victoria Land, Antarctica. *U.S. Geol. Surv. Profess. Paper,* **456-B.**

———, and W. Mountjoy, 1965. Alkali content of alpine ultramafic rocks: *Geochim. Cosmochim. Acta,* **29,** 661–671.

Hammer, W., 1921. Eklogit und Peridotit in den mittleren Ötztaler Alpen. *Jahrb. Geol. Bundesanstalt,* (*Austria*) **76,** 98.

Handin, J., 1964. "Strength at high confining pressure and temperature of serpentinite from Mayaguez, Puerto Rico," in Burk, C. A., ed., *A study of serpentinite.* Natl. Acad. Sci.—Natl. Res. Council Publ. **1188,** 126–131.

Hargraves, R. B., 1962. Petrology of the Allard Lake anorthosite suite, Quebec. *Geol. Soc. Am.* **Buddington Vol.,** 163–189.

Harker, A., 1904. The Tertiary igneous rocks of Skye. *Geol. Surv. U. K. Mem.*

———, 1909. *The natural history of igneous rocks.* Macmillan Co., New York.

Harrington, B. J., 1907. Isomorphism as illustrated by certain varieties of magnetite. *Mineral. Mag.*, **14,** 373–377.

Harris, P. G., 1957. Zone refining and the origin of potassic basalts. *Geochim. Cosmochim. Acta,* **12,** 195–205.

———, 1962. Increase of temperature in ascending basalt magma. *Am. J. Sci.,* **260,** 783–786.

———, 1966. The importance of minerals other than olivine in the upper mantle. *Trans. Am. Geophys. Union,* **47,** 176. (Abstr. Preprint of complete paper distributed at the 47th Annual Meeting of *Am. Geophys. Union.*)

———, and J. A. Rowell, 1960. Some Geochemical Aspects of the Mohorovicic Discontinuity. *J. Geophys. Res.,* **65,** 2443–2459.

Harrison, J. C., 1955. An interpretation of the gravity anomalies in the eastern Mediterranean. *Phil. Trans. Roy. Soc.* London, Ser. A, **248,** 283.

Hart, S. R., 1964. Ultramafic rocks of St. Paul's Island. *Carnegie Inst. Wash. Yearbook,* **63,** 330–331.

———, 1965. Potassium, rubidium, and strontium in the ultramafic rocks of St. Paul's Islands. *Geol. Soc. Am., Spec. Paper* **82,** 86–87. (Abstr.)

———, L. T. Aldrich, G. R. Tilton, G. L. Davis, T. E. Krogh, and M. Yamaguchi, 1965. Potassium-Rubidium studies of ultrabasic rocks in Japan. *Carnegie Inst. Wash. Yearbook,* **64,** 293–296.

Harvie, R., 1909. On the origin and relations of the Palaeozoic breccia of the vicinity of Montreal. *Trans. Roy. Soc. Can.,* 3rd ser., **3,** 249–299.

Haskin, L. A., and F. A. Frey, 1966. Dispersed and not-so-rare earths, *Sci.,* **152,** 299–314.

Hayashi, H., 1955. Ejecta around Itinome-gata in Oga Peninsula, Akita Prefecture. *Geol. Soc. Japan J.,* **61,** 240–248. (Japanese.)

Heard, H. C., and W. W. Rubey, 1966. Tectonic implications of gypsum dehydration. *Bull. Geol. Soc. Am.,* **77,** 741–760.

Heckroodt, R. O., 1959. The geology around the dunite pipe on Driekop (Eastern Transvaal). *Trans. Geol. Soc. S. Africa,* **62,** 59–73.

Hedge, C. E., and F. G. Walthall, 1963. Radiogenic strontium-87 as an index to geologic processes. *Science,* **140,** 1214–1217.

Heier, K. S., 1963. Uranium, thorium and potassium in eclogitic rocks. *Geochim. Cosmochim. Acta,* **27,** 849–860.

Heier, K. S., and W. Compston, 1966. K/Rb ratios of eclogites. Submitted to *Geochim. Cosmochim. Acta.*

———, and I. McDougall, 1965. Thorium and uranium concentrations, and the isotopic composition of strontium in the differentiated Tasmanian dolerites. *Geochim. Cosmochim. Acta* **29,** 643–659.

Hentschel, H., 1937. Der Eklogite von Gilsberg im Sachs. Granulitgebirge und seine metamorphen Umwandlungsstofen. *Mineral. Petrog. Mitt.,* **49,** 42–88.

Herz, Norman, 1950. The petrology of the Baltimore gabbro and the petrography of the Baltimore-Patapsco aqueduct. Ph.D. thesis, Johns Hopkins Univ., 127p.

———, 1951. Petrology of the Baltimore gabbro, Maryland. *Bull. Geol. Soc. Am.,* **62,** 979–1016.

Hess, H. H., 1933. The problem of serpentinization and the origin of certain chrysotile asbestos, talc, and soapstone deposits. *Econ. Geol.,* **28,** 634–657.

———, 1938. A primary peridotite magma. *Am. J. Sci.,* 5th ser., **35,** 321–344.

———, 1939. Extreme fractional crystallization of a basaltic magma, the Stillwater igneous complex. *Trans. Am. Geophys. Union,* **20,** 430–432. (Abstr.)

———, 1941. Pyroxenes of common mafic magmas. *Am. Mineral.,* **26,** 515–535, 573–594.

———, 1949. Chemical composition and optical properties of common clinopyroxenes, pt. I. *Am. Mineral.,* **34,** 621–666.

———, 1950. Vertical mineral variation in the Great Dyke of Southern Rhodesia. *Trans. Geol. Soc. S. Africa,* **53,** 159–166.

———, 1952. Orthopyroxenes of the Bushveld type, ion substitutions and changes in unit cell dimensions. *Am. J. Sci.,* **Bowen vol.,** 173–187.

———, 1955a. Serpentines, orogeny and epeirogeny. *Geol. Soc. Am., Spec. Paper* **62,** 391–408.

———, 1955b. The oceanic crust, *J. Marine Res.,* **14,** 423–439.

———, 1956. The magnetic properties and differentiation of dolerite sills—Discussion. *Am. J. Sci.,* **254,** 446–451.

———, 1960a. Stillwater igneous complex, Montana, a quantitative mineralogical study. *Geol. Soc. Am., Mem.* **80,** 230p.

———, 1960b. Caribbean research project: Progress report. *Bull. Geol. Soc. Am.,* **71,** 235–240.

———, 1962. History of ocean basins: *Geol. Soc. Am.,* **Buddington vol.,** 599–620.

———, 1964. "The oceanic crust, the upper mantle and the Mayaguez serpentinized peridotite" in Burk, C. A., ed., *A Study of Serpentinite.* Natl. Acad. Sci.—Natl. Res. Council Publ. **1188,** 169–175.

———, and Otalora, G., 1964. "Mineralogical and Chemical Composition of the Mayaguez Serpentinite Cores," in Burk, C. A., ed., *A Study of Serpentinite.* Natl. Acad. Sci.—Natl. Res. Council Publ., **1188,** 152–168.

Hiemstra, S. A., and W. J. van Biljon, 1959. The geology of the upper Magaliesberg Stage and the lower Bushveld Complex in the vicinity of Steelpoort. *Trans. Geol. Soc. S. Africa,* **62**, 239–255.

Hiessleitner, G., 1952. Serpentin- und Chromerz-Geologie der Balkanhalbinsel und eines Teiles von Kleinasien. *Jahb. Geol. Bundesanstalt, (Austria) Sonderbd.* 1, T. 1, 2, 683p.

Higazy, R. A., 1954. Trace elements of volcanic ultrabasic potassic rocks of south-western Uganda and adjoining part of the Belgian Congo. *Bull. Geol. Soc. Am.,* **65**, 39–70.

Hodder, R. W., 1961. Alkaline rocks and niobium deposits near Nemegos, Ontario. *Geol. Surv. Can., Bull.* **70**, 1–75.

Hoering, T. C., and P. L. Parker, 1961. The geochemistry of the stable isotopes of chlorine. *Geochim. Cosmochim. Acta,* **23**, 186–199.

Hogarth, D. D., 1964a. Intrusive carbonate rock near Ottawa, Canada. *Proc. 4th Gen. Meeting Intern. Mineral. Assoc.,* New Delhi, 1964, (*Indian Mineral.,* in press).

———, 1964b. Normal and reverse pleochroism in biotite. *Can. Mineral.* **8**, pt. 1, 136.

Hogbom, A. G., 1895. Über das Nephelinsyenitgebiet auf der Insel Alnö. *Geol. Fören. Stockholm Förh.,* **17**.

Holmes, A., 1936. A contribution to the petrology of kimberlite and its inclusions. *Trans. Geol. Soc. S. Africa,* **39**, 379–428.

———, 1937. The petrology of katungite. *Geol. Mag.,* **74**, 200–219.

———, 1950. Petrogenesis of katungite and its associates. *Am. Mineral.,* **35**, 772–792.

———, 1956. The ejectamenta of Katwe crater, south-west Uganda. *Kon. Ned. Geol. Mijnbouwk, Genootschap., Geol. Ser.,* **16**, 139–166.

———, and H. F. Harwood, 1932. Petrology of the volcanic fields east and south-east of Ruwenzori, Uganda. *Quart. J. Geol. Soc. London,* **88**, 370–442.

———, 1937. The volcanic area of Bufumbira: The petrology of the volcanic field of Bufumbira, South-west Uganda. *Geol. Surv. Uganda Mem.,* no. 3, pt. II, 300p.

Holyk, W., and L. H. Ahrens, 1953. Potassium in ultramafic rocks. *Geochim. Cosmochim. Acta,* **4**, 241–250.

Hopson, C. A., 1964. "Crystalline rocks," in *Geology of Howard and Montgomery Counties,* Maryland Geol. Surv. County Rept. 257p.

Horai, K., 1964. Studies of the thermal state of the earth. The 13th paper: terrestrial heat flow in Japan. *Bull. Earthquake Res. Inst., Tokyo Univ.,* **42**, 93–132.

Hornal, R. W., 1967. The gravity anomaly field of the Coppermine area, N.W.T. *Gravity map series of the Dominion Observatory no. 45.* Ottawa, Canada.

Hotstetler, P. B., R. G. Coleman, F. A. Mumpton, and B. W. Evans, 1966. Brucite in Alpine serpentinites. *Am. Mineral.,* **51**, 75–98.

Howard, W. V., 1922. Some outliers of the Monteregian Hills. *Trans. Roy. Soc. Can.,* **16**, 47–95.

Howie, R. A., 1963. Kaersutite from the Lugar Sill and from Alnöite Breccia, Alnö Island. *Mineral. Mag.* 33, no. 263.

Howland, A. L., 1954. Relations of regional and thermal metamorphism near the base of the Stillwater complex, Montana. *Bull. Geol. Soc. Am.* **65**, 1264–1265. (Abstr.)

———, 1955. Chromite deposits in central part of the Stillwater complex, Sweet Grass County, Montana. *U.S. Geol. Surv. Bull.* **1015-D**, 99–121.

———, R. M. Garrels, and W. R. Jones, 1949. Chromite deposits of the Boulder River area, Sweetgrass County, Montana. *U.S. Geol. Surv. Bull.* **948-C**, 63–82.

Huang, W. T., 1962. *Petrology,* McGraw-Hill Book Co., New York, 480p.

Hubbert, M. K., and W. W. Rubey, 1959. Role of fluid pressure in mechanics of overthrust faulting. *Bull. Geol. Soc. Am.,* **70**, 115–166.

Huckenholz, H. G., 1966. Der petrogenetische Werdegang der Klinopyroxene in den tertiaren Vulkaniten der Hocheifel. III. Die Klinopyroxene der Pikritbasalte (Ankaramite). *Contr. Mineral. Petrol.,* **12**, 73–95.

Hughes, C. J., 1956. Geological investigations in east Greenland, pt. VI: A differentiated basic sill enclosed in the Skaergaard Intrusion, east Greenland and related sills injecting the lavas. *Medd. Grønland,* **137**, 2.

Hunahashi, M., 1948. Contact metasomatism associated with the pyroxene peridotite in the Horoman region in Hidaka metamorphic zone. *J. Fac. Sci., Hokkaido Univ. Ser. 4,* **8**, 31–61. (Japanese.)

Huntting, M. T., W. A. G. Bennett, V. E. Livingston, and W. S. Moon, 1961. Geologic map of Washington. *State of Washington. Div. Mines Geol.*

Hurley, P. M., 1957. Test on the possible chondritic composition of the earth's mantle and its abundance of uranium, thorium and potassium. *Bull. Geol. Soc. Am.,* **68**, 379–382.

———, et al, 1959. Age of the Monteregian Hills. 7th Ann. Rept. for 1959, U.S. At. Energy Comm., NYO-3940, Mass. Inst. Tech. 217p.

Hurley, P. M., H. W. Fairbairn, and W. H. Pinson, 1964. "Rb-Sr relationships in serpentinite from Mayaguez, Puerto Rico, and dunite from St. Paul's rocks: a progress report." in Burk, C. A., ed., *A study of serpentinite.* Natl. Acad. Sci.—Natl. Res. Council Publ. **1188**, 149–151.

Irvine, T. N., 1959. The ultramafic complex and related rocks of Duke Island, southeastern

Alaska. Ph.D. thesis, Calif. Inst. of Technology, 320p.

Irvine, T. N., 1963. Origin of the ultramafic complex at Duke Island, southeastern Alaska. *Mineral. Soc. Am. Spec. Paper* **1**, 36–45.

———, 1965. Sedimentary structures in igneous intrusions with particular reference to the Duke Island ultramafic complex. *Soc. Econ. Paleontol. Mineral. Spec. Publ.* **12**, 220–232.

———, 1966. Chromian spinel as a petrogenetic indicator. Part 2: Petrologic applications. *Can. J. Earth Sci.* In preparation.

Jackson, E. D., 1960. X-ray determinative curve for natural olivine of composition Fo_{80-90}. *U.S. Geol. Surv. Profess. Paper* **400-B**, B432-B434.

———, 1961a. Primary textures and mineral associations in the Ultramafic zone of the Stillwater complex, Montana. *U.S. Geol. Surv. Profess. Paper* **358**, 106p.

———, 1961b. X-ray determinative curve for some natural plagioclases of composition An_{60-85}. *U.S. Geol. Surv. Profess. Paper* **424-C**, C286–C288.

———, 1963. Stratigraphic and lateral variation of chromite composition in the Stillwater complex. *Mineral. Soc. Am. Spec. Paper* **1**, 46–54.

———, 1964. "Primary features of stratiform chromite deposits," in Woodtli, R., ed., *Methods of prospection for chromite,* Organization for Economic Cooperation and Development, Paris, 111–132.

———, A. L. Howland, J. W. Peoples, and W. R. Jones, 1954. Geologic maps and sections of the eastern part of the Stillwater complex, in Stillwater County, Montana. *U.S. Geol. Surv.,* Open-file report.

Jacobs, E. C., 1914. Talc, and the talc deposits of Vermont. *Vermont State Geologist 9th Bienn. Rept.* 1913–14, 382–429.

———, 1916. The talc and verd antique deposits of Vermont. *Vermont State Geologist 10th Bienn. Rept.* 1915–16, 232–280.

Jaeger, J. C., 1958. "The solidification and cooling of intrusive sheets," in *Dolerite: a Symposium.* Hobart, Tasmania, 77–87.

———, and G. Joplin, 1956. The magnetic properties and differentiation of dolerite sills—discussion. *Am. J. Sci.,* **254**, 443–446.

Jahns, R. H., 1955. The study of pegmatites, in pt. 2 of A. M. Bateman, ed., *Econ. Geol. 50th anniv. vol.,* 1025–1130.

———, 1956. Resurgent boiling and the formation of magmatic pegmatites, *Bull. Geol. Soc. Am.,* **67**, 1172 (Abstr.)

———, and C. W. Burnham, 1961. Experimental studies of pegmatite genesis: A model for the crystallization of granitic pegmatites, *Geol. Soc. Am. Spec. Paper* **68**, 206 (Abstr.)

Janse, A. J. A., 1964a. Monticellite-peridotite from Mt. Brukkavos, South West Africa. *Ann. Rept. Res. Inst. African Geol., Univ. Leeds,* **8**, 21–24.

Janse, A. J. A., 1964b. Kimberlites and related rocks of the Nama Plateau, South-West Africa. Ph.D. thesis, University of Leeds.

Jérémine, E., 1938. Sur les lherzolites en voie de serpentinisation des Vosges Lorraines. *C.R. Acad. Sci., Paris,* **206**, 441–443.

Johannsen, A., 1938. *A Descriptive Petrography of the Igneous Rocks: The Feldspathoid Rocks, and the Peridotites and Perknites, vol. IV.* The University of Chicago Press, 523p.

Johnson, R. L., 1961. The geology of the Darowa and Shawa carbonatite complexes, Southern Rhodesia. *Trans. Geol. Soc. S. Africa,* **64**, 101–145.

Johnson, R. W., Jr., and C. Milton, 1955. Dike rocks of central-western Virginia *Bull. Geol. Soc. Am.,* **66**, 1689–1690.

Johnston, R., 1953. The olivines of the Garbh Eilean Sill, Shiant Isles. *Geol. Mag.,* **90**, 161–171.

Jones, W. R., J. W. Peoples, and A. L. Howland, 1960. Igneous and tectonic structures of the Stillwater complex, Montana. *U.S. Geol. Surv. Bull.* **1071-H**, 281–340.

Joplin, G. A., 1959. On the origin and occurrence of basic bodies associated with discordant bathyliths. *Geol. Mag.,* **96**, 361–373.

Junner, N. R., 1943. The diamond deposits of the Gold Coast. *Bull. Geol. Surv., Gold Coast,* no. **12.**

Kalkowsky, E., 1880. Ueber die Erforschung der archäischen Formationen. *Neues Jahrb. Mineral. Geol. Paleontol.,* **1**, 1–28.

Kanamori, H., 1963. Study on the crustal-mantle structure in Japan. Pt 2: Interpretation of the results obtained by seismic refraction studies in connection with the study of gravity and laboratory experiments. *Bull. Earthquake Res. Inst., Tokyo Univ.,* **41**, 761–779.

Kapp, H. E., 1961. A petrographic comparison of a tertiary alkaline igneous complex in Northeastern Greenland with the Monteregian Hills of Eastern Canada. *Can. Mineral.,* **6**, 582–594.

Karnis, A., H. L. Goldsmith, and S. G. Mason, 1963. Axial migration of particles in Poiseuille flow. *Nature,* **200**, 159–160.

Kashkarov, I. F., and Yu. A. Polkanov, 1964. On the discovery of diamond in titanium-zircon sand. *Dokl. Akad. Nauk SSSR,* **157**, 1129–1130. (Russian.)

Katsura, T., 1956. Geochemical study of Japanese volcanoes (pt 35). Vanadium contents of volcanic rocks in the region north of Huzi Volcanic Zone. *J. Chem. Soc. Japan,* **77**, 1196–1201. (Japanese.)

Keep, F. E., 1930. The geology of the chromite and asbestos deposits of the Umvukwe Range,

Lomagundi and Mazoe Districts. *Southern Rhodesia Geol. Surv. Bull.* **16**, 98p.

Keil, K., and K. Fredriksson, 1964. The iron, magnesium and calcium distribution in coexisting olivines and rhombic pyroxenes of chondrites. *J. Geophys. Res.*, **69**, 3487–3515.

Keith, M. L. 1954. Phase equilibria in the system MgO-Cr_2O_3-SiO_2. *J. Am. Ceram. Soc.*, **37**, 490–496.

Kemp, J. F., and V. F. Marsters, 1893. The trap dikes of the Lake Champlain region. *U.S. Geol. Surv. Bull.* **107**, 62p.

Kemp, J. F., and J. G. Ross, 1907. A peridotite dike in the Coal Measures of southwestern Pennsylvania. *Ann. N.Y. Acad. Sci.*, **17**, 509–518.

Kennedy, G. C., 1955. "Some aspects of the role of water in rock melts," in A. Poldervaart, ed., Crust of the Earth, *Geol. Soc. Am. Spec. Paper*, **62**, 489–503.

———, and M. S. Walton, 1946. Geology and associated mineral deposits of some ultramafic rock bodies in southeastern Alaska, *U.S. Geol. Surv. Bull.* **947-D**, 65–84.

Kennedy, W. Q., 1938. Crustal layers and the origin of magmas: petrological aspects of the problem. *Bull. Volcanol.*, **3**, 24–41.

King, B. C., 1949. The Napak area of Southern Karamoja, Uganda. *Uganda Geol. Surv. Mem.* **5**, 57p.

———, 1965. Petrogenesis of the alkaline igneous rock suites of the volcanic and intrusive centres of Eastern Uganda. *J. Petrol.* **6**, 67–100.

Kitsul, V. I., 1964. "Geochronological significance of ultrabasic alkalic intrusions of the Aldan shield": in *Geology and Geochronology of the Precambrian*, 228–235. Acad. Sci., Moscow (Russian.)

Kitahara, S., S. Takenouchi, and G. C. Kennedy, 1966. Phase relations in the system MgO-SiO_2-H_2O at high temperatures and pressures. *Am. J. Sci.*, **264**, 223–233.

Kodym, O., 1960. "Platform development of the Czech Massif" in V. Zoubek, ed., *Tectonic Development of Czechoslovakia.* Nakladatestvi Ceskoslovenske Akad. Ved., Prague, 122–138.

Koenig, J. B., 1956. The petrography of certain igneous dikes of Kentucky. *Kentucky Geol. Surv. Bull.* **21**, 1–57.

Kokta, J., and K. Němec, 1936. Gránat ultrabasickyćk hornin od. Černina. *Veda. Priodni Praka.*, **17**, 176–180.

Kokubu, N., T. Mayeda, and H. C. Urey, 1961. Deuterium content of minerals, rocks and liquid inclusions from rocks. *Geochim. Cosmochim. Acta*, **21**, 247–256.

Kopecký, L., 1960. Diamond prospects in the Czech massif. *Izvest. Akad. Nauk S.S.S.R., Ser. Geol., no.* 12, 46–55.

———, and V. Sattran, 1962. On the genesis of pyrope in the Czech Mittelgebirge. *Věstník Ústředního Ústavu Geologiskéno*, **37**, 269–283. Prague. Acad. Sci. (Czech with Russian summary.)

Koster van Groos, A. F., and P. J. Wyllie, 1963. Experimental data bearing on the role of liquid immiscibility in the genesis of carbonatites. *Nature*, **199**, 801–802.

———, 1966. Liquid immiscibility in the system Na_2O-Al_2O_3-SiO_2-CO_2 at pressures up to 1 kilobar. *Am. J. Sci.*, **264**, 234–255.

Kovach, R. L., and D. L. Anderson, 1965. The interiors of the terrestrial planets, *J. Geophys. Res.*, **70**, 2873–2882.

Koval'skii, V. V., 1963. *Kimberlitic Rocks of Yakutia.* Acad. Sci., Moscow, 184p. (Russian.)

Kranck, E. H., 1929. On turjaite and the ijolite stem of Turja, Kola. *Fennia*, **51**, 1–102.

Kretz, R., 1961. Some applications of thermodynamics to coexisting minerals of variable composition. Examples: orthopyroxene-clinopyroxene and orthopyroxene-garnet. *J. Geol.*, **69**, 361–387.

———, 1963. Distribution of magnesium and iron between orthopyroxene and calcic pyroxene in natural mineral assemblages. *J. Geol.*, **71**, 773–785.

Kryukov, A. B., 1964. "Geology of the Kongarovsk explosive pipe," in *Geology and Metallogeny of Effusive-Sedimentary Formations of Siberia.* Nedra Moscow, 190–202. (Russian.)

Kuenen, Ph. H., 1952. Significant features of graded bedding: *Am. Assoc. Petroleum Geol. Bull.*, **37**, 1044–1066.

Kulp, J. L., W. U. Ault, and H. W. Feely, 1956. Sulfur isotope abundances in sulfide minerals. *Econ. Geol.*, **51**, 139–149.

Kuno, H., 1959a. Discussion of paper by J. F. Lovering: The nature of the Mohorovicic discontinuity. *J. Geophys. Res.*, **64**, 1071.

———, 1959b. Origin of Cenozoic petrographic province of Japan and surrounding areas. *Bull. Volcanol., 2d ser.*, **20**, 37–76.

———, 1960. High-alumina basalt. *J. Petrol.* **1**, 121–145.

———, 1963. Crustal and upper mantle rocks beneath the Hawaiian Volcanoes; paper delivered to the *Upper Mantle Symposium, 13th Gen. Assembly, I.U.G.G.*, Berkeley, Calif.

———, et al, 1957. Differentiation of Hawaiian magmas. *Jap. J. Geol. Geogr.*, **28**, 179–218.

Kupferbürger, W., and B. V. Lombaard, 1937. The chromite deposits of the Bushveld Igneous Complex, Transvaal. S. *Africa Dept. Mines Geol. Surv. Bull.* **10**, 48p.

Kupletsky, B. M., 1936. Knopite in basic magma rocks. *Bull. Acad. Sci. URSS, Classe Sci. Mathematiques et Natureles. Serie Geologique.* no. 1, 104–110. (Russian; English summary 110–111)

Kupletsky, B. M., 1937. "The Afrikanda pyroxenite intrusion," in A. A. Polkanov, Guide to the Northern Excursion, Kola Peninsula. *17th Intern. Geol. Congr.* U.S.S.R., 41–50.

Kuroda, P. K., and W. H. Crouch, Jr., 1962. On the chronology of the formation of the solar system, 2. Iodine in terrestrial rocks and the Xenon 129/136 formation interval of the Earth. *J. Geophys. Res.*, **67**, 4863–4866.

Kuschke, G. S. J., 1939. The Critical Zone of the Bushveld Igneous Complex, Lydenburg District. *Trans. Geol. Soc. S. Africa,* **42**, 57–81.

Kushiro, I., 1964a. The system diopside-forsterite-enstatite at 20 kilobars. *Carnegie. Inst. Wash. Yearbook,* **63**, 101–108.

———, 1964b. Stability field of akermanite. *Carnegie Inst. Wash. Yearbook,* **63**, 84–86.

———, 1964c. "The join wollastonite-enstatite at 20 kilobars. *Carnegie Inst. Wash. Yearbook,* **63**, 103–105.

———, 1965. Clinopyroxene solid solutions at high pressures, *Carnegie Inst. Wash. Yearbook,* **64**. In press.

———, and H. Kuno, 1963. Origin of primary basalt magmas and classification of basaltic rocks. *J. Petrol.*, **4**, 75–89.

Kushiro, I., and J. F. Schairer, 1963. New data on the system diopside-forsterite-silica. *Carnegie Inst. Wash. Yearbook,* **63**, 95–103.

Kushiro, I., and H. S. Yoder, Jr., 1964a. Experimental studies on the basalt-eclogite transformation. *Carnegie Inst. Wash. Yearbook,* **63**, 108–114.

———, 1964b. Breakdown of monticellite and akermanite at high pressures. *Carnegie Inst. Wash. Yearbook,* **63**, 81–83.

———, 1964c. Pressure-temperature plane for anorthite + forsterite composition. *Carnegie Inst. Wash. Yearbook,* **63**, 109–111.

———, 1964d. Pressure-temperature plane for anorthite + 2 enstatite composition. *Carnegie Inst. Wash. Yearbook,* **63**, 112–114.

———, 1965. The reactions between forsterite and anorthite at high pressures. *Carnegie Inst. Wash. Yearbook,* **64**. In press.

Lacroix, A., 1893. Les enclaves des roches volcaniques. Macon.

———, 1894. Etude minéralogique de la lherzolites et les ophites des Pyrénées et ses phénomènes de contact. *Nouv. Arch. Mus. Hist. Nat. Paris,* **6**, 204–308.

———, 1900. Les roches basiques accompagnant les lherzolites et les ophites des Pyrénées. *Rept. 8th Intern. Geol. Congr.*, Paris, 806–838.

———, 1917. Les peridotites des Pyrénées et les autres roches intrusives non-feldspathiques qui les accompagnant. *C.R. Acad. Sci., Paris.*, **165**, 381–387.

———, 1923. *Minéralogie de Madagascar.* Soc. Editions Geograph. Maritimes Coloniales, Paris, 3, 450p.

Ladurner, J., 1954. Das Verhalten des Olivins als Gefugekorn in einigen Olivingesteinen. *Tschermaks Mineral. Petrog. Mitt.*, Folge **3**, Bd. 5, 21–36.

Lanphere, M. A., and G. D. Eberlein, 1966. Potassium-argon ages of magnetite-bearing ultramafic complexes in southeastern Alaska. *Geol. Soc. Am., Spec. Paper,* **93** (Abstr.). In press.

Lapham, D. M., and W. A. Bassett, 1964. K-Ar dating of rocks and tectonic events in the Piedmont of southeastern Pennsylvania. *Geol. Soc. Am. Bull.*, **75**, 661–668.

Lapham, D. M., and H. L. McKague, 1964. Structural patterns associated with the serpentinites of southeastern Pennsylvania. *Bull. Geol. Soc. Am.*, **75**, 639–660.

Lappin, M. A., 1962. The eclogites, dunites and anorthosites of the Selje and Almklovdalen districts, Nordfjord, S.W. Norway. Ph.D. thesis, University of Durham.

Larochelle, A., 1962. Palaeomagnetism of the Monteregian Hills, Southeastern Quebec. *Geol. Surv. Can., Bull,* **79**, 44p.

Larsen, E. S., 1942. Alkalic rocks of Iron Hill, Gunnison County, Colorado. *U.S. Geol. Surv. Profess. Paper* **197-A**, 1–64.

———, and E. A. Goranson, 1932. The deuteric and later alterations of the uncompahgrite of Iron Hill, Colorado. *Am. Mineral.*, **17**, 343–356.

Larsen, E. S., and J. T. Pardee, 1929. The stock of alkaline rocks near Libby, Montana. *J. Geol.*, **37**, 97–112.

Larsen, O., and H. Sørensen, 1960. Principles of classification and norm calculations of metamorphic rocks: a discussion. *J. Geol.*, **68**, 681–683.

Larsson, W., 1943. Zur Kenntnis der alkalinen ultrabasischen Ganggesteine der Kalix-Gebiets, Nord-Schweden. *Sveriges Geol. Undersökn, Arsbok, Ser. C,* no. **456.**

LeBas, M. J., 1962. The role of aluminum in igneous clinopyroxenes with relation to their parentage. *Am. J. Sci.*, **260**, 267–288.

Lebedev, A. P., 1964. Kimberlites of north-eastern USSR and their problems. *Liverpool Geol. J.*, **4**, 87–104.

Lehmann, I., 1959. Velocities of longitudinal waves in the upper parts of the Earth's mantle. *Ann. Geophys.*, **15**, 93–118.

———, 1961. S and the structure of the upper mantle. *Geophys. J.*, **4**, 124–138.

Lemberg, J., 1875. Ueber die serpentine von Zoblitz, Griefendorf und Waldheim. *Zts. dt. geol. Ges.*, **27**, 531–549.

Leontiev, L. N., and A. A. Kadensky, 1957. On the nature of kimberlite pipes of Yakutia: *Dokl. Akad. Nauk SSSR,* **115**, 368–371.

Lessing, P., and E. J. Catanzaro, 1964. Sr^{87}/Sr^{86} ratios in Hawaiian lavas. *J. Geophys. Res.* **69,** 1599–1601.

Lessing, P., R. W. Decker, and R. C. Reynolds, 1963. Potassium and rubidium distribution in Hawaiian lavas. *J. Geophys. Res.,* **68,** 5851–5855.

Lewis, C., 1887. On a diamantiferous peridotite, and the genesis of the diamond. *Geol. Mag.* **4,** 22–24.

———, 1888. The matrix of the diamond. *Geol. Mag.,* new ser., **5,** 129–131.

Lightfoot, B., 1940. The Great Dyke of Southern Rhodesia. *Proc. Geol. Soc. S. Africa,* **43,** xxvii–xlv.

Lindgren, W., 1933. *Mineral Deposits.* 4th ed., McGraw-Hill Book Co., New York, 930p.

Lindsley, D. H., and F. R. Boyd, 1965. Orthoclino inversion in ferrosilite and enstatite, *Trans. Amer. Geophys. Union,* **46,** 181. (Abstr.)

Lindsley, D. H., I. D. MacGregor, and B. T. C. Davis, 1964. Synthesis and stability of ferrosilite, *Carnegie Inst. Wash. Yearbook,* **63,** 174–176.

Lipman, P. W., 1964. Structure and origin of an ultramafic pluton in the Klamath Mountains, California. *Am. J. Sci.,* **262,** 199–222.

Litinski, V. A., 1961. On the content of Ni, Cr, Ti, Nb and some other elements in kimberlites and the possibility of geochemical prospecting for kimberlite bodies. *Geochemistry,* 813–822.

Little, H. W., 1949. The ultrabasic rocks of the Middle River range, British Columbia. *Am. J. Sci.,* **247,** 802–823.

Lombaard, A. F., 1950. Die geologie van die Bosfeldkompleks langs Bloedrivier. *Trans. Geol. Soc. S. Africa,* **52,** 343–376.

Lombaard, B. V., 1934. On the differentiation and relationships of the rocks of the Bushveld Complex. *Trans. Geol. Soc. S. Africa,* **37,** 5–52.

Longchambon, M., 1912. Contribution à l'étude du métamorphism des terrains secondaires dans les Pyrénées orientales et ariégoises. *Bull. Carte Géol., France,* **131,** 1–68.

Lovering, J. F., 1958. The nature of the Mohorovicic discontinuity. *Trans. Am. Geophys. Union,* **39,** 947–955 .

———, 1964. The eclogite-bearing basic igneous pipe at Ruby Hill near Bingara, New South Wales. *J. Proc. Roy. Soc. N.S.W.,* **97,** 73–79.

———, and J. W. Morgan, 1963a. Uranium and thorium abundances in possible upper mantle materials. *Nature,* **197,** 138–140.

———, 1963b. Comparative uranium and thorium analyses of basic and ultra-basic rocks. *Nature,* **199,** 479–480.

Lovering, J. F. and J. R. Richards, 1964. Potassium-argon age study of possible lower-crust and upper mantle inclusions in deep seated intrusions. *J. Geophys. Res.,* **69,** 4895–4901.

Lovering, J. F., and A. J. R. White, 1964. The significance of primary scapolite in granulitic inclusions from deep seated pipes. *J. Petrol.,* **5,** 195–217.

Lovering, T. S., 1936. Heat conduction in dissimilar rocks and the use of thermal models. *Bull. Geol. Soc. Am.,* **47,** 87–100.

Lowdon, J. A., 1960. Age determinations by the Geological Survey of Canada. Report 1, Isotopic Ages. *Geol. Surv. Can., Paper* **60-17,** 51p.

———, 1961. Age determinations by the Geological Survey of Canada. Report 2, Isotopic Ages. *Geol. Surv. Can., Paper* **61-17,** 127p.

Macdonald, G. A., 1944. The 1840 eruption and crystal differentiation in the Kilauean magma column. *Am. J. Sci.,* **242,** 177–189.

———, 1949. Petrography of the Island of Hawaii. *U.S. Geol. Surv., Profess. Paper,* **214-D,** 76.

———, 1963. Physical properties of erupting Hawaiian magmas. *Bull. Geol. Soc. Am.,* **74,** 1071–1078.

———, and T. Katsura, 1964. Chemical composition of Hawaiian lavas. *J. Petrol.,* **5,** 82–133.

MacDonald, G. J. F., 1959a. "Chondrites and the chemical composition of the earth," in P. H. Abelson, ed., *Researches in Geochemistry.* John Wiley and Sons, New York, 476–494.

———, 1959b. Calculations on the thermal history of the Earth. *J. Geophys. Res.,* 1959, **64,** 1967–2000.

MacGregor, A. M., 1921. The geology of the diamond-bearing gravels of the Somabula Forest. *S. Rhodesia Geol. Surv. Bull.,* no **8.**

———, J. C. Ferguson, and F. L. Amm, 1937. The geology of the country round the Queen's Mine, Bulawayo District. *S. Rhodesia Geol. Surv. Bull.,* no. **30.**

MacGregor, I. D., 1964. The reaction 4 enstatite + spinel $\rightleftharpoons$ forsterite + pyrope. *Carnegie Inst. Wash. Yearbook,* **63,** 157.

———, 1965a. Stability fields of spinel and garnet peridotites in the synthetic system MgO-CaO-Al_2O_3-SiO_2. *Carnegie Inst. Wash. Yearbook,* **64,** in press.

———, 1965b. Aluminous diopsides in the three phase assemblage diopside + forsterite + spinel. *Carnegie Inst. Wash. Yearbook,* **64,** in press.

———, and A. E. Ringwood, 1964. The natural system enstatite-pyrope. *Carnegie Inst. Wash. Yearbook,* **63,** 161–163.

MacGregor, I. D. and C. H. Smith, 1963. The use of chrome spinels in petrographic studies of ultramafic intrusions. *Can. Mineral.* **7,** 403–412.

Macgregor, M., and A. G. MacGregor, 1948. *British regional geology: the Midland Valley of Scotland* (2nd ed., rev.). H. M. Stationery Office, Edinburgh, 92p.

MacKenzie, D. B., 1960. High-temperature alpine-type peridotite from Venezuela. *Bull. Geol. Soc. Am.*, **71**, 303–318.

Mace, D., 1939. Gravity measurements in Cyprus. *Monthly Notices Roy. Astron. Soc. Geophys. Suppl.*, **4**, 473.

Machado, F. J. de Sousa, 1958. The volcanic belt of Angola and its carbonatites. *C.C.T.A. Assoc. Serv. Geol. Africains.* (Unpublished.)

Majer, V., 1960. Magmatic rocks in the region of Bassit between Latakia and Kessab in northwestern Syria. *Fac. Sci. Univ. Skopje, Yugoslavia Spec. Ed.*, no. **10**.

Makhlayev, L. V., and N. P. Surina, 1963. Maymecha-Kotuy province of ultrabasic and alkalic rocks—a new region of kimberlite magmatism. *Dokl. Akad. Nauk SSSR,* **153**, 1172–1174. (*Am. Geol. Inst. Translation,* 1964, 178–180.)

Malakhov, I. A., 1964. Content and distribution of aluminum in the Ural ultrabasic rocks. *Geokhimiya,* **1964**, 266–275.

Malde, H. E., 1954. Serpentine pipes at Garnet Ridge, Arizona. *Science,* **119**, 618.

———, and R. E. Thaden, 1963. "Serpentine at Garnet Ridge," in Witkind, I. J., and R. E. Thaden, Geology and uranium-vanadium deposits of the Monument Valley area, Apache and Navajo Counties, Arizona. *U.S. Geol. Surv. Bull.,* **1103**, 54–61.

Manson, V., and A. Poldervaart, 1965. Geochemistry of basalts and dolerites, *Geol. Soc. Am. Spec. Paper* **82**, 12. (Abstr.)

Marinos, G., and G. Maratos, 1957. Greek olivinites. *Inst. Geol. Subsurface Res.* (Athens), *Geol. Geophys. Res.*, **5**, no. 2, 12p. (Greek.)

Marsters, V. F., 1895. Camptonite and other intrusives of Lake Memphremagog. *Am. Geol.*, **16**, 25–39.

Martens, J. H. C., 1924. Igneous rocks of Ithaca, New York, and vicinity. *Bull. Geol. Soc. Am.*, **35**, 305–320.

Martin, H., M. Mathias, and E. S. W. Simpson, 1960. The Damaraland subvolcanic ring complexes in South-West Africa. *21st Intern. Geol. Congr.*, Copenhagen, *Repts.* **13**, 156–174.

Mason, B., 1962. *Meteorites.* John Wiley and Sons, New York, 274p.

Mathews, W. H., S. Thorarinsson, and N. B. Church, 1964. Gravitative settling of olivine in pillows of an Icelandic basalt. *Am. J. Sci.*, **262**, 1036–1040.

Mathur, S. M., 1962. Geology of the Panna diamond deposits. *Records Geol. Surv. India.* **87**, 787–818.

Matuzawa, T., 1959. On the crustal structure in north-east Japan by explosion seismic observations. *Bull. Earthquake Res. Inst., Tokyo Univ.*, **37**, 123–154.

Maxwell, J. C., and A. Azzaroli, 1963. Submarine extrusion of ultramafic magma. *Geol. Soc. Am. Spec. Paper,* **73**, 203–204. (Abstr.)

McCall, G. J. H., 1964. Are cryptovolcanic structures due to meteoric impact? *Nature,* **201**, 251–254.

———, 1965. A reconsideration of certain aspects of the Rangwa and Ruri carbonatite complexes in western Kenya. *Geol. Mag.*, **100**, 181–185.

McDougall, I., and W. Compston, 1965. Strontium isotope composition and potassium-rubidium ratios in some rocks from Reunion and Rodriguez, Indian Ocean. *Nature,* **207**, 252–253.

McDougall, I. and D. H. Green, 1964. Excess radiogenic argon in pyroxenes and isotopic ages on minerals from Norwegian eclogites. *Norsk. Geol. Tiddsskr.*, **44**, 183–196.

McKinlay, A. C. M., 1955. Kimberlite intrusions cutting Karroo sediments in the Ruhuhu depression of south-west Tanganyika. *Records Geol. Surv. Tanganyika*, **5**, 63–80.

McKinstry, H. E., 1961. Structure of the Glenarm series in Chester County, Pennsylvania. *Bull. Geol. Soc. Am.*, **72**, 557–578.

McLean, D., 1962. *Mechanical properties of metals.* John Wiley and Sons Ltd., London, 403p.

Melcher, G. C., 1954. Nota sobra o distrito alcalino de Jacupiranga, Estado de São Paulo. *Dept. Naçional de Produção Mineral, Divisão de Geologia e Mineralogia.* no. **84**, 1–20.

Menyailov, A. A., 1961, ed. *The Diamonds of Yakutia.* Acad. Sci., Moscow, 227p. (Russian.)

———, 1962. *Tuffs and Kimberlites of the Siberian Platform and their Genesis.* Acad. Sci., Moscow, 228p. (Russian.)

Mercy, E. L. P. and M. J. O'Hara, 1965a. Olivines and orthopyroxenes from garnetiferous peridotites and related rocks. *Norsk. Geol. Tiddskr.*, **45**, 457–461.

———, 1965b. Chemistry of some garnet-bearing rocks from the South Norwegian peridotites. *Norsk. Geol. Tiddskr.*, **45**, 323–332.

Meyer de Stadelhofen, C., 1963. Les brèches kimberlitiques du territoire de Bakwanga (Congo). *Arch. Sci.*, **16**, 87–143.

Mikhailov, N. P., 1962. Intrusive ophiolite complexes of eastern Kazakhstan. *Trans. Vses. Nauchn.-Issled. Geol. Inst.*, **80**, 109–223.

Mikheyenko, V. I. and N. I. Nenashev, 1961. Absolute age of specimens and relative age of emplacement of kimberlites in Yakutia. *Trans. 9th Session Committee on Absolute Age Acad. Sci. USSR*, 146–164.

———, 1962. Absolute age of the kimberlites of Yakutia. *Intern. Geol. Rev.*, **4**, 916–924.

Mikkola, T., 1955. Origin of ultrabasics in the Orijärvi region. *C. R. Soc. Géol. Finland,* **28**, 39–51.

Milashev, V. A., 1965. *Petrochemistry of the Kimberlites of Yakutia.* Nedra, Leningrad, 160p. (Russian.)

———, M. A. Krutoyarski, M. I. Rabhkin, and Z. N. Zirlich, 1963. Kimberlitic rocks and picritic porphyries of the north-eastern part of the Siberian platform. *Trudy Nauchno-Issled. Inst. Geol. Artik.*, **126**, 1–215. (Same title published 1963 by Gosgeoltekhizdat, Moscow, 216p.)

Milliard, Y., 1959. Les massifs metamorphiques et ultrabasiques de la zone paleozoique interne du Rif. *Notes Serv. Geol. Maroc.* no. **147**, 125–160.

Misch, P., 1960. Large overthrusts in the northwestern Cascades near the 49th parallel (Whatcom and Skagit Counties, Washington and lower Tomyhoi Creek area, British Columbia). *Bull. Geol. Soc. Am.*, **71**, p. 2069. (Abstr.)

———, 1962. Unusual imbrication patterns displayed by pre-Devonian crystallines and upper Paleozoic rocks below Mount Shuksan overthrust in Mount Larrabee (Red Mountain)—Tomyhoi Peak area of northwestern Cascades, Whatcom County, Washington. *Geol. Soc. Am., Spec. Paper*, **73**, 53. (Abstr.)

Miser, H. D. and C. S. Ross, 1923. Diamond-bearing peridotite in Pike County, Arkansas. *U.S. Geol. Surv. Bull.*, **735**, 279–322.

Miyashiro, A., 1966. Some aspects of peridotite and serpentinite in orogenic belts. *Jap. J. Geol. Geogr.*, **37**, 45–61.

———, and Y. Seki, 1958. Mineral assemblages and subfacies of the glaucophane-schist facies. *Jap. J. Geol. Ceogr.*, **29**, 199–208.

Monster, J., E. Anders, and H. G. Thode, 1965. S^{34}/S^{32} ratios for the different forms of sulfur in the Orgueil meteorite and their mode of formation. *Geochim. Cosmochim. Acta*, **29**, 773–779.

Moody, C. L., 1949. Mesozoic igneous rocks of northern Gulf Coastal Plain. *Bull. Am. Assoc. Petrol. Geologists*, **33**, 1410–1428.

Moor, G. G., 1940. Perspective of diamond resources of northern Central Siberia. *Problemy Arktiki*, **3.** (Russian.)

———, 1941. Micaceous kimberlite in the north of central Siberia. *Dokl. Akad. Nauk SSSR*, **31**, 363–365.

Moores, E. M., H. H. Hess, and J. C. Maxwell, 1966. Petrology of an ultramafic-mafic (ophiolite) sequence (abstr). *Program of Geol. Soc. Am. Ann. Mtg.*, San Francisco, Nov. 1966.

Morkovkina, V. F., 1962. Metasomatitzeckije preobrazovanija giperbasitov poljarnogo Urala. *Trudy Inst. Geol. Mest. Petr. Min. Geoch.*, **77**, 130–224.

Muan, A., and E. F. Osborn, 1956. Phase equilibria at liquidus temperatures in the system MgO-FeO-Fe_2O_3-SiO_2. *Am. Ceram. Soc. J.*, **39**, 121–140.

Mügge, O., and F. Heide, 1931. Einfache Schiebung am Anorthit. *Neues Jahrb. Mineral. Geol. Paläont*, **64A**, 163–169.

Muir, I. D., and C. E. Tilley, 1957. Contributions to the petrology of Hawaiian basalts: I. The picrite-basalts of Kilauea. *Am. J. Sci.*, **255**, 241–253.

———, 1963. Contributions to the petrology of Hawaiian basalts: II. The tholeiitic basalts of Mauna Loa and Kilauea. *Am. J. Sci.*, **261**, 111–128.

———, 1964. Basalts from the northern part of the rift zone of the mid-Atlantic ridge. *J. Petrol.*, **5**, 409–434.

Murata, K. J., and D. H. Richter, 1961. Magmatic differentiation in the Uwekahuna Laccolith, Kilauea caldera, Hawaii. *J. Petrol.*, **2**, 424–437.

———, 1966. Chemistry of the lavas of the 1959–60 eruption of Kilauea volcano, Hawaii. *U.S. Geol. Surv., Profess. Paper*, **537-A**, 26p.

Murina, N. P., 1966. The structural-tectonic position of kimberlites and their inter-relationship with rocks of the alkalic-ultrabasic formation in the Maimecha-Kotui region. *Sovetskaya Geol.*, no. **3**, 140–144. (Russian.)

Murray, R. J., 1954. The clinopyroxenes of the Garbh Eilean sill, Shiant Isles. *Geol. Mag.*, **91**, 17–31.

Mushkin, I. V., et al, 1964. On volcanic pipes of south Gissar (southern Tyan'-Shan'). *Dokl. Akad. Nauk*, **158**, 633–635. (Russian.)

Nagy, B., and G. T. Faust, 1956. Serpentines: Natural mixtures of chrysotile and antigorite. *Am. Mineral.*, **41**, 817–838.

Naidu, P. R. J., 1955. Minerals of charnockites from India. *Schweiz. Mineral. Petrog. Mitt.*, **34**, 203–279.

Nelson, B. W., and Roy, R., 1958. Synthesis of the chlorites and their structural and chemical constitution. *Am. Mineral.*, **43**, 707–725.

Neumann, H., 1960. Apparent ages of Norwegian minerals and rocks. *Norsk Geol. Tidsskr.*, **40**, 173–191.

———, J. Mead and C. J. Vitaliano, 1954. Trace element variation during fractional crystallization as calculated from the distribution law. *Geoch. Cosmochim. Acta*, **6**, 90–99.

Nicholls, G. D., 1965. Basalts from the deep ocean floor, *Mineral. Mag.* **34**, 373–388.

Nicolaysen, L. D., J. W. L. de Villiers, A. J. Burger, and F. W. E. Strelow, 1958. New measurements relating to the absolute age of the Transvaal System and of the Bushveld Igneous Complex. *Trans. Geol. Soc. S. Africa*, **61**, 137–163.

Nixon, P. H., O. von Knorring and J. M. Rooke, 1963. Kimberlites and associated inclusions of

Basutoland; a mineralogical and geochemical study. *Am. Mineral.*, **48**, 1090–1132.

Noble, J. A., and H. P. Taylor, Jr., 1960. Correlation of the ultramafic complexes of southeastern Alaska with those of other parts of North America and the world. *21st Intern. Geol. Congr.*, Copenhagen, *Repts.*, **13**, 188–197.

Nockolds, S. R., 1954. Average chemical compositions of some igneous rocks. *Bull. Geol. Soc. Am.*, **65**, 1007–1032.

Noe-Nygaard, A., 1942. On the geology and petrography of the West Greenland Basalt Province: pt III, The plateau basalts of Svartenhuk Peninsula. *Medd. Grønland,* **137**, 3.

———, and H. Ramberg, 1961. Geological reconnaissance map of the country between latitudes 69°N and 63°45N, West Greenland. *Medd. Grønland.*, **123,5**, 1–9.

Odintsov, M. M., 1965. Geological features and possibilities of diamond formations of the southwestern part of the Siberian Platform. *Sov. Geol.*, **5**, 71–82.

Oen, Ing Soen, 1962. Hornblendic rocks and their polymetamorphic derivatives in an area NW of Ivigtut, South Greenland. *Medd. Grønland,* **169,6**, 1–84.

O'Hara, M. J., 1961. Zoned basic and ultrabasic gneiss masses in the early Lewisian metamorphic complex at Scourie, Sutherland. *J. Petrol.*, **2**, 248–276.

———, 1963a. Melting of garnet-peridotite at 30 kilobars. *Carnegie Inst. Wash. Yearbook,* **62**, 71–76.

———, 1963b. The join diopside-pyrope at 30 kilobars. *Carnegie Inst. Wash. Yearbook,* **62**, 116–118.

———, 1963c. Distribution of iron between coexisting olivines and calcium-poor pyroxenes in peridotites, gabbros and other magnesian environments. *Am. J. Sci.*, **261**, 32–46.

———, 1963d. Melting of bimineralic eclogite at 30 kilobars. *Carnegie Inst. Wash. Yearbook,* **62**, 76–77.

———, 1964. Non-equivalence of distribution coefficients and tie-lines of coexisting pyroxenes. *Geol. Mag.*, **101**, 472–473.

———, 1965a. Primary magmas and the origin of basalts. *Scot. J. Geol.*, **1**, 19–40.

———, 1965b. Origin of ultrabasic and basic gneiss masses in the Lewisian. *Geol. Mag.*, **102**, 296–314.

———, 1966. Origin of ultrabasic and basic gneiss masses in the Lewisian. *Geol. Mag.*, **103**, 284.

———, and E. L. P. Mercy, 1963. Petrology and petrogenesis of some garnetiferous peridotites. *Trans. Roy. Soc. Edinburgh,* **65**, 251–314.

———, 1965. On diamantiferous diatremes. *Econ. Geol.*, **60**, 830–832.

———, 1966. Eclogite, peridotite and pyrope from the Navajo Country, Arizona and New Mexico. *Am. Mineral.* **51**, 336–352.

O'Hara, M. J., and J. F. Schairer, 1963. The join diopside-pyrope at atmospheric pressure. *Carnegie Inst. Wash. Yearbook,* **62**, 107–115.

O'Hara, M. J., and H. S. Yoder, Jr., 1963. Partial melting of the mantle. *Carnegie Inst. Wash. Yearbook,* **62**, 66–71.

Oliver, D. R., 1962. Influence of particle rotation on radial migration in the Poiseuille flow of suspensions. *Nature,* **194**, 1269–1271.

Olsen, Edward, 1963. Equilibrium calculations in the system Mg, Fe, Si, O, H, and Ni. *Am. J. Sci.*, **261**, 943–956.

O'Neil, J. R., and R. N. Clayton, 1964. "Oxygen isotope geothermometry," in *Isotopic and Cosmic Chemistry* (*Urey Volume*), ed. H. Craig et al, North Holland, Amsterdam. 157–168.

O'Neill, J. J., 1914. St. Hilaire (Beloeil) and Rougemont Mountains, Quebec. *Geol. Surv. Can., Mem.* **43**, 108p.

Onuki, H., 1965. Petrochemical research on the Horoman and Miyamori ultramafic intrusives, northern Japan. *Sci. Rept. Tohoku Univ.*, Ser. III, **9**, 217–276.

———, 1966. On the iron-rich peridotites in the Sanbagawa metamorphic belt of the Kanto Mountains. *J. Jap. Assoc. Mineral. Pet. Econ. Geol.*, **55**, 39–47.

———, and Tiba, T., 1965. Notes on petrochemistry of ultramafic intrusives—specially, aluminum distribution in co-existing pyroxenes. *J. Jap. Assoc. Mineral. Pet. Econ. Geol.*, **53**, 215–227.

Oosterom, M. G., 1963. The ultramafites and layered gabbro sequences in the granulite facies rocks on Stjernoy (Finnmark, Norway). *Leidse Geol. Mededel.*, **28**, 177–296.

Osborn, E. F., 1959. Role of oxygen pressure in the crystallization and differentiation of basaltic magma. *Am. J. Sci.*, **257**, 609–647.

———, 1962. Reaction series for subalkaline igneous rocks based on different oxygen pressure conditions. *Am. Mineral.*, **47**, 211–226.

———, and A. Muan, 1960. Phase equilibrium diagrams of oxide systems. Plate 2. The system $CaO-MgO-SiO_2$. *Am. Ceram. Soc.* Columbus, Ohio.

Osborn, E. F., and D. B. Tait, 1952. The system diopside-forsterite-anorthite. *Am. J. Sci.* **Bowen vol.**, 413–433.

Osborne, F. F., 1935. Anemousite in essexite. *Can. J. Res.*, **12**, 668–675.

———, and T. H. Clark, 1960. New Glasgow-St. Lin area. *Quebec Dept. Mines, Geol. Rept.* **91**, 41p.

Osborne, F. F., and R. Grimes-Graeme, 1936. The breccia on St. Helen Island, Montreal. *Am. J. Sci.*, **32**, 43–54.

Osborne, F. F., and N. L. Wilson, 1934. Some dyke rocks from Mount Johnson. *J. Geol.*, **42**, 180–187.

Oxburgh, E. R., 1964. Petrological evidence for the presence of amphibole in the upper mantle and its petrogenetic and geophysical implications, *Geol. Mag.*, **101**, 1–19.

Panagos, A., 1965. Contribution to the knowledge of Greek chromite. *Ann. Géol. Pays Helleniques.* **18**, 1–42. (Greek, German summary.)

Pardee, J. T., 1941. *Preliminary geologic map of the Sumpter quadrangle, Oregon.* Oregon Dept. Geology and Mineral Industries. (Geologic map with text.)

Paterson, M. S., 1964. Triaxial testing of materials at pressures up to 10,000 kg/cm². *J. Inst. Engrs., Australia*, **36**, 23–29.

Patte, E., 1924. Description de l'île des Cendres, volcan apparci en mer au large de lá côte d'Annam. *Bull. Volcanol.*, **2**, 162–172.

Patterson, E. M., 1946. The teschenite-picrite sill of Saltcoats, Ayrshire. *Trans. Geol. Soc. Glasgow*, **21**, 1–27.

Peach, B. N., J. Horne, W. Gunn, C. T. Clough, and L. W. Hinkman, 1907. The geological structure of the North West Highlands of Scotland. *Mem. geol. Surv., U.K.*

Peach, P. A., 1963. A volcano of recent age in Eastern British Columbia. *Can. Prog. Rep., Intern. Upper Mantle Project*, 6p.

Peacock, A., 1931. Classification of igneous rock series. *J. Geol.*, **39**, 54–67.

Pearre, N. C., and A. V. Heyl, Jr., 1960. Chromite and other mineral deposits in serpentine rocks of the Piedmont Upland, Maryland, Pennsylvania, and Delaware. *U.S. Geol. Surv. Bull.*, **1082-K**, 707–833.

Pecherskii, V. P., 1965. On the discovery of micaceous diamondiferous kimberlites in the foothills of eastern Sayan. *Sov. Geol.*, **4**, 131–133. (Russian)

Peoples, J. W., 1936. Gravity stratification as a criterion in the interpretation of the structure of the Stillwater complex, Montana: *Rept. 16th Intern. Geol. Congr.*, Washington, D.C., 1933, **1**, 353–360.

———, and A. L. Howland, 1940. Chromite deposits of the eastern part of the Stillwater complex, Stillwater County, Montana. *U.S. Geol. Surv. Bull.*, **922-N**, 371–416.

———, W. R. Jones, and D. Flint, 1954. Geologic map, sections, and map of underground workings of the Mountain View Lake area, Stillwater County, Montana. *U.S. Geol. Surv.* (Open-file report.)

Perrin, R., and M. Roubault, 1955. Observations nouvelles sur des serpentines des Alpes françaises et d'Algérie. *Coll. Pétr. Sci. Terre*, nr. hors série, 151–167.

Peters, Tj., 1963. Mineralogie und Petrographie des Totalp Serpentins bei Davos. *Schweiz. Mineral. Petrog. Mitt.*, **43**, 529–685.

———, and E. Niggli, 1964. Spinellführende Pyroxenite (Ariégite) in den Lherzolith körpern von Lherz und Umgebung (Ariège, Pyrenean) und der Totalp (Graubünden, Schweiz), ein Vergleich. *Schweiz. Mineral. Petrog. Mitt.*, **44**, 513–517.

Peterson, D. W., 1960. Descriptive modal classification of igneous rocks. *Geotimes*, **5**, 30–36.

Pettijohn, F. J., *Sedimentary Rocks.* Harper and Bros., New York, 1957, 718p.

Phillips, A. H., and H. H. Hess, 1936. Metamorphic differentiation at contacts between serpentinite and siliceous country rocks. *Am. Mineral.*, **21**, 333–362.

Phillips, B., and A. Muan, 1959. Phase equilibria in the system CaO-iron oxide-SiO_2 in air. *J. Am. Ceram. Soc.*, **42**, 413–423.

Pinson, W. H., C. C. Schnetzler, E. Beiser, H. W. Fairbairn, and P. M. Hurley, 1965. Rb-Sr age of stony meteorites. *Geochim. Cosmochim. Acta*, **29**, 455–466.

Pittman, E. F., 1901. The mineral resources of New South Wales. *Geol. Surv. New South Wales*, 487p.

Poiseuille, J. L. M., 1836. Recherches sur les causes du mouvement du sang dans les vaisseaux capillaires. *Ann. Sci. Nat.*, Ser. 2, **5**, 111–115.

Poldervaart, A., 1944. The petrology of the Elephant's Head dyke and the New Amalfi sheet (Matatiele). *Trans. Roy. Soc. S. Africa*, **30**, 85–119.

Polutoff, N., 1964. Die sibirischen Diamantlagerstätten. *Z. Erzbergbau Metallhüttenwesen*, **17**, 440–443.

Pouliot, G., 1962. The thermal history of the Monteregian intrusives, based on a study of the feldspars. Ph.D. thesis, McGill University, Montreal.

Powell, J. L., 1967. Isotopic composition of strontium in carbonatites and kimberlites. *Proc. 4th Gen. Meeting Intern. Mineral. Assoc.*, New Delhi, 1964 (*Indian Mineral.*, in press).

———, G. Faure, and P. M. Hurley, 1965. Strontium 87 abundance in a suite of Hawaiian volcanic rocks of varying silica content. *J. Geophys. Res.*, **70**, no. 6, 1509–1513.

Powell, J. L., P. M. Hurley, and H. W. Fairbairn, 1967. "The strontium isotopic composition and origin of carbonatites," in Tuttle, O. F., and J. Gittins, eds., *The Carbonatites.* Wiley-Interscience, New York, 365–378.

Presnall, D. R., 1966. The join forsterite-diopside-iron oxide and its bearing on the crystallization of basaltic and ultramafic magmas. *Am. J. Sci.*, **264**, 753–809.

Prostka, H. J., 1962. *Geology of the Sparta quadrangle, Oregon.* Oregon Dept. Geology and Mineral Industries. (Geologic map.)

Pulfrey, W., 1949. Ijolitic rocks near Homa Bay, Western Kenya. *Quart. J. Geol. Soc. London,* **105**, 425–459.

Rabhkin, M. I., M. A. Krutoyarski, and V. A. Milashev, 1962. Classification and nomenclature of Yakutian kimberlites. *Trudy Issled. Inst. Geol. Arktik.,* **121**, 154–164.

Ragan, D. M., 1963. Emplacement of the Twin Sisters dunite, Washington. *Am. J. Sci.,* **261**, 549–565.

Raleigh, C. B., 1963. Fabrics of naturally and experimentally deformed olivine. Ph.D. dissertation, Univ. Calif. at Los Angeles.

———, 1965a. Structure and petrology of an alpine peridotite on Cypress Island, Washington, U.S.A. *Beitr. Mineral. Petrog.,* **11**, 719–741.

———, 1965b. Glide mechanisms in experimentally deformed minerals. *Science,* **150**, 739–741.

———, and M. S. Paterson, 1965. Experimental deformation of serpentinite and its tectonic implications. *J. Geophys. Res.,* **70**, 3965–3985

Ramberg, H., 1952. *The Origin of Metamorphic and Metasomatic Rocks.* Univ. Chicago Press, 317p.

———, 1960. Energy transfer from differentiation in a differential pressure system under non-equilibrium conditions: A discussion of "partial quantities." *J. Geol.,* **68**, 110–113.

———, and G. de Vore, 1951. The distribution of Fe and Mg between coexisting olivines and pyroxenes. *J. Geol.,* **59**, 193–210.

Randall, B. A. O., 1960. Sagvandites of Lyngen, Troms, North Norway. *21st Intern. Geol. Congr.,* Copenhagen, *Repts.* **13**, 443–451.

Ravier, J., 1954. Le métamorphisme des terrains secondaires des Pyrénées. *Congr. Géol. Intern. Algeria* 1952, **15**, 457–470.

———, 1959. Le métamorphisme des terrains secondaires des Pyrénées. *Mem. Soc. Geol. France,* **38**, 1–250.

———, 1964. Ariégites et éclogites. *Bull. Soc. Franç. Minéral. Crist.,* **87**, 212–215.

Read, H. H., 1934. On zoned associations of antigorite, talc, actinolite, chlorite, and biotite in Unst, Shetland Islands. *Mineral. Mag.,* **23**, 519–540.

Reay, A., and P. G. Harris, 1964. The partial fusion of peridotite. *Bull. Volcanol.,* **27**, 115–127.

Reid, A. M., 1961. The petrology of the Mount Megantic igneous complex, Southern Quebec. M.Sc. thesis, Univ. of Western Ontario, London, Ontario.

Reinisch, R., 1908. Petrographische Beschreibung d. Gaussbergesteine. *Neues Jahrb. Mineral.,* **1**, 75.

Reitan, P. H., and J. J. C. Geul, 1959. On the formation of a carbonate-bearing ultrabasic rock at K[illegible], Lyngen, Northern Norway. *Norg. Geol. Undersøkelse,* **205**, 111–1[illegible]7

Reuss, 1852. Quoted by Schadler, 1913.

Reuter, J. H., S. Epstein, and H. P. Taylor, Jr., 1965. O^{18}/O^{16} ratios of some chondritic meteorites and terrestrial ultramafic rocks. *Geochim. Cosmochim. Acta,* **29**, 481–488.

Reynolds, J. H. and J. Verhoogen, 1953. Natural variations in the isotopic constitution of silicon. *Geochim. Cosmochim. Acta,* **3**, 224–234.

Richardson, C. H., 1918. The terranes of Roxbury, Vermont. Vermont State Geologist 11th Bienn. Rept., 1917–18, 120–140.

Rickard, M. J., 1965. Taconic orogeny in the western Appalachians: experimental application of microtextural studies to isotopic dating. *Bull. Geol. Soc. Am.,* **76**, 523–536.

Ricker, R. W., 1952. Phase equilibria in the quaternary system $CaO\text{-}MgO\text{-}FeO\text{-}SiO_2$. Ph.D. thesis, The Pennsylvania State University.

Rimann, E., 1915. Über Kimberlit und Alnöit in Brasilien. *Tscherm. Mineral. Petrog. Mitt.,* **33**, 244–262.

———, 1931. Über das Muttergestein der Diamanten von Minas Gerais, Brasil. *Fortsch. Mineral. Krist. Petrog.,* **16**, 93–96.

Ringwood, A. E., 1959. On the chemical evolution and densities of the planets. *Geochim. Cosmochim. Acta,* **15**, 257–283.

———, 1962a. "Present status of the chondritic Earth model," in Moore, C. B., ed., *Researches on Meteorites.* John Wiley and Sons, New York, 198–216.

———, 1962b. A model for the upper mantle. *J. Geophys. Res.,* **67**, 857–867.

———, 1962c. A model for the upper mantle, 2. *J. Geophys. Res.,* **67**, 4473–4477.

———, 1966. "Mineralogy of the Mantle," in Hurley, P. M., ed., *Advances in Earth Science,* 357–399. The M.I.T. Press, Cambridge, Mass.

———, and D. H. Green, 1964. Experimental investigations bearing on the nature of the Mohorovicic Discontinuity. *Nature,* **201**, 566–567.

Ringwood, A. E., I. D. MacGregor, and F. R. Boyd, 1964. Petrological composition of the upper mantle. *Carnegie Inst. Wash. Yearbook,* **63**, 147–152.

Ringwood, A. E., and M. Seabrook, 1962. Olivine-spinel equilibria at high pressure in the system $NiGeO_4\text{-}Mg_2SiO_4$. *J. Geophys. Res.,* **67**, 1975–1985.

———, 1963. High pressure phase transformations in germanate pyroxenes and related compounds. *J. Geophys. Res.,* **68**, 4601–4609.

Riordon, P. H., 1957. The structural environment of the Thetford-Black Lake asbestos deposits. *Proc. Geol. Assoc. Can.,* **9**, 83–93.

———, 1962. Geology of the asbestos belt in

Southeastern Quebec. *Bull. Can. Inst. Mining Met.*, **55**, no. 601, 311–313.

Rittman, A., 1962, *Volcanoes and their Activity.* Wiley-Interscience, New York, 305p.

Robertson, E. C., F. Birch, and G. J. F. MacDonald, 1957. Experimental determination of jadeite stability relations to 25,000 bars. *Am. J. Sci.*, **255**, 115–137.

Roe, G. D., 1964. Rubidium-strontium analyses of ultramafic rocks and the origin of peridotites. Ph.D. thesis, Mass. Inst. Tech.

———, W. H. Pinson, and P. M. Hurley, 1965. Rb-Sr evidence for the origin of peridotites. *Trans. Am. Geophys. Union,* **46**, 186. (Abstr.)

Roedder, E., 1965. Liquid CO_2 inclusions in olivine bearing nodules and phenocrysts from basalts. *Am. Mineral.*, **50**, 1746–1782.

Romanov, B. M., 1949. A gabbro-peridotite formation in the Urals. *Sov. Geol.*, **40.**

Roots, E. F., 1954. Geology and mineral deposits of Aiken Lake Map-area, British Columbia, *Geol. Surv. Can., Mem.*, **274**, 246p.

Rosenfeld, J. L., and A. B. Chase, 1961. Pressure and temperature of crystallization from elastic effects around solid inclusions in minerals? *Am. J. Sci.*, **259**, 519–541.

Ross, C. S., M. D. Foster, and A. T. Myers, 1954. Origin of dunites and of olivine-rich inclusions in basaltic rocks. *Am. Mineral.*, **39**, 693–737.

Ross, C. S., H. D. Miser, and L. W. Stephenson, 1929. Water-laid volcanic rocks of early Upper Cretaceous age in southwestern Arkansas, southeastern Oklahoma, and northeastern Texas. *U.S. Geol. Surv., Profess. Paper,* **154**, 175–202.

Rossello, G., 1964. Guides pétrographiques et structuraux applicables a la recherche des gisements de chromite de type "alpin." *Chron. Mines Rech. Minière,* **32**, 219–224.

Rossman, D. L., N. S. Fernandez, C. A. Fontanos, and Z. C. Zepeda, 1959. Chromite deposits on Insular Chromite Reservation Number One, Zambales, Philippines. *Philippine Bur. Mines,* Spec. project Ser., Pub. no. 19, Chromite, 12p.

Rost, F., 1961. Chlorit und Granat in ultrabasischen Gesteinen. *Fortschr. Mineral.*, **39**, 112–126.

Rothstein, A. T. V., 1957. The Dawros peridotite, Connemara, Eire. *Geol. Mag.*, **95**, 456–462.

———, 1958. Pyroxenes from the Dawros peridotite and some comments on their nature. *Geol. Mag.*, **95**, 456–462.

———, 1961. A synorogenic peridotite at Dawros, Connemara. *Acta Geologica, Budapest,* **7**, 221–232.

———, 1962. *Magmatic facies in ultrabasic igneous rocks of the tholeiitic series.* Acad. Sci., Moscow, 42p. (Russian, English summary.)

Routhier, P., 1954. Volcanicité et embryotectonique paléogène en Nouvelle-Cáledonie. *Congr. Géol. Intern. Alger,* **17**, 43–52.

Rowe, R. B., 1958. Niobium (columbium) deposits of Canada. *Geol. Surv. Can., Econ. Geol.*, Ser. no. 18, 108p.

Rozhkov, I. S., et al, *The Geology of Diamond Deposits.* Acad Sci., Moscow, 187p. (Russian.)

Ruckmick, J. C., and J. A. Noble, 1959. Origin of the ultramafic complex at Union Bay, southeastern Alaska. *Bull. Geol. Soc. Am.*, **70**, 981–1018.

Russell, H. D., S. A. Hiemstra, and D. Groeneveld, 1954. The mineralogy and petrology of the carbonatite at Loolekop, Eastern Transvaal. *Trans. Geol. Soc. S. Africa,* **57**, 197–208.

Saether, E., 1957. The alkaline rock province of the Fen area in southern Norway. *Norsk. Vidensk. Selsk. Skrifter,* no. **1**, 1–150.

Saggerson, E. P., 1963. Geology of the Simba-Kibweki Area. *Rept. Min. Com. Ind., Geol. Surv. Kenya.*, **58**, 70p.

———, and L. A. J. Williams, 1964. Ngurumanite from Southern Kenya and its bearing on the origin of rocks in the Northern Tanganyika alkaline district. *J. Petrol.*, **5**, 40–81.

Sahama, Th. G., 1945. Spurenelemente der Gesteine im südlichen Finnisch-Lapland. *Bull. Comm. Géol. Finlande,* **135.**

———, 1962. Petrology of Mt. Nyiragongo. *Trans. Edinburgh Geol. Soc.*, **19**, 1–28.

Salmon, L., 1957. The determination of sodium and potassium in a sample of dunite by radioactivation analysis. *Atomic Energy Research Establishment C/M 323, United Kingdom Atomic Energy Establishment,* 1–7.

Sampson, D. N., 1958. The volcanic hills at Igwisi, *Records Geol. Surv. Tanganyika,* **3**, 48–53.

Sarsadskikh, N. N., et al, 1966. On the absolute age of Yakutian kimberlites. *Dokl. Akad. Nauk,* **168**, 420–423. (Russian.)

Satterley, J., 1948. Geology of Michaud Township. *Ontario Dept. Mines Ann. Rept.*, **57**, pt. 4.

Schadler, Von Jas., 1913. Zur Kenntnis der Einschlüsse im den südsteirischen Basalttuffen und ihrer Mineralien. *Mineral. Petrog. Mitt.*, **230**, 33.

Schairer, J. F., and H. S. Yoder, 1964. Crystal and liquid trends in simplified alkali basalts. *Carnegie Inst. Wash. Yearbook,* **63**, 65–74.

Schmitt, R. A., G. G. Goles, and R. H. Smith, 1966. Elemental abundances in stone meteorites. *Geochim. Cosmochim. Acta.* In press.

Schmitt, R. A., R. H. Smith, J. E. Lasch, A. W. Mosen, D. A. Olehy, and J. Vasilevskis, 1963. Abundances of the fourteen rare-earth elements, scandium, and yttrium in meteoritic and terrestrial matter. *Geochim. Cosmochim. Acta,* **27**, 577–622.

Schuiling, R. D., 1964. Serpentinization as a possible cause of high heat-flow values in and near the oceanic ridges. *Nature,* **201**, 807–808.

Schüller, A., 1961. Die Druck-, Temperatur- und Energie-felder der Metamorphose. *Neues. Jahrb. Mineral. Abhand.*, **96**, 250–290.

Schwellnus, J. S. I., L. J. N. Engelbrecht, F. J. Coertze, H. D. Russell, S. J. Malherbe, D. P. van Rooyen, and R. Cooke, 1962. The geology of the Olifants River area, Transvaal. S. *Africa Dept. Mines Geol. Surv. Expl. Sheets,* **2429B** and **2430A**, 87p.

Sclar, C. B., L. C. Carrison, and C. M. Schwartz, 1964. High-pressure stability field of clinoenstatite and the orthoenstatite-clinoenstatite transition. *Trans. Am. Geophys. Union,* **45**, 121. (Abstr.)

Sclar, C. B., A. P. Young, L. C. Carrison, and C. M. Schwartz, 1962. Synthesis and optical crystallography of stishovite, a very high pressure polymorph of SiO_2. *J. Geophys. Res.*, **67**, 4049–4054.

Scott Blair, G. W., 1958. The importance of the sigma phenomenon in the study of the flow of blood. *Rheol. Acta,* **1**, 123–126.

Scrope, G. P., 1825, *Considerations on Volcanos.* W. Phillips, London, 270p.

Segré, G., and A. Silberberg, 1961. Radial particle displacements in Poiseuille flow of suspensions. *Nature,* **189**, 209–210.

———, 1962. Behavior of macroscopic rigid spheres in Poiseuille flow, II. Experimental results and interpretation. *J. Fluid Mech.*, **14**, 136–157.

———, 1964. The tubular pinch effect in the Poiseuille flow of a suspension of spheres. *Biblio. Anat.*, **4**, 83–93.

Shand, S. J., 1934. The heavy minerals of kimberlite. *Trans. Geol. Soc. S. Africa,* **37**.

———, 1947. *Eruptive Rocks,* 3rd ed. John Wiley and Sons, New York, 488p.

Shaw, H. R., 1965. Comments on viscosity, crystal settling, and convection in granitic magmas. *Am. J. Sci.*, **263**, 120–151.

Shcherbakov, Yu. G., and G. A. Perezhogin, 1964. Gold geochemistry. *Geokhimiya,* **1964**, 518–528.

Sheinmann, Yu. M., 1957. Location and age of alkalic ultrabasic rocks of the Siberian platform: *Razvedka i Okrana Nedra,* **23**, 12–16.

Sheinmann, M. Yu., et al, 1961. *Geology of Deposits of the Rare Elements: Alkalic Intrusions.* Gosgeoltekhizdat, Moscow, **12**, 178p. (Russian.)

Shido, F., 1958. Notes on rock forming minerals (9). Hornblende-bearing eclogite from Gangenyama of Higasi-Akaisi in the Bessi district, Sikoku. *J. Geol. Soc. Jap.*, **65**, 701–703.

Shields, R. M., 1964. The Rb^{87}-Sr^{87} age of stony meteorites, Ph.D. thesis, Mass. Inst. Tech.

Shima, M., W. H. Gross, and H. G. Thode, 1963. Sulfur isotope abundances in basic sills, differentiated granites, and meteorites. *J. Geophys. Res.*, **68**, 2835–2847.

Shoemaker, E. M., 1956. "Occurrence of uranium in diatremes on the Navajo and Hopi Reservations, Arizona, New Mexico, and Utah," in Page, L. R., H. E. Stocking, and H. B. Smith, Contributions to the geology of uranium and thorium by the United States Geological Survey and Atomic Energy Commission for the United Nations international conference on peaceful uses of atomic energy, Geneva, Switzerland, 1955. *U.S. Geol. Surv. Profess. Paper,* **300**, 179–185.

———, C. H. Roach, and F. M. Byers, Jr., 1962. "Diatremes and uranium deposits in the Hopi Buttes, Arizona," in Engel, A. E. J., H. L. James, and B. F. Leonard, eds., *Petrologic Studies.* Geol. Soc. Am., **Buddington vol.**, 327–355.

Simkin, T., 1964. Flow differentiation in the picritic sills of North Trotternish, Isle of Skye, Scotland. *Geol. Soc. Am. Spec. Paper,* **82**, 186.

———, 1965. The picritic sills of Northwest Trotternish, Isle of Skye, Scotland. Ph.D. thesis, Princeton University, 139p.

Simmons, G., 1964a. Velocity of compressional waves in various minerals at pressures to 10 kilobars, *J. Geophys. Res.*, **69**, 1117–1121.

———, 1964b. Velocity of shear waves in rocks to 10 kilobars, II, *J. Geophys. Res.*, **69**, 1123–1130.

Simpson, E. S. W., 1954. On the graphical representation of differentiation trends in igneous rocks. *Geol. Mag.*, **91**, 238–244.

Sinclair, W. E., 1959. *Asbestos. Its Origin, Production and Utilization.* Mining Publications Ltd. (The Mining Magazine), London, 512p.

Smales, A. A., D. Mapper, and A. J. Wood, 1957. The determination, by radioactivation, of small quantities of nickel, cobalt and copper in rocks, marine sediments and meteorites. *Analyst,* **82**, 75–88.

Smirnov, G. I., 1959. Mineralogy of the Siberian kimberlites. *Intern. Geol. Rev.*, **1**, 21–39.

Smit, P. J., 1962. The gravity survey of the Republic of South Africa, Pt. 1. S. *Africa Dept. Mines Geol. Surv. Handbook* 3, 354p.

Smith, C. H., 1958. Bay of Islands igneous complex, western Newfoundland. *Geol. Surv. Can. Mem.* **290**, 132p.

———, 1962a. Notes on the Muskox intrusion, Coppermine River area, District of Mackenzie. *Geol. Surv. Can., Paper* **61-25**, 16p.

———, 1962b. Ultramafic intrusions in Canada and their significance to Upper Mantle studies. *Can. Geophys. Bull.*, **14**, 157–169.

———, T. N. Irvine, and D. C. Findlay, 1966. Geologic maps of the Muskox intrusion. *Geol. Surv. Can.*, Maps 1213A and 1214A.

Smith, C. H., and H. E. Kapp, 1963. The Muskox intrusion, a recently discovered layered intrusion in the Coppermine River area, Northwest

Territories, Canada. *Mineral. Soc. Am., Spec. Paper* **1**, 30–35.

Smith, C. H., and I. D. MacGregor, 1960. Ultrabasic intrusive conditions illustrated by the Mount Albert ultrabasic pluton, Gaspé, Quebec. *Bull. Geol. Soc. Am.*, **71**, 1978. (Abstr.)

Smith, J. V., and P. Gay, 1958. The powder patterns and lattice parameters of plagioclase felspars, II. *Mineral. Mag.*, **31**, 744–762.

Smyth, C. H., Jr., 1902. Petrography of recently discovered dikes in Syracuse, N.Y.; with note on the presence of melilite in the Green Street dike. *Am. J. Sci.*, 4th ser., **14**, 26–30.

Snyder, F. G., and P. E. Gerdemann, 1965. Explosive igneous activity along an Illinois-Missouri-Kansas axis. *Am. J. Sci.*, **263**, 465–493.

Sobolev, N. V., 1963. Rhombic pyroxenes from garnet-peridotite and eclogite. *Dokl. Akad. Nauk SSSR* (A.G.I. transl., 1964, 110–111).

———, 1964. *Paragenetic Types of Garnet.* Nauka, Moscow, 218p. (Russian.)

———, and I. K. Kuznetsova, 1966. Mineralogy of diamond-bearing eclogites. *Dokl. Akad. Nauk SSSR,* **167**, 1365–8. (Russian, A.G.I. transl., 1966, 112–115)

Sobolev, V. S., 1960a. Role of high pressure in metamorphism: *21st. Intern. Geol. Congr.*, Copenhagen, *Repts.*, **14**, 72–82.

———, 1960b. Conditions of formations of diamond. *Geol. Geofiz.*, 1960, no. 1.

Sørensen, H., 1953. The ultrabasic rocks at Tovqussaq, West Greenland. A contribution to the peridotite problem. *Medd. Grønland,* **136,4**, 1–86.

———, 1954. The border relations of the dunite at Siorarssuit, Sukkertoppen District, West Greenland. *Medd. Grønland,* **135,4**, 1–47.

———, 1955a. A petrographical and structural study of the rocks around the peridotite at Engenbrae, Holandsfjord, Northern Norway. *Norg. Geol. Undersøkelse,* **191**, 71–102.

———, 1955b. A preliminary note on some peridotites from Northern Norway. *Norsk Geol. Tidsskr.,* **35**, 93–104.

———, 1955c. On sapphirine from West Greenland. *Medd. Grønland,* **137,1**, 1–32.

Sosman, R. B., 1938. Evidence on the intrusion-temperature of peridotites. *Am. J. Sci.*, 5th ser., **35**, 353–359.

Stansfield, J., 1923. Extensions of the Monteregian petrographical province to the west and northwest. *Geol. Mag.*, **60**, 433–453.

Starkey, John, and W. L. Brown, 1964. Künstliche Erzeugung Mechanischer Zwillinge in Anorthit, $CaAl_2Si_2O_8$. Z. *Krist.*, **120**, 388–392.

Starkey, T. V., 1956. The laminar flow of streams of suspended particles. *Brit. J. Appl. Phys.*, **7**, 52–55.

Stearns, H. T., and K. N. Vaksvik, 1935. Geology and ground-water resources of the island of Oahu, Hawaii. *Bull. Hydrol. Div. Hawaii,* **1**.

Stebbins, R. H., 1957. Field description of the Percy Islands ultramafic complex, southeastern Alaska. M.A. thesis, Columbia University.

Stishov, S. M., 1963. Equilibrium line between coesite and rutilelike modification of silica. *Dokl. Akad. Nauk SSSR,* **148**, no. 5, 1186–1188.

Stockwell, C. H., 1957. Geology and economic minerals of Canada. *Geol. Surv. Can., Econ. Geol.*, Ser. no. 1, 4th ed.

———, 1964. "Fourth report on structural provinces, orogenies, and time-classification of rocks of the Canadian Precambrian Shield," in Age determinations and geological studies. *Geol. Surv. Can., Paper* **64-17**, pt. 2, 1–21.

Strauss, C. A., and F. C. Truter, 1950. The alkali complex at Spitskop, Sekukuniland, eastern Transvaal. *Trans. Geol. Soc. S. Africa,* **53**, 81–125.

Stueber, A. M., 1965. A geochemical study of ultramafic rocks. Ph.D. thesis, Univ. of California, San Diego.

———, and G. G. Goles, 1967. Abundances of Na, Mn, Cr, Sc, and Co in ultramafic rocks. *Geochim. Cosmochim. Acta,* **31**, 75–93.

Stueber, A. M., and V. R. Murthy, 1965. Strontium isotope and alkali element abundances in ultramafic rocks. *Trans. Am. Geophys. Un.,* **46**, 186. (Abstr.)

———, 1966a. Potassium-rubidium ratios in ultramafic rocks and the differentiation history of the upper mantle. Submitted to *Science.*

———, 1966b. Strontium isotope and alkali element abundances in ultramafic rocks. *Geochim. Cosmochim. Acta,* **30**, 1243–1259.

Sugimura, A., 1960. Zonal arrangement of some geophysical and petrological features in Japan and its environs; *J. Faculty Sci., Univ. Tokyo,* sect. II, **XII**, pt. 2, 133–153.

Sutton, J., and J. Watson, 1951. The pre-Torridonian metamorphic history of the Loch Torridon and Scourie areas in the North West Highlands of Scotland, and its bearing on the chronological classification of the Lewisian. *Quart. J. Geol. Soc. London,* **106**, 241–308.

Talbot, J. L., B. E. Hobbs, H. G. Wilshire, and T. R. Sweatman, 1963. Xenoliths and xenocrysts from lavas of the Kerguelen Island Archipelago. *Am. Mineral.*, **48**, 159–179.

Taljaard, M. S., 1936. South African melilite basalts and their relations. *Trans. Geol. Soc. S. Africa,* **39**, 281–316.

Tatsumoto, M., C. E. Hedge, and A. E. J. Engel, 1965. Potassium, rubidium, strontium, thorium, uranium, and the ratio of strontium-87 to strontium-86 in oceanic tholeiitic basalt. *Science,* **150**, 886–888.

Taubeneck, W. H., 1965. An appraisal of some

potassium-rubidium ratios in igneous rocks. *J. Geophys. Res.*, **70,** 475–478.

Taylor, H. P., Jr., 1966. Oxygen isotope studies of volcanic and plutonic igneous rocks. (Manuscript in preparation.)

———, M. B. Duke, L. T. Silver, and S. Epstein, 1965. Oxygen isotope studies of minerals in stony meteorites. *Geochim. Cosmochim. Acta,* **29,** 489–512.

Taylor, H. P., Jr., and S. Epstein, 1962. Relationship between O^{18}/O^{16} ratios in coexisting minerals of igneous and metamorphic rocks; Pt 1. *Bull. Geol. Soc. Am.*, **73,** 461–480.

———, 1963. O^{18}/O^{16} ratios in rocks and coexisting minerals of the Skaergaard intrusion, East Greenland. *J. Petrol.*, **4,** 51–74.

———, 1966. Deuterium-hydrogen ratios in coexisting minerals of metamorphic and igneous rocks. (Manuscript in preparation.)

Taylor, H. P., Jr., J. Frechen, and E. T. Degens, 1966. Oxygen and carbon isotope studies of carbonatites from the Laacher See District, West Germany, and the Alnö District, Sweden. *Geochim. Cosmochim. Acta.* In press.

Taylor, H. P., Jr., and R. L. Nielsen, 1956. Geological map of the Annette Island dunite body. (Unpub. report.)

Taylor, H. P., Jr., and J. A. Noble, 1960. Origin of the ultramafic complexes in southeastern Alaska. *21st Intern. Geol. Congr.*, Copenhagen, *Repts.* **13,** 175–187.

Taylor, H. P., Jr., and R. H. Stebbins, 1956. Geological map of the Klukwan pyroxenite body. (Unpub. report.)

Taylor, R. B., 1964. Geology of the Duluth Gabbro Complex near Duluth, Minnesota. *Minn. Geol. Surv. Bull.* **44,** 63p.

Taylor, S. R., 1964. Trace element abundances and the chondritic Earth model. *Geochim. Cosmochim. Acta.* **28,** 1989–1998.

Tex, E. den, 1965. Metamorphic lineages of orogenic plutonism. *Geol. Mijnbouw,* **44,4,** 105–132.

Thayer, T. P., 1946. Preliminary chemical correlation of chromite with the containing rocks. *Econ. Geol.*, **41,** 202–217.

———, 1956. Preliminary geologic map of the John Day quadrangle, Oregon. *U.S. Geol. Surv. Mineral inv. field studies,* Map MF 51.

———, 1960. Some critical differences between alpine-type and stratiform peridotite-gabbro complexes. *21st Intern. Geol. Congr.*, Copenhagen, *Repts.*, **13,** 247–259.

———, 1961. Application of geology in chromite exploration and mining. *Symp. Chrome Ore,* Central Treaty Organization, Ankara, 197–223.

———, 1963a. Flow layering in alpine peridotite-gabbro complexes. *Mineral. Soc. Am., Spec. Paper,* **1,** 55–61.

———, 1963b. The Canyon Mountain Complex, Oregon, and the alpine mafic magma stem. *U.S. Geol. Surv., Profess. Paper,* **475-C,** C82–C85.

———, 1964. Principal features and origin of podiform chromite deposits, and some observations on the Guleman-Soridağ district, Turkey. *Econ. Geol.*, **59,** 1497–1524.

———, 1966. Serpentinization considered as a constant-volume metasomatic process. *Am. Mineral.*, **51,** 685–710.

———, and C. E. Brown, 1961. Is the Tinaquillo, Venezuela, "pseudogabbro" metamorphic or magmatic? *Bull. Geol. Soc. Am.*, **72,** 1565–1570.

———, 1964. Pre-Tertiary orogenic and plutonic intrusive activity in central and northeastern Oregon. *Bull. Geol. Soc. Am.*, **75,** 1255–1262.

Thiessen, P. A., G. Heinicke, and K. Meyer, 1960. Chemische Wirkungen aus mechanischen Ursachen. *Festschr. Humboldt-Univ.*

Thode, H. G., H. B. Dunford, and M. Shima, 1962. Sulfur isotope abundances in rocks of the Sudbury District and their geological significance. *Econ. Geol.*, **57,** 565–578.

Thode, H. G., J. Monster, and H. B. Dunford, 1961. Sulfur isotope geochemistry. *Geochim. Cosmochim. Acta,* **25,** 159–174.

Thompson, G. A., 1963. Geophysical Investigations at Twin Sisters, Washington. *Geol. Soc. Am., Spec. Paper* **76,** 227–228. (Abstr.)

Thompson, G. R., 1964. Investigations of potassium-rubidium ratios in carbonate rocks of problematical origin. M.A. thesis, Dartmouth College, Hanover, New Hampshire.

Thompson, L. S. 1928. The upland diamond deposits of the Diamantina district, Minas Gerais, Brazil. *Econ. Geol.*, **23,** 705–723.

Thorne, R. L., and R. R. Wells, 1956. Studies of the Snettisham magnetite deposit, southeastern Alaska. *U.S. Bur. Mines, Rept. Invest.* **5195,** 41p.

Tilles, D., 1961. Natural variations in isotopic abundances of silicon. *J. Geophys. Res.*, **66,** 3003–3013.

Tilley, C. E., 1947. The dunite-mylonite of St. Paul's Rock (Atlantic). *Am. J. Sci.*, **245,** 483–491.

———, and H. F. Harwood, 1931. The dolerite-chalk contact at Scawt Hill, C. Antrim. The production of basic alkali-rocks by the assimilation of limestone by a basaltic magma. *Mineral. Mag.* **22,** 439–468.

Tilley, C. E., and I. D. Muir, 1962. The Hebridean plateau magma type. *Trans. Edinburgh Geol. Soc.*, **19,** 208–215.

Tilley, C. E., and H. S. Yoder, 1964. Pyroxene fractionation in mafic magma at high pressures and its bearing on basalt genesis. *Carnegie Inst. Wash. Yearbook,* **63,** 114–120.

Tilton, G. R., and G. W. Reed, 1963. "Radioactive Heat Production in Eclogite and Some Ultramafic Rocks," in Geiss, J., and E. D. Goldberg, eds., *Earth Science and Meteoritics.* North-Holland Publishing Co., Amsterdam, 31–43.

Du Toit, A. L., 1954. *The Geology of South Africa.* Oliver and Boyd, Edinburgh.

Tomkeiieff, S. I., 1928. The volcanic complex of Colton Hill, Derbyshire. *Quart. J. Geol. Soc. London,* **84,** 703.

———, 1949. The volcanoes of Kamchatka. *Bull. Volcanol.,* ser. 2, **8,** 87–112.

———, 1961. Alkalic ultrabasic rock and carbonatites in the U.S.S.R. *Intern. Geol. Rev.,* **3,** 739–758.

Törnebohm, A. E., 1882. Mikroskopiska Bergartsstudier. XVII. Melilitbasalt fran Alnö. *Geol. Fören. Stockholm Förh.,* Bd. **VI.**

Tröger, W. E., 1935. *Spezielle Petrographie der Eruptivgesteine—Ein Nomenklatur-Kompendium.* Verlag der Deutschen Mineralogischen Gesellschaft, Berlin, 360p.

Truswell, J. F., 1955. A petrological study of dolerite sills in the Jagersfontein diamond mine, Orange Free State. *Trans. Roy. Soc. S. Africa,* **34,** 409–416.

Truter, F. C., 1955. Modern concepts of the Bushveld Igneous Complex: C.C.T.A. *Southern Reg. Comm. Geol.,* Salisbury, **1,** 77–92.

Tryggvason, T., 1943. Das Skjaldbreid-Gebietauf Island; eine petrographische studie. *Upsala Univ. Geol. Inst.,* B, **30,** 273–320.

Turekian, K. K., 1963. The chromium and nickel distribution in basaltic rocks and eclogites. *Geochim. Cosmochim. Acta,* **27,** 835–846.

———, and M. H. Carr, 1961. Chromium, cobalt and strontium in some Bureau of Standards rock reference samples. *Geochim. Cosmochim. Acta,* **24,** 1–9.

Turekian, K. K., and K. H. Wedepohl, 1961. Distribution of the elements in some major units of the Earth's crust. *Bull. Geol. Soc. Am.,* **72,** 175–192.

Turner, F. J., 1942. Preferred orientation of olivine crystals in peridotites with special reference to New Zealand examples. *Trans. Roy. Soc. New Zealand,* **72,** 280–300.

———, H. C. Heard, and D. T. Griggs, 1960. Experimental deformation of enstatite and accompanying inversion to clinoenstatite. *21st Intern. Geol. Congr.,* Copenhagen, *Repts.,* **18,** 399–408.

Turner, F. J., and J. Verhoogen, 1960. *Igneous and Metamorphic Petrology,* 2nd ed. McGraw-Hill Book Co., New York, 694p.

Turner, F. J., and L. E. Weiss, 1963. *Structural Analysis of Metamorphic Tectonites.* McGraw-Hill Book Co., New York, 545p.

Turnock, A. C., and H. P. Eugster, 1962. Fe-Al Oxides: Phase relations below 1000°C. *J. Petrol.,* **3,** 533–565.

Tuttle, O. F., and J. Gittins, 1967. *The Carbonatites.* John Wiley and Sons, New York.

Tweto, O., 1951. Form and structure of sills near Pando, Colorado. *Bull. Geol. Soc. Am.,* **62,** 507–531.

Tyndale-Biscoe, R., 1949. The geology of the country around Gwelo. *Geol. Surv. S. Rhodesia, Bull.* **39,** 145p.

Tyrrell, G. W., 1912. The late Palaeozoic alkaline igneous rocks of the west of Scotland. *Geol. Mag.,* **9,** 120–131.

———, 1916. The picrite-teschenite sill of Lugar (Ayrshire). *Quart. J. Geol. Soc. London,* **72,** 84–131.

———, 1923. Classification and age of the analcite-bearing igneous rocks of Scotland. *Geol. Mag.,* **60,** 249–260.

———, 1929. *The Principles of Petrology,* 2nd ed. P. Dutton and Co., New York, 349p.

———, 1948. A boring through the Lugar sill. *Trans. Geol. Soc. Glasgow,* **21,** 157–202.

———, 1952. A second boring through the Lugar sill. *Trans. Edinburgh Geol. Soc.,* **25,** 374–392.

Urey, H. C., 1952. *The Planets, their Origin and Development,* Yale University Press, 245p.

Van Bemmelen, R. W., 1949. *The Geology of Indonesia.* 2 vols., Govt. Printing Office, Den Haag, Holland.

Van Wambeke, L., J. W. Brinck, et al, 1964. The alkaline rocks and the carbonatites of the Kaiserstuhl. *Euratom Rept.* **1827,d,f,e,** 232p.

Varlakov, A. S., and M. F. Zhuzhgova, 1964. Geochemistry of boron in the ultramafic rocks of the Orenburg District. *Geokhimiya,* **1964,** 795–801.

Verhoogen, J., 1938. Les pipes de kimberlite du Katanga: *Com. Spec. Katanga. Ann. Serv. Mines,* **9,** 1–50.

———, 1948. Geological significance of surface tension. *J. Geol.,* **56,** 210–217.

Vilminot, J. C., 1965. Les enclaves de péridotite et de pyroxénotite à spinelle dans le basalte du Rocher du Lion (Chaîne du Devès, Haute-Loire). *Bull. Soc. Franç. Minéral. Crist.,* **88,** 109–118.

Vincent, E. A., and J. H. Crocket, 1960. Studies in the geochemistry of gold–II. The gold content of some basic and ultrabasic rocks and stone meteorites. *Geochim. Cosmochim. Acta,* **18,** 143–148.

Vinogradov, A. P., 1962. Average contents of chemical elements in the principal types of igneous rocks of the Earth's crust. *Geochemistry* (transl. of *Geokhimiya*), **1962,** 641–664.

———, M. S. Chupakhin, and V. A. Grinenko, 1957. Some data on the isotopic composition of the sulfur of sulfides. *Geokhimiya,* **3,** 183–186.

Vinogradov, A. P., K. P. Florenskii, and V. F. Volynets, 1963. Ammonia in meteorites and igneous rocks. *Geokhimiya,* **1963,** 875–885.

Vinogradov, A. P., O. I. Kropotova, and V. I. Ustinov, 1965. Possible sources of carbon in natural diamond by C^{12}/C^{13} isotope data. *Geokhimiya,* **1965,** 643–651.

Visher, G. S., 1962. Petrology of the Moxie pluton, west-central Maine. *Geol. Soc. Am., Spec. Paper,* **68,** 289. (Abstr.)

Visser, H. N., J. J. Spies, G. P. Fourie, J. J. Viljoen, A. P. G. Söhnge, and F. A. Venter, 1961. Die geologie van die gebied tussen Middelburg en Cullinan, Transvaal. S. *Africa Dept. Mines Geol. Surv. Toel., Blad* **2528D, 2529C,** 73p.

Vogt, J. H. L., 1921. The physical chemistry of the crystallization and magmatic differentiation of igneous rocks: Pt III. *J. Geol.,* **29,** 515–539.

———, 1923. The physical chemistry of the crystallization and magmatic differentiation of igneous rocks: Pt VIII. *J. Geol.,* **31,** 407–419.

Voll, G., 1961. Zur Frage des Stofftransports auf den Korngrenzen metamorpher Gesteine. *Geol. Rundschau,* **51,** 395–405.

Vorobyeva, O. A., 1961. On the magmatic nature of the platinum-bearing belt of the gabbro-peridotite formation of the Urals. *Izv. Akad. Nauk SSSR. Geol.,* Ser. no. **7,** 16–29. (English trans.)

Vuagnat, M., 1953. Sur un phénomène de metasomatisme dans les roches vertes du Montgenèvre (Hautes-Alpes). *Bull. Soc. Franç. Minéral. Crist.,* **76,** 438–450.

Wade, A., and R. T. Prider, 1940. The leucite-bearing rocks of the West Kimberley area, Western Australia, *Quart. J. Geol. Soc. London,* **96,** 39–98.

Wager, L. R., 1956. A chemical definition of fractionation stages as a basis for comparison of Hawaiian, Hebridean and other basic lavas. *Geochim. Cosmochim. Acta,* **9,** 217–248.

———, 1958. Beneath the earth's crust. *Brit. Assoc. Advan. Sci., Pres. Address Section C,* no. **58,** 31–45.

———, 1963. The mechanism of adcumulus growth in the layered series of the Skaergaard intrusion. *Mineral. Soc. Am., Spec. Paper,* **1,** 1–9.

———, and G. M. Brown, 1967. *Layered Igneous Rocks.* Oliver and Boyd, Edinburgh and London.

———, and W. J. Wadsworth, 1960. Types of igneous cumulates, *J. Petrol.,* **1,** 73–85.

Wager, L. R., and W. A. Deer, 1939. Geological investigations in East Greenland, Pt III. The petrology of the Skaergaard intrusion, Kangerdlugssuaq, East Greenland. *Medd. Grønland,* **105,** no. 4, 352p.

Wager, L. R., and R. L. Mitchell, 1951. The distribution of trace elements during strong fractionation of basic magma—a further study of the Skaergaard intrusion, East Greenland, *Geochim. Cosmochim. Acta,* **1,** 129–208.

Wagner, P. A., 1914. *The Diamond Fields of Southern Africa.* The Transvaal Leader, Johannesburg, 347p.

———, 1916. The geology and mineral industry of South-West Africa. *S. Africa Dept. Mines Ind., Mem.,* **7.**

Walker, F., 1930. The geology of the Shiant Isles (Hebrides). *Quart. J. Geol. Soc. London,* **86,** 355–398.

———, 1932. Differentiation in the sills of northern Trotternish (Skye). *Trans. Roy. Soc. Edinburgh.* **57,** 241–257.

———, 1940. Differentiation of the Palisade disbase, New Jersey. *Bull. Geol. Soc. Am.,* **51,** 1059–1106.

———, 1956. The magnetic properties and differentiation of dolerite sills—a critical discussion. *Am. J. Sci.,* **254,** 433–443.

———, and L. O. Nicolaysen, 1954. The petrology of Mauritius. *Colonial Geol. Mineral. Resources (Gt. Brit.),* **4,** 3–43.

Walker, F., and A. Poldervaart, 1942. The petrology of the Karroo dolerites between Sutherland and Middelburg, C. P. *Trans. Geol. Soc. S. Africa,* **45,** 55–64.

———, 1949. Karroo dolerites of the Union of South Africa. *Bull. Geol. Soc. Am.,* **60,** 591–706.

Walker, G. P. L., 1959. Some observations on the Antrim basalts and associated dolerite intrusions. *Proc. Geologists' Assoc. (Engl.)* **70,** 179–205.

Walton, M. S., 1951. The Blashke Islands ultrabasic complex. Ph.D. thesis, Columbia University.

Washington, H. S., 1901. The foyaite-ijolite series of Magnet Cove: A chemical study in differentiation. *J. Geol.,* **9,** 607–622.

———, 1927. The italite locality of Villa Senni. *Am. J. Sci.,* 5th ser., **14,** 173–198.

Wasserburg, G. J., G. J. F. MacDonald, F. Hoyle, and W. A. Fowler, 1964. Relative contributions of uranium, thorium, and potassium to heat production in the Earth. *Science,* **143,** 465–467.

Watson, K. D., 1955. Kimberlite at Bachelor Lake, Quebec. *Am. Mineral.,* **40,** 565–579.

———, 1957. Hornblende lamprophyre dykes in southwestern Lesueur Township, Quebec. *Can. Mineral.,* **6,** pt. 1, 15–30.

———, 1960. Eclogite inclusions in serpentine pipes at Garnet Ridge, northeastern Arizona. *Bull. Geol. Soc. Am.,* **71,** 2082–2083.

Webster, R. K., 1960. "Mass Spectrometric Isotope Dilution Analysis," in Smales, A. A., and L. R. Wager, eds., *Methods in Geochemistry.* Wiley—Interscience, New York, 202–246.

Wedepohl, K. H., 1963. Die Nickel- und Chromgehalte von basaltischen Gesteinen und deren

Olivin-führenden Einschlüssen. *Neues Jahrb. Mineral., Monatsh.*, **1963**, 237–242.

Weedon, D. S., 1960. The Gars-bheinn ultrabasic sill, Isle of Skye. *Quart. J. Geol. Soc. London,* **116**, 37–54.

Weidmann, M., 1964. Géologie de la région située entre Tigssaluk Fjord et Sermiligârssuk Fjord (Partie Médiane), SW-Groenland. *Medd. Grønland,* **169,5**, 1–146.

Weiss, O., 1940. Gravimetric and earth-magnetic measurements on the Great Dyke of Southern Rhodesia. *Trans. Geol. Soc. S. Africa,* **43**, 143–151.

Welby, C. W., 1961. Bedrock geology of the Central Champlain Valley of Vermont. *Vermont Develop. Dept. Bull.*, **14**, 296p.

Wells, R. R., and R. L. Thorne, 1953. Concentration of Klukwan, Alaska, magnetite ore. *U.S. Bur. Mines. Rept. Invest.* **4984**, 15p.

White, A. J. R., 1959. Scapolite-bearing marbles and calc-silicate rocks from Tungkillo and Milendella, South Australia. *Geol. Mag.*, **96**, 285–306.

White, W. S., 1949. Cleavage in east-central Vermont: *Trans. Am. Geophys. Union,* **30**, 587–594.

———, and R. H. Jahns, 1950. Structure of central and east-central Vermont. *J. Geol.*, **58**, 179–220.

Whittaker, E. J. W., and J. Zussman, 1956. The characterization of serpentine minerals by X-ray diffraction. *Mineral. Mag.*, **31**, 107–126.

Wigglesworth, Edward, 1916. The serpentines of Vermont. Vermont State Geologist, 10th bienn. Rept. 1915–16, 281–292.

Wiik, H. B., 1953. Composition and origin of soapstone. *Bull. Comm. Géol. Finlande,* **165**, 1–57.

Wijkerslooth, P. de, 1947. The chromite deposits of the Guleman concession (Vilâyet Elâzig), Turkey. *Koninkl. Ned. Akad. Wetenschap., Proc. Ser. B,* **50**, 215–224.

Wilkinson, J. F. G., 1953. Some aspects of the alpine-type serpentinites of Queensland. *Geol. Mag.*, **90**, 305–321.

———, 1956. Clinopyroxenes of alkali olivine-basalt magma. *Am. Mineral.*, **41**, 724–743.

———, 1957. The clinopyroxenes of a differentiated teschenite sill near Gunnedah, New South Wales. *Geol. Mag.*, **94**, 123–134.

———, 1958. The petrology of a differentiated teschenite sill near Gunnedah, New South Wales. *Am. J. Sci.*, **256**, 1–39.

Willemse, J., 1959. The "floor" of the Bushveld igneous complex and its relationships, with special reference to the eastern Transvaal. *Proc. Geol. Soc. S. Africa,* **62**, xxi–lxxx.

Williams, A. F., 1932. The *Genesis of the Diamond* (2 vols.). Ernest Benn Ltd., London, 636p.

———, 1934. Discussion of S. J. Shand's paper "The heavy minerals of kimberlite." *Proc. Geol. Soc. S. Africa,* **37**, li–lvii.

Williams, G. C., 1939. The kimberlite province and associated diamond deposits of Tanganyika Territory. *Geol. Surv. Tanganyika Bull.*, **12**, 38p.

Williams, G. H., 1886. The gabbros and associated hornblende rocks occurring in the vicinity of Baltimore, Maryland. *U.S. Geol. Surv. Bull.* **28**, 78p.

———, 1895. General relations of the granitic rocks in the Middle Atlantic Plateau. *U.S. Geol. Surv. 15th Ann. Rept., 1893–1894,* 657–684.

Williams, H., 1936. Pliocene volcanoes of the Navajo-Hopi country. *Bull. Geol. Soc. Am.*, **47**, 111–171.

———, F. J. Turner, and C. M. Gilbert, 1954. *Petrography.* W. H. Freeman and Co., San Francisco, 406p.

Wilshire, H. G., 1963. Internal structure of a differentiated teschenite intrusion, Prospect Hill, New South Wales. *Mineral. Soc. Am., Spec. Paper,* **1**, 134. (Abstr.)

———, and R. A. Binns, 1961. Basic and ultrabasic xenoliths from volcanic rocks of New South Wales. *J. Petrol.*, **2**, 185–208.

Wilson, G. V., 1939 in *Geol. Surv. Gt. Brit. Sum. Progr. for 1938,* 74–76.

Wilson, H. D. B., 1956. Structure of lopoliths. *Bull. Geol. Soc. Am.*, **67**, 289–300.

Wilson, J. T. 1954. "The development and structure of the crust," in Kuiper, G., ed., *The Earth as a Planet,* vol. II (in *The Solar System*), Univ. of Chicago Press, 138–214.

Wilson, N. W., 1960. The diamond deposits of Yakutia. *Mining Mag.* (London), **103**, 205–213.

Wilson, R. A. M., 1959. The geology of the Xeros-Troodos area. *Cyprus Geol. Surv. Dep. Mem.*, **1**, 1–135.

———, and F. T. Ingham, 1959. The geology and mineral resources of the Xeros-Troodos area. *Cyprus Geol. Surv. Dep. Mem.*, **1**, 184p.

Winchell, A. N., 1951. *Elements of Optical Mineralogy, pt. II: Description of Minerals.* John Wiley and Sons, Inc., New York, 551p.

Woodland, B. C., 1962. Lamprophyric dikes of the Burke area, Vermont. *Am. Mineral.*, **47**, 1094–1110.

Woollard, G. P., and W. E. Strange, 1963. Gravity anomalies and the crust of the earth in the Pacific Basin. *Am. Geophys. Union, Geophys. Monogr.* **6**.

Worst, B. G., 1958. The differentiation and structure of the Great Dyke of Southern Rhodesia. *Trans. Geol. Soc. S. Africa,* **61**, 283–354.

———, 1960. The Great Dyke of Southern Rhodesia. *Geol. Surv. S. Rhodesia Bull.*, **47**, 234p.

Wyllie, P. J., 1960. The system CaO-MgO-FeO-SiO_2 and its bearing on the origin of ultrabasic and basic rocks. *Mineral. Mag.*, **32**, 459–470.

———, 1961. Fusion of Torridonian sandstone by a picrite sill in Soay (Hebrides). *J. Petrol.*, **2**, 1–37.

———, 1963. Effects of the changes in slope occurring on liquidus and solidus paths in the system diopside-anorthite-albite. *Mineral. Soc. Am., Spec. Paper,* **1**, 204–212.

———, 1966. Experimental data bearing on the petrogenetic links between kimberlites and carbonatites. *Proc. 4th Gen. Meeting Intern. Mineral. Assoc.*, New Delhi, 1964 (*Indian Mineral.*, in press).

———, and H. I. Drever, 1963. The petrology of picritic rocks in minor intrusions—A picrite sill on the Island of Soay (Hebrides). *Trans. Roy. Soc. Edinburgh,* **65**, 155–177.

Wyllie, P. J., and O. F. Tuttle, 1960. The system CaO-CO_2-H_2O and the origin of carbonatites. *J. Petrol.*, **1**, 1–46.

Wyssotsky, N., 1913. The platinum deposits of the Isovsk and Nizhne-Tagil regions in the Urals. *Tr. Geol. Kom.*, Ser. **62.**

Yamaguchi, M., 1964. Petrogenetic significance of ultrabasic inclusions in basaltic rocks from south west Japan. *Mem. Fac. Sci. Kyushu Univ.*, **D.15**, 163–219.

Yefimov, A. A., and T. I. Kuuspalu, 1962. Nature of the anorthite gabbros at Serebryanskiy Kamen and of the associated copper mineralization. *Dokl. Akad. Nauk SSSR,* **145**, 143–145. (English trans.)

Yoder, H. S., Jr., 1952. The MgO-Al_2O_3-SiO_2-H_2O system and the related metamorphic facies. *Am. J. Sci.*, **Bowen vol.**, 569–627.

———, 1955. The role of water in metamorphism, *Geol. Soc. Am., Spec. Paper,* **62**, 505–524.

———, and G. A. Chinner, 1960a. Grossularite-pyrope-water system at 10,000 bars. *Carnegie Inst. Wash. Yearbook* **59**, 78–81.

———, 1960b. Almandite-pyrope-water system at 10,000 bars, *Carnegie Inst. Wash. Yearbook,* **59**, 81–84.

Yoder, H. S., Jr., and C. E. Tilley, 1962. Origin of basalt magmas: an experimental study of natural and synthetic rock systems. *J. Petrol.* **3**, 342–532.

Yoshino, G., 1961. Structural-petrological studies of peridotite and associated rocks of the Higashi-akaishi-yama district, Shikoku, Japan. *J. Sci. Hiroshima, Univ.*, **C.3**, 343–402.

———, 1964. Ultrabasic mass in the Higashi-akaishi-yama district, Shikoku, Southwest Japan. *J. Sci. Hiroshima Univ.*, **C.4**, 333–364.

Young, G. A., 1906. The geology and petrography of Mount Yamaska. *Geol. Surv. Can. Ann. Rept.*, 1904, **16**, pt. H, 43p.

Zachos, K., 1954. "Chromite deposits of Vourinon (Kozani) area," in Mineral Wealth of Greece. *Inst. Geol. Subsurface Res.*, **3**, 1–82.

Zartman, R. E., M. Brock, A. V. Heyl, and H. H. Thomas, 1965. K-Ar and Rb-Sr ages of some alkalic intrusive rocks from Central and Eastern United States. *Geol. Soc. Am.*, Ann. Meeting, Kansas City, Missouri, 187–188. (Abstr.)

Zavaritsky, A. N., 1928. Principal platinum deposits of the Urals. *Geol. Kom. Materialy Obshch. Prikl. Geol.*, **108.**

———, and A. G. Betekhtin, 1937. The Nizhne-Tagil dunite massif. *17th Intern. Geol. Congr. Guidebook, Uralian excursion, northern part,* 66–67.

Zealley, A. E. V., 1919. The geology of the Selukwe mineral belt. S. *Rhodesia Geol. Surv. Bull.* 3, 24p.

Zwaart, H. J., 1953. La géologie du Massif du Saint-Barthélemy (Pyrénées France). *Leidse Geol. Mededel.*, **18**, 1–228.

———, 1954. Les lherzolites et ophites des Pyrénées. *Leidse. Geol. Mededel.*, **18**, 281–286.

Author Index

Subject Index